*Readings in Anthropology*

$2_d$ *edition*

# Readings in Anthropology

*Jesse D. Jennings*
UNIVERSITY OF UTAH

*E. Adamson Hoebel*
UNIVERSITY OF MINNESOTA

*McGraw-Hill Book Company*

NEW YORK / ST. LOUIS / SAN FRANCISCO / TORONTO / LONDON / SYDNEY

*Readings in Anthropology*

*To Our Colleagues in Anthropology*

# *Preface*

When Professor E. Adamson Hoebel, the late Professor Elmer R. Smith, and I were compiling the first version of the *Readings*, we were aware of two things. First, we undertook the task because we felt the need of a selection of readings to be used in conjunction with introductory anthropology texts since, from experience, we knew that any text requires supplementary material. Therefore we tried to pull together a reader composed of well-written classic articles that were interesting and readable and that contained solid documentation of certain ideas. Second, we realized that any piece of good anthropological writing could be used to exemplify or clarify more than one idea or concept and would often be used by various teachers to make theoretical points quite different from those which led to its inclusion. Therefore, we decided against the preparation of explanatory materials either for the major sections of the book, or for the individual excerpts.

In preparing this revision, the same considerations are held as valid, but through the years, I have come to see another value in *Readings*. Whereas the textbook by its very nature tends to represent orthodoxy or, one should possibly say, widely held and agreed upon ideas, the reader can "run ahead" of generally agreed upon concepts. This helps the student to move beyond the orthodoxy of the text. I have also learned that students are stimulated and excited when they discover strong differences of opinion and real controversies raging beneath the placid prose of the day-to-day text. Therefore, I have included a few articles which are contradictory. Many of the added excerpts offer the student a view of subareas within anthropology which I expect to become stronger and to contribute importantly to the understanding of human behavior although they may receive scant, if any, attention in standard texts. Articles included in the present edition have been selected not only for relevance but for the interest they may have in broader terms for the undergraduate.

Editorial changes have involved deletion of some passages and the elimination of explicit bibliographic citations. The author being quoted, of course, is indicated as he is in the original, but source citations have been removed. Other deletions involve references to figures that are not reproduced. Footnotes are also removed.

Because Professor Smith had passed away and Professor Hoebel was committed to other work, I undertook this revision alone. The selections include some of the many I have found interesting, readable, and helpful over the years.

Although each author's permission to use his material is appropriately acknowledged, I should like to mention here with extreme gratitude the generosity that my friends and colleagues have shown in allowing me to draw freely on their professional writings. My especial thanks go to the several anonymous reviewers whose candid advice guided me in the final selection of the articles included. This assistance has made possible a reader which can support and supplement any of the standard introductory texts in anthropology.

And with appreciation, I mention the assistance of Caralee Price who efficiently took care of voluminous correspondence needed in securing permissions, checked copyrights, and did other chores. To my wife, Jane C. Jennings, who assembled the manuscript, reviewed my editing and assisted with all other phases of the job, I offer my special thanks.

JESSE D. JENNINGS

# Contents

## Part 6    Primitive Society

## Part 7    Language

## Part 8    Society and Culture

## Part 9    Economic Anthropology

## Part 10    Applied Anthropology

*part 1*

# *The Study of Anthropology*

# Anthropology and an Education for the Future

## Margaret Mead

*From The Teaching of Anthropology.* American Anthropological Association Memoir 94. *1963, pp. 595–607.* © *1963, David G. Mandelbaum. By permission of the author, the publisher, and the copyright holder.*

. . . Anthropology is a uniquely situated discipline, related in diverse ways to many other disciplines, each of which, in specializing, has also inadvertently helped to fragment the mind of modern man. Anthropology is a *humanity* [italics added], represented in the American Council of Learned Societies, concerned with the arts of language and with the versions that human cultures have given of the definition of man and of man's relationship to the universe; anthropology is a science, concerned with discovering and ordering the behavior of man-in-culture; anthropology is a *biological science* [italics added], concerned with the physical nature of man, with man's place in evolution, with the way genetic and racial differences, ecological adaptations, growth and maturation, and constitutional differences are implicated in man's culture and achievements; anthropology is a *historical discipline* [italics added], concerned with reading the record of man's far past and establishing the links which unite the potsherd and the first inscription on stone, in tying together the threads between the preliterate and the literate world wherever the sequence occurs, in Egypt, in China, in Crete, or in a modern African state. Anthropology is a *social science* [italics added], although never only a social science, because in anthropology man, as part of the natural world, as a biological creature, is not separated from man as a consumer or producer, member of a group, or possessor of certain psychological faculties. Anthropology is an art. The research skills which go into good field work are as complex as the skills of a musician or a surgeon; a disciplined awareness of self is as essential.

Partly because anthropology is a late comer on the scene, including a curiously assembled set of subject matters—such as the preliterate past, the body of man, the behavior of preliterate surviving people, the formal study of spoken language—and partly because of the diversity of anthropological interests, it is an uncommitted discipline. Because it includes all of them, it does not fall, with relentless traditionalism, into any category of science or of humanities or of social science. It has sheltered under the wings of philosophy and anatomy, botany and history, aesthetics and geology. Wherever it has been placed it has been restive, not for the simple imperialistic reasons that all part-departments seek to be whole departments but because there was always, when anthropology was placed within any category, such a large part that did not fit. How did a course in primitive art fit into a sociology curriculum, a course in the diffusion of material culture into a psychology department, a course in child training into philosophy?

It is in this very anomalousness that I believe anthropology can make a unique contribution to a liberal education. As a part of liberal education, it is peculiarly fitted to fill a tremendous need.

I should like to review briefly some of the gaps in the knowledge and understanding of modern man, so fragmented, so myopically limited and specialized, even at this very moment when we are journeying into space. Then I will consider how anthropology can be taught not by professional anthropologists alone, but by those who have studied under anthropologists and, like all great teachers of the adolescent mind, are willing to immerse themselves in their material sufficiently to convey it to their students "with the dew still on it."

The gaps in men's minds and imagination which we need to bridge are appallingly conspicuous today: the gap between the understanding of the past, the grasp of the present, and an ability to deal with the future; the gap between the lively pursuit of natural science wherever it leads and the statesmanship which will be able to control the results of such pursuits; the gap between the mathematical and formal analyses of systems and the ability to analyze and predict the behavior of human beings; the gap between the scientist who "understands" a single approach to the natural world and the poet and painter who can find no foothold in modern man's response to changes which he does not understand; the gap between man's knowledge of things and his knowledge of people; between his awareness of the external world, which has never been so great, and his awareness of himself, which has seldom been so impoverished; the gap between our small ethnocentric, narrowly racial, class and time bound senses of identity and the grandeur of our membership in one human species, now bound together as denizens of one planet. On the verge of leaving that planet, we still fail to conceive our full place upon it, in time and in space.

The fully educated man, whether he was the young adult male member of a primitive tribe who had learned all that the elders had to tell him, the man of Greece or Rome, thinking about and understanding the known world, Renaissance man stirred to an aware excitement of the ancient world from which he had been cut off, and moved by the new discoveries—the great and the small seen for the first time through telescopes and microscopes—all of these had, in different measure, what we now seek to re-establish for our own time. In contrast, many members of great societies—the peasant, taught for centuries that his is a limited place in the world, the urban proletarian, starved and cynical in his slums near the palace, the bitter contentious member of one of the cults and sects that seek to narrow truth to the limits of their own impoverished emotions and intellects—these have never, no matter how great the civilization within which they resided, been men of a liberal education. The essence of a liberal education is to share the full identity made possible by the state of civilization within which one lives: today that identity stretches back to the beginning of life on this planet, and soon perhaps in other parts of the universe; it comprises all members of the human species, all their work and marvels of hand and brain, heart and eye, the intricacy of their languages, the significance of their myriad experiments in human relationships, the cunningness with which their bodies are made, their relationships to all living creatures —to birds who are bipeds and build nests, and dolphins who, handless and lipless, devise ballets of their own in the sea; it reaches back into the past, out into the present, deeper beneath the sea and farther into the atmosphere than man has ever gone, and onward into a future for which each one of us, and each nation, holds today a terrible responsibility. Modern man is offered today an identity far greater than he has ever known. It is a task of a liberal education to help him develop it.

In order to appreciate fully how anthropology can contribute to this stupendous but rewarding task, something must be said of the way in which an anthropologist is educated, and what he does, when, as a research worker, he goes into the field. Every smallest research report, and every more generalized publication for the layman, bears the stamp of this education, of the presuppositions on which his work is based, and of the methods that, whatever his temperamental bent, he must pursue in the field. It is this experience of the field anthropologist, particularly of the field cultural anthropologist, which provides the possibility of integration. It is not that the anthropologist is widely read in the literature of the world, that he has an encyclopedic grasp of the history of science, that he has traveled and understood the ancient ruins of Angkor Wat or Crete, or undergone the rigorous disciplines of medicine, or one of the arts. His inclusiveness and universality are of quite another order. It is in his education and his research, based as they are in the whole of human history, embedded in the simplest and the most solemn moments of human life, that his integration lies.

In the United States anthropology has remained an inclusive and integrating discipline by successfully resisting the fragmentation which has occurred in most disciplines, which, as they became more specialized, with more workers, in more countries of the world, have progressively shattered into mutually non-communicating parts. Anthropology has kept its own media of intradisciplinary communication. Just as the fragmented and over specialized biological sciences can still communicate through observation of scientific canons

of presentation, argument, and experimental style, and the humanists in many tongues can still invoke the names of Plato and Aristotle, or physicians refer to a well-described case and lawyers to a carefully stated legal precedent, so too anthropologists have remained in communication with each other through the concrete materials with which they deal. They work not only with generalizations about culture, but also with the descriptions of particular cultures; not only with generalizations about language, but also with the auditory records of the speech of particular Indians or particular South Sea Island tribes; not only with tables of prehistoric time, but also with the actual artifacts and skeletal bits from which these tables are constructed. In their field work they go to various parts of the world, among living peoples who are different and speak different languages, or at a second remove, to the detailed accounts of those who did travel, and to the concrete specimens that they brought back.

Although it looked during the 1940's as if American anthropology, which had stood for such a unified approach to man in all his aspects, might fragment, it did not fragment. Graduate students in our universities today still learn about man's past, his place in evolution, the remains of his past civilization, the complexity of his languages, the nature of his culture and how to study it, and, increasingly, how to apply this knowledge, professionally, [to] various contemporary social problems as practitioners. In such an education the student is not lectured about the various parts of the subject but is forced to experience some small part of each, to read monographs about the Chukchee and the Koryak, to learn the shape of a bone, to undergo the discipline of analyzing an unknown language straight from an informant's lips, to arrange an assemblage of potsherds and/or the contents of a single archaelogical dig. Where this ideal is not fully realized, contact with those who have spent many years doing just these concrete things serves, to some extent, as a surrogate for the experience itself. . . .

*selection 2*

# The World into Which
# Darwin Led Us

*George Gaylord Simpson*

*From* Science, *Vol. 131,
No. 3405, 1960, pp.
966–974. Copyright 1960,
American Association for
the Advancement of
Science. By permission
of the author, the
publisher and copyright holder.*

. . . It has often been said that Darwin changed the world. It has less often been made clear just what the change has been. Darwin did not—to his credit he did not—make any of the discoveries that have led to our present overwhelming physical peril. Most, although not quite all, of our technology would be the same if Darwin's work had not been done, by him or anyone else. . . . The influence of Darwin, or more broadly of the concept of evolution, has had effects more truly profound. It has literally led us into a different world.

How can that be? If evolution is true, it was as true before Darwin as it is today. The physical universe has not changed. But our human universes, the ones in which we really have our beings, depend at least as much on our inner perceptions as on the external, physical facts. That can be made evident by an elementary example. Suppose a stone is seen by a small boy, an artist, and a petrologist. The small boy may perceive it as something to throw, the artist as something to carve into sculpture, the petrologist as a mixture of minerals formed under conditions. The stone is three quite different things to the three people, and yet they are seeing exactly the same thing. The stone has identical properties whatever anyone thinks about it.

In that trivial example all three conceptions of the stone, although profoundly different, are equally true. The stone can indeed be thrown, be sculptured, or be analyzed petrologically by procedures suitable to each of the three perceptions. But there are differing perceptions of objects and of our whole world that are not equally true in the same sense, which is the scientific sense of material testability. Perceptions that are not materially testable or that have been contradicted by adequate tests are not rationally valid. As they petrify into tradition and dogma they become superstitions. Perception of the truth of evolution was an enormous stride from superstition to a rational universe.

## The Changing Universe

Years ago I lived for a time with a group of uncivilized Indians in South America. Their world is very different from ours: in space, a saucer a few miles across; in time, from a few years to a few generations back into a misty past; in essence, lawless, unpredictable, and haunted. Anything might happen. The Kamarakoto Indians quite believe that animals become men and men become stones; for them there is neither limitation nor reason in the flux of nature. There is also a brooding evil in their world, a sense of wrongness and fatality that they call *kanaima* and see manifested in every unusual event and object.

That level of invalid perceptions might be called the lower superstition. It is nevertheless superior in some respects to the higher superstitions celebrated weekly in every hamlet of the United States. The legendary metamorphoses of my Indian friends are grossly naive, but they do postulate a kinship through all of nature. Above all, they are not guilty of teleology. It would never occur to them that the universe, so largely hostile, might have been created for their benefit.

It is quite wrong to think that uncivilized Indians are, by that token, primitive. Nevertheless, I suppose that the conceptual world of the Kamarakotos is more or less similar to that of ancient, truly primitive men. Indeed, even at the dawn of written history in the cradles of civilization, the accepted world pictures do not seem very different from that of those Indians.

The world in which modern, civilized men live has changed profoundly with increasingly rational, which is to say eventually scientific, consideration of the universe. The essential changes came first of all from the physical sciences and their forerunners. In space, the small saucer of the savage became a large disc, a globe, a planet in a solar system, which became one of many in our galaxy, which in turn became only one nebula in a cosmos containing uncounted billions of them. The astronomers have finally located us on an insignificant mote in an incomprehensible vastness—surely a world awesomely different from that in which our ancestors lived not many generations ago.

As astronomy made the universe immense, physics itself and related physical sciences made it lawful. Physical effects have physical causes, and the relationship is such that when causes are adequately known effects can be reliably predicted. We no longer live in a capricious world. We may expect the universe to deal consistently, even if not fairly, with us. If the unusual happens, we need no longer blame *kanaima* (or a whimsical god or devil) but may look confidently for an unusual or hitherto unknown physical cause. That is, perhaps, an act of faith, but it is not superstition. Unlike recourse to the supernatural, it is validated by thousands of successful searches for verifiable causes. This view depersonalizes the universe and makes it more austere, but it also makes it dependable. . . .

To those discoveries and principles, which so greatly modified concepts of the cosmos, geology added two more of fundamental, world-changing importance: vast extension of the universe in time, and the idea of constantly lawful progression in time. Estimates of geological time have varied greatly, but even in the 18th century it became clear to a few that the age of the earth must be in millions of years rather than the thousands then popularly accepted from Biblical exegesis. Now some geological dates are firmly established, within narrowing limits, and no competent geologist considers the earth less than 3 billion years old. (Upper estimates for the solar system range from 5 to 10 billion.) That is still only a moment in eternity, but it characterizes a world very different from one conceived as less than 6000 years old.

With dawning realization that the earth is really extremely old, in human terms of age, came the knowledge that it has changed progressively and radically but usually gradually and always in an orderly, a natural, way. The fact of change had not earlier been denied in Western science or theology—after all, the Noachian Deluge was considered a radical change. But the Deluge was believed to have supernatural causes or concomitants that were not operative throughout earth's history. The doctrine of geological uniformitarianism, finally established early in the 19th century, widened the recognized reign of natural law. The earth has changed throughout its history under the action of material forces, only, and of the *same* forces as those now visible to us and still acting on it.

## The Higher Superstition and the Discovery of Evolution

The steps that I have so briefly traced reduced the sway of superstition in the conceptual world of human lives. The change was slow, it was unsteady, and it was not accepted by everyone. Even now there are nominally civilized people whose world was created in 4004 B.C. Nevertheless, by early Victorian times the physical world of a literate consensus was geologically ancient and materially lawful in its history and its current operations. Not so, however, the world of life; here the higher (or at least later) superstition was still almost unshaken. Pendulums might swing with mathematical regularity and mountains might rise and fall through millennia, but living things belonged outside the realm of material principles and secular history. If life obeyed any laws, they were supernal and not bound to the physics of inert substance. Beyond its original, divine creation, life's history was trivial. Its kinds were each as created in the beginning, changeless except for minor and obvious variations.

Perhaps the most crucial element in man's world is his conception of himself. It is here that the higher superstition offers little real advance over the lower. According to the higher superstition, man is something quite distinct from nature. He stands apart from all other creatures; his kinship is supernatural, not natural. It may, at first sight, seem anomalous that those scientists who held this view did classify man as an animal. Linnaeus, an orthodox upholder of the higher superstition, even classified *Homo* with the apes and monkeys. No blood relationship was implied. The system of nature was the pattern of creation, and it included all created things, without any mutual affinities beyond the separate placing of each in one divine plan.

Another subtler and even more deeply warping concept of the higher superstition was that the world was created for man. Other organisms had no separate purpose in the scheme of creation. Whether noxious or useful, they were to be seriously considered only in their relationship to the supreme creation, the image of God. It required considerable ingenuity to determine why a louse, for example, was created to be a companion for man, but the ingenuity was not lacking. A world made for man is no longer the inherently hostile and evil world of *kanaima*, but that again is offset in some versions of the higher superstition by the belief that man himself is inherently evil or, at least, sinful.

Those elements of the higher superstition dominated European thought before publication of *The Origin of Species*, but various studies of the centennial year have exhaustively demonstrated that evolutionary ideas existed and were slowly spreading among a minority of *cognoscenti* long before Darwin. Some believed that a species, although divinely and separately created, might change, and in particular might degenerate from its form in the original plan of creation. That is not a truly evolutionary view, since it does not really involve the origin of one species from another, but it does deserve to be called pro-evolutionary in that it recognized the fact that each separate species may change. In the 18th century Buffon went that far, but hardly further, in spite of some apologists who now hail him as an evolutionist.

Some 18th-century worthies—among them Linnaeus in his later years—did go one step further. They conceived that each of the separately created "kinds" of Genesis might later have become considerably diversified, so that the unit of separate creation might be what we now call a genus or even a family or higher group, and the species or subgroups might have arisen, or indeed evolved, since the creation. Just as the many breeds of domesticated dogs are all dogs and of common origin, so the wolves, coyotes, foxes, jackals, and other wild species might all descend from a single creation of the dog-kind. That would still admit no relationship between the dog-kind and the now likewise diversified but singly and separately created cat-kind, for example. . . .

By the end of the 18th century there were a few true and thorough-going evolutionists— Charles Darwin's grandfather Erasmus was one, as has so often been pointed out. Their number increased during the first half of the 19th century. Some of them even had glimmerings of Darwin's great discovery, natural selection, although (contrary to some recent historians whose aim seems to be to denigrate Darwin) none of them elucidated that principle clearly and fully.

## Darwin

Practically all of the ideas in *The Origin of Species* had been dimly glimpsed, at least, by someone or other before 1859. . . .

The reason why *The Origin of Species* carried conviction was that it did supply sufficient evidence of evolution and also provided an explanation of the phenomena of evolution. That twofold nature of Darwin's accomplishment has certainly been pointed out often enough, but the statement has also been criticized, and perhaps some small notice should here be given to some of the criticisms. It has, for one thing, been maintained that previous evidence *was* sufficient. It had persuaded Erasmus Darwin, Lamarck, Chambers . . . and others, so (some critics say) it should have persuaded anyone without Charles Darwin's needing to recompile it. That conclusion is simply ridiculous. What anyone thinks *should* have happened has nothing to do with the question of historical fact. Previous evidence *did not* convince a majority of interested scientists; therefore it was insufficient for that purpose. Darwin's evidence *did* in fact convince them; therefore it was sufficient. (It may of course be recognized, as Darwin himself implied, that the way had been prepared by a changing climate of opinion and that even his evidence might have been insufficient if adduced at an earlier date.)

It has further been suggested that evolution could have been, perhaps should have been, established as a fact without requiring an explanation, and also that Darwin's explanation was not really adequate. The first proposition is debatable, certainly, and examples can be produced to support both sides. The inheritance of acquired characters was accepted by practically everyone, down to and including Darwin, even though no one had adequately explained it. Darwin himself did not like to deal with unexplained facts, and he did belatedly attempt to explain the inheritance of acquired characters. Since in this case the "facts" were not true, that particular Darwinian theory is now charitably forgotten. (Fortunately it was not really essential to his broader theory explanatory of evolution as whole.) In any case, belief in the inheritance of acquired characters did not depend on any explanation of the supposed phenomena. (Is there perhaps a warning in the fact that the unexplained phenomena did not in truth occur?) On the other side of the argument is the modern example of extrasensory perception. A great mass of facts is claimed to demonstrate the reality of that unexplained phenomenon, and yet it is not generally accepted. It seems quite clear that it will not carry conviction unless some credible explanation is produced.

It does seem to me highly improbable that the fact of evolution would have been accepted so widely and quickly if it had been unaccompanied by an explanatory theory. Again, to question whether it *should* have been would be childish arguing with history. . . .

## The Fact of Evolution

The fact—not theory—that evolution has occurred and the Darwinian theory as to how it has occurred have become so confused in popular opinion that the distinction must be stressed. The distinction is also particularly important for the present subject, because the effects on the world in which we live have been distinct. The greatest impact no doubt has come from the fact of evolution. It must color the whole of our attitude toward life and toward ourselves, and hence our whole perceptual world. That is, however, a single step, essentially taken a hundred years ago and now a matter of simple rational acceptance or superstitious rejection. How evolution occurs is much more intricate, still incompletely known, debated in detail, and the subject of most active investigation at present. Decision here has decidedly practical aspects and also affects our worlds even more intimately, and in even more ways, than the fact of evolution. The two will be separately considered.

The import of the fact of evolution depends on how far evolution extends, and here there are two crucial points: does it extend from the inorganic into the organic, and does it extend from the lower animals to man? In

*The Origin of Species* Darwin implies that life did not arise naturally from nonliving matter, for in the very last sentence he wrote, ". . . life . . . having been originally breathed by the Creator into a few forms or into one. . . ." (The words *by the Creator* were inserted in the second edition and are one of many gradual concessions made to critics of that book.) Later, however, Darwin conjectured (he did not consider this scientific) that life will be found to be a "consequence of some general law"—that is, to be a result of natural processes rather than divine intervention. . . .

Until comparatively recently, many and probably most biologists agreed with Darwin that the problem of the origin of life was not yet amenable to scientific study. Now, however, almost all biologists agree that the problem can be attacked scientifically. The consensus is that life did arise naturally from the nonliving and that even the first living things were not specially created. The conclusion has, indeed, really become inescapable, for the first steps in that process have already been repeated in several laboratories. . . .

At the other end of the story, it was evident to evolutionists from the start that man cannot be an exception. In *The Origin of Species* Darwin deliberately avoided the issue, saying only in closing, "Light will be thrown on the origin of man and his history." Yet his adherents made no secret of the matter and at once embroiled Darwin, with themselves, in arguments about man's origin from monkeys. Twelve years later (in 1871) Darwin published *The Descent of Man*, which makes it clear that he was indeed of that opinion. No evolutionist has since seriously questioned that man did originate by evolution. Some, notably the Wallace who shared with Darwin the discovery of natural selection, have maintained that special principles, not elsewhere operative, were involved in human origins, but that is decidedly a minority opinion about the causes or explanations, not the fact, of evolution.

It is of course also true that the precise ancestry of man is not identified in full detail and so is subject to some disagreement. That is a minor matter of no real importance for man's image of himself. No one doubts that man is a member of the order Primates along with lemurs, tarsiers, monkeys, and apes. Few doubt that his closest living relatives are the apes. On this subject, by the way, there has been too much pussyfooting. Apologists emphasize that man cannot be a descendant of any living ape—a statement that is obvious to the verge of imbecility—and go on to state or imply that man is not really descended from an ape or monkey at all, but from an earlier common ancestor. In fact, that common ancestor would certainly be called an ape or monkey in popular speech by anyone who saw it. Since the terms *ape* and *monkey* are defined by popular usage, man's ancestors *were* apes or monkeys (or successively both). It is pusillanimous if not dishonest for an informed investigator to say otherwise.

Evolution is, then, a completely general principle of life. (I refer here, and throughout, to organic evolution. Inorganic evolution, as of the stars or the elements, is quite different in process and principle, a part of the same grand history of the universe but not an extension of evolution as here understood.) Evolution is a fully natural process, inherent in the physical properties of the universe, by which life arose in the first place and by which all living things, past or present, have since developed, divergently and progressively.

This world into which Darwin led us is certainly very different from the world of the higher superstition. In the world of Darwin man has no special status other than his definition as a distinct species of animal. He is in the fullest sense a part of nature and not apart from it. He is akin, not figuratively but literally, to every living thing, be it an ameba, a tapeworm, a flea, a seaweed, an oak tree, or a monkey—even though the degrees of relationship are different and we may feel less empathy for forty-second cousins like the tapeworms than for, comparatively speaking, brothers like the monkeys. This is togetherness and brotherhood with a vengeance, beyond the wildest dreams of copy writers or of theologians.

Moreover, since man is one of many millions of species all produced by the same grand process, it is in the highest degree improbable that anything in the world exists specifically for his benefit or ill. It is no more true that fruits, for instance, evolved for the delectation of men than that men evolved for the delectation of tigers. Every species, including our own, evolved for its own sake, so to speak. Different species are intricately interdependent, and also some are more successful than others, but there is no divine favoritism. The rational world is not teleological in the old sense. It certainly has purpose, but the purposes are not imposed from without or anticipatory of the future. They are internal to each species separately, relevant only to its functions and usually only to its present condition. Every species is unique, and it is true that man is unique in new and very special ways. Among these peculiarities, parts of the definition of *Homo sapiens*, is the fact that man does have his own purposes that relate to the future. . . .

**Synthesis**

Adaptation and the apparent purposefulness of evolution are basic problems that a successful theory *must* solve. The rising science of genetics early in this century not only failed to solve the problem but also made it appear insuperably difficult. That explains why almost no students of other disciples were inclined to accept mutationism, and why Neo-Lamarckism, an elegant but as we now know incorrect solution, hung on for so long. It also was one of several reasons for continued popularity of non-naturalistic theories, to which I allude below.

The way out of the dilemma seems simple now that it has been found. Mutationism is not an alternative to Neo-Darwinism but a supplement to it. If mutation is the source of new variation and yet is substantially non-adaptive, and if the actual course of evolution is to a large extent adaptive, then some additional factor or process must frequently intervene between the occurrence of mutations and the incorporation of some of them into evolving populations. The intervening process must be literally selective, because it must tend (not necessarily with full efficiency) to weed out disadvantageous mutations and genetic combinations and to multiply those that are advantageous in existing circumstances. Natural selection is just such a process, and the principal modern theory of evolution, although it contains much besides,

is in large part a synthesis of selection theory and mutation theory.

Evolution is an extremely complex process, and we are here interested mainly in the effects of the concept on our world rather than in the process for its own sake. For that purpose I must, however, briefly note the main elements of the process now known. Genetic systems, governing heredity in each individual case, are composed of genes and chromosomes, discrete but complexly interacting units at different levels of size and complexity. The genes themselves, their organized associations in chromosomes, and whole sets of chromosomes have a large degree of stability as units, but all the kinds of units are shuffled and combined in various ways by the sexual processes of reproduction in most organisms. Thus, a considerable amount of variation is maintained, and, so to speak, genetic experimentation occurs in all natural populations. Mutations, in the broadest sense, affecting individual genes, chromosomes, or sets of chromosomes, introduce wholly new variation, which is fed into the processes of recombination.

Populations of similar animals, usually interbreeding among themselves and definable as species, have genetic pools, characterized by the total of genetic units in the included individuals and the distribution of combinations of those units through the population. Evolutionary change involves changes in the genetic pool, in kinds of included units, in frequencies of them, and in kinds and frequencies of combinations of them. Recombination alone does not tend to change the gentic pool. Only three processes are known to do so: mutation, fluctuation in genetic frequencies (what are known statistically as "sampling errors"), and differential reproduction. The first two of those processes are not oriented toward adaptation. They are in that sense essentially random, and are usually inadaptive, although they may rarely and coincidentally be adaptive. By "differential reproduction" is meant the consistent production of more offspring, on an average, by individuals with certain genetic characteristics than by those without those particular characteristics. That is the modern understanding of natural selection, including but broader than the Darwinian or Neo-Darwinian concept, which emphasized mortality and survival more than reproduction. Natural selection in the Darwinian sense and still more in this expanded sense is nonrandom, and its trend is adaptive. It also tends, not always with complete success, to counteract the random effects of mutation and sampling error.

Evolutionary processes are tremendously more complicated in detail than this bald outline suggests. The point of the outline is that here is a mechanism, involving only materials and processes known beyond a doubt to occur in nature, capable (as one of its proponents has said) of generating just the degree of improbability evident in the phenomena of evolution.

Further information pertinent to our theme is provided by paleontology, the actual record of events in the history of life. Observation and experimentation with living organisms can extend over a few years, at most. There is always a possibility that processes there evident worked out differently over spans of millions of years, or that the actual history involved principles undetectable in shorter periods of time. There is admittedly some difference of opinion, but I think it fair to say that there is now a consensus for the view that the fossil record is fully consistent with the modern synthetic theory of evolution and that it neither requires nor suggests any alternative explanation.

There is one thing demonstrated by the fossil record that is decidedly pertinent here and that probably would never have been inferred from study of living organisms. Throughout the whole history of life most species have become extinct, without issue. The statistically usual outcome of evolution is not, then, the progressive appearance of higher forms but simply obliteration. There has, indeed, been progression and even (still more rarely) progress, but this has been in the comparatively few, exceptional lines of descent. The adaptive mechanism of natural selection has guaranteed that some lineages would win, that the world would indeed be filled and kept filled with adapted organisms, but just as inexorably it has insured that most lineages would lose. It has, moreover, had the result that even the winners, the lineages that have survived so far, have not necessarily been progressive, from a human point of view at least. The primitive ameba

has remained adapted, hence has survived, while the lordly dinosaurs lost adaptation and therefore life. The degenerate tapeworm is to all appearances as well adapted as the—we like to think—progressive man. . . .

## The World of Man

Let me summarize and conclude as to this world into which Darwin led us. In it man and all other living things have evolved, ultimately from the nonliving, in accordance with entirely natural, material processes. In part that evolution has been random in the sense of lacking adaptive orientation. As a rule, however, it has been oriented or directed toward achieving and maintaining adaptive relationships between populations of organisms and their whole environments. Nevertheless, this blind, amoral process has not guaranteed indefinite maintenance of adaptation for any given lineage of populations. On the contrary, it usually leads to eventual extinction and a repeopling of the world by the newly divergent offspring of a minority of earlier successful lineages. The mechanism of orientation, the nonrandom element in this extraordinarily complex history, has been natural selection, which is now understood as differential reproduction.

Man is one of the millions of results of this material process. He is another species of animal, but not just another animal. He is unique in peculiar and extraordinarily significant ways. He is probably the most self-conscious of organisms, and quite surely the only one that is aware of his own origins, of his own biological nature. He has developed symbolization to a unique degree and is the only organism with true language. This makes him also the only animal who can store knowledge beyond individual capacity and pass it on beyond individual memory. He is by far the most adaptable of all organisms because he has developed culture as a biological adaptation. Now his culture evolves not distinct from and not in replacement of but in addition to biological evolution, which also continues.

Concomitant with these developments is the fact that man has unique moral qualities. The evolutionary process is not moral—the word is simply irrelevant in that connection—but it has finally produced a moral animal. Conspicuous among his moral attributes is a sense of responsibility, which is probably felt in some way and to some degree by every normal human being. There has been disagreement and indeed confusion through the ages regarding to whom and for what man is responsible. The lower and the higher superstitions have produced their several answers. In the post-Darwinian world another answer seems fairly clear: man is responsible to himself and for himself. "Himself" here means the whole human species, not only the individual and certainly not just those of a certain color of hair or cast of features.

The fact that man knows that he evolves entails the possibility that he can do something to influence his own biological destiny. The fact that uncontrolled evolution often leads to degeneration and usually to extinction makes it highly advisable that man take a hand in determining his own future evolution. If man proceeds on the wrong evolutionary assumptions—for instance, on those of Neo-Lamarckism or Michurinism—whatever he does is sure to be wrong. If he proceeds on the right assumptions, what he does may still

be wrong, but at least it has a chance of being right.

A world in which man must rely on himself, in which he is not the darling of the gods but only another, albeit extraordinary, aspect of nature, is by no means congenial to the immature or the wishful thinkers. That is plainly a major reason why even now, a hundred years after *The Origin of Species*, most people have not really entered the world into which Darwin led—alas!—only a minority of us. Life may conceivably be happier for some people in the older worlds of superstition. It is possible that some children are made happy by a belief in Santa Claus, but adults should prefer to live in a world of reality and reason.

Perhaps I should end on that note of mere preference, but it is impossible to do so. It is a characteristic of this world to which Darwin opened the door that unless *most* of us do enter it and live maturely and rationally in it, the future of mankind is dim, indeed—if there is any future.

*selection* 3

# Universals of Culture

## George P. Murdock

*From The Common Denominator of Cultures. In Ralph Linton (ed.),* The Science of Man in the World Crisis, *Columbia University Press, 1945, pp. 123–125. By permission of the author and the publisher.*

Early reports of peoples lacking language or fire, morals or religion, marriage or government, have been proved erroneous in every instance. Nevertheless, even today it is not generally recognized how numerous and diverse are the elements common to all known cultures. The following is a partial list of items, arranged in alphabetical order to emphasize their variety, which occur, so far as the author's knowledge goes, in every culture known to history or ethnography: age-grading, athletic sports, bodily adornment, calendar, cleanliness training, community organization, cooking, cooperative labor, cosmology, courtship, dancing, decorative art, divination, division of labor, dream interpretation, education, eschatology, ethics, ethnobotany, etiquette, faith healing, family, feasting, fire making, folklore, food taboos, funeral rites, games, gestures, gift giving, government, greetings, hair styles, hospitality, housing, hygiene, incest taboos, inheritance rules, joking, kingroups, kinship nomenclature, language, law, luck superstitions, magic, marriage, mealtimes, medicine, modesty concerning natural functions, mourning, music, mythology, numerals, obstetrics, penal sanctions, personal names, population policy, postnatal care, pregnancy usages, property rights, propitiation of supernatural beings, puberty customs, religious ritual, residence rules, sexual restrictions, soul concepts, status differentiation, surgery, tool making, trade, visiting, weaning, and weather control.

Cross-cultural similarities appear even more far-reaching when individual items in such a list are subjected to further analysis. For example, not only does every culture have a language, but all languages are resolvable into identical kinds of components, such as phonemes or conventional sound units, words or meaningful combinations of phonemes, grammar or standard rules for combining words into sentences. Similarly funeral rites always include expressions of grief, a means of disposing of the corpse, rituals designed to protect the participants from supernatural harm, and the like. When thus analyzed in detail, the resemblances between all cultures are found to be exceedingly numerous. . . .

The true universals of culture, then, are not identities in habit, in definable behavior. They are similarities in classification, not in content. They represent categories of historically and behaviorally diverse elements which nevertheless have so much in common that competent observers feel compelled to classify them together. There can be no question, for example, that the actual behavior exhibited in acquiring a spouse, teaching a child, or treating a sick person differs enormously from society to society. Few would hesitate, however, to group such divergent acts under the unifying categories of marriage, education, and medicine. All of the genuinely widespread or universal resemblances between cultures resolve themselves upon analysis into a series of such generally recognized categories. What cultures are found to have in common is a uniform system of classification, not a fund of identical elements. Despite immense diversity in behavioristic detail, all cultures are constructed according to a single fundamental plan—the "universal culture pattern" as Wissler has so aptly termed it.

The essential unanimity with which the universal culture pattern is accepted by competent authorities, irrespective of theoretical divergences or other issues, suggests that it is not a mere artifact of classificatory ingenuity but rests upon some substantial foundation. This basis cannot be sought in history, or geography, or race, or any other factor limited in time or space, since the universal pattern links all known cultures, simple and complex, ancient and modern. It can only be sought, therefore, in the fundamental biological and psychological nature of man and in the universal conditions of human existence. . . .

# Ethnological Field Techniques

*Cornelius Osgood*

*From Ingalik Material Culture.* Yale University Publications in Anthropology, *No. 22, Yale University Press, 1940, pp. 50–54. By permission of the author and the publisher.*

To estimate the validity of data one must give some consideration to the manner in which they are gained. My preparations, besides previous years of field work among the Northern Athapaskans, included a survey of the information to be obtained on the Ingalik area by previous writers from the first commentary, the few but important paragraphs of the Russian creole explorer Glazunov, to the outstanding contributions of the missionary John Chapman. My problem was to find an informant who knew the old culture and who had not only the ability to verbalize his knowledge but a personality which would make the long and arduous task psychologically acceptable to him. The difficulties of finding good informants among the Northern Athapaskans are so great that it is naïveté for an ethnologist to decide to work in a particular village, however large. He must rather go from one to another until he can find an individual who will supply enough information so that contributions from others can be built around it to make a connected whole. One may find a village often enough where the linguistic barrier alone renders pursuit of ethnography futile, or where seasonal economic activities such as salmon fishing cut the possibility of buying an informant's time to a point where it is a waste not to move on. Thus one may understand that the basic factor in doing successful ethnography among the Athapaskans is to find good informants. How I came upon one who even surpassed my hopes seems to justify a bit of personal narrative.

On my first day at Anvik, which happened to be a Sunday, I was entertained at tea with the resident missionary by the owner of the village store and his wife, all of whom were kind enough to consider which Indians in the neighborhood might supply me with information. One by one the Indians were disqualified for some reason or another. Frequently would come the typical remark known to all ethnographers who deal in reconstructions: "Old So-and-so, he would have been just the person for you. He knew everything and would be glad to tell you, but he died last year." And then some considerable reminiscences about "old So-and-so." I was becoming discouraged when my kind hostess said, "I know the man for you," and she mentioned his name. Someone protested that he could hardly be considered as honest. Also his morals were apparently questionable and it was clear that he was not a good Christian. I sensed immediately that the man under discussion had stirred up more emotion among my companions than they cared to verbalize, that rather than really disliking the man, they had respect for him but regretted him as a disturbing influence. My hostess went on something in this vein: "It is strange about that Billy. You know in the winter when he sells a fox skin, instead of leaving as the others do, he will stand around for an hour if you will listen and tell you about that fox, how it came around the trap the first time and was suspicious, and went away, and how he fixed the trap, and how the fox came back and finally was caught."

"Yes," her husband joined in, "you can depend on what he said about that fox being absolutely so. He knows foxes better than they know themselves." Everyone agreed that Billy was smarter than a fox and the conversation turned to other things. The commentary on this man excited me, for it sounded like what I had been waiting to hear for so many years that I had begun to think I never would—an Athapaskan Indian who wanted to talk about his world in which foxes and men competed on a somewhat equal basis. It was easy to find out where Billy lived and I shortly excused myself. Any further introduction would have placed my hopes in jeopardy. When I found his house I knocked and went in. It was a single room cabin singularly well ordered and richly furnished for a native of that country. Sitting in the center of the floor was an Indian surrounded by a pile of clean fresh spruce shavings which had resulted from his whittling.

"You are Billy Williams?" I asked questioningly.

"Yes," he answered without hesitation, looking up at me with a twisted expression resulting from his one blind eye.

"I have come a long way to see you because I think you can teach me some things I want to know."

He immediately rose and placed a homemade chair for me beside the stove and drew up another for himself. There was nothing in the act that gave any suggestion that he wanted me to be impressed by the fact that he was the most sophisticated Indian in the north, a man who could build his own house and furnish it with chairs and cupboards trimly painted in red and blue and green with a few designs deftly added to give them a character of their own. Neither was there any note of insecurity, none of any apology for what differences might appear between the way of life of this widower and his visitor. I had a feeling that I had met an equal.

In the conversation that followed Billy said little while I explained my interest in Indian life, by habit avoiding aspects which I thought might create suspicion. We soon arranged that he would act as informant at a fixed fee per hour starting the next morning at nine, and I left to make my own living arrangements. This was most satisfactorily done, the resident missionary generously turning over his house to me, as he himself was living in the boy's dormitory of the school. As I planned for the morning, I wondered how much trouble I would have in finding Billy. The only informant I had ever had in all my previous experience that I could depend on for an appointment was totally blind, and even he was frequently led off somewhere by his relatives. The next morning, having slept poorly and risen late in my new surroundings, I was just about to set off when there was a knock on the door and I opened it to find Billy. I was astonished but managed to invite him to a seat across a table suitable for our work. I made out a schedule to keep track of the time and then looked at my watch. It was exactly nine o'clock.

"You came early," I said, but he answered with so slight a smile I wondered if he had heard me.

Within three days our schedule shifted and we were working intensely for clocked hours from eight to twelve and one to five. This meant that my copying and arranging questions for the following day lasted often into the early hours of the morning. Billy tried coming at seven, but I was too exhausted. Within a few days Billy had come to know almost exactly what I was trying to do, and I discovered that for some strange reason it was as important to him as it was to me. It is written on my time sheets that we have spent more than five hundred practically uninterrupted hours together recording data between eight and five. This does not include the days we spent together in the woods nor the social occasions in his or some other person's house.

During the period we were engaged in a discussion of manufactured objects, Billy would spend his evenings making models, bringing them the next day. He took a special pleasure in pulling them from underneath his jacket and putting them on the table. We also had a sandbox in which he excavated house pits and built little dwellings, carving the sticks as he talked. If women's work was involved, he would ask his mother or sister to help us. He also did something else which proved a surprise to me. It was the general opinion that the genuine old articles of the culture were gone but sometimes I would see him paddle by the house in his little hunting canoe soon after supper to return in the dusk of the northern midnight. I knew he had been off to some fish camp along the river and that the next day I would get a present, perhaps an old knife or some piece of woman's work he had remembered was in someone's possession. Sometimes he would go off into the woods and come back with an old bowl that he knew had been cached and forgotten long years ago. In this way was built up the collection of hundreds of Ingalik objects now in the Peabody Museum at Yale University.

We generally began the week by reviewing what had been done previously. I would ask him to repeat the key parts of the procedure, and he would do so with amazing fidelity in the same step by step, logical manner without giving any sign of the strain of repetition. A particularly telling incident as to his character as an informant comes to mind in connection with the recording of a rather long and complicated ceremonial performance. There had been day after day of writing, of going back and repeating, all the agony of making an intelligent and coherent whole out of something that the ethnographer had never

seen and had not learned fully to understand. Billy had made repetition after repetition until it was hateful to ask him to repeat again. Finally one night I finished the record and wrote it up so that it seemed satisfactory. A few days later I read it to Billy but he pointed out some important errors and we went to work on them. The results made the whole thing illogical and I was in poor humor because my time as always seemed too short for my task. Billy was tired also and I was afraid he might not stand for any more of my stupidity, so I asked him what we had better do. His face relaxed slightly as he answered, "I think we had better start all over from the beginning," which, of course, was the only intelligent thing to do, and in a few days we both felt we had achieved something, and I that I had found a colleague.

Another notable instance of his powers as an informant may be indicated by the following circumstance. Before I had ever seen the *kashim*, or most complicated structure of the Ingalik, I had spent days in recording its details down to the native term for each of the pieces of which it is composed. Sometime later we made a visit to a place where there was an old *kashim*. When I checked the interior construction carefully I found only two points of disagreement and asked my informant about the matter. He took me outside and showed me the modern entryway. "When the Russians came they began to make the doors this way, and with this door the inside can no longer be arranged as it should be." It was obvious when he pointed out the technicalities of the construction. When we left I could not help feeling that I had better stay at home and listen carefully, for if I trusted only my eyes I would be certain to get things wrong.

The great majority of my data comes directly from Billy Williams. Some comes from other Indians by direct questioning and a great deal more with Billy really acting as interpreter. It is particularly significant that on disputable points Billy would collect opinions and present them as such. Most informants I have dealt with treat information as something peculiarly theirs, not to be questioned, and they are insulted if someone else is asked about the matter. Billy, on the contrary, had an almost scientific dispassionateness about data. He had a great confidence in his own knowledge, but if someone else was supplying information which was in contradiction to his own, he would state it apparently with little feeling except for a kind of curiosity about the informant, and, when asked to explain later, he would say, "Well maybe them fellows did that way." Sometimes after several days, in an unexpected moment, he would interpolate some perfectly simple explanation of the contradiction which apparently he had thought out or learned from some old man. When praised for it he was imperturbable.

Apart from his own experience in life, Billy's principal teacher was his mother's father, who lived in Shageluk where Billy was born about 1884. Billy complains that he made him sit and listen to him hour after hour and would tell him the same old things over and over until Billy had a headache from listening and wanted to get away, but his grandfather would make him sit and listen just the same. This went on until Billy was about fifteen, when he ran away from home.

The grandfather must have been an exceptional character. He had been orphaned at the age of one in the great smallpox epidemic of 1838–39 and was raised in Shageluk by his sister. He was a conservative in his viewpoint, a tradition so strongly impressed upon Billy in his early years that it undoubtedly contributed to his revolt from his family. Billy's compensatory action in becoming engrossed in the pattern of ancient life, and his willingness to have it recorded, seem but the final steps in a logical sequence of his reaction to a changing culture.

*part 2*

*Prehistory*

# Radiocarbon Dating

## Robert F. Heizer

*From Long-range Dating in Archeology. In A. L. Kroeber (ed.), Anthropology Today, University of Chicago Press, 1953, pp. 14–17. By permission of the author and publisher.*

The determination of the duration of geological time by measurement of the disintegration products of radioactive elements has long been used, and the methods and results can be easily located. Of primary interest to archeologists are two methods of time-reckoning by radioactivity, since they will yield dates within the recent past. These are the radiocarbon (carbon 14) technique for calculating the age of organic materials and the radium ratio method for calculating the age of certain stratified sediments, such as glacial-varved clays and ocean-floor deposits.

### Radioactive Carbon (C$^{14}$) Method

The development of this technique dates to 1931, when, at the University of Chicago, an unknown radioactivity was detected. In the following decade this was identified as that of carbon 14 whose source lay in the high atmosphere, where cosmic radiation produces neutrons which are converted to radiocarbon by reaction with nitrogen according to the formula: neutron + N$^{14}$ = proton + C$^{14}$. These carbon atoms unite with oxygen in the atmosphere to form carbon dioxide in the same manner as does ordinary carbon (C$^{12}$), and as such are circulated through the biosphere. An extended technical account of the principles has been recently published by W. F. Libby, Institute for Nuclear Studies, University of Chicago, who has been largely responsible for the development and application of the method.

The C$^{14}$ atoms have a half-life of 5,568 ± 30 years. In the life-process of oxygen exchange in plants and animals, the amount of radiocarbon uptake is sufficient to effect a level of equilibrium with that in the atmosphere. Thus organisms during life possess a specific activity of 15.6 disintegrations per minute per gram of carbon in their bodies. After life and $C^{14}$ intake cease and the equilibrium is halted, radioactive disintegration of the $C^{14}$ occurs, and after 5,568 years this activity will have decreased to 7.8 disintegrations per minute per gram of carbon. Once these facts were established, some very extensive laboratory testing of organic samples of living material from various latitudes, altitudes, and geographical situations was performed, with the result that the $C^{14}$ value for living matter was confirmed. The next step was to assay ancient samples whose age was already known, in order to assess the assumption that the radiocarbon level in the recent past has been the same as at present. These tests confirmed this assumption, in that the amount of radioactive carbon present was equal to that predicted. The final phase of the research by Libby has been to determine the age of numerous samples of unknown age, and as of mid-1951 some 300 samples had been dated. The age of these samples ranged from a few hundred years to over 20,000 years. The list of materials and their radiocarbon dates have been published on several occasions. Expert critical assessment of the radiocarbon date series has been performed in a series of articles. The majority opinion is that the method is sound, provided that the proper precautions are observed in selecting samples which have not been contaminated by the addition of radiocarbon from more recent materials.

Libby recommends the following amounts and materials as most desirable (in the order given) for age determination: charcoal (1 ounce) or charred organic material such as heavily burned bone (2 pounds); well-preserved wood (2 ounces); grasses, cloth, and peat (2 ounces); well-preserved antler and similar horny substances (2 or 3 pounds); well-preserved, unaltered shell (4 ounces).

The dates derived through measurement of the level of radioactivity of $C^{14}$ are not precise and absolute dates but are in each instance accompanied by a $\pm$ error of 100 to 1,200 years, the magnitude of the error being in part a function of the age of the material. This error is assumed not to exceed the sampling error in counting in runs of 48 hours. If the counting period were extended, the error could be reduced in the direction of greater accuracy. On the other hand, the assumption that nothing but random events is responsible for the errors may easily be erroneous. The significance of this error has been commented on by Collier as follows:

"The error figure given represents the standard deviation of the mean (one sigma). This means that there is one chance in three that the true date will fall outside of one sigma and one chance in twenty that it will fall outside of two sigma. To use sample 75 (2665 $\pm$ 200) as an example, there is one chance in three that the true date of the sample is outside the range 2465–2865, and one in twenty that it is outside the range 2265–3065." . . .

# New World Prehistory

## Gordon R. Willey

*From* Science, *Vol. 131, No. 3393, 1960, pp. 73–85. Copyright 1960, American Association for the Advancement of Science. By permission of the author, the publisher and copyright holder.*

The prehistory of the New World is so multi-faceted and complex that synthesis demands not only compression but rigorous selection. What strands of human activity can be followed most easily through the maze of the past? Which elements are the significant ones? These are always troublesome questions for the archeologist, and in the present case they are made more so by the tremendous range of space and time and by the quantity and quality of the data with which we are dealing. It is difficult to fix consistently upon criteria of comparison. The best we can do is to adhere to those universal themes of man's existence that leave their mark in or upon the earth: technology, environmental adaptation, subsistence, and settlement. These were not necessarily determinative of the form and elaboration of other aspects of man's life, but they provide a background and a base which is necessary to the understanding of societies and cultures in pre-Columbian America.

### Major Problems in New World Archeology

Before beginning this account of New World prehistory it will be well to review some of the major problems confronting the American archeologist, for it will be evident that the tentative conclusions which I have reached about these problems give the outline and structure to the present article. They are problems not unlike those of Old World prehistory in that they are concerned with the great changes in man's adaptations to his natural and social environments.

Most briefly, and in approximate chronological order, these problems are as follows.

1. Who were the earliest inhabitants of the New World? Were they food gatherers comparable in their simple subsistence technology

to the peoples of the Old World lower and middle Paleolithic?

2. Where and at what time did the American big-game-hunting specialization of the Pleistocene arise? What were its relationships to the possible earlier food gatherers mentioned above? What were its relationships to the big-game-hunting tradition of the Old World? What happened to the pattern?

3. What were the origins and relationships of the specialized food-collecting subsistence patterns of the post-Pleistocene? Did Asiatic diffusions and migrations play a part in these developments, especially in the Arctic and Boreal zones?

4. Where and when were food plants first domesticated in the New World, and what was the effect of this on society and culture?

5. What is the history of pottery in the New World?

6. At what period and in what regions did sedentary village life based upon farming arise in the New World, and what was the history of the spread of this pattern in native America?

7. What was the nature of sedentary village life in the New World in those areas or regions where plant cultivation was poorly developed or lacking, and when did it occur? To what extent were such cultures and societies dependent upon the diffusion of ideas and elements from the village-farming pattern?

8. When and how did the native civilizations of Nuclear America come into being? What were their relationships within the Nuclear sphere? What were their relationships to non-Nuclear America?

In the statement of these problems and in the discussion that follows, certain terminology is used that needs explanation. This terminology also relates to the three diagrammatic charts (Figs. 1–3) which summarize New World prehistory in broad eras or stages of subsistence technology (earlier chronological ranges) or settlement types (later chronological ranges). The term *food gathering* is applied to subsistence patterns where the gathering of wild plant foods or the hunting of animal life lacked regional specialization or technological diversification. This usage follows that of Braidwood in Old World archeology. *Food collecting,* in contradistinction, implies both specialization and diversification in the taking and utilization of wild plant and animal foods. The other terms descriptive of types of subsistence and settlement—*incipient cultivation, village farming, towns and temples, cities,* and a few other special terms of this nature—are defined below.

The geographical arrangements and the designations of the charts deserve a word. Figure 1 is a cross section for an area that runs north and south through the western axis of the hemisphere. The name *Nuclear America* refers to the southern two-thirds of Mexico, all of Central America, and Andean and coastal Colombia, Ecuador, and Peru, with adjacent portions of Bolivia. This was the heartland of native American agriculture and the seat of the two pre-Columbian centers of civilization, one in Middle America (Mexico-Guatemala) and the other in Peru-Bolivia. There is a column for each of these two centers on the chart, and the column between, headed "Intermediate," refers to what I am calling the "Intermediate area" of southern Central America, Colombia, and Ecuador. To the north of Nuclear America is western North America, divided into the Southwest culture area and the adjacent Great Basin area. Under "Southern South America" are columns headed "South Andes" and "Pampas-Patagonia." Figure 2 is a cross section for an area extending from the Intermediate area of Nuclear America eastward across Venezuela, then southeastward to the Amazon drainage basin and eastern Brazil, and finally south to the Pampas-Patagonia region. In Fig. 3 the "Middle America" column is repeated under "Nuclear America," and the cross section is extended to include the North American eastern woodlands and plains areas. The charts are highly schematic, and only a small number of archeological cultures, or phase names, have been entered in the columns for various areas. (These names appear in small letters.)

The point should be made that the diagonal and curving lines which mark off the major subsistence and settlement types on the charts are not impermeable ones. Influences and traits crossed these lines, frequently moving outward from areas of cultural complexity and intensity into areas of simpler cultures. Such traits were often assimilated by the receiving groups without effecting basic changes in subsistence or settlement. In some instances suspected diffu-

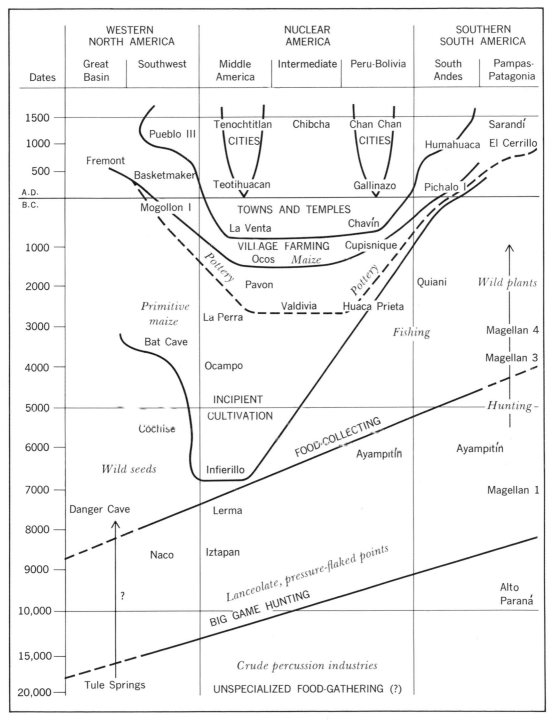

**Figure 1** Subsistence and settlement type levels in native America: cross-section for western North America, Nuclear America, and southern South America. The first appearance of pottery is indicated by the dotted line.

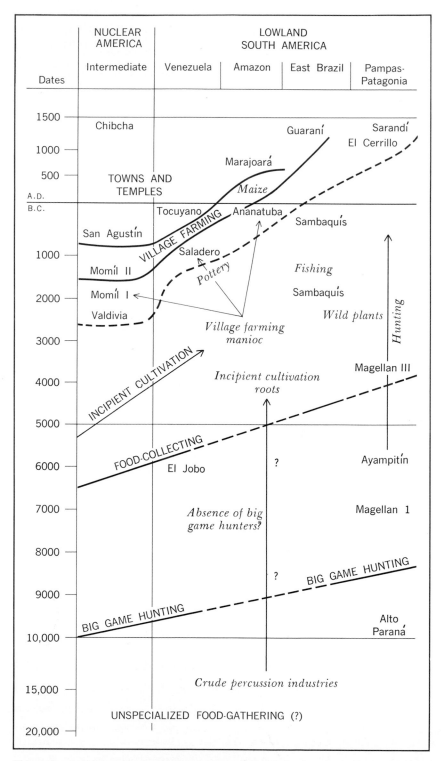

**Figure 2** Subsistence and settlement type levels in native America: cross-section for Nuclear America and lowland South America. The first appearance of pottery is indicated by the dotted line.

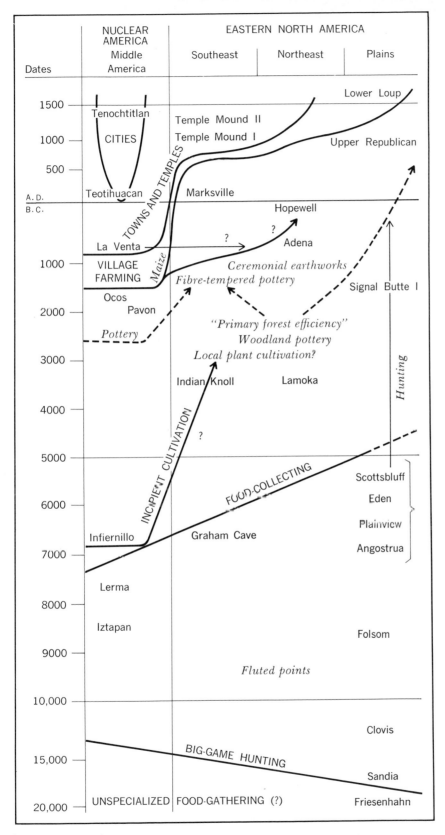

**Figure 3** Subsistence and settlement type levels in native America: cross-section for Nuclear America and eastern North America. The first appearance of pottery is indicated by the dotted line.

sions of this kind are indicated on the charts by means of arrows.

## Pleistocene Food Gathering (?)

There are scattered finds in the Americas which suggest by their typology and chronological position that they may be the remains of early food-gathering societies. These artifacts include rough, percussion-chipped flint choppers, scrapers, and possibly knives or points, and occasional worked bone splinters. In some places, such as Tule Springs, Nevada, or Friesenhahn Cave, Texas, these crude weapons and tools have been found associated with the bones of extinct Pleistocene mammals, so it is likely that some hunting, even of large game, was practiced. In general, however, the technological aspects of the implements show a lack of specialization toward hunting or toward any other particular means of obtaining food. In this the artifacts, and the inferences made from them, are analogous to those for the food-gathering cultures of the Old World lower and middle Paleolithic.

In age and geological placement, such putative early food gatherers in the Americas are not, however, comparable to those of Asia or any part of the Old World. At Tule Springs, a radiocarbon date (22,000 B.C.) indicates a context in the early substages of the Wisconsin glaciation, but in other localities, such as the lowest levels of Danger Cave, Utah, or Fishbone Cave, Nevada, the assemblage can be no older than the final Wisconsin advance. Still other artifact assemblages that suggest an unspecialized food-gathering economy are not satisfactorily dated.

## Pleistocene Big-Game Hunting

Sometime during the last Wisconsin interglacial era, or possibly even earlier, inhabitants of the North American continent entered upon a way of life that was based upon the pursuit and killing of the great ice-age mammals, such as the mammoth, the mastodon, the camel, and later the buffalo. The origins of this life pattern are unknown. There are no visible antecedents in the possible earlier food-gathering cultures of the Americas. There is, it is true, a general correspondence between this New World specialized hunting of Pleistocene fauna and what was going on in

the Old World in the approximately coeval upper Paleolithic stage; yet even this possibility of a connection with the Old World does not provide a reasonable source for the big-game-hunting complexes of the New World, with their distinctive and highly specialized equipment. Apparently the forms which are most indicative of the American big-game-hunting technology are New World inventions.

The technical equipment associated with big-game hunters in the Americas includes lanceolate projectile points shaped by pressure-flaking. These are frequently distinguished by a channel fluting on both faces of the blade. A variety of skin-scraping tools accompanies the points as they are found in camp sites, "kills," and butchering stations. The best documented of these discoveries come from the North American high plains in eastern New Mexico, Colorado, and Texas, and there are others from southern Arizona southward into Mexico. Some finds, such as those of the lower layer of Sandia Cave, New Mexico, may date back to before 15,000 B.C. The Sandia complex is characterized by a lanceolate single-shouldered projectile point. Other discoveries, such as Clovis and Folsom, appear to be later, ranging perhaps, from 15,000 to 7000 B.C. The projectile points of both the Clovis and Folsom complexes are of the fluted form. There are also a variety of lanceolate, unfluted points that appear to mark a horizon subsequent to the Folsom. These include the Angostura, Scottsbluff, Plainview, and Eden types (see Fig. 3).

The spread of big-game hunting in the Americas took place during, and in the first or second millennium after, the final Wisconsin substage, the Mankato-Valders. The total span of time of this dissemination appears to have been from about 9000 to 5000 B.C. Finds of fluted projectile points throughout the eastern woodlands of North America indicate the former prevalence of the pattern there. The Iztapan and Lerma remains in central and northeastern Mexico, the El Jobo points of Venezuela, the Aympitín industry of the Andes and southern South America, and the Magellan I culture of the Straits give the geographical range of the early big-game-hunting societies.

The fate of the big-game-hunting pattern is better known than its beginnings. After 7000 B.C. and the glacial retreats, there was a shrinkage of the total territory in which the big herbivores could be hunted. The inter-montane basins and the range country of western North America became more arid, and a similar climatic shift took place in southern South America. After 5000 B.C., with a still greater increase in warmth and dryness, big-game hunting persisted in the central zones of the old continental grasslands, such as the North American plains and the Argentine pampas. In these areas a modified hunting pattern, based, respectively, on the buffalo and the guanaco, continued into later times. Elsewhere, populations of hunters probably were forced into new environmental situations and new subsistence habits.

## Later Food Collecting and Hunting

These new subsistence patterns can best be described as food collecting. They are differentiated from the possible earlier food-gathering pattern in that they show specialization in the exploitation of regional environments and much more effective technological equipment. Although the taking of game is a means of subsistence in some of these patterns, it is not the old big-game hunting of the Pleistocene. The food collectors, for the most part, developed cultures of greater material wealth, larger communities, and more stable settlements than their predecessors. There were exceptions to this, particularly in areas or regions of severe natural limitations and in the earlier periods of the food-collecting patterns; but on the average, and certainly at the optimum, these generalizations hold true.

Chronologically, most of the food-collecting patterns had their beginnings in the span of time between about 6000 and 2000 B.C. There were, however, exceptions to this, as in the North American Great Basin, where the specialized collecting of wild seeds was well established as early as 7000 or even 8000 B.C. As this is the same general area where clues to the most ancient food gatherers are found, it may be that there is a continuity in the Great Basin from the unspecialized gathering of the early Pleistocene to the later food collecting. According to this interpretation big-game hunting would be only partially represented or would be absent in an intervening sequence position. This relationship is expressed in Fig. 1.

This possibility of continuities between the North American desert food collectors and earlier resident cultures and populations brings attention to the larger question of the origins of the New World food-collecting patterns and peoples in general. There are three logical possibilities: (i) food-collecting societies and cultures were derivative, arising from the earler food gatherers; (ii) members of such societies were the descendants of big-game hunters who were forced by the changing climatic conditions that followed the end of the Wisconsin glaciation to make readjustments; or (iii) they were more recent arrivals from the Old World by way of the Bering Strait. It seems quite likely that all three explanations may be useful, according to the particular geographical areas involved, and I have already mentioned the first two. The third explanation, that new arrivals from Asia played a part, is very probably correct insofar as the development of food-collecting cultures in northern North America is concerned. I have in mind particularly the northeastern woodlands, the northwest Pacific coast, and the subarctic and arctic. Elsewhere Asiatic influences were almost certainly of less direct account.

There are several major food-collecting patterns in the New World, and we can only skim over these very briefly. I have referred to what has been called a Desert pattern. The long depositional histories at Danger Cave, Utah, Leonard Rock Shelter, Nevada, and Fort Rock Cave, western Oregon are representative, and the basketry and crude milling stones found at these sites testify to a seed-collecting and seed-grinding subsistence. A similar story is recorded in the Cochise culture of southern Arizona-New Mexico, and there are evidences of this Desert pattern in Mexico as well.

In the woodlands of eastern North America there is another collecting pattern that shows an adaptation to forest and riverine conditions in hunting, utilization of wild plants, fishing, and catching shellfish. Such sites as the Graham Cave, in Missouri, suggest that there was a transition in the eastern woodlands area, at about 7000 B.C., from big-game hunting to food collecting. In the ensuing millennia these Eastern Woodland collecting cultures, subsumed under the name *Archaic* in much of the literature, underwent progressive adaptations to regional conditions. By 3000 B.C.

they were characterized not only by rough grinding stones and specialized projectile points but by numerous items of polished stone, such as vessels, celts, weights for throwing sticks, and various ornamental or ceremonial objects. The Indian Knoll, Kentucky, and Lamoka, New York, phases are typical of their particular regions. Many of the Archaic sites are huge heaps of shells situated along rivers or on the Atlantic coast. Such locations were undoubtedly suitable for a semisedentary, or even sedentary, existence.

Along the Pacific coast of North America there was another food-collecting pattern which paralleled in many ways that of the Eastern Woodlands. Here, by 2000 B.C. if not earlier, semisedentary societies based upon fishing and acorn gathering were established all along the coast from southern Alaska to southern California. In South America there were also ancient fishing societies along the coasts. The Quiani phase of northern Chile displays this adjustment. On the Brazilian coast are the huge *sambaquis*, piles of shell refuse containing the skeletons and artifactual remains of food-collecting peoples who lived along these shores probably as much as two millennia before the beginning of the Christian Era. Coastal shell-mound dwellers are also known from Venezuela at about this same period.

I have mentioned that in both the North American and the South American plains there were retentions of big-game-hunting patterns into later times; even these cultures, however, show the result of contact with the neighboring food collectors in their possession of an increasing number of food-grinding implements. This is exemplified in the later North American Plains phases, such as the Signal Butte I, and by the later phases in the Strait of Magellan sequence and on the Argentine pampas.

## Incipient Cultivation

The change from food collecting to a subsistence based upon plant cultivation was one of the great turning points in human prehistory. This is true of the New World as well as the Old, and there are indications in both hemispheres that this switch-over was not a rapid one, but that it was effected only over a period of experimentation. It is this era of experimental or incipient cultivation in the New World that I now wish to examine.

In the Americas it would appear that there may be at least four distinct and semi-independent traditions of incipient farming. Two of these are Nuclear American. The northern one, the probable propagator of maize, was located in Middle America and in the adjacent deserts of northern Mexico and the southwestern United States; the southern one had its focus on the Peruvian coast. A third incipient-cultivation tradition centered somewhere in the tropical forests of the Amazon or Orinoco. Its existence is difficult to demonstrate archeologically, but such a tradition is needed to explain the domestication of manioc and other root crops. A fourth, and distinctly lesser, tradition rose in eastern North America in the Mississippi Valley system.

The earliest evidence for incipient cultivation in any of these traditions comes from northern Nuclear America. The region is the northeastern periphery of Middle America, in the semiarid hill country of Tamaulipas. Here, preserved plant remains were taken from the refuse deposits of dry caves. In the Infiernillo phase, dating from 7000 to 5000 B.C., there are traces of domesticated squash (*Cucurbita pepo*) and of possible domesticates of peppers, gourds, and small beans. The cultural context is that of North American desert food collectors. There are, in addition to flint implements, net bags of yucca and maguey cords and woven baskets of a rod-foundation type. In the succeeding Ocampo phase, from about 5000 to 3000 B.C., beans were definitely domesticates. After this, between 3000 and 2000 B.C., a primitive small-eared maize came into the sequence in the La Perra and Flacco phases. R. S. MacNeish, who excavated and studied the Tamaulipas caves, has estimated the composition of food refuse of the La Perra phase to be as follows: 76 percent wild plants, 15 percent animals, and 9 percent cultigens. The La Perra and Flacco artifact inventories are not strikingly different from inventories of the earlier phases, although they demonstrate a somewhat greater variety of manufactures and an increased concern for seed foods. A few centuries later, at about 1500 B.C., an archeological complex which is representative of fully settled village farming appears in the region. Thus, the Tamaulipas sequence offers a more or less unbroken story of the very slow transition from food collecting supplemented with incipient cultivation to the patterns of established cultivation.

Early and primitive maize is also found to the north of Tamaulipas, actually outside of Nuclear America, in New Mexico. At Bat Cave, corncobs from refuse of a Cochise-affiliated culture date between 3500 and 2500 B.C. This is as early as the La Perra maize, or even earlier.

As yet, neither archeologists nor botanists have been able to determine the exact center of origin for domestication of maize in the New World, and it may be that this important event first took place in northern Middle America and in southwestern North America, where the intensive use of wild seeds in a food-collecting economy in a desert area provided a favorable setting. There remains, nevertheless, the very good possibility that a territory nearer the heart of Nuclear America and more centrally situated for the spread of maize in the hemisphere—an area such as southern Middle America—played this primary role in the cultivation of maize. The great difficulty is, of course, that the archeological record is so uneven, owing to the rarity of sites and environments where such things as plant remains are preserved in the earth. Such findings have not yet been reported in southern Middle America.

Coastal Peru, at the southern end of Nuclear America, provides a rainless climate and splendid conditions for preservation of organic materials in open archeological sites, and it is in Peru that we have glimpsed what appears to be a second tradition of incipient plant cultivation in Nuclear America. At Huaca Prieta, in a great hill of marine shells, sea-urchin spines, ash, and other debris, cultivated squash, peppers, gourds, cotton, and a local bean (*Canavalia*) were found, along with an abundance of wild root plants and fruits. The people who raised and gathered these crops and seafoods lived at Huaca Prieta at least 2000 years before the Christian Era. Whether there was, however indirectly, an exchange of domesticated plants between these early Peruvians and their contemporaries in Middle America is not certain. Such connections could have existed; or the beginnings of cultivation may have been truly independent of each other in these two areas of Nuclear America. Definite connections between early farmers of Middle America and of Peru appear, however, by 700 B.C. with the sudden presence of maize in Peru. This maize was not, like that at Bat Cave or in the La Perra culture of Tamaulipas, of an extremely primitive kind. It was brought, or it spread, to Peru as a relatively well-developed plant, and it serves as a link to Middle America. We may conclude that Nuclear America possessed, from this time forward, a single major horticultural tradition, but by this time we have also passed beyond the chronological limits of cultivation incipience.

An ancient tradition of plant cultivation in the South American tropical forest is based upon the presumption that a long period of experimentation was necessary for the domestication of such tropical root crops as bitter and sweet manioc (*Manihot utilissima, M. Api*) and the yam (*Ipomoea batatas*). It seems reasonably certain that these domesticates date back to before 1000 B.C. in lowland Venezuela. This is inferred from the presence of pottery griddles, of the sort used for cooking manioc cakes in later times, in the Saladero phase at the Orinoco Delta by this date. Also, the early archeological phase of Momíl I, in Caribbean Colombia, has the pottery manioc griddle. The dating of Momíl I is debatable, but some of the ceramic traits suggest a date as early as 2000 B.C. Saladero and Momíl I are, however, outside the chronological and development range of incipient cultivation patterns. They appear to be village sites based upon the cultivation of root crops, and as such they are comparable to, although historically separate from, village farming based on maize. I shall return to this point farther along. For the present I bring these sites into the discussion because their existence implies centuries, or even millennia, of prior incipient root-crop cultivation in tropical northern South America.

A fourth tradition of incipient cultivation for the New World derives from the cultivation of local plants in the Mississippi Valley by as early as 1000 B.C. These plants include the sunflower, the goosefoot (*Chenopodium*), and the pumpkin (*Cucurbita pepo*). This domestication may have been in response to stimuli from Middle America, or it may have been an entirely independent development. This Eastern Woodland incipient-cultivation tradition was undoubtedly but a minor part of the food-collecting economy for a long time. Just how important it ever became, or how important the early diffusion of maize was to eastern United States cultures of the 1st millennium B.C., are crucial problems in the understanding of the area. I shall return to them later.

### Appearance of Pottery

Before taking up the rise of village farming in Nuclear America and its subsequent spread to other parts of the hemisphere, let us review the first appearances of pottery in the New World. Obviously, the line indicating the presence of pottery on the charts is not comparable to the lines indicating type of subsistence or settlement (Figs. 1–3). American archeologists no longer consider pottery to be the inevitable concomitant of agricultural village life, as was the fashion some years ago. Still, ceramics, because of their very ubiquity and durability, are an important datum in many prehistoric sequences. Their presence, while not a necessary functional correlate of farming, at least implies a certain degree of cultural development and sedentary living.

At the present writing there seem to be two pottery traditions for native America. Curiously, the ages of these two pottery traditions —in the broadest sense of that term—may be about the same, 2500 B.C.

One of these pottery traditions, which we shall call the Nuclear American, is believed to be indigenous, but we can be no more specific about its geographic point of origin than to state this is somewhere in the central latitudes of the New World. Actually, the earliest radiocarbon dates on the Nuclear American pottery tradition come from coastal Ecuador, in the Valdivia phase, and are from about 2400 to 2500 B.C. There are also early dates on pottery generally similar to that of Valdivia from Panama (about 2100 B.C.) Thus, these earliest ceramic datings for Nuclear America are not from Middle America or Peru but from the Intermediate area, and this may be significant in following up origins, although the record is still too incomplete to say for sure. Both the Ecuadorean and the Panamanian early potteries are found in coastal shell-mound sites, and in connection with cultures about whose means of subsistence it is not easy to draw inferences, except to say that full village

farming was unlikely. Possibly marine subsistence was supplemented with incipient cultivation, although we have no proof of this. The Valdivia and the Panamanian (Monagrillo) pottery is reasonably well made and fired, the forms are rather simple, and the vessels are decorated with incisions, excisions, punctations, and very simple band painting. These early Ecuadorean and Panamanian styles may be part of a stratum of ancient Nuclear American pottery that underlies both Middle America and Peru. There are some indications that this may be the case, although the oldest pottery so far known in the Middle American and Peruvian areas dates from several centuries later. In Fig. 1 the interpretation is offered that Nuclear American pottery is oldest in southern Middle America (for this there is as yet no evidence) and in the Intermediate area for this there is evidence). Whatever the point of origin for pottery in Nuclear America, there is fairly general agreement that the ceramic ideas generated there carried to much of outlying North and South America.

The second major pottery tradition of the Americas is widely recognized by the term *Woodland*. Apparently not indigenous, but derived from northern Asia, it is best known from the eastern woodlands of New York and the Great Lakes region. So far, its presumed long trek from the arctic down through Canada has not been traced. Woodland pottery is generally of simpler design than the early Nuclear American wares. Of an elongated form, it is frequently finished only with cord-marked surfaces. As already noted, the oldest of this cord-marked pottery in the Americas may go back to 2500 B.C. Even if this early dating is not accepted, there is little doubt but that Woodland pottery was well established in eastern North America before 1000 B.C.

In spite of the fact that the Nuclear American and Woodland pottery traditions are so radically different, there are, interestingly, a few similarities. The most notable of these is the technique of rocker-stamping combined with incised zoning of plain surface areas, known in Nuclear America and in the eastern United States. The distinctive rocker-stamped treatment of pottery was accomplished by impressing the soft, unfired surface of a vessel with either a small straight-edged implement manipulated rocker-fashion or, possibly, with a fine-edged disk used like a roulette. The impressions left on the pottery may be either plain or dentate, and they always have a characteristic "zigzag" appearance. Rocker-stamping is found in the Valdivia phase in Ecuador, and it also occurs at about 1000 B.C. in parts of Middle America and in Peru. In eastern North America it is not found on the earliest Woodland pottery but is found on vessels which date from just a few centuries before the beginning of the Christian Era. Thus, the Nuclear American rather than the Woodland tradition has chronological priority in this trait in the New World. Again, as with so many other problems that perplex Americanists we can only refer to this without coming to any conclusions as to the timing and direction of the flows of possible diffusions. Nuclear American and Woodland ceramics may in some way be related, but at the present state of knowledge they appear to have different origins and substantially separate histories.

## Village Farming in Nuclear America

Braidwood and others have stressed the importance in the Old World of the threshold of the village-farming settled community. Although in its beginnings the agricultural village had a subsistence base that was no more adequate, if as ample, as that of some of the food-collecting communities, this base offered the potential in certain Old World localities that led, eventually, to civilization. In the New World a similar development was repeated in Nuclear America.

In the New World the line between incipient cultivation and village farming has been drawn at that theoretical point where village life is, in effect, sustained primarily by cultivated food plants. In archeology this distinction must be made by an appraisal of the size and stability of a settlement as well as by direct or indirect clues as to the existence of agriculture. In Nuclear America the earliest time for which we can postulate the conditions of village farming is the 2nd millennium B.C. For example, in Middle America in the Tamaulipas sequence the change-over from incipient cultivation to established cultivation takes place at about 1500 B.C. Elsewhere in Middle America the known sequences begin with the village-farming stage, as at Early Zacatenco (Valley of Mexico), Las Charcas (Guatemalan Highlands), Ocos (Pacific coast of Guatemala), and Mamom (Maya lowlands). In Peru the village-farming level is reasonably well defined with the appearance of maize in the Cupisnique phase and the shift of settlements back from the coast to the valley interiors. The date for this event is shortly after 1000 B.C.; this suggests that the horizon for village farming may have sloped upward in time from Middle America to Peru (Fig. 1). For the Intermediate area, where I have noted the earliest occurrence of pottery in Nuclear America, the threshold of village farming is difficult to spot. In Ecuador, the phases succeeding Valdivia have a different ecological setting, being inland in the river valleys rather than on the immediate shores. Perhaps, as in Peru, this correlates with the primary economic importance of plant cultivation. In Colombia, the Momíl II phase, which is represented by a stable village site area, is believed to have possessed maize.

The foregoing discussion carries the implication that village farming was a pattern diffused through Nuclear America from a single area or region. Essentially, this is the point of view expressed in this article. This is not to overlook the possibility that village agricultural stability may have risen independently in more than one place in the New World. In fact, as I point out below, it apparently did just that in the tropical forests of South America. I am of the opinion, however, that in the Nuclear American zone the maize plant, genetically developed and economically successful, became the vital element in a village-farming way of life that subsequently spread as a complex. For the present, I would hazard the guess that this complex developed in southern Middle America and from there spread northward to Mexico and southward as far as Peru. This was, in a sense, its primary diffusion or spread. Afterward, there were secondary diffusions to other parts of the Americas.

## The Village in Non-Nuclear America

These secondary disseminations of the Nuclear American pattern of village farming were responsible for the establishment of similar communities in areas such as southwestern North America, the southern Andes, lowland tropical South America, and the eastern woodlands of North America (see Figs. 1–3). This process was relatively simple in southwestern North America and the southern Andes. The agricultural patterns were diffused to, or carried and superimposed upon, peoples with food-collecting economies of limited efficiency. In the Southwest, village farming and ceramics first appear at about the same time in such cultures as the Vahki, the Mogollon I, and the Basketmaker. This was between 200 B.C. and A.D 300. Moving from the south, the village-farming pattern pushed as far as the Fremont culture of the northern periphery of the Southwest. In the southern Andes there is, as yet, no good hint of an early incipient-cultivation tradition, and, apparently, pottery and agriculture arrive at about the same time, integrated as a village-farming complex. This flow of migration or diffusion was from Peru-Bolivia southward. Pichalo I of northern Chile marks such an introduction, as do the earliest of the Barreales phases in northwest Argentina. The time is about the beginning of the Christian Era. Beyond the southern Andes the village-farming pattern did not diffuse onto the plains of the pampas or Patagonia.

The relationship of Nuclear American village farming to the tropical lowlands of South America was much more complex. There the maize-farming pattern was projected into an area in which village life already existed. This is indicated in Fig. 2 by the entry "Village Farming—Manioc" in the columns headed "Venezuela" and "Amazon." Sedentary village life based upon root-crop farming is estimated to be as old as 2500 B.C. This is a guess, and, if it is correct, these villages are older than the Nuclear American village sustained by maize. Perhaps the estimated date is too early; however, at 2000 and 1000 B.C., respectively (see Fig. 2), we have the villages of Momíl I and Saladero, which, apparently, were supported by root-crop cultivation. It is of interest to note that Momíl I, near the mouth of the Sinù River in Colombia, lies within the axis of Nuclear America; yet it differs from the succeeding Momíl II phase at the same site in being oriented toward manioc rather than maize. This suggests that, in the Intermediate area at least, tropical-forest farming patterns may have preceded farming patterns for maize in Nuclear America.

Relationships between village farming in Nuclear America and in eastern North America, are also complicated. It is unlikely that the local incipient-cultivation tradition in eastern North America ever matured into a subsistence pattern that could have supported fully sedentary village life. J. R. Caldwell has argued that, in its place, a steadily increasing efficiency in forest collecting and hunting climaxed at about 2000 B.C. in a level of "Primary Forest Efficiency" (see Fig. 3). Such a level, he concludes, offered the same opportunities for population stability and cultural creativity in the eastern woodlands as were offered by village farming. While agreeing with Caldwell that the efflorescence of Adena-Hopewell (about 800 B.C. to A.D. 200) is the brilliant end product of a mounting cultural intensity in eastern North America that originated in the food-collecting or Archaic societies, I am not yet convinced that plant cultivation did not play an important role in this terminal development. And by plant cultivation I am referring to maize, brought or diffused from Nuclear America. There is, as yet, no good direct evidence of maize associated with either the Adena or the contemporary Poverty Point culture. Maize is, however, found with Hopewellian cultures, although it has been assumed that it was of relatively little importance as subsistence at this time. I would argue that the riverine locations of Adena and Hopewell sites, together with the great size and plan of the ceremonial earthworks that mark many of them, make it difficult to infer an adequate subsistence if maize agriculture is ruled out.

To sum up briefly, the amazing cultural florescence of the Eastern Woodlands in the 1st millennium B.C. has not yet been satisfactorily explained. This florescence rests upon a chronologically deep series of Archaic food-collecting cultures which were at least semisedentary, and it contains elements, such as pottery, which are probably of Asiatic derivation and which added to the richness of the Archaic continuum. But the sudden burst of social and cultural energy which marks the Adena culture cannot be interpreted easily without adding other factors to the equation, and perhaps these missing factors are maize agriculture and other stimuli from Middle America (see Fig. 3).

Village life is, of course, present in native America in the non-Nuclear areas under conditions where plant cultivation may be ruled out entirely. Settled villages developed on the northwest coast of North America, with population supported by the intensive food-collecting economy of the coast and rivers. The same is also true for the coast and interior valleys of California. It is significant, however, that in neither of these areas did aboriginal cultivation ever make much headway, while in eastern North America it became a staple of life in the later pre-Columbian centuries.

**Temples, Towns, and Cities**

In Nuclear America the town and eventually the city had beginnings in the settled farming village. A centralizing factor in this development was undoubtedly the temple. This earliest form of permanent structure usually had a flat-topped pyramidal mound of earth or rock as a base, and these mound bases of temples are found associated with some, but not all, of the village-farming cultures in Middle America. At first, the importance of such a mound, and of the temple that stood on it, was probably limited to the immediate village. Sometimes these villages were small, concentrated clusters of dwellings; in other instances the settlement pattern was a dispersed one, with a number of small, hamlet-like units scattered at varying distances from the temple center. Later on, the temple, or temple and palace structures, became the focal point of what might be called a town.

In Nuclear America the towns, like their antecedent villages, were either concentrated or dispersed. The former pattern developed in parts of Middle America, such as the Valley of Mexico or the Guatemalan Highlands, and in Peru; the latter was characteristic of the Veracruz-Tabasco lowlands or the Peten-Yucatan jungles of Middle America. In the towns the temple or ceremonial precinct was devoted to religious and governmental matters and to the housing of priests and of rulers and their retainers. The surrounding settlement zone, either scattered or concentrated, grew with increase in the numbers of farmers, artisans, or both. Trade was an important function of these towns.

In Nuclear America the town-and-temple community dates back to 800 B.C., a date that is applicable both to Middle America and to Peru. In the Intermediate area, between these two, town life was certainly pre-Columbian, but its date of origin is difficult to determine

because there is a lack of adequate archeological chronologies.

In lowland South America, town-and-temple communities also antedate the Conquest, and it seems likely that these communities were, in part, the result of contact with and stimulus from the Nuclear American axis. In the southern Andes the tightly planned clusters of rock and adobe buildings of the late archeological periods of northwestern Argentina reflect town and city life in Peru and Bolivia. Similarly, towns of the pre-historic southwestern United States relate to the Nuclear American zone. Development of these towns dates from sometime after A.D. 500, with an apogee in the Pueblo III and IV periods and in the Classic Hohokam phases.

On the other great periphery of Nuclear America, eastern North America, Middle American town life, with its temple mound-and-plaza complex, entered the Mississippi Valley sometime between A.D. 500 and 1000 and climaxed in the Mississippian or Temple Mound cultures shortly afterwards. Maize cultivation was an established part of this complex. Thus, in a sense, the thresholds of village farming and of the town-and-temple complex in the eastern woodlands, when these beginnings can be identified indisputably as of Nuclear American inspiration, are synchronous (Fig. 3).

There remains, however, as in our consideration of the village-farming level, the puzzle of the Adena-Hopewell cultures. As we have already noted, the Adena-Hopewell ceremonial mounds and earthworks, built between 800 B.C and A.D. 200, are of impressive size. Some of them are comparable in dimensions, and in the amount of coordinated manpower necessary to build them, with the contemporary mounds of Middle America. Although the mounds of Middle America were usually temple platforms while the Adena-Hopewell tumuli were mounds heaped up to cover tombs and sacred buildings, this dichotomy should not be overstressed. Some mounds of Middle America also were tombs, or combined tombs and temples. In any event, it is safe to conclude that the Adena-Hopewell mounds were structures which memorialized social and religious traditions and served as community nuclei, as the ceremonial building did in Middle America. Was there a historical connection between Middle America and the Eastern

Woodlands at this time, and was Adena-Hopewell ceremonial construction influenced by the emergence of the town-and-temple concept of Middle America? There is no satisfactory answer at present, but the possibilities cannot be dismissed (see Fig. 3).

In Nuclear America the city developed from the town and temple, and there is no sharp division between the two. Size is, assuredly, one criterion but not the only one. These cities were the nerve centers of civilizations. They were distinguished by great public buildings and the arts. Formal pantheons of deities were worshipped in the temples under the tutelage of organized priesthoods. Populations were divided into social classes. Trade, in both raw materials and luxury items, was carried on in these cities, and science and writing were under the patronage of the leaders. Not all of these criteria are known or can be inferred for any one city in the New World, but many of them do properly pertain to Middle American and Peruvian sites from as early as the first centuries of the Christian Era.

Cities in the New World seem to have been of two types, and these types may have their antecedents in the earlier dispersed and concentrated towns. The dispersed city, with its ceremonial center and outlying hamlets, appears to have been orthogenetic in its traditions and to have drawn upon, and commanded, a relatively limited geographical territory. The great lowland Mayan centers of the Classic period, such as Tikal or Palenque, are representative. The concentrated city adheres more to the concept of the city in the western European definition of the term. It was a truly urban agglomeration. Its traditions were heterogenetic, and its power extended over a relatively large territorial domain. The city was, in effect, the capital of an empire. Peruvian Chanchan, Aztec Tenochtitlan, and, probably, the more ancient Mexican city of Teotihuacan represent the type.

Although the cities and civilizations which developed in Middle America and Peru in the 1st millennium A.D. were unique and distinct entities in their own right, it is obvious that they also drew upon a common heritage of culture which had begun to be shared by all of Nuclear America at the level of village-farming life. This heritage was apparently built up over the centuries, through bonds of interchange and contact, direct and indirect.

There are substantial archeological evidences in support of this supposition. During the era of city life these relationships continued, so that a kind of cosmopolitanism, resulting from trade, was just beginning to appear in Nuclear America in the last few centuries before Columbus.

In the outlands beyond Nuclear America, trade and influences from the cities followed old routes of contact and penetrated and were assimilated in varying degrees. In the south Andes there was the very direct impact of the Inca state in the final hundred years before the Spanish conquest, and northward from Mexico, Toltec-derived influences reached the North American Southwest in relatively unadulterated form. But, for the most part, the potentialities of the New World city for influencing and acculturating the "barbarian outlanders" were still unrealized when the European entered the American continents.

## Comments

Conclusions are inappropriate to a synthesis which, by its nature, is an outline of opinion, however tentative. Retrospective comment seems more in order.

A few things stand out. The early inhabitants of the New World were not remarkably different in their mode of life from the food gatherers and hunters of the Old World; yet even on these early horizons, and despite the relatively limited cultural inventories available, dissimilarities of form are striking. The interrelationships of the two hemispheres during the Pleistocene are still very vague.

Plant cultivation in the New World—its incipient rise and its culmination as the most effective subsistence base of the Americas—is, of course, analogous to happenings in the Old World. The important American plants, however, are of local origin. In the Western Hemisphere the incipience of cultivation followed the end of the Pleistocene, and was not a great deal later, perhaps, than in the Old World Middle East. Yet the period of incipience was longer here; over 5000 years elapsed before village life was sustained by crop cultivation. Is this because the first New World cultigens were inadequate as foodstuffs, and it was necessary to develop, first, the cereal maize before agriculture was made profitable?

Although there is a high correlation between village life and agricultural subsistence in the New World, there were New World societies and cultures which maintained villages without plant cultivation. In at least one instance, that of the ancient Adena-Hopewell development of eastern North America, community centers comparable to those of the contemporary farmers of Middle America may have been built and supported without a full-fledged farming subsistence.

I have slighted in this presentation the relationships between Asia and the Americas which were probably maintained from Pleistocene times down to the European conquest. This is particularly true of the cultures of the northern half of North America, where it is certain that there were contacts between the Old World and the arctic, subarctic, and northwest Pacific coasts. For Nuclear America nothing at all has been said of the possibility of trans-Pacific contacts between the Old World civilizations of China and Southeast Asia and those of Middle America and Peru. This undoubtedly reflects my own bias, but I remain willing to be convinced of such events and their importance to the history of culture in the New World.

*selection* 7

# Microenvironments and Mesoamerican Prehistory

## Michael D. Coe and Kent V. Flannery

*From* Science, *Vol. 143, No. 3607, 1964, pp. 650–651.* Copyright 1964, American Association for the Advancement of Science. By permission of the authors, the publisher, and copyright holder.

A crucial period in the story of the pre-Columbian cultures of the New World is the transition from a hunting-and-collecting way of life to effective village farming. We are now fairly certain that Mesoamerica is the area in which this took place, and that the time span involved is from approximately 6500 to 1000 B.C., a period during which a kind of "incipient cultivation" based on a few domesticated plants, mainly maize, gradually supplemented and eventually replaced wild foods. Beginning probably about 1500 B.C., and definitely by 1000 B.C., villages with all of the signs of the settled arts, such as pottery and loomweaving, appear throughout Mesoamerica, and the foundations of pre-Columbian civilization may be said to have been established.

Much has been written about food-producing "revolutions" in both hemispheres. There is now good evidence both in the Near East and in Mesoamerica that food production was part of a relatively slow *evolution*, but there still remain several problems related to the process of settling down. For the New World, there are three questions which we would like to answer.

1. What factors favored the early development of food production in Mesoamerica as compared with other regions of this hemisphere?

2. What was the mode of life of the earlier hunting-and-collecting peoples in Mesoamerica, and in exactly what ways was it changed by the addition of cultivated plants?

3. When, where, and how did food production make it possible for the first truly sedentary villages to be established in Mesoamerica?

The first of these questions cannot be answered until botanists determine the habits and preferred habitats of the wild ancestors of maize, beans, and the various cucurbits which were domesticated. To answer the other questions, we must reconstruct the human-ecological situations which prevailed.

Some remarkably sophisticated, multidisciplinary projects have been and still are being carried out elsewhere in the world, aimed at reconstructing prehistoric human ecology. However, for the most part they have been concerned with the adaptations of past human communities to large-scale changes in the environment over very long periods—that is, to alterations in the *macroenvironment*, generally caused by climatic fluctuations. Such alterations include the shift from tundra to boreal conditions in northern Europe. Nevertheless, there has been a growing suspicion among prehistorians that macroenvironmental changes are insufficient as an explanation of the possible causes of food production and its effects, regardless of what has been written to the contrary.

### Ethnography and Microenvironments

We have been impressed, in reading anthropologists' accounts of simple societies, with the fact that human communities, while in some senses limited by the macroenvironment —for instance, by deserts or by tropical forests—usually exploit several or even a whole series of well-defined *microenvironments*

in their quest for food. These microenvironments might be defined as smaller subdivisions of large ecological zones; examples are the immediate surroundings of the ancient archeological site itself, the bank of a nearby stream, or a distant patch of forest.

An interesting case is provided by the Shoshonean bands which, until the mid-19th century, occupied territories within the Great Basin of the American West. These extremely primitive peoples had a mode of life quite similar to that of the peoples of Mesoamerica of the 5th millennium B.C., who were the first to domesticate maize. The broadly limiting effects of the Great Basin (which, generally speaking, is a desert) and the lack of knowledge of irrigation precluded any effective form of agriculture, even though some bands actually sowed wild grasses and one group tried an ineffective watering of wild crops. Consequently, the Great Basin aborigines remained on a hunting and plant-collecting level, with extremely low population densities and a very simple social organization. However, Steward's study shows that each band was not inhabiting a mere desert but moved on a strictly followed seasonal round among a vertically and horizontally differentiated set of microenvironments, from the lowest salt flats up to piñon forest, which were "niches" in a human-ecological sense.

The Great Basin environment supplied the potential for cultural development or lack of it, but the men who lived there selected this or that microenvironment. Steward clearly shows that *how* and *to what* they adapted influenced many other aspects of their culture, from their technology to their settlement pattern, which was necessarily one of restricted wandering from one seasonally occupied camp to another.

Seasonal wandering would appear to be about the only possible response of a people without animal or plant husbandry to the problem of getting enough food throughout the year. Even the relatively rich salmon-fishing cultures of the Northwest Coast (British Columbia and southern Alaska) were without permanently occupied villages. Contrariwise, it has seemed to us that only a drastic reduction of the number of niches to be exploited, and a concentration of these in space, would have permitted the establishment of full-time village life. The ethnographic data suggest that an analysis of microenvironments or niches would throw much light on the processes by which the Mesoamerican peoples settled down.

## Methodology

If the environment in which an ancient people lived was radically different from any known today, and especially if it included animal and plant species which are now extinct and whose behavior is consequently unknown, then any reconstruction of the subsistence activities of the people is going to be difficult. All one could hope for would be a more-or-less sound reconstruction of general ecological conditions, while a breakdown of the environment into smaller ecological niches would be impossible. However, much if not most archeological research concerns periods so recent in comparison with the million or so years of human prehistory that in most instances local conditions have not changed greatly in the interval between the periods investigated and the present.

If we assume that there is a continuity between the ancient and the modern macroenvironment in the area of interest, there are three steps which we must take in tracing the role of microenvironments.

1. Analysis of the present-day microecology (from the human point of view) of the archeological zone. Archeological research is often carried out in remote and little known parts of the earth, which have not been studied from the point of view of natural history. Hence, the active participation of botanists, zoologists, and other natural scientists is highly recommended.

The modern ethnology of the region should never be neglected, for all kinds of highly relevant data on the use of surrounding niches by local people often lie immediately at hand. We have found in Mesoamerica that the workmen on the "dig" are a mine of such information. There may be little need to thumb through weighty reports on the Australian aborigines or South African Bushmen when the analogous custom can be found right under one's nose. The end result of the analysis should be a map of the microenvironments defined (here aerial photographs are of great use), with detailed data on the seasonal possibilities each offers human com-

munities on certain technological levels of development.

2. Quantitative analysis of food remains in the archeological sites, and of the technical equipment (arrow or spear points, grinding stones for seeds, baskets and other containers, and so on) related to food-getting. It is a rare site report that treats of bones and plant remains in any but the most perfunctory way. It might seem a simple thing to ship animal bones from a site to a specialist for identification, but most archeologists know that many zoologists consider identification of recent faunal remains a waste of time. Because of this, and because many museum collections do not include postcranial skeletons that could be used for identification, the archeologist must arrange to secure his own comparative collection. If this collection is assembled by a zoologist on the project, a by-product of the investigation would be a faunal study of microenvironments. Similarly, identification of floral and other specimens from the site would lead to other specialized studies.

3. Correlation of the archeological with the microenvironmental study in an overall analysis of the ancient human ecology.

## The Tehuacán Valley

An archeological project undertaken by R. S. MacNeish, with such a strategy in mind, has been located since 1961 in the dry Tehuacán Valley of southern Puebla, Mexico. The valley is fringed with bone-dry caves in which the food remains of early peoples have been preserved to a remarkable degree in stratified deposits. For a number of reasons, including the results of his past archeological work in Mesoamerica, McNeish believed that he would find here the origins of maize agriculture in the New World, and he has been proved right. It now seems certain that the wild ancestor of maize was domesticated in the Tehuacán area some time around the beginning of the 5th millennium B.C.

While the Tehuacán environment is in general a desert, the natural scientists of the project have defined within it four microenvironments (Fig. 1).

1. *Alluvial valley floor*, a level plain sparsely covered with mesquite, grasses, and cacti, offering fairly good possibilities, especially

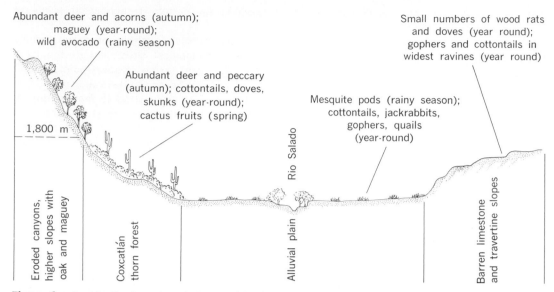

Abundant deer and acorns (autumn);
maguey (year-round);
wild avocado (rainy season)

Small numbers of wood rats
and doves (year round);
gophers and cottontails in
widest ravines (year round)

Abundant deer and peccary
(autumn); cottontails, doves,
skunks (year-round);
cactus fruits (spring)

Mesquite pods (rainy season);
cottontails, jackrabbits,
gophers, quails
(year-round)

1,800 m

Río Salado

Eroded canyons,
higher slopes with
oak and maguey

Coxcatlán
thorn forest

Alluvial plain

Barren limestone
and travertine slopes

**Figure 1** An idealized east-west transsection of the central part of the Tehuacán Valley, Puebla, Mexico, showing microenvironments and the seasons in which the food resources are exploited. East is to the left. The length of the area represented is about 20 kilometers.

along the Río Salado, for primitive maize agriculture dependent on rainfall.

2. *Travertine slopes*, on the west side of the valley. This would have been a niche useful for growing maize and tomatoes and for trapping cottontail rabbits.

3. *Coxcatlán thorn forest*, with abundant seasonal crops of wild fruits, such as various species of *Opuntia*, pitahaya, and so on. There is also a seasonal abundance of whitetail deer, cottontail rabbits, and skunks, and there are some peccaries.

4. *Eroded canyons*, unsuitable for exploitation except for limited hunting of deer and as routes up to maguey fields for those peoples who chewed the leaves of that plant.

The correlation of this study with the analysis, by specialists, of the plant and animal remains (these include bones, maize cobs, chewed quids, and even feces) found in cave deposits has shown that the way of life of the New World's first farmers was not very different from that of the Great Basin aborigines in the 19th century. Even the earliest inhabitants of the valley, prior to 6500 B.C., were more collectors of seasonally gathered wild plant foods than they were "big game hunters," and they traveled in microbands in an annual, wet-season-dry-season cycle. While slightly more sedentary macrobands appeared with the adoption of

simple maize cultivation after 5000 B.C., these people nevertheless still followed the old pattern of moving from microenvironment to microenvironment, separating into microbands during the dry season.

The invention and gradual improvement of agriculture seem to have made few profound alterations in the settlement pattern of the valley for many millennia. Significantly, by the Formative period (from about 1500 B.C. to A.D. 200), when agriculture based on a hybridized maize was far more important than it had been in earlier periods as a source of food energy, the pattern was still one of part-time nomadism. In this part of the dry Mexican highlands, until the Classic period (about A.D. 200 to 900), when irrigation appears to have been introduced into Tehuacán, food production had still to be supplemented with extensive plant collecting and hunting.

Most of the peoples of the Formative period apparently lived in large villages on the alluvial valley floor during the wet season, from May through October of each year, for planting had to be done in May and June, and harvesting, in September and October. In the dry season, from November through February, when the trees and bushes had lost their leaves and the deer were easy to see and track, some of the population must have moved to hunting camps, principally in the Cox-

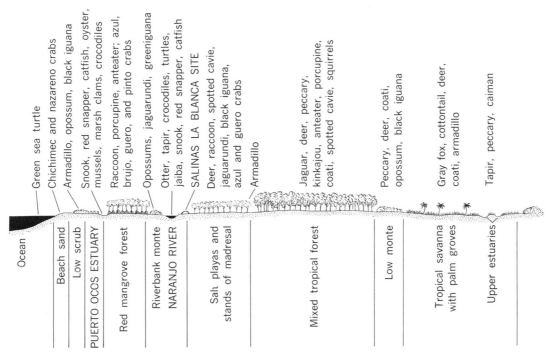

**Figure 2** Northeast-southwest transsection of the Ocós area of coastal Guatemala, showing microenvironments in relation to the site of Salinas La Blanca. Northeast is to the right. The length of area represented is about 15 kilometers.

catlán thorn forest. By February, hunting had become less rewarding as the now-wary deer moved as far as possible from human habitation; however, in April and May the thorn forest was still ripe for exploitation, as many kinds of wild fruit matured. In May it was again time to return to the villages on the valley floor for spring planting.

Now, in some other regions of Mesoamerica there were already, during the Formative period, fully sedentary village cultures in existence. It is clear that while the Tehuacán valley was the locus of the first domestication of maize, the origins of full-blown village life lie elsewhere. Because of the constraining effects of the macroenvironment, the Tehuacán people were exploiting, until relatively late in Mesoamerican prehistory, as widely spaced and as large a number of microenvironments as the Great Basin aborigines were exploiting in the 19th century.

## Coastal Guatemala

Near the modern fishing port of Ocós, only a few kilometers from the Mexican border on the alluvial plain of the Pacific coast of Guatemala, we have found evidence for some of the oldest permanently occupied villages in Mesoamerica. We have also made an extensive study of the ecology and ethnology of the Ocós area.

From this study we have defined no less than eight distinct microenvironments (Fig. 2) within an area of only about 90 square kilometers. These are as follows:

1. *Beach sand and low scrub.* A narrow, infertile strip from which the present-day villagers collect occasional mollusks, a beach crab called *chichimeco* and one known as *nazareño,* and the sea turtle and its eggs.

2. *The marine estuary-and-lagoon system,* in places extending considerably inland and ultimately connecting with streams or rivers coming down from the Sierra Madre. The estuaries, with their mangrove-lined banks, make up the microenvironment richest in wild foods in the entire area. The brackish waters abound in catfish (*Arius* sp. and *Galeichthys* sp.), red snapper (*Lutjanus colorado*), several species of snook (*Centropomus* sp.), and many other kinds of fish. Within living memory,

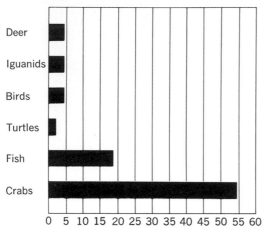

Deer
Iguanids
Birds
Turtles
Fish
Crabs

0  5  10 15 20 25 30 35 40 45 50 55 60

Number of individuals represented

**Figure 3** Animal remains, exclusive of mollusks, found in Cuadros phase levels at Salinas La Blanca.

crocodiles (*Crocodylus astutus*) were common, but they have by now been hunted almost to extinction. The muddy banks of the estuaries are the habitat of many kinds of mollusks, including marsh clams (*Polymesoda radiata*), mussels (*Mytella falcata*), and oysters (*Ostrea columbiensis*), and they also support an extensive population of fiddler and mud crabs.

3. *Mangrove forest*, consisting mainly of stilt-rooted red mangrove, which slowly gives way to white mangrove as one moves away from the estuary. We noted high populations of collared anteater (*Tamandua tetradactyla*) and arboreal porcupine (*Coendu mexicanus*). A large number of crabs (we did not determine the species) inhabit this microenvironment; these include, especially, one known locally as the *azul* (blue) crab, on which a large population of raccoons feeds.

4. *Riverine*, comprising the channels and banks of the sluggish Suchiate and Naranjo rivers, which connect with the lagoon-estuary system not far from their mouths. Freshwater turtles, catfish, snook, red snapper, and mojarra (*Cichlasoma* sp.) are found in these waters; the most common animal along the banks is the green iguana (*Iguana iguana*).

5. *Salt playas*, the dried remnants of ancient lagoon-and-estuary systems which are still subject to inundation during the wet season, with localized stands of a tree known as *madresal* ("mother of salt"). Here there

is an abundance of game, including whitetail deer and the black iguana (*Ctenosaura similis*), as well as a rich supply of salt.

6. *Mixed tropical forest*, found a few kilometers inland, in slightly higher and better drained situations than the salt *playas*. This forest includes mostly tropical evergreens like the ceiba, as well as various zapote and fan palms, on the fruit of which a great variety of mammals thrive—the kinkajou, the spotted cavy, the coatimundi, the raccoon, and even the gray fox. The soils here are highly suitable for maize agriculture.

7. *Tropical savannah*, occupying poorly drained patches along the upper stream and estuary systems of the area. This is the major habitat in the area for cottontail rabbits and gray foxes. Other common mammals are the coatimundi and armadillo.

8. *Cleared fields and second growth*, habitats which have been created by agriculturists, and which are generally confined to areas that were formerly mixed tropical forest.

Among the earliest Formative cultures known thus far for the Ocós area is the Cuadros phase, dated by radiocarbon analysis at about 1000 to 850 B.C. and well represented in the site of Salinas La Blanca, which we excavated in 1962. The site is on the banks of the Naranjo River among a variety of microenvironments; it consists of two flattish mounds built up from deeply stratified refuse layers representing house foundations of a succession of hamlets or small villages.

From our analysis of this refuse we have a good idea of the way in which the Cuadros people lived. Much of the refuse consists of potsherds from large, neckless jars, but very few of the clay figurines that abound in other Formative cultures of Mesoamerica were found. We discovered many plant remains; luckily these had been preserved or "fossilized" through replacement of the tissues by carbonates. From these we know that the people grew and ate a nonhybridized maize considerably more advanced than the maize which was then being grown in Tehuacán. The many impressions of leaves in clay floors in the site will, we hope, eventually make it possible to reconstruct the flora that immediately surrounded the village.

The identification of animal remains (Fig. 3), together with our ecological study and with the knowledge that the people had a well-developed maize agriculture, gives a great deal of information on the subsistence activities of these early coastal villages. First of all, we believe they had no interest whatever in hunting, a conclusion reinforced by our failure to find a single projectile point in the site. The few deer bones that have been recovered are all from immature individuals that could have been encountered by chance and clubbed to death. Most of the other remains are of animals that could have been collected in the environs of the village, specifically in the lagoon-estuary system and the flanking mangrove forest, where the people fished, dug for marsh clams, and, above all, caught crabs (primarily the *azul* crab, which is trapped at night). Entirely missing are many edible species found in other microenvironments, such as raccoon, cottontail rabbit, peccary, spotted cavy, and nine-banded armadillo.

There is no evidence at all that occupation of Salinas La Blanca was seasonal. An effective food production carried out on the rich, deep soils of the mixed tropical forest zone, together with the food resources of the lagoon-estuary system, made a permanently settled life possible. Looked at another way, developed maize agriculture had so reduced the number and spacing of the niches which had to be exploited that villages could be occupied the year round.

Conditions similar to those of the Ocós area are found all along the Pacific Coast of Guatemala and along the Gulf Coast of southern Veracruz and Tabasco in Mexico, and we suggest that the real transition to village life took place there and not in the dry Mexican highlands, where maize was domesticated initially.

## Conclusion

The interpretation of archeological remains through a fine-scale analysis of small ecological zones throws new light on the move toward sedentary life in Mesoamerican prehistory. In our terms, the basic difference between peoples who subsist on wild foods and those who dwell in permanent villages is that the former must exploit a wide variety of small ecological niches in a seasonal pattern—niches which are usually scattered over a wide range of territory—while the latter may, because of an effective food production, concentrate on one or on only a few microenvironments which lie relatively close at hand.

Fine-scale ecological analysis indicates that there never was any such thing as an "agricultural revolution" in Mesoamerica, suddenly and almost miraculously resulting in village life. The gradual addition of domesticates such as maize, beans, and squash to the diet of wild plant and animal foods hardly changed the way of life of the Tehuacán people for many thousands of years, owing to a general paucity of the environment, and seasonal nomadism persisted until the introduction of irrigation. It probably was not until maize was taken to the alluvial, lowland littoral of Mesoamerica, perhaps around 1500 B.C., that permanently occupied villages became possible, through reduction of the number of microenvironments to which men had to adapt themselves.

selection 8

# Early Civilizations, Subsistence, and Environment

## Robert M. Adams

. . . My task is to describe briefly some of the major ecological relationships which sustained the growth of civilizations in a number of "nuclear" areas. In addition to Mesopotamia and Egypt, the choice of pre-Spanish Mesoamerica and Peru seems most appropriate. It is supported not only by the volume and historical-archeological depth of relevant data that are available from the latter two areas but also by the likelihood that extreme geographic separation reduced their dependence on Old World precursors to a minimum. In spite of this separation there is a striking similarity, in scope and form, of nuclear American sociopolitical attainments to those of the Fertile Crescent area at a much earlier time.

J. H. Steward has argued convincingly that even the demonstrated fact of diffusion between two cultural traditions is insufficient to "explain" their likenesses. "One may fairly ask," he maintains, "whether each time a society accepts diffused culture, it is not an independent recurrence of cause and effect." From this point of view, it is possible to regard all four areas as historically distinct examples regardless of the ultimate "origins" of particular traits. This is especially true for our purposes, since cultural-environmental relationships within an area are pre-eminently a matter of independent adjustment to local conditions and resources.

Moreover, the substantive evidence in these cases for the presence of diffusion from some outside source as a determinative factor is either lacking or at best equivocal. Each of the four areas stood out over its surroundings as a highly creative rather than a passively receptive center. While the complete

From Carl H. Kraeling and Robert M. Adams (eds.), City Invincible: A Symposium on Urbanization and Cultural Development in the Ancient Near East. *The University of Chicago Press, 1960, pp. 269–295.* © 1960, University of Chicago Press. By permission of the author, the publisher and copyright holder.

absence of trans-Pacific stimuli for New World high cultural development cannot be assured, the conclusion of most Americanists today is that the latter "stands clearly apart and essentially independent from the comparable culture core of the Old World." There is certainly no suggestion of any New World–Old World contact as important as the relatively brief but catalytic influence of Mesopotamia on Egypt at about 3000 B.C., yet in the latter case Frankfort took pains to point out the selective, qualified, and generally transient character of the borrowing. With respect to interrelations between Peru and Mesoamerica, it is sufficient to state that not a single object or record of influence or contact between these areas has been accepted as authentic from the long time span between the Formative (or Early Village) period and the coming of the Spaniards, although the over-all tempo of development in each is remarkably similar. In short, it is both reasonable on a priori theoretical grounds and justified by present evidence to use Mesopotamia, Egypt, Mesoamerica, and Peru as essentially independent examples for a discussion of their internal ecological relationships.

Within the limits of this discussion it is neither possible nor necessary to explore fully the similarities in cultural development among these four areas. All clearly became civilizations, in the sense in which that term is defined here as a functionally interrelated set of social institutions: class stratification, marked by highly different degrees of ownership of control of the main productive resources; political and religious hierarchies complementing each other in the administration of territorially organized states; a complex division of labor, with full-time craftsmen, servants, soldiers, and officials alongside the great mass of primary peasant producers. Each was a complex, deeply rooted cultural tradition displaying most or all of V. G. Childe's more inclusive civilizational criteria as well: monumental public works, the imposition of tribute or taxation, "urban" settlements, naturalistic art, the beginnings of exact and predictive sciences, a system of writing suitable at least for rudimentary records and accounts. The attainment of civilization, from a diachronic point of view, was expressed in each of the four areas by a series of parallel trends or processes: urbanization, militarization, stratification, bureaucratization, and the like. Of course, these processes were truncated in the New World by the Spanish Conquest—as a plausible approximation, after a level of development had been reached which was functionally equivalent to Old Kingdom Egypt or southern Mesopotamia under the Dynasty of Agade. However, this does not affect our comparisons here, which will be limited to earlier periods in the Near East for which New World equivalents are available.

It thus seems possible to group the four civilizations as representatives of a single type or class of social system. (Other members of the class would include the unknown Indus Valley polity of Harappa and Mohenjo Daro, Shang China, and perhaps certain West African city-states.) To be sure, this stress on structural and functional similarities needs supplementing by the traditional humanistic emphasis on the unique and relatively timeless qualities of each civilization for a properly balanced view. One example of the latter emphasis is the invocation of particular environmental features of different civilizations to account in part for their differing views of the natural world as reconstructed from works of ancient literature or art, for the distinctive structuring of their formal cosmologies, and perhaps even for dominant psychological attitudes. A typological approach necessarily neglects, although certainly cannot deny, the unique total patterning of every culture irrespective of what proportion of its constituent elements may have close parallels elsewhere. Probably this patterning is expressed most systematically, concisely, and impersonally in stylistic or configurational terms. But in any case these widely ramifying, largely ideational, aspects of the interrelations between man and the natural world are beyond the scope of this paper. Here we are concerned only with the generalized social order common to a group of autochthonous civilizations and with its relations to the environment.

### Climate, Physiography, Resources, and Population

Beyond the limitation of each of the nuclear areas to subtropical latitudes, the combined gross catalogue of environmental features is characterized mainly by its diversity. If Egyptian and Sumero-Babylonian civilizations are restricted to great arid or semi-arid river valleys, no such uniform description holds for the zones occupied by either Mesoamerican or Peruvian civilization. Both of the latter range from sea level to high mountain slopes, with tropical, temperate, or even cold-temperate climates corresponding to their altitudes. If coastal Peru and much of highland Mesoamerica are sufficiently dry to be closely comparable with the Old World centers, this is progressively less true in the Peruvian sierra with increasing altitude and distance from the Pacific coast and not true at all in the Gulf Coastal lowlands of Middle America.

Both of the New World areas lack great inclusive river systems comparable to Egypt and the Nile or Mesopotamia and the Tigris-Euphrates. Instead, short, steeply descending watercourses that drain relatively small watersheds are common, and many of the largest of these are reduced in their pre-Hispanic importance by geographic factors. The main valley of the Rio Balsas and the intermontane basins of the Bajío on the Rio Lerma in Mexico, for example, were lightly occupied before the Spanish introduction of draft animals and the iron-tipped plow made it possible for agriculturalists to deal with heavy soils and sod. The Amazon headwaters in the eastern sierra and Montaña of Peru may be found to provide a more significant exception when they have been explored more adequately but at least the lowland rain forest of the Amazon basin proper acted as a major ecological barrier to the expansion of Peruvian civilization. Since the potentialities of the Old World rivers for disastrous floods, for large-scale irrigation, and as arteries of commerce are often thought to have promoted political unification and the growth of trade in the ancient Orient, it is worth noting that the same cultural phenomena appeared independently in regions where these potentialities were absent or at least far less important.

With respect to natural resources, it is sufficient to recall the absence of even stone in the alluvial soil of southern Mesopotamia, as well as the extremely poor quality for building of the soft and quick-growing woods that alone were available locally. In contrast, parts at least of the New World nuclear regions were well favored, although with great alti-

tudinal variation local self-sufficiency was often replaced by patterns of regional specialization and exchange. As with climate and terrain, then, we cannot identify a fixed constellation of raw materials which acted as a necessary precondition (much less as a "cause"!) for the emergence of civilization in every area.

While relatively continuous settlement in linear patterns coinciding with the positions of the watercourses was possible in southern Mesopotamia and Egypt, enclaves of dense occupation separated by stretches of relatively inhospitable terrain were more characteristic of Mesoamerica and Peru. The best known and largest of the Mesoamerican enclaves is the interior drainage basin called the Valley of Mexico, which has provided the bulk of population and subsistence resources successively for the great religious center of Teotihuacan, the Toltec realm with Tula as its capital, the widespread conquests and incipient empire formation of the Aztecs, and present-day Mexico City. Yet in spite of the unparalleled importance of this region its area does not exceed 8,000 sq. km. In Peru the areas of intensive settlement and cultivation were all still smaller. Perhaps the largest of the mountain basins able to support a concentrated population is that of Huancayo, in the central highlands, with an area of only 1,200 sq. km. The arable area of the Chicama Valley, the largest in the North Coastal lowlands, is approximately the same.

In all of nuclear America, only along the Gulf Coast and on the low-lying Yucatan Peninsula were the conditions suitable for relatively uniform and continuous settlement. There, too, the rivers most nearly resemble the Nile or the Euphrates in regularity of flow and ease of control. But the lateritic soils and heavy rain-forest vegetation impose a very long recovery period after brief use for slash-and-burn agriculture, which materially reduces population density and perhaps helped to postpone for a considerable time the onset of urbanization processes which had been initiated in adjacent Mesoamerican highlands. A sharper contrast would be hard to imagine than that between Sumerians clustering in cities and Classic Mayans living in dispersed, essentially rural, hamlets while only a small elite permanently inhabited the elaborate religious centers. Yet both were civilized. In short, the distribution of population and settlements within the nuclear areas appears to have been as variable as the general environmental conditions within which they occurred, although average density in each case was surely much higher than in surrounding areas.

## Variations in Agricultural Subsistence Patterns

While the essential basis for subsistence in every civilization is obviously to be found in sedentary agriculture, this rubric covers impressive technical, botanical, and zoölogical differences when it is applied to the high cultures of both the New and the Old World. Largely following C. O. Sauer, we may summarize these differences briefly.

New World agriculture, in the first place, essentially did not involve stockbreeding or the utilization of such animal products as dung fertilizer or milk. Domesticated Andean camelids such as the llama were used mainly for transport and were largely confined to the higher slopes; hence they cannot be regarded as important exceptions. Also missing in nuclear America, therefore, is the unique and powerful ambivalence of relations between herdsman and farmer, involving both symbiosis and hostility, which has shaped the social life, tinctured the history, and enriched the literature of the civilizations of the Fertile Crescent.

Second, nuclear American agriculture involves an entirely different range of cultivated plants, which nonetheless seem to have provided as balanced and adequate a diet as the cereal-date-vegetable-livestock complexes of the ancient Orient.

Third, basically different methods of cultivation were employed in the New World. In the absence of draft animals, the major implements were the digging stick and the hoe instead of the plow. Instead of a definite brief harvest season, crop-gathering was prolonged by the use of the major food crops also as green vegetables during earlier stages of their growth and by the widespread practice of interspersing different crops within a single field.

Finally, corresponding to the greater variations in climate because of altitude, New World agriculture was far more variable. There is little difference in at least the potential yields of the Assyrian uplands and the Mesopotamian alluvial plain other than that due to the inability of the date palm to flourish beyond the northern limit of the alluvium and to the greater (but not exclusive) reliance on barley rather than wheat south of that limit. By contrast, coastal Peruvian agriculture essentially revolved around a maize-beans-squash-cotton-fruits complex, while in the sierra subsistence depended on an entirely different complex composed of root crops like potatoes, oca, and quinoa. Similarly, maize, beans, and squash were the staple foods in both highland and lowland Mesoamerica, but they had been differentiated very early into altitudinally specialized varieties. Moreover, the cultivation of cotton, cacao, and many fruits was restricted to the lowlands.

## Similarities in Subsistence Patterns

In spite of these profound differences, common features are not lacking. Perhaps something can be learned of the general place of subsistence in the growth of civilizations by outlining three common elements which seem to be of greatest importance.

One such significant common feature is that "farmers were persuaded or compelled to wring from the soil a surplus above their own domestic requirements and [that] this surplus was made available to support new economic classes not directly engaged in producing their own food." It must be understood that the notion of a surplus is related to fixed biological needs and the level of productive efficiency only in very general terms and that both the kinds and the quantities of available surpluses were determined to a considerable degree by the broad social contexts —"noneconomic" as well as "economic"— within which they occurred. Yet the institutional forms for the concentration and redistribution of surpluses show a high degree of uniformity among the early civilizations and serve to distinguish the latter sharply from societies in which no full-time activity other than primary food production finds sanction. Although it is impossible to quantify, it is only reasonable to assume that the proliferation of nonagricultural specialists common to all the early civilizations was correlated with a general increase in agricultural efficiency. It is, of course, quite another matter to assume that improved efficiency was independent of and prior to the whole ramifying network of concurrent social changes. Even purely technological advances, which in most instances these increased surpluses probably do not reflect, are usually linked with the social and cultural milieu, as Kroeber's study of independent and relatively simultaneous inventions was first to show.

A second common feature of some importance may be the complexity of the subsistence base on which each of the civilizations seems to have rested. We are dealing in no case with a single-crop economy or with one in which the bulk of the population normally could supply the entire range of agricultural produce for themselves. Perhaps the diversity of resources is partly to be understood as the protection against natural calamity necessary for long-term cultural growth. But also in part it must have been responsible for the development of trade, exchange, and redistributive institutions which in turn enhanced the growth of some form of centralized authority.

Mesopotamia is perhaps the best-documented example. The complementarity of dates and grain finds symbolic expression in the alabaster "Uruk vase," of late Protoliterate date, where alternate palm and cereal shoots in the bottom register figuratively support the abundant ceremonial life illustrated above. Fishing was another essential subsistence pursuit; of the 1,200 or so members of the Baba temple community in Girsu in the mid-third millennium B.C., more than 100 were fishermen. The precise role of fishing in earlier times is difficult to ascertain, but quantities of fish offerings found in a late Ubaid temple at Eridu may indicate that it had already attained considerable importance by that remote period. Slightly less numerous than the Baba temple fishermen were its shepherds and herdsmen, but their numbers in that specific case do not adequately reflect the crucial position of sheep, donkeys, and oxen in the mixed economy of ancient Mesopotamia for plowing, transport, wool, and fertilizer as well as meat. Surely the prominence of the shepherd-and-byre motif in Protoliterate glyptic art reflects a high antiquity for husbandry as an essential part of the configuration of subsistence activities. In all of these cases it is interesting to note that the temple and state institutions played a vital part in the collection and redistribution of the agricultural produce.

To the far more limited degree to which there are pertinent data on diversification and specialization of subsistence in Old Kingdom Egypt, the picture is at least not inconsistent with what has been described for Mesopotamia. The idealized representations in the tombs of life on the estates of court officials record a great variety of craft activities and subsistence pursuits; since an organization of the work under foremen is sometimes illustrated, there must have been at least a partial specialization of function in the real world as well. While the great bulk of the peasant's caloric intake may always have been derived from grain, the cultivation of vegetables and fruits and fowling, fishing, and animal husbandry also play a substantial part in the tomb scenes of Old Kingdom officials. The importance of herding, in particular, may have been obscured by its limited modern role under very different conditions of land use. For obvious reasons the main center of husbandry was in the Nile Delta, and the close concern of the state for husbandry is clearly to be seen in the emphasis on livestock in lists of claimed tribute and loot, in periodic censuses of the herds, and in the appointment of numerous officials charged with responsibility of one kind or another for domestic animals.

In the New World the differentiation of subsistence pursuits seems to have been mainly on a regional basis, perhaps as a consequence of the greater environmental diversity that has previously been alluded to. But the necessity for a wide interchange of agricultural products remained the same, and the organization of this interchange similarly must have helped to expand and consolidate the position of centralized social authority. In North Coastal Peru, for example, llamas from the sierra were already being ceremonially buried in a community shrine or public building in Late Formative times. In another case, the only llama bones from a contemporary site of the same period were found in association with the burial of an individual whose relatively elaborate *Beigaben* suggest a priestly status. By the succeeding Florescent era, the relative abundance of llama bones, wool, and droppings indicates that trading contacts with the highland centers of domestication for these animals had been regularized and enlarged. Presumably cotton, maritime products, peppers, fruits, and coca were among the commodities moving in the reverse direction, as they were at the time of the Conquest. To some degree, regional specialization with regard to subsistence extended into craft production as well, as is implied by the importation of a colony of Chimu craftsmen to work for the Inca government in Cuzco. It is interesting to note that a high degree of specialization still characterizes the Quechua community.

Similar patterns of differentiation in specialized production can be identified in Mesoamerica. Cotton from the lower-lying valleys of Puebla and Morelos was already being interchanged with the Valley of Mexico in Early Formative times, and the securest archeological dating horizons of later periods are provided by distinctive pottery wares that were traded widely from their different centers of manufacture. For the Conquest period these traces of evidence can be greatly amplified with eyewitness accounts of, for example, the great and diversified market at Tlatelolco with its separate vendors for many varieties of fruit, meat, maize, vegetables, and fish and with a reputed daily attendance of 60,000 persons. From a different point of view, the heterogeneity of native resources is also underlined by the *matricula de tributos*. Although it accounts for tribute levied by the Aztecs rather than for trade, the general concentration of assignments for particular kinds of produce (other than the ubiquitous mantles) to a very few provinces surely reflects earlier patterns for the interchange of normal regional surpluses. And by Aztec times, if not earlier, the integration of interregional trading with the needs and policies of the expanding state is well known.

A third significant feature common to the agricultural pursuits of the early civilizations was the development of some degree of intensive land use. Whether or not this was accompanied by a general increase in agricultural efficiency (output/labor input), certainly it must have increased at least the total agricultural output. However, the point of current interest is not so much the effect of intensive methods of cultivation on the volume of available surplus as their effect directly on social organization. The argument, following

Ralph Linton's [this volume, p. 327ff.] lucid portrayal of the introduction of wet rice cultivation in Madagascar, is that under conditions of intensive cultivation plots of land acquire different values based, for example, on cumulative improvements and the availability of water. Since water, or good bottom land, or some other similar resource was almost always relatively scarce, well-favored and improved plots came to be regarded as capital investments. While unimproved land was allotted equitably among all members of the village or extended kin group, under conditions of intensive cultivation the cohesiveness of the older social units broke down and tended to be replaced by a small number of individual families as the hereditary landholding units. The emergence of an authoritarian "king," of rudimentary social classes including nobles, commoners, and war-captive slaves, and increasing expenditures on warfare are some of the further consequences which Linton traces to the basic shift in cultivation practices. Under at least some circumstances, in other words, the social processes we have identified with the beginnings of civilization are closely interconnected with the beginning of intensive agriculture. No necessary distinction into "cause" and "effect" is implied, be it understood, between subsistence change and institutional change. The investment of labor in land improvement and the adoption of intensive cultivation techniques were as much influenced by contemporary social forms as they influenced the latter.

Intensive agriculture, in the case of the earlier civilizations, usually is taken to be roughly synonymous with irrigation. Indeed, without some kind of irrigation agriculture is and probably always was impossible in southern Mesopotamia, Egypt, and coastal Peru. But we shall attempt to show that in most cases irrigation was part of a broader range of intensive techniques and that some of the assumed implications of irrigation as a single, gross category are misleading when applied to the four nuclear areas where the civilizations with which this paper is concerned had their beginnings. Here, then, irrigation is subsumed under the general rubric of intensive cultivation rather than equated with it.

It is important to distinguish between the functional significance of different kinds of irrigation if we are to understand better the relations between ecology and cultural growth. Small-scale irrigation, including flood-water techniques and the construction of short lengths of canal serving small landholdings, does not seem essentially different in its social effects from those observed by Linton in Madagascar. It may make available for agricultural purposes only a fraction of the potentially irrigable land surface, since it will seldom extend very far from the streams and since short canals will not be sufficient everywhere to bring the water to fields at a high enough level. Alluvial situations, in which rivers tend to raise their beds above the level of the surrounding land, are particularly favorable for small-scale irrigation. For the same reason, they invite destruction of existing canals by silting and flooding, although this is not critical where canals do not represent a heavy investment in labor and can be quickly replaced. The construction and maintenance of this kind of irrigation, we submit, requires no elaborate social organization and does not depend on labor resources larger than those at the disposal of the individual community, kin group, or even family—or, at most, those easily available locally through patterns of reciprocity. To the extent that this kind of irrigation is important, its chief influence on social development would seem to arise from its encouragement of stratification based on differentiation of landholdings. Perhaps also it encouraged the growth of militarism associated with increasing competition for developed canal networks and the most fertile and easily irrigated lands.

Large-scale irrigation, on the other hand, imposes technical and social demands of a different order. Masses of labor must be mobilized from many scattered communities, and their activities need close co-ordination. The problem of maintenance and supervision is a continuous one and again demands a superordinate authority. Some kind of equitable distribution of the available irrigation water must be imposed on many competing communities, and disputes must be adjudicated. Since downstream users are inherently at the mercy of those higher up, large-scale irrigation networks are only durable where the entire area they serve is a politically integrated unit. As has often been observed, large-scale canal networks can only be associated with formal state superstructures in which the ultimate authority rests with an administrative elite.

The problem for us is an absolutely basic one, however sparse, refractory, and ambiguous most of the present evidence may be. To the extent that large-scale irrigation is found to have begun very early, its social requirements may be adduced as a convincing explanation for the origin of primitive states in the ancient civilizations. Processes of class stratification associated with intensive agriculture then might be a secondary and derivative phenomenon on this reconstruction; because of its monopoly over hydraulic facilities, the state bureaucracy is identified as the strongest social force. Largely following Karl Wittfogel, Julian Steward took this position with respect to Mesopotamia and Peru although not to Mesoamerica. Our view is firmly to the contrary. It is beyond the scope of a paper dealing with cultural ecology to argue that the primitive state is mainly linked instead with the emergence of a stratified society, but at least it will be suggested here that the introduction of great irrigation networks was more a "consequence" than a "cause" of the appearance of dynastic state organizations—however much the requirements of large-scale irrigation subsequently may have influenced the development of bureaucratic elites charged with administering them. The admittedly still inadequate evidence for this proposition now needs to be briefly summarized.

Our present understanding of the antiquity of irrigation in Mesopotamia is derived mainly from surface reconnaissance in Akkad and the Diyala basin and is obscured by the heavy and continuous alluviation with which the northern part of the alluvial plain has been particularly affected over the millenniums intervening since Sumerian times. At least in this region, however, there appears to have been little change in settlement pattern between the beginning of widespread agricultural occupation in the Ubaid period and the end of the third millennium B.C., or even later. There is historical documentation for the construction of occasional large canals and irrigation works as early as the Protoimperial period, but on the whole the settlements followed closely the shifting, braided channels of the major rivers.

In other words, for a long time irrigation

seems to have been conducted principally on an *ad hoc* small-scale basis, which would have involved periodic cleaning and perhaps straightening of clogged natural channels, adjusting the location of fields and settlements in the closest possible conformity with the existing hydraulic regime, and for the most part constructing and maintaining only relatively small-scale field and feeder canals that were wholly artificial. Where the king explicitly claims credit for initiating dredging operations on either a canal or a natural watercourse (as in modern Iraq, the same word is used for both!), it is noteworthy that the aspect of canals as providers of irrigation water is entirely unmentioned. Moreover, whatever the rhetoric of the king's claimed responsibilities, the necessary labor forces for the maintenance work were apparently organized and directed by the individual temples. No Early Dynastic or Protoimperial record has survived of the mode of allocation of irrigation water, but at least in Ur III times this was separately handled in each temple constituency by a special official in charge of sluice gates. In short, there is nothing to suggest that the rise of dynastic authority in southern Mesopotamia was linked to the administrative requirements of a major canal system.

There are very few data yet available on the character or extent of Egyptian irrigation during the period for which it might be compared with New World equivalents, that is, up to the beginning of the Middle Kingdom. Prior to the opening of the Fayyum depression to irrigation in the Twelfth Dynasty, there is nothing less ambiguous to demonstrate state responsibility for irrigation than the statement of a Sixth-Dynasty royal architect that he had dug two canals for the king. Unfortunately, the inscription fails to make clear whether the canals were intended for irrigation or only for the movement of royal supplies like building stone, as was the case with five contemporary canals dug to bypass the First Cataract of the Nile. Still another possible explanation of the significance of the passage is that it refers to land reclamation by swamp drainage, much as a very late (and therefore doubtful) tradition credits Menes with having drained the territory around Memphis. Yet swamp drainage began long before any pharaoh appeared on the scene—if the obvious meaning is attached to the claim of a Third-Dynasty official that he

"founded" twelve estates in nomes of Lower Egypt—and continued afterward without the necessity of royal initiative. In considering alternatives other than irrigation we are also confronted with a protodynastic scorpion macehead ostensibly showing the king breaking ground for a waterway of some kind. Again, an immunity charter of Pepi I protects the priesthood of the two pyramids of Snefru against any obligation for labor service on what may be a canal; here it is neither clear that the putative canal was for irrigation nor that the pharaoh was responsible for its construction. Interestingly enough, the same charter continues with an injunction against enumerating canals, lakes, wells, hides, and trees belonging to the priesthood for tax purposes and thus suggests that all of those categories were under purely local jurisdiction.

In short, considering the number of known records of royal building activity in the Old Kingdom, it seems only fair to regard their silence on the construction of irrigation works as strange if the demands of large-scale irrigation had indeed been responsible for the initial emergence of a pharaoh at the head of a unified state. On the assumption of a centrally administered irrigation system, the failure of officials with long and varied careers of public service to refer to administrative posts connected with canal maintenance or water distribution is equally puzzling. To the degree that an *argumentum ex silentio* ever carries conviction, the Egyptian case parallels that of Mesopotamia.

Although there is serious danger of overgeneralizing from it, the data on Peruvian irrigation are reasonably consistent with what has been adduced from Mesopotamia and Egypt. Drawing principally from Gordon Willey's pioneer study of settlement patterns in a typical small valley transecting the arid North Coastal strip, we cannot presently trace large-scale irrigation earlier than the Florescent era (beginning probably at about the time of Christ). The distribution of Late Formative sites suggests, however, that small-scale experimentation with canal-building had begun in a few advantageous locales several centuries prior to this time, and some success with at least flood-water irrigation on the river flats is implied by the slow expansion inward from the valley mouth which began a millennium earlier. The Early Florescent (Gallinazo) canals, it is interesting to note, were built as integral parts of an elaborate and impressive complex of monumental construction which included fortifications and ceremonial pyramids as well; on present evidence, both of the latter types of monumental construction antedated the large canals. By mid-Florescent times at least, valley-wide systems of irrigation were in use on the North Coast (although our particular example comprises only 98 sq. km. of arable land!), and some individual canals are large by any standards: the canal of La Cumbre in the Chicama Valley, for example, is 113 km. long. A subsequent development, probably dating only from the Militaristic era (beginning after A.D. 700), was the still more extensive reshaping of natural drainage patterns through the introduction of intervalley irrigation systems in which urban zones occupied by a governing elite were set off from areas for agricultural exploitation.

Irrigation apparently developed more slowly in highland Peru than on the North Coast, although the sharpness of the contrast may be a reflection in part of the lesser amount of archeological attention that the sierra has received. Terraces for soil conservation have been reported first for the Tiahuanaco horizon, at the outset of the Militaristic era. In the characteristically steep and narrow Andean valleys rapid runoff was perhaps a more serious problem than paucity of rainfall, but in general the later terraces seem to have been associated with irrigation channels as well. The elaborate, well-cut, and extensive terrace-irrigation system for which Peru is famous all were products of the labor-service obligation imposed by the Inca state as a tax in the final century or so of its successful expansion before the coming of the Spaniards. Even the Early Inca terraces, probably postdating the onset of the Tiahuanaco horizon by four or more centuries, have been described as "small and irregular, and probably the work of individual family groups." As in North Coastal Peru, Egypt, and southern Mesopotamia, we seem to have evidence here of a very gradual evolution of irrigation practices beginning with local and small-scale terracing which emphatically did not require political organization embracing a large group of communities. Large-scale, integrated programs of canalization and terracing apparently were attempted only after the perfection of the Inca

state as a political apparatus controlling the allocation of mass-labor resources. They are consequences, perhaps, of the attainment of a certain level of social development; we repeat that they cannot be invoked to explain the processes by which that level was attained.

For Mesoamerica the situation is more complex and not a little contradictory. The traditional view is that "there is little evidence that irrigation was of basic importance anywhere in Mexico, in pre-Spanish times, and that it is erroneous to speak of maize culture as having flourished most in arid or subarid regions of that country." Recently this conclusion has been controverted effectively by a number of investigators, although the full significance of their empirical findings is still open to dispute. On the whole though, the situation seems to be quite similar to that described for the other nuclear areas; in fact, it was primarily the recent findings in Mesoamerica which stimulated the reconsideration of irrigation that this paper represents.

The question of the role of irrigation in the formation of Mesoamerican civilization takes us back at least to the beginning of the Classic era (*ca.* A.D. 100?), if not earlier, and revolves particularly around the population and ceremonial center of Teotihuacan in the Valley of Mexico. The Pyramid of the Sun there, one of the largest pre-Hispanic structures in Mesoamerica, apparently antedates that era. It has been estimated that before its abandonment in Late Classic times (*ca.* A.D. 700) the site occupied 750 hectares or more of religious and civic buildings, residential "palaces," workshops, and clusters of ordinary rooms and patios housing "at least" 50,000 inhabitants. True, the observed limits of surface debris may reflect only the aggregate area of the center over a period of several centuries and not its maximum size at any one period. Moreover, the proportion of residential units within the built-up area of the site is still not at all clear. But even if the estimate is scaled down considerably, it certainly reflects an urban civilization in being. To what extent, if at all, did it depend on irrigation agriculture? No direct evidence for canal irrigation has yet been reported. Instead we have the observations that irrigation is necessary today for cultivation of even a single yearly crop in the subregion of which

Teotihuacan is a part, that according to paleoclimatic studies based on pollen analysis and fluctuating lake levels it was even more necessary during the time of emergence of Teotihuacan as a great center, and hence that the use of irrigation must be assumed. The difficulty is that a center of the enormous size of Teotihuacan must have developed on a sustaining area far larger than its immediate subregion and that a major contribution from its immediate surroundings cannot be assumed to have been indispensable for the growth of the site. Monte Alban, Xochicalco, and other examples can be found which approach Teotihuacan in size but which lie at some distance from their main agricultural hinterland. A second argument is still less conclusive. It consists of the suggestion that irrigation is implied by representation of cacao and fruit trees along the banks of streams or canals in a mural from a Teotihuacan "palace." Even if the identification of cacao is accepted as correct, the location of the scene is unknown and the crucial question of whether the waterways are natural or artificial is unanswered. There remains only a distributional argument, based on the wide extent of Mesoamerican irrigation practices at the time of the Conquest. Like all distributional arguments, it is loaded with presuppositions and provides no real clue to the antiquity of the trait in question. And so for Formative and Classic times the existence of canal irrigation still remains to be demonstrated.

For the final, or Historic, era (beginning *ca.* A.D. 900 with the founding of Tula), on the other hand, the evidence for large-scale irrigation agriculture and other hydraulic works is incontrovertible. Perhaps such works are already implied by the legendary account of the formation of Tula in the Codex Ramirez which describes the damming-up of a river in order to form an artificial lake stocked with fish and waterfowl. In any case, the Spanish conquerors were full of admiration for the scale and intricacy of the system of dikes and aqueducts that by 1519 was both supplying Tenochtitlan with potable water and controlling fluctuations in the salt- and fresh-water levels of the lakes surrounding the city. The sequence of construction of these works can be traced in some detail in historical sources, and the conclusion seems justified that they should be viewed "not so much as the result

of many small-scale initiatives by small groups, but as the result of large-scale enterprise, well-planned, in which an enormous number of people took part, engaged in important and prolonged public works under centralized and authoritative leadership." Elsewhere in the Valley of Mexico, an irrigation complex in the Old Acolhua domain has been described that was roughly contemporary with the Aztec construction and also seems to have been initiated by a dynastic authority and carried out as a planned large-scale enterprise. Finally, an impressive list of places, with a wide distribution throughout Mesomerica outside the Maya area, can be assembled for which irrigation is definitely identified or can reasonably be inferred in Spanish contact sources. In short, the position that irrigation was not important anywhere or at any period in pre-Spanish Mexico no longer seems tenable.

It needs to be stressed again, however, that distribution is a highly unreliable index to antiquity and that even the examples from the Valley of Mexico appertain only to the final century before the Conquest. Moreover, with the exception of the above-mentioned Aztec system all the known Mesoamerican irrigation networks are quite small in comparison with those of the Old World and Peru. On present evidence, then, Wolf and Palerm rightly tend to regard planned large-scale canal irrigation not as a primary cause of Mesoamerican civilization but merely as its culminating activity in the economic sphere. They recognize, to be sure, that political controls in turn probably were centralized and intensified by the introduction of major irrigation works.

But if large-scale canalization is late in Mesoamerica, there are indications that other forms of irrigation and intensive cultivation— as in Peru and Mesopotamia also—can be traced to a more remote antiquity. Canal irrigation probably never became as important a technique in the Valley of Mexico as chinampa agriculture, that is, the cultivation of artificial islands made out of plant debris and mud scooped from the lake beds. Modern chinampas are largely devoted to truck gardening, but, since the tasks of construction and maintenance do not require extensive organization and capital, they may have been used aboriginally as highly productive subsistence plots for kin groups or even families. The only example of an apparent chinampa so far subjected to archeological scrutiny contained occupational refuse dating to about the beginning of the Classic period and suggests that the technique is sufficiently old to have been a factor in the subsistence of Teotihuacan. The means were at hand early enough, in other words, for differential returns from specialized farming to have provided the material basis for the growth of a stratified society.

Since chinampas were unknown elsewhere in Mesoamerica (or depended on conditions not repeated elsewhere), their high and perennial productivity may not have been a direct factor in the development of civilization throughout the whole area. At the same time, the Valley of Mexico was in many other respects the key area of development for the greater part of Mesoamerica, for a very long time the center of its most advanced political forms, its widest and most closely intercommunicating trade network, its densest population. To a degree, then, it may have set the course of development which elsewhere was merely followed with more or less local innovation. To that degree, chinampa agriculture may far exceed in importance its highly circumscribed geographical limits. Unfortunately, having largely set aside simple diffusion studies, anthropologists are only beginning to develop more functional approaches to the analysis of interregional relations, through which the supposed primacy of the Valley of Mexico might be understood and evaluated.

Another, and broader, aspect of intensive cultivation in Mesoamerica is perhaps to be seen in the maintenance of dooryard garden plots in close symbiosis with individual houses, which augment the production of foodstuffs through the use of leavings as fertilizer and encourage stability of residence. Although not subject to archeological confirmation at present, this practice was apparently well established at the time of the Conquest and is possibly very old. Again, crudely made terraces for erosion-control purposes have been observed at many places in highland Mesoamerica and in at least one instance in the lowland rain forest of the Yucatan Peninsula. Certainly in many cases of considerable pre-Spanish antiquity, they suggest agricultural

regimes of greater intensity than the milpa system as it is practiced today. Although at present impossible to document for pre-Conquest times, a more intensive application of labor in the form of hand-weeding would have prolonged cultivation and increased output, particularly in the tropical lowlands. This might make less inexplicable or even "explain" the extraordinary cultural achievements of the Classic Maya in the lowlands.

By assisting in the establishment of residential stability and in the production of surpluses, all the above-mentioned practices would have provided at least a receptive hinterland within which the new and more complex social forms could expand and consolidate. The origin of innovations such as the primitive state might then be sought in a few small strategic regions such as the Valley of Mexico where the inducements to accumulate surpluses and institutionalize class differences were probably greatest. In a wider sense, it may be granted, the florescence of the state could only take place where conditions in the hinterland were also propitious, so that the pinpointing of precise points of origin is probably misleading.

Briefly to recapitulate, we have attempted to show that developments in modes of subsistence within Mesoamerica were substantially similar to those in Mesopotamia, Egypt, and Peru in that large-scale canal irrigation was a culminating, rather than an early and persistent, form of intensive cultivation. It is conceded that differences in the rate of development existed, probably in large part because of the fewer inducements and opportunities to depend on irrigation that Mesoamerica offered. But these, we suggest, are quantitative and not qualitative differences. In North Coastal Peru the culmination came in the mid-Florescent era—or even later, in the Militaristic era, if the introduction of intervalley irrigation systems is accepted as a significant later innovation. In Mesoamerica it came in late Historic or Militaristic times, as it also seems to have done in *highland* Peru. According to our Mesopotamian data, admittedly inadequate in detail and based on a possibly retarded Akkad instead of Sumer, the onset of large-scale artificial canalization did not occur until after the time of Hammurabi. Even in Sumer itself there is no justification for supposing that this process began any earlier than the late Early Dynastic or the Protoimperial period—a sound equivalent for the New World Historic or Militaristic era. In *no* area, then, at least on present evidence, was large-scale irrigation early enough to "explain" the emergence of the great theocratic centers of the Classic era or the dynastic states which closely followed them. The concern of Wolf and Palerm, and latterly of Steward, over the distinction between "Theocratic Irrigation States" (Protoliterate Mesopotamia and Florescent Peru) and "Ceremonial Trade States" (Classic Mesoamerica) thus seems groundless.

## Reciprocal Effects of Human Culture on Environment

This discussion so far has assumed that the natural physiography and resources of the four nuclear areas were relatively stable. The different cultural traditions have been regarded implicitly as evolving successive patterns of ecological adjustment and land use entirely according to some internal dynamic of their own. The effect of environment, in these terms, is merely that of providing a fixed framework of potentialities and limiting conditions which somehow is then exploited selectively by the creative cultural growth within it. Such a view is obviously an over-simplification of the processes of interaction between man and the natural world, even if decisive climatic shifts no longer are regarded as likely to have occurred during the span of time that led to the emergence of any civilization.

Unfortunately the reciprocal effects of changing patterns of human activity on the land and flora cannot be traced continuously for any area. Perhaps the clearest and best-documented example is provided by recent work in central Mexico, where it has been shown that intensive hill-slope cultivation during the last centuries of Aztec dominance had gone far to destroy the capacity of the soil to sustain agriculture even before the arrival of the Spaniards. But the more remote history of occupance in even this relatively well-studied region is still insufficiently known for its environmental effects to be understood. The abandonment of the central Peten region by the lowland Classic Maya furnishes an even more dramatic case, with ecological processes such as sheet erosion, the silting-up of fresh-water sources, and the gradual replacement of forest vegetation by uncultivable savanna in the course of slash-and-burn agriculture all having been suggested as contributing factors. But in spite of a generation of speculation and interest these factors still exist only as hypotheses, and in a recent general work on the Maya it is interesting to note that they are largely rejected in favor of an explanation of the collapse of at least the elaborate ceremonial life in purely historical terms.

In the alluvial valleys of the Old World civilizations, processes of erosion are less likely to have affected directly the course of cultural development. It is not impossible, however, that deforestation at the headwaters of the Tigris and Euphrates increased both the silt loads carried by those rivers and their flooding potential. In turn, this would have affected the continuity of occupation in the alluvium and the problems associated with constructing and maintaining irrigation systems. But, although deforestation undoubtedly went on, there are no empirical data at present on its rate nor on its consequences for the alluvial plain as a whole. Even the traditional assumption that the area of the plain has been continuously enlarged by the deposition of silt along the margin of the Persian Gulf has now been challenged by evidence that extensions of the land have been roughly counterbalanced by subsidence.

On the other hand, a group of different and important reciprocal effects is likely to have been initiated directly by the introduction of various techniques of intensive cultivation. Depletion of soil nutrients by inadequate crop rotation or fallowing cycle is one example. Salinization of poorly drained land as a result of continuous irrigation is another. Still a third may be the disturbance of natural patterns of drainage by the slow rise of canal beds and banks as a result of silting. To some degree all of these processes must have gone on, but their importance can only be gauged against the background of a far better understanding of ancient agriculture than we have at present for any area. To begin with, empirical studies are necessary of changes in the intensity of land use and of the exact nature of the full agricultural cycle over a long period in the past. At the time of this writing, a study along these lines has been undertaken for a small section of the Meso-potamian plain but not for any other nuclear area.

For the present, therefore, the distortions of a picture in which cultures are conceived as having evolved within a static environmental framework must remain uncorrected. If several possible types of correction have been mentioned, their effects cannot even be demonstrated satisfactorily with the evidence available from most areas, and in any case they are virtually impossible to quantify. One can only conclude that attempts to invoke changing ecological factors as "causes" of cultural development — however convenient they may appear as heuristic hypotheses—are still no more than a priori speculations.

In a broader sense, the lack of data on population density and land use underlines the purely speculative character of all those heuristic hypotheses which regard cultural change as an adaptive response to direct environmental forces. One account of the rise of militarism, for example, sees it as a consequence of the displacement of a population surplus, although there is absolutely no evidence of a concurrent reduction in the sustaining capacity of the environment or of a trend toward overpopulation in any of the nuclear areas. Another recent synthesis, going still farther, attributes not only the rise of large-scale warfare but also the cyclical character of the early empires in large part to population pressure. How population "pressure" can be defined usefully except by reference to real patterns and intensities of land utilization and settlement pressing against clearly defined ecological limits—for which, we must emphasize again, the evidence is still almost entirely lacking—is not apparent.

There is always an attraction for explanations of historical and cultural phenomena that stem from "outside" the immediate field of study. They have the advantage of providing fixed points from which analysis may proceed in a straightforward chain of cause-and effect processes. But on closer inspection many such fixed points will be found to dissolve into shifting relationships which are not as separate and distinct from cultural influences as they may appear. Premature dependence upon explanations in terms of the external environment only diverts the historian or anthropologist from unraveling the complex stresses within human institutions. In all but the simplest societies, it is forces within the social order rather than direct environmental factors which have provided the major stimulus and guide to further growth.

## Conclusion

In retrospect, the significant common features of land use among the early civilizations of the Old and the New World are so general that they are almost trite. If we have attempted to define the terms more closely than is usual, there is certainly nothing unusual about finding that all the great civilizational traditions rested on surpluses made available through sedentary, diversified, intensive agriculture. In addition, of course, it is implicit in this discussion that the common social institutions and processes of development identified in each of the four civilizations were bound up together with this general constellation of subsistence practices in a functionally interacting network which characterizes early civilization as a sort of cultural type.

Against this simple and limited finding of regularity, the diversity of other environmental subsistence features and the huge proliferation of cultural forms stand in sharp contrast. History is not a mathematical exercise in the application of "laws," and the meaning of human experience is not to be found by suppressing its rich variety in the search for common, implicitly deterministic, denominators. From this point of view, perhaps the lack of closer specificity in the ecological relationships that are common to the early civilizations is the single most important point to be made. Much of sociocultural development seems to proceed very largely on its own terms, including even some important aspects of ecological adjustment. Societal growth is a continuously creative process, conditioned far more by past history than by directly felt environmental forces. On the whole, then, one may reasonably conclude that for an understanding of the meaning of the early civilizations—both in their own terms and for the modern world—the natural environment serves as no more than a backdrop.

# The Legacy of Sumer

## Samuel Noah Kramer

*From* The Sumerians.
*University of Chicago
Press, n.d., pp. 269–299.*
© *1963, University of
Chicago. By permission
of the author, and
the publisher and
copyright holder.*

On the assumption that civilization is of some value for man, the long-dead Sumerians might well point with "fingerless" pride to the numerous innovations, inventions, and institutions which they helped to originate. To be sure, it might be said that these would have come to be in any case, Sumerians or no Sumerians. But this hardly seems to the point—the Sumerians were there first, and it seems not unfair to give credit where credit is due. Be that as it may, in this chapter I shall attempt to sketch rather briefly and hesitatingly some of their more palpable and significant contributions to the culture of man. . . .

It was a Semitic people—the Amorites—who put an end to the Sumerians as a political, ethnic, and linguistic entity. To be sure, the conquered conquered the conquerors, and the Amorites, commonly known as Babylonians because their capital was the city of Babylon, took over Sumerian culture and civilization lock, stock, and barrel. Except for the language, the Babylonian educational system, religion, mythology, and literature are almost identical with the Sumerian, excluding, of course, the expected changes and variations due to political developments and the passing of time. And since these Babylonians, in turn, exercised no little influence on their less cultured neighbors, particularly the Assyrians, Hittites, Hurrians, and Canaanites, they, as much as the Sumerians themselves, helped to plant the Sumerian cultural seed everywhere in the ancient Near East. And this brings us to the legacy of Sumer down through the ages, including our own, although in our age this heritage is no longer an active and creative source of cultural growth but a rather melancholy if not altogether uninspiring theme for antiquarian history.

The tracking-down of Sumer's legacy may well begin with the socio-political institution commonly known as the city-state which, in

Sumer, developed out of the village and town in the second half of the fourth millennium B.C. and was a flourishing institution throughout the third millennium. The city—with its free citizens and assembly, its nobles and priests, its clients and slaves, its ruling god and his vicar and representative on earth, the king, its farmers, craftsmen, and merchants, its temples, walls, and gates—is found all over the ancient world from the Indus to the western Mediterranean. Some of its specific features may vary from place to place, but by and large it bears a strong resemblance to its early Sumerian prototype, and it seems not unreasonable to conclude that not a few of its elements and counterparts go back to Sumerian roots. It may well be, of course, that the city would have come into being in the ancient world whether Sumer had existed or not. But this is not at all certain; in Egypt, for instance, the city-state never took root, and the same might have happened in other parts of the ancient world.

One of the most characteristic features of the Sumerian city-state throughout the greater part of the third millennium B.C. was written law, beginning with the writing of legal documents such as sales and deeds and culminating in the promulgation of specially prepared law codes. Written legal documents and law codes are found in later periods all over the ancient Near East, and there is little doubt that although these may differ in details they all go back to Sumerian prototypes; even Greece and Rome would probably never have had their written laws had it not been for the Sumerian penchant for keeping a record of their legal transactions.

In the matter of scientific achievement, it is probably in the field of mathematics that the Sumerians made their major contribution to future generations by devising the sexagesimal system of place notation, which may have been the forerunner of the Hindu-Arabic decimal system now in use. Traces of the Sumerian sexagesimal system exist even today in the measurement of the circle and angle by degrees and in some of the weights and measures that were current until relatively recent times.

In the field of technology, the potter's wheel, the wheeled vehicle, and the sailboat are all probably Sumerian inventions. And while met-allurgy is certainly not of Sumerian origin, the products of the Sumerian metalworkers were dispersed all over the ancient Near East, and some even reached as far as Hungary and Central Europe.

Architecture was the major art of Sumer from earliest times, in particular the construction of temples with their stone foundations and platforms, niched cellas, painted walls and altars, mosaic-covered columns, and impressive façades; it would not seem unlikely that at least some of these architectural techniques were diffused over the ancient world. Sumerian architects also made use of the dome, vault, and arch, and it is not improbable that the arch first came to Greece and Rome from contact with Babylonia, which had inherited it from Sumer. Near Eastern sculpture, too, particularly the practice of fashioning statues of gods and men, may go back to Sumerian origins, since it was the Sumerian theologians who first conceived of the idea that the statue represented the ruler, or even some other high official, standing before his god in unceasing prayer, as it were, for his life. The Sumerian cylinder seal "rolled" its way all over the ancient world from India to Cyprus and Crete, and there is many a church in Europe today whose capitals are ornamented with conventionalized motifs going back to scenes first imagined and engraved by the Sumerian artist and craftsman.

The achievements of the Sumerians in the areas of religion, education, and literature left a deep impress not only on their neighbors in space and time but on the culture of modern man as well, especially through their influence, indirect though it was, on the ancient Hebrews and the Bible. The extent of the Hebrew debt to Sumer becomes more apparent from day to day as a result of the gradual piecing together and translation of the Sumerian literary works; for as can now be seen, they have quite a number of features in common with the books of the Bible. This chapter will close, therefore, with a sketch of the Biblical parallels found in Sumerian literature by isolating and analyzing the various beliefs, tenets, themes, motifs, and values which seem to be common to the ancient Hebrews and the much more ancient Sumerians.

The form and content of the Sumerian literary works have been discussed and analyzed in great detail [not included in this text], and no further elaboration is needed at this point. It goes without saying that a written literature so varied, comprehensive, and time-honored as the Sumerian left a deep impress on the literary products of the entire Near East. Particularly was this so since at one time or another practically all the peoples of western Asia—Akkadians, Assyrians, Babylonians, Hittites, Hurrians, Canaanites, and Elamites (to name only those for which positive and direct evidence is available at the moment)—had found it to their interest to borrow the cuneiform script in order to inscribe their own records and writings. The adoption and adaptation of this syllabic and logographic system of writing, which had been developed by the Sumerians to write their own agglutinative and largely monosyllabic tongue, demanded a thorough training in the Sumerian language and literature. To this end, no doubt, learned teachers and scribes were imported from Sumer to the schools of the neighboring lands, while the native scribes traveled to Sumer for special instruction in its more famous academies. The result was a wide dissemination of Sumerian culture and literature. The ideas and ideals of the Sumerians—their cosmology, theology, ethics, and system of education—permeated to a greater or lesser extent the thoughts and writings of all the peoples of the ancient Near East. So, too, did the Sumerian literary forms and themes—their plots, motifs, stylistic devices, and aesthetic techniques. And the Hebrews of Palestine, the land where the books of the Bible were composed, redacted, and edited, were no exception.

To be sure, even the earliest parts of the Bible, it is generally agreed, were not written down in their present form much earlier than 1000 B.C., whereas most of the Sumerian literary documents were composed about 2000 B.C. or not long afterward. There is, therefore, no question of any contemporary borrowing from the Sumerian literary sources. Sumerian influence penetrated the Bible through the Canaanite, Hurrian, Hittite, and Akkadian literatures—particularly through the latter, since, as is well known, the Akkadian language was used all over Palestine and its environs in the second millennium B.C. as the common language of practically the entire literary world. Akkadian literary works must therefore have been well known to Palestinian men of letters, including the Hebrews, and not a few of these Akkadian literary works can be traced back to Sumerian prototypes, remodeled and transformed over the centuries.

However, there is another possible source of Sumerian influence on the Bible which is far more direct and immediate than that just described. In fact, it may well go back to Father Abraham himself. Most scholars agree that while the Abraham saga as told in the Bible contains much that is legendary and fanciful, it does have an important kernel of truth, including Abraham's birth in Ur of the Chaldees, perhaps about 1700 B.C., and his early life there with his family. Now Ur was one of the most important cities of ancient Sumer; in fact, it was the capital of Sumer at three different periods in its history. It had an impressive *edubba;* and in the joint British-American excavations conducted there between the years 1922 and 1934, quite a number of Sumerian literary documents have been found. Abraham and his forefathers may well have had some acquaintance with Sumerian literary products that had been copied or created in their home town academy. And it is by no means impossible that he and the members of his family brought some of this Sumerian lore and learning with them to Palestine, where they gradually became part of the traditions and sources utilized by the Hebrew men of letters in composing and redacting the books of the Bible.

Be that as it may, here are a number of Biblical parallels from Sumerian literature which unquestionably point to traces of Sumerian influence:

1 CREATION OF THE UNIVERSE The Sumerians, like the ancient Hebrews, thought that a primeval sea had existed prior to creation. The universe, according to the Sumerians, consisted of a united heaven and earth engendered in some way in this primeval sea, and it was the air-god, Enlil—perhaps not unlike the *ruachelohim* of Genesis—who separated heaven from earth.

2 CREATION OF MAN Man, according to both the Hebrews and the Sumerians, was conceived as having been fashioned of clay and

imbued with the "breath of life." The purpose for which he was created was to serve the gods—or Jahweh alone, in the case of the Hebrews—with prayer, supplication, and sacrifices.

3 CREATION TECHNIQUES   Creation, according to both Biblical and Sumerian writers, was accomplished primarily in two ways: by divine command and by actual "making" or "fashioning." In either case, the actual creation was preceded by divine planning, though this need not have been explicity stated.

4 PARADISE   No Sumerian parallels to the story of the Garden of Eden and the Fall of Man have yet been found. There are, however, several paradise motifs that are significant for comparative purposes, including one that may help to clarify the rib episode in Genesis 2:21–23. Moreover, there is some reason to believe that the very idea of a divine paradise, a garden of the gods, is of Sumerian origin.

5 THE FLOOD   As has long been recognized, the Biblical and Sumerian versions of the Flood story show numerous obvious and close parallels. Noteworthy, too, is the fact that according to at least one Mesopotamian tradition there were ten antediluvian rulers, each with a life span of extraordinary length, which is reminiscent of some of the Biblical antediluvian patriarchs.

6 THE CAIN-ABEL MOTIF   The rivalry motif depicted in the undoubtedly much abbreviated Cain-Abel episode of the Bible was a high favorite with the Sumerian writers and poets.

7 THE TOWER OF BABEL AND THE DISPERSION OF MANKIND   The story of the building of the Tower of Babel originated, no doubt, in an effort to explain the existence of the Mesopotamian ziggurats. To the Hebrews, these towering structures, which could often be seen in a state of ruin and decay, became symbols of man's feeling of insecurity and the not unrelated lust for power which brings upon him humiliation and suffering. It is most unlikely, therefore, that a parallel to this story will be found among the Sumerians, to whom the ziggurat represented a bond between heaven and earth, between god and man. On the other hand, the idea that there was a time

when all peoples of the earth "had one language and the same words" and that this happy state was brought to an end by an irate deity may have a parallel in a golden-age passage which is part of the Sumerian epic tale "Enmerkar and the Lord of Aratta."

8 THE EARTH AND ITS ORGANIZATION   The Sumerian myth "Enki and the World Order: The Organization of the Earth and Its Cultural Processes" provides a detailed account of the activities of Enki, the Sumerian god of wisdom, in organizing the earth and in establishing what might be termed law and order on it; this poem has its Biblical echoes in, for example, Deuteronomy 32:7–14 (note especially verse 8) and Psalm 107.

9. PERSONAL GOD   To judge from the covenant between God and Abraham—note, too, the reference to a "god of Nahor" in Genesis 31:53—the ancient Hebrews were familiar with the idea of a personal god. The belief in the existence of a personal god was evolved by the Sumerians at least as early as the middle of the third millennium B.C. According to Sumerian teachers and sages, every adult male and family head had his "personal god," or a kind of good angel whom he looked upon as his divine father. This personal god was in all probability adopted by the Sumerian paterfamilias as the result of an oracle or a dream or a vision involving a mutual understanding or agreement not unlike the covenant between the Hebrew patriarchs and Jahweh.

To be sure, there could have been nothing mutually exclusive about the covenant between the Sumerian and his tutelary deity, and in this respect, therefore, it differed very significantly from that between Abraham and his god. All that the Sumerian expected of his personal god was that he speak in his behalf and intercede for him in the assembly of the gods whenever the occasion demanded and thus insure for him a long life and good health. In return, he glorified his god with special prayers, supplications, and sacrifices, although at the same time he continued to worship the other deities of the Sumerian pantheon. Nevertheless, as the Sumerian literary document "Man and His God" indicates, there existed a close, intimate, trusting and even tender relationship between the Sumerian and his personal god, one which bears no little resemblance to that between Jahweh and the Hebrew patriarchs and, in later days, between Jahweh and the Hebrew people as a whole.

10  LAW  That the Biblical laws and the long-known Hammurabi law code show numerous similarities in content, terminology, and even arrangement is recognized by practically all students of the Bible. But the Hammurabi code itself, as has been shown in recent years, is an Akkadian compilation of laws based largely on Sumerian prototypes. In fact, there is good reason to infer that the extraordinary growth and development of legal concepts, practices, precedents, and compilations in the ancient Near East goes back largely to the Sumerians and their rather one-sided emphasis on rivalry and superiority.

11  ETHICS AND MORALS  The ethical concepts and moral ideals developed by the Sumerians were essentially identical with those of the Hebrews, although they lacked their almost palpable ethical sensitivity and moral fervor, especially as these qualities are exemplified in the Biblical prophetic literature. Psychologically, the Sumerian was more distant and aloof than the Hebrew—more emotionally restrained, more formal and methodical. He tended to eye his fellow men with some suspicion, misgiving, and even apprehension, which inhibited to no small extent the human warmth, sympathy, and affection so vital to spiritual growth and well-being. And in spite of his high ethical attainments, the Sumerian never reached the lofty conviction that a "pure heart" and "clean hands" were more worthy in the eyes of his god than lengthy prayers, profuse sacrifices, and elaborate ritual.

12  DIVINE RETRIBUTION AND NATIONAL CATASTROPHE  Jahweh's wrath and the humiliation and destruction of the people that incurs it constitute an often repeated theme in the Biblical books. Usually the national catastrophe comes about through a violent attack by some neighboring people, especially selected as Jahweh's scourge and whip. to this theme the historiographic document "The Curse of Adage" offers a rather interesting parallel: Enlil, the leading deity of the Sumerian pantheon, having been deeply angered by the blasphemous act of a ruler of Agade, lifted his eyes to the mountains and brought down the barbarous and cruel Gutians, who proceeded to destroy not only Agade but almost all of Sumer as well.

13  THE PLAGUE MOTIF  The Sumerian myth "Inanna and Shukalletuda: The Gardener's Mortal Sin" contains a plague motif which parallels to some extent the Biblical plague motif in the Exodus story: in both cases, a deity angered by the misdeeds and obduracy of an individual sends a series of plagues against an entire land and its people.

14  SUFFERING AND SUBMISSION: THE "JOB" MOTIF  Quite recently, a Sumerian poetic essay which is of rather unusual significance for Biblical comparative studies has become available. Its central theme, human suffering and submission, is identical with that treated so sensitively and poignantly in the Biblical Book of Job. Even the introductory plot is the same: A man—unnamed in the Sumerian poem—who had been wealthy, wise, righteous, and blessed with friends and kin is overwhelmed one day, for no apparent reason, by sickness, suffering, poverty, betrayal, and hatred. Admittedly, however, the Sumerian essay, which consists of less than one hundred and fifty lines, compares in no way with the Biblical book in breadth, depth, and beauty; it is much closer in mood, temper, and content to the more tearful and plaintive psalms of the Book of Psalms.

15  DEATH AND THE NETHER WORLD  The Biblical Sheol, and, for that matter, the Hades of the Greeks, has its counterpart in the Sumerian Kur. Like the Hebrew Sheol, the Kur was the dark, dread abode of the dead. It was a land of no return, from which only exceptionally the shade of a once prominent figure might be called up for questioning. In the Sumerian literary documents, there are several other interesting parallels with Hebrew ideas relating to the nether world: its depiction as the pitiful home of former kings and princes; the raising of the shades of the dead from it; and the imprisonment in it of the god Dumuzi, the Biblical Tammuz, for whom the women of Jerusalem were lamenting as late as the days of the prophet Ezekiel. . . .

# Human Society before the Urban Revolution

## Robert Redfield

What can be said that is general and true about the condition of mankind before civilization? The question is directed to a time from five to six thousand years ago. At that time human populations were to be found on all the world's continents, with the possible exception of Australia. Greenland had not yet been invaded by man, and some of the islands of the Pacific were as yet without human occupants. But there were people in a great many widely scattered parts of the habitable earth, not very many of them in any one place, and not very many of them altogether. No city had yet been built anywhere.

The question is whether anything can be said, with show of reason and evidence, about *all* the human beings that were there then, whether they lived in the arctic or in the tropics, whether they hunted, fished, or farmed, and whatever may have been the color of their skins, the languages they spoke, or the particular beliefs and customs that they had. The question demands a positive characterization of their manner of life. The description should be more than a mere statement of the things that those early men did not have that we today do have. It should say: this is what they did; this is how they felt; this is the way the world looked to them.

The question, so understood, appears to require more than can be provided from trustworthy evidence, but I do not think that it really does. It can be answered from two sources of information. The archaeologists dig up the material things that men of those times made and used, and from these things draw reasonable inferences about their manner of life. And, secondly, the ethnologists tell us a good deal about the ways of life of those peo-

*From* The Primitive World and Its Transformations. *Cornell University Press, 1953, pp. 1–23. Copyright 1953, Cornell University. By permission of Mrs. Robert Redfield, the publisher and copyright holder.*

ple who until recent times have remained uncivilized: the primitive, the preliterate—or, to
use the old-fashioned terms—the savage and
the barbaric peoples. To learn what pre-civilized men were like, we may look to the accounts of the remains of ancient camps and
settlements unaffected by cities, either because they were there before there were any
cities anywhere, or because they stood remote
and unreached by ancient cities already arisen.
And also we may look to what has been written in great detail about many hundreds of
present-day tribes and bands and villages,
little communities of the never civilized. I do
not assume that these latter people have experienced no changes in the several thousands
of years since the first cities were built. The
particular thoughts and beliefs of the present-
day preliterates have probably changed a good
deal during many hundreds of generations.
The customs of these people are not "earlier"
than is our own civilization, for they have had
as long a history as have we. But what I do
assert is that the surviving primitive peoples
have remained substantially unaffected by civilization. Insofar as the conditions of primitive
life remain—in the smallness of the community, and in its isolation and nonliteracy—so,
too, the kind of thoughts and beliefs, however changed in specific content, remain of a
kind characteristic of primitive society. That
there is such a kind is evidenced to us from
the fact that we can generalize as to this manner of thought and belief from the surviving
primitive peoples, in the face of the very great
variety of content of thought and belief which
these exhibit. These surviving primitive peoples provide us with instances of that general
and primordial kind of human living which it
is my immediate purpose to describe.

Now it is fortunate for the present enterprise that these two sources of information,
the archaeological and the ethnological, supplement each other. Where the former is weak,
the latter is strong; and where the ethnologist
may be insufficiently impressed by the influence of technology on the manner of life of a
human community, the archaeologist can
hardly fail to be impressed. This is what he
sees: the material things. Moreover, of the
many meanings which are locked in the artifacts that ancient peoples made, it is those
meanings which relate to practical action, especially the getting of foods, which commu-

nicate themselves most readily to the archaeologist who finds them. A Plains Indian medicine bundle or an Australian totemic design
as an archaeological object by itself would
convey only a little of the very great deal
which the ethnologist who can talk to a living
Indian or Australian can find out that it
means. So the archaeologist's view of the
manner of life of the precivilized peoples will
emphasize the practical aspects of living and
the material influences on change. An archaeologist should make a little effort to lean deliberately away from a materialist view of human life and a conception of history in simple
terms of economic determinism. His work in-
clines him toward it. On the other hand, the
ethnologist is often in a position where he can
find out little or nothing of the history of the
people he is studying, as they have written
nothing down about it, having no means to do
so; and so it may sometimes appear to him
that they are to be explained chiefly in terms
of the kinds of marriage choices he finds them
making when he finds them, or the potlatches
they give. In the absence of a history, the way
the material conditions of living limited that
people here or gave them a chance to develop
something there may not be apparent.

Archaeologist and ethnologist, however, do
often talk to each other, and indeed in some
cases are the same person. So the separation
of work, the difference in emphasis, is not so
great as I have perhaps made it sound. In the
attempt to characterize the precivilized manner of life, I will begin by following Childe, an
archaeologist. Professor Childe is interested
in the effects on human development of
changes in the technology by which food is
produced. He makes a separation of importance between that period in human history
when men were hunters and fishers only (savagery), and that period when men had learned
how to be agriculturalists or animal breeders
(barbarism). The change from the one kind of
life to the other he calls a revolution, "the
food-producing revolution."

The discovery of how to produce food was,
of course, of enormous importance in human
history, and it is not too much to call it a revolution and to group it, as Childe does, with
the "urban revolution," when civilization came
into being, and with the industrial revolution
of modern times. Yet certain qualifications or
additions need to be made. It has been

pointed out that the food-producing revolution was the more notable event in that from the condition of food collecting one could not predict that food producing would be achieved, but that when once food production had increased human population and made leisure possible, civilization was bound to come about. And it is also necessary to recognize that some of the changes characteristic of each stage may have taken place, in one community or another, before the revolution in technology that Childe stresses had occurred there. Thus we know that a sedentary village life is possible to a people who know nothing of agriculture or animal husbandry. The fishing Indians of our Northwest coast lived a village life and developed certain aspects of their culture very highly. In prehistoric times there existed on the Scandinavian coast sessile communities, quite comparable with Neolithic farmers in the village character of life, with pottery and the polishing of flint, but without crops or herds. Also, it is not unlikely that with the advent of agriculture there began some of those changes which we are able to see only when cities and writing have made them visible to us. The excavations in Iraq, already mentioned, suggest this possibility. As the changes in technology, so also the changes in the human mind which are the subject of these pages may have well begun before the urban revolution, even before the food-producing revolution.

Nevertheless, within the wide generalizations that I am here attempting, the food-producing revolution and the urban revolution may be considered as two parts of one great transformation. To one interested in changes in human habits and capacities of mind, the urban revolution is the more important part, for it is with the coming of city life that we are able to see novel and transforming attitudes taken toward life and the universe. That these novel attitudes began earlier is likely, and farther on in these pages indications will be drawn from present-day primitive societies that occasional beginnings of these civilized attitudes were to be found in the precivilized societies had we been there to look for them. The question as to the relative importance of Childe's two first revolutions may be set aside with this statement: the food-producing revolution was perhaps the turning point in the human career, but it was through the urban

revolution that the consequences of the turn were realized.

Now let us attempt a characterization of mankind in precivilized times. Let us begin with the simple statement that in the primary condition of mankind the human community was small. As Childe says, writing of the food-collecting period, hunters and vegetable-food collectors usually live in small roving bands. Even the more stable settlement of Pacific coast Indian fishing people, of recent times exceptionally well provided with food, includes hardly more than thirty occupied houses and several hundred people. Nor does the immediate transition to food producing increase substantially the size of the community, now a group of farmer's huts or a center of cattle raising.

On the whole the growth of population was not reflected so much in the enlargement of the settlement unit as in a multiplication of settlements. In ethnography neolithic villages can boast only a few hundred inhabitants. . . . In prehistoric Europe the largest neolithic village yet known, Barkaer in Jutland, comprised fifty-two small, one-roomed dwellings, but sixteen to thirty houses was a more normal figure; so the average local group in neolithic times would average two hundred to four hundred members.

Certain food-producing town centers well on the way to civilization do give indication of larger populations, but hunters' bands or food producers' settlements are alike in general contrast to the far larger community which was the ancient city with its seven thousand to twenty thousand inhabitants. What is here worth emphasizing is that until the rise of civilization mankind lived in communities so small that every adult could, and no doubt did, know everybody else.

These communities were isolated from one another. Again Childe gives us to understand that the change in this regard with the coming of agriculture was a change in some degree, but at first not a radical change. Throughout both Paleolithic and Neolithic times each little group was largely self-contained and self-supported, as the surviving primitive societies, whether hunters or growers of vegetable or animal food, are largely self-contained and self-supported. The trade that occurred in Paleolithic times was chiefly trade in nonessentials; with Neolithic times the trade intensified and included some staple commodities, such as stone for querns and flint for hand axes. But the trade did not greatly limit the essential separateness of the local community. The isolation of the Neolithic settlement continued into the medieval English village. Villagers of primitives or peasants today are still relatively isolated, and, on the whole, when such people have more than casual association with outsiders, it is with people who are much like themselves, in neighboring bands or settlements that are like their own community.

So we may characterize mankind in its primary condition as living in small and isolated communities. These communities were of course without writing. I do not say more of this absence of literacy and literature; its importance as a criterion of primitive as contrasted with civilized living is familiar. To these qualities others may be added. The precivilized community was composed of one kind of people. If this fact is not to be deduced from the archaeologist's data, it follows from what we know of isolated primitive communities seen today. Small and isolated communities are intimate communities; people come to have the same ways of doing things; they marry with and live almost entirely with others like them in that community.

Next we may say that the members of the precivilized community had a strong sense of group solidarity. No doubt they thought of themselves as naturally belonging together, and so far as they were aware of people different from themselves, they thought their own ways to be better than the ways of others. These things also may be said, not only because they are necessary consequences of the isolation and the smallness of the community, but because we see them to be true of contemporary primitive communities. Civilized communities are more heterogeneous, and the sense of group solidarity is qualified by the number and variety of kinds of groups to which the individual makes attachment—or by the difficulty of making firm attachments to groups in some urban situations.

Let us follow Professor Childe further in his characterization of precivilized man. We see that now he must make increasing use of reasonable deduction and of the evidence from ethnology. He tells us that in the precivilized community there were no full-time specialists. He asserts this for the reason that in communities with simple hunting or even farming "there simply will not be enough food to go round unless every member of the group contributes to the supply." In the primitive societies of the present day there are rarely full-time specialists. So the assumption is fairly well founded that in the early condition of mankind what men did was customarily different from what women did, but what one man did was much like what another did. There were men with special skills at activities carried on by all men, and there were probably shamans or other part-time practitioners in the spiritual and healing arts. Differences among individuals with respect to the depth of understanding of cosmogonic and religious ideas may have been very considerable; this is a matter to which we shall recur on a later page. But, on the whole, all men shared the same essential knowledge, practiced the same arts of life, had the same interests and similiar experiences.

Yet another characteristic of precivilized living may be asserted. Within those early communities the relationships among people were primarily those of personal status. In a small and intimate community all people are known for their individual qualities of personality. Few or no strangers take part in the daily life. So men and women are seen as persons, not as parts of mechanical operations, as city people see so many of those around them. Indeed, this disposition to see what is around one as human and personal like oneself is not, in precivilized or primitive society, limited to people; a great deal of what we call "nature" is more or less so regarded. The cosmos is personal and human-like.

Also in this connection it may be said that the groupings of people within the primitive community is one that depends on status and on role, not on mere practical usefulness. There are fathers, or older people, or shamans, or priests; each such kind of person is accorded prestige. In civilized societies the network of relationships of utility—the numbers and kinds of people who produce goods and services are so great and are at such remote distances—that many of the relationships that keep people provided with what they use are not involved in status at all, for those who use the goods. In primitive societies the status relationships are universal and dominant; the exceptions to be made would be those relatively few that arise out of trade with foreign communities.

Furthermore, in this personal universe where categories of relationships involve status, the forms and groupings of kinship provide the basic classifications. The original human society was one of kinsmen. Childe speaks of the "sentiment of kinship" which in considerable part held the group together. Within the precivilized society, it is safe to assume that relationships were essentially familial. The primary arrangements of personal status and role are those connected with that universally persistent kind of family anthropologists now call "nuclear" and the extensions of this primary kinship into many, possibly even all, of the other relationships within the community. Moreover, the categories of kinship may include elements of nature, as some animals, and supernatural beings. Of course we cannot say just what were the kinship institutions in the thousands of bands and settlements that constituted precivilized society. In his latest book Childe with ingenuity and prudence draws reasonable inferences as to elements of social organization in precivilized societies known only archaeologically. The result suggests the presence in one place of single-family households, in another of large households including several or many nuclear families, and a variety of forms of marriage. Nevertheless the very smallness and isolation of the precivilized community everywhere allows us to say that in the early condition of humanity, the community, as well as the cosmos of which its members felt it to be a part, was essentially made up of personal relationships, and that the patterning of these relationships was primarily accomplished by developments derived from the differences of age, sex, and familial connection. Today, among western Australian peoples, "the whole society forms a body of relatives," and the intimate connection between the body of relatives and nature, through the water hole or other center of animal multiplication, and the totemic rites, is familiar to readers of Australian ethnology.

What, essentially, held together this primordial human community? Was it the mutual usefulness to one another of those few hunters or fishers or farmers? To answer, Yes, is to recognize what is obviously true: "Co-operation is essential to secure food and shelter and for defense against foes, human and subhuman." But to answer, Yes, is also to suggest a possible misconception. The "identity of economic interests" of which Childe writes in the paragraph in which he so interestingly characterizes the mode of life of man before civilization, is a fact which any of us would have observed had we been there to see the precivilized community, and which is an obvious inference from what we know more directly about it. But this does not mean that in those communities men worked primarily for material wealth. The incentives to work and to exchange labor and goods are, in primitive and precivilized society especially, various and chiefly noneconomic (in the narrow sense). They arise from tradition, from a sense of obligation coming out of one's position in a system of status relationships, especially those of kinship, and from religious considerations and moral motivations of many kinds. The point has been put very convincingly by Karl Polanyi. Let us then add to our characterization of the precivilized society that it was a society in which the economy was one determined by status (as contrasted with the society imagined and in part realized in nineteenth-century Europe and America, in which the economy was determined by the market). In the precivilized or the primitive society "man's economy is, as a rule, submerged in his social relations." Essentially and primarily, man "does not aim at safeguarding his individual interest in the acquisition of material possessions, but rather at ensuring social good-will, social status, social assets. He values possessions primarily as a means to that end." We are talking now of a time before the acquisitive society.

To answer only that the precivilized community was held together by reason of mutual usefulness is to fail to say what it is that most importantly and characteristically holds such a community together. Indeed, Childe sees and states succinctly, in terms which Durkheim caused many of us to use, the difference in this regard between the precivilized settlement and the city. It is not the former, but the earliest cities that "illustrate a first approximation to an organic solidarity based upon functional complementarity and interdependence between all its members such as subsist between the constituent cells of an organism." It is the urban community that rests upon mutual usefulness. The primitive and precivilized communities are held together essentially by common understandings as to the ultimate nature and purpose of life. The precivilized society was like the present-day primitive society in those characteristics—isolation, smallness, homogeneity, persistence in the common effort to make a way of living under relatively stable circumstances—to which we have already attended, and therefore it was like the parallel societies which we can observe today in that its fundamental order was a matter of moral conviction. In both cases the society

exists not so much in the exchange of useful functions as in common understandings as to the ends given. The ends are not stated as matters of doctrine, but are implied by the many acts which make up the living that goes on in the society. Therefore, the morale of a folk society—its power to act consistently over periods of time and to meet crises effectively—is not dependent upon discipline exerted by force or upon devotion to some single principle of action, but to the concurrence and consistency of many or all of the actions and conceptions which make up the whole round of life.

For the homogeneity of such a society is not that homogeneity in which everybody does the same thing at the same time. The people are homogeneous in that they share the same tradition and have the same view of the good life. They do the same kinds of work and they worship and marry and feel shame or pride in the same way and under similar circumstances. But at any one time the members of a primitive community may be doing notably different things: the women looking for edible roots while the men hunt; some men out on a war party while others at home perform a rite for its success. And when there is a familial ceremonial or a magico-religious ritual affecting the whole community, the differences in what is being done may be very great. In the activities to gain a material living, labor, as between man and man or woman and woman, may be divided. But the total specialization of functions, as among people of different sexes and age-or-kinship positions, and as among participants in a rite, may be very considerable. The point to be stressed is that all these activities conduce to a purpose, express a view of man's duty, that all share, and to which each activity or element of institution contributes.

We can safely say these things of the precivilized societies as we can say them of the primitive societies because these things follow from the other characteristics which we have already conceded, and are attested in every very isolated, undisturbed primitive society we observe today. For the same reasons it is possible to add yet other attributes to the characterization. In the most primitive societies of living men into which we may enter and which we can come directly to understand, the controls of each are informal; they rest on the traditional obligations of largely inherited status, and are expressed in talk and gesture and in the patterns of reciprocal action. Political institutions are few and simple, or even entirely absent. The members of these societies "believe in the sacred things; their sense of right and wrong springs from the unconscious roots of social feeling, and is therefore unreasoned, compulsive and strong." People do the kind of things they do, not because somebody just thought up that kind of thing, or because anybody ordered them to do so, but because it seems to the people to flow from the very necessity of existence that they do that kind of thing. The reasons given after the thing is done, in the form of myth and the dress of ceremony, assert the rightness of the choice. Particular things are done as a result of decision as to that particular action, but as to the class of action, tradition is the source and the authority. "The Indians decide now to go on a hunt; but it is not a matter of debate whether one should, from time to time, hunt." So the principles of rightness which underlie the activities are largely tacit. And they are not the subject of much explicit criticism, nor even of very much reflective thought. Institutions are not planned out, nor is their modification a matter of much deliberate choice and action. Legislation, though it may occur, is not the characteristic form of legal action in primitive societies. And what Malinowski refers to as "science" in connection with the primitive peoples is better distinguished as practical knowledge. And these things too may with confidence be attributed to the precivilized societies. Yet, because in them thought and action were largely traditional and uncritical, it does not follow that activities were automatic or empty of meaning. Rather we must suppose that activity with them as with us involved lively and variable subjective states. Ruth Bunzel, studying Pueblo potters, found that the Indian woman who was in fact copying the designs of other potters with only the smallest variation was unaware that she copied, condemned copying as wrong, and had a strong conviction that she was in fact inventive and creative. And as for the meaning of life—that was, so to speak, guaranteed. One did what tradition said one did, making a multitude of interesting and particular choices. But all of it fell within and was motivated by the common understandings of the little community as to the nature and purpose of life.

The attempt to gather together some of the attributes of that form of human living which prevailed before the first civilizations arose may now be halted. Later we shall examine some of the respects in which it is necessary to qualify this characterization. Enough of the characterization for the needs of these pages has been assembled. There results a picture, very generalized, of the organization of life, social control, and motivation among most of the societies of mankind during most of human history. The point upon which we are to insist, for its importance in considering the topics of the following lectures, is that in this early condition of humanity the essential order of society, the nexus which held people together, was moral. Humanity attained its characteristic, long-enduring nature as a multitude of different but equivalent systems of relationships and institutions each expressive of a view of the good. Each precivilized society was held together by largely undeclared but continually realized ethical conceptions.

Professor Childe unfortunately happened upon a figure of comparison that leads in the direction just opposite to the truth when he wrote that the solidarity of the precivilized community was "really based on the same principles as that of a pack of wolves or a herd of sheep." Even the little glimpses of religion and sense of obligation to do right which are accorded the archaeologist show us that twenty-five thousand years ago the order of society was moral order. That of wolves or sheep is not. Childe's facts prove that this was so and that his comparison of precivilized

society with that of animals is misleading. Describing the wall paintings, the personal adornments, the trade in cowrie shells, and the hints these things give of a life of the mind and the spirit among the Western Europeans of the Ice Age, Childe says, "Savagery produced a dazzling culture." It is Childe who uses this adjective for the cultures at the end of the Ice Age that found expression in necklaces of animal teeth, in well-executed realistic paintings of the animals that were hunted, in stone-weighted skeletons of reindeer cast into a German lake, "presumably as an offering to the spirit of the herd or the genius of the land," according to Childe.

The antiquity of the moral order is not fully attested by archaeology. A people's conceptions as to the good are only meagerly represented in the material things that they make. A tribe of western Australia, the Pitjendadjara, today carry on a religious and moral life of great intensity, but they make and use material objects so few and so perishable that were these people exhibited to us only through archaeology, we would barely know that they had existed and we would know nothing of their moral life. As described by Charles P. Mountford in his charming book, these aborigines perform their rites to increase animal and plant food, and they follow a morality of personal relations with dignity and conscience. Mountford says that they make but five tools: a spear, a spear thrower, a wooden carrying dish, a stone slab on which to grind food, and a digging stick. Perhaps this investigator overlooked some of the articles made by these aborigines, but it is certainly true that naked and wandering, with almost none of the material possessions and power which we associate with the development of humanity, they are nevertheless as human as are you and I.

We may suppose that fifty thousand years ago mankind had developed a variety of moral orders, each expressed in some local tradition, and comparable to what we find among aborigines today. Their development required both the organic evolution of human bodily and cerebral nature and also the accumulation of experience by tradition. As the tradition began to accumulate while the organic evolution was still going on, the moral order—and the technical order—began to be established among the apelike men of the early Pleistocene. On the other hand, until bodily and cerebral nature equivalent to that of men living today had been developed, we cannot fairly attribute to those earliest humanoid societies a moral order comparable, let us say, with that of the Australian blackfellow. Even in the case of so relatively late a being as Neanderthal man there was a factor of biological difference which would have limited the development of culture. But by a time seventy-five or fifty thousand years ago, the biological evolution of mankind had reached a point at which the genetic qualities necessary for the development of fully human life had been attained. This reaches the conclusion that for a period of time at least five times as long as the entire period of civilization man has had the capacity for a life governed by such moral orders as we see in primitive societies today. The men who left the paintings of Altamira were fully human and not very different from us. And I follow Eliseo Vivas when he writes:

That does not mean, of course, that they pursued the identical values and were capable of the same theoretical sophistication of which we are capable; it merely means that they probably had the same degree of moral sensibility, though perhaps focused toward different objects than those toward which we, the men of contemporary technological society, focus ours.

In recognizing that every precivilized society of the past fifty or seventy-five millenniums had a moral order to which the technical order was subordinate, I do not say that the religious and ethical systems of these societies were equally complex. Then, as now, there were "thin cultures" and "rich cultures." Childe sees certain of the mesolithic cultures as "thin" in comparison with the cultures that preceded them. It is not, of course, clear that the thinness lay in the moral life. Maybe they had a religious and personal life that is not represented in the archaeology. However this may be in that particular case, we are to recognize that the development of technology had, even in precivilized times, an important influence on the moral life. While the Australians show us how little material culture is needed for the development of a moral order, such a contrast as that between the Haida and the Paiute Indians reminds us that generally speaking a people desperately concerned with getting a living cannot develop a rich moral or esthetic life. The moral order of a hard-pressed people may be itself simple. But I insist that it is there in every case.

One other point is to be made about the moral orders that preceded civilization. Morality has had its developmental history. I shall return to this development in the last chapter. Here I say that when the moralities of primitive or precivilized peoples are judged by men of the present day, some are found to be better than others; and the judgment makes allowances for practical difficulties encountered by the primitive people. In primitive societies known today where the food quest is all absorbing one does not condemn the people for failing to develop much creative art or for failing to show a particularly humane consideration for other people. The Siriono of Bolivia, as recently reported by Allen R. Holmberg, live a harsh and precarious life in a tropical rain forest. They have their moral order—systems of intense inhibition as to sexual relations with certain relatives, ideas as to the rights and duties of relatives to share food, fearful attitudes toward invisible spirits, and so forth. But men's activities "remain on the same monotonous level day after day and year after year, and they are centered largely around the satisfaction of the basic needs of hunger, sex and avoidance of fatigue and pain." Holmberg saw a band of Indians walk out of a camp leaving a woman, sick to death, alone in her hammock. "Even the husband departed without saying good-bye." It is stern necessity that makes for this conduct; children, who can be cared for, are tenderly treated at much expenditure of effort. On the other hand, elsewhere we are reminded of the degree to which respect for personal integrity may develop among primitive food collectors. Among the Yagua, another people living under difficult conditions in the tropical forest of South America, although the entire clan lives in a single long house, Fejos tells us that the members of the large household "are able to obtain perfect privacy whenever they wish it simply by turning their faces to the wall of the house. Whenever a man, woman or child faces the wall, the others regard that individual as if he were no longer present."

I turn now to the distinction between the technical order and the moral order, and from that proceed to contrast precivilized and primitive living with civilized living in terms of this distinction. Technical order and moral order name two contrasting aspects of all human societies. The phrases stand for two distinguishable ways in which the activities of men are co-ordinated. As used by C. H. Cooley and R. E. Park, "the moral order" refers to the organization of human sentiments into judgments as to what is right. Describing how the division of labor puts an organization of society based on occupation and vocational interests in place of an older kind of organization of society, Park contrasts these newer ties, based on common interests, with "forms of association like the neighborhood, which are based on contiguity, personal association, and the common ties of humanity." The division of labor modifies this older moral order. Here we will extend the significance of the phrase, and make it cover all the binding together of men through implicit convictions as to what is right, through explicit ideals, or through similarities of conscience. The moral order is therefore always based on what is peculiarly human—sentiments, morality, conscience—and in the first place arises in the groups where people are intimately associated with one another. The word "values," is a related conception, but the phrase "moral order" points to the nature of the bonds among men, rather than to a category of the content of culture. We may conceive of the moral order as equally present in those societies in which the rules for right conduct among men are supported by supernatural sanctions and in those in which the morality of human conduct is largely independent of the religion (in the sense of belief and cult about the supernatural). "Moral order" includes the binding sentiments of rightness that attend religion, the social solidarity that accompanies religious ritual, the sense of religious seriousness and obligation that strengthens men, and the effects of a belief in invisible beings that embody goodness. The moral order becomes vivid to us when we think of the Australian Arunta assembling, each man to do his part, denying himself food, making the sacred marks or performing the holy dances, that the witchetty-grub may become numerous and the whole band thus continue to find its food. Or of the old Chinese family performing the rituals for the an-

cestors. Or of the members of the boys' gang refusing, even in the face of threats from the police, to "tell on" a fellow member.

By a corresponding extension of another and more familiar term, all the other forms of co-ordination of activity which appear in human societies may be brought together and contrasted with the moral order under the phrase "the technical order." The bonds that co-ordinate the activities of men in the technical order do not rest on convictions as to the good life; they are not characterized by a foundation in human sentiments; they can exist even without the knowledge of those bound together that they are bound together. The technical order is that order which results from mutual usefulness, from deliberate coercion, or from the mere utilization of the same means. In the technical order men are bound by things, or are themselves things. They are organized by necessity or expediency. Think, if you will, of the orderly way in which automobiles move in response to the traffic light or the policeman's whistle, or think of the flow of goods, services, and money among the people who together produce, distribute, and consume some commodity such as rubber.

Civilization may be thought of as the antithesis of the folk society. It may also, and consistently with the first antithesis, be thought of as that society in which the relations between technical order and moral order take forms radically different from the relationships between the two which prevail in precivilized society.

Civilization (conceived now as one single thing and not—as by Toynbee—as twenty-one different things) may be said to exist to the extent, to the degree, and in the respects in which a society has developed away from the kind of precivilized society which I have been describing. Civilization is, of course, things added to society: cities, writing, public works, the state, the market, and so forth. Another way of looking at it is from the base provided by the folk society. Then we may say that a society is civilized insofar as the community is no longer small, isolated, homogeneous and self-sufficient; as the division of labor is no longer simple; as impersonal relationships come to take the place of personal relationships; as familial connections come to be modified or supplanted by those of political affiliation or contract; and as thinking has become reflective and systematic. I do not mention all of the characteristics of folk societies which I named in foregoing paragraphs; these are enough to suggest the point of view we might adopt. If we do adopt this way of conceiving civilization, we shall think of Toynbee's twenty-one civilizations as different developments away from the folk society. We see then that civilizations do not depart from the nature of the folk society evenly or in the same way. In Chinese civilization the organization of social relationships according to the categories and attitudes of kinship retained its importance while philosophy and the fine arts passed through long histories of development. The Andean civilization developed political and administrative institutions of impressive complexity and far-reaching influence while yet the Indians who developed them were without writing. The Mayan peoples, in contrast, extended their political institutions little beyond that attained by the ordinary tribe while their intellectual specialists carried some parts of mathematics and astronomy to heights that astonish us. In short, the several civilizations start up from their folk bases into specialized developments in which some elements of the folk society are left behind while others are retained. Yet this fact does not destroy the impression that, as a manner of life taken as a whole, civilization is one kind of thing different from the life of the folk society.

The contrast between technical order and moral order helps us to understand the general kind of thing which is civilization. In the folk society the moral order is great and the technical order is small. In primitive and pre-civilized societies material tools are few and little natural power is used. Neither the formal regulations of the state or church nor the nonmoral ordering of behavior which occurs in the market plays an important part in these societies. It is civilization that develops them.

It is civilization, too, that develops those formal and apparent institutions which both express the moral order and are means toward its realization. The technical order appears not only in tools, power, and an interdependence of people chiefly or wholly impersonal and utilitarian, but also in greater and more varied apparatus for living—apparatus both physical and institutional. Under ten headings Childe has summarized the characteristics of civilized life whether lived at Uruk, Mohenjo-daro, or Uxmal among the Mayans. One, the reappearance of naturalistic art, has a significance not immediately plain, and may be a little doubtful. Of the other nine, six plainly announce the growth of the technical order: (1) the great increase in the size of the settlement (the material equipment for human association becomes far larger); (2) the institution of tribute or taxation with resulting central accumulation of capital; (3) monumental public works; (4) the art of writing; (5) the beginnings of such exact and predictive sciences as arithmetic, geometry, and astronomy; and (6) developed economic institutions making possible a greatly expanded foreign trade. Each of these six suggests the increasing complexity of social organization, and the remaining three criteria explicitly declare features of that social organization which are characteristic of civilization; (7) full-time technical specialists, as in metal working; (8) a privileged rulng class; and (9) the state, or the organization of society on a basis of residence in place of, or on top of, a basis of kinship.

In folk societies the moral order predominates over the technical order. It is not possible, however, simply to reverse this statement and declare that in civilizations the technical order predominates over the moral. In civilization the technical order certainly becomes great. But we cannot truthfully say that in civilization the moral order becomes small. There are ways in civilization in which the moral order takes on new greatness. In civilization the relations between the two orders are varying and complex.

The great transformations of humanity are only in part reported in terms of the revolutions in technology with resulting increases in the number of people living together. There have also occurred changes in the thinking and valuing of men which may also be called "radical and indeed revolutionary innovations." Like changes in the technical order, these changes in the intellectual and moral habits of men become themselves generative of far-reaching changes in the nature of human living. They do not reveal themselves in events as visible and particular as do material inventions, or even always as increasing complexity in the systems of social relationships. Nor is it perhaps possible to associate the moral transformations with limited periods of time as we can associate technological revolutions with particular spans of years. Yet the attempt to identify some of the transformations in men's minds can be made.

One might begin such an attempt by examining the manner of life of the most primitive people we know today, and perhaps also something that is told us about ancient peoples, for evidence of the appearance of forms of thought, belief, or action which a little knowledge of the history of some civilization shows us became influential in changing human life. We see some far-reaching change in the moral or intellectual life of the Western world, perhaps, and so guided we return to the primitive societies to see if it had a beginning there. So we might come to some understanding of some of the relations in history between the two kinds of orders.

As to the trend of this relationship throughout history, I have one general impression. It is that the moral order begins as something pre-eminent but incapable of changing itself, and becomes perhaps less eminent but more independent. In folk society the moral rules bend, but men cannot make them afresh. In civilization the old moral orders suffer, but new states of mind are developed by which the moral order is, to some significant degree, taken in charge. The story of the moral order is attainment of some autonomy through much adversity.

# part 3
# Physical Anthropology

# The New Physical Anthropology

## Sherwood L. Washburn

*From* Transactions of the New York Academy of Sciences, *Series II, Vol. 13, No. 7, 1951, pp. 298–304. By permission of the author and the publisher.*

Recently, evolutionary studies have been revitalized and revolutionized by an infusion of genetics into paleontology and systematics. The change is fundamentally one of point of view, which is made possible by an understanding of the way the genetic constitution of populations changes. The new systematics is concerned primarily with process and with the mechanism of evolutionary change, whereas the older point of view was chiefly concerned with sorting the results of evolution. Physical anthropology is now undergoing the same sort of change. Population genetics presents the anthropologist with a clearly formulated, experimentally verified, conceptual scheme. The application of this theory to the primates is the immediate task of physical anthropology.

In the past, physical anthropology has been considered primarily as a technique. Training consisted in learning to take carefully defined measurements and in computing indices and statistics. The methods of observation, measurement, and comparison were essentially the same, whether the object of the study was the description of evolution, races, growth, criminals, constitutional types, or army personnel. Measurements were adjusted for various purposes, but measurement of the outside of the body, classification, and correlation remained the anthropologists' primary tools. The techniques of physical anthropology were applied to a limited group of problems, and any definition or statement of traditional anthropology must include both the metrical methods and the problems for which the methods were used. Further, anthropology was characterized by theories, or rather by a group of attitudes and assumptions.

There has been almost no development of theory in physical anthropology itself, but the dominant attitude may be described as static, with emphasis on classification based on types. Any such characterization is over-simplified, and is intended only to give an indication of the dominant techniques, interests, and attitudes of the physical anthropologist. Except for emphasis on particular animals, physical anthropology shared much with the zoology of the times when it developed. Much of the method was developed before the acceptance of the idea of evolution, and all of it before the science of genetics.

Physical anthropology should change, just as systematic zoology has changed. The difficulties which accompany the necessary modifications can be greatly reduced if their nature is clearly understood. Naturally, in a time of rapid flux there will be numerous doubts and disagreements as to what should be done. This is natural, and what I have to offer is a tentative outline to indicate how parts of the new physical anthropology may differ from the old.

The old physical anthropology was primarily a technique. The common core of the science was measurement of external form with calipers. The new physical anthropology is primarily an area of interest, the desire to understand the process of primate evolution and human variation by the most efficient techniques available.

The process of evolution, as understood by the geneticist, is the same for all mammals. The genetic composition of a population may be described in terms of gene frequencies. The modification of these frequencies results in evolution, which is caused by *selection*, mutations, drift, and migrations. Mutations and migrations introduce new genetic elements into the population. But selection on the phenotype, adapting animals to their environment, is the primary cause of alteration in gene frequencies.

This is essentially a return to Darwinism, but with this important difference: Darwin wrote in a pregenetic era. Therefore, he did not understand the mechanism which makes possible the production of variation and the possibility of selection. Since Darwin's ideas could not be proved in detail by the techniques available in his time, the concept of selection did not become fully effective. Therefore, some pre-evolutionary ideas continued in full force. More Linnaean species were described from types after Darwin than before. The idea of evolution created interest in species, but the species were described in pre-evolutionary terms. Further, it is possible for people to hold a variety of theories in place of, or in addition to, Darwin's. For example, Lamarckian ideas have continued right down to today. Orthogenesis has been widely believed and irreversibility has been regarded as a law.

It has been claimed that evolution should be described in terms of non-adaptive traits, yet this is impossible if evolution is largely due to selection. The first great achievement of the synthesis of genetics, paleontology, and systematics is in clearing away a mass of antiquated theories and attitudes which permeate the writings of the older students of evolution. Further, the new evolutionary theory shows which aspects of past work are worth using, extending, and strengthening. This is possible because much of the mechanism of evolutionary change is now understood, clearly formulated, and *experimentally verified*. The logic of Darwin's great theory could only become fully effective when techniques had been developed to prove that selection was right and that other ideas of evolution were wrong. A change in theory, no matter how popular, is not enough. The new ideas must be implemented by effective techniques.

If a new physical anthropology is to differ effectively from the old, it must be more than the adoption of a little genetic terminology. It must change its ways of doing things to conform with the implications of modern evolutionary theory. For example, races must be based on the study of populations. There is no way to justify the division of a breeding population into a series of racial types. It is not enough to state that races should be based on genetic traits; races which can not be reconciled with genetics should be removed from consideration. If we consider the causes of changes in gene frequency as outlined above, and if we are concerned with the process of evolution, the task of the anthropologist becomes clear. He has nothing to offer on mutation, but can make contributions with regard to migration, drift, and selection.

The migrations of man made possible by

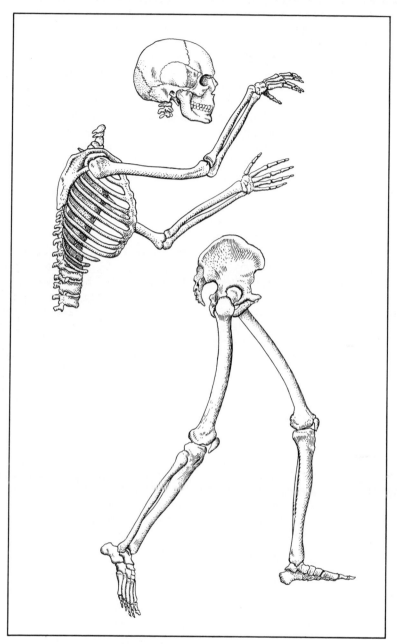

culture have vastly confused the genetic picture. Before selection can be investigated, it is necessary to know how long a people has been in an area and under what conditions they have been living. For example, the spread of European people, of Bantu speakers, or of Eskimo, all have changed the distribution of the blood groups. The interpretation of the genetic situation demands an understanding of history. Whether people became adapted to cold by selection or by change in their way of life completely alters the interpretation of the distribution of physical traits. This has been widely recognized by anthropologists, and the solution of this difficulty requires the active collaboration of archaeologists, ethnologists, linguists, and students of the physical man.

Drift is related to population size, and this depends on the way of life. Again, as in the case of migration, the situation in which drift may have taken place cannot be specified by the physical anthropologist alone, but requires the active collaboration of many specialists. The adoption of modern evolutionary theory will force a far closer and more realistic collaboration between the branches of anthropology than ever before.

Although much of the present distribution of races may be explained by migration and although drift probably accounts for some differences, selection must be the explanation of long term evolutionary trends and of many patterned variations as well. Anthropologists have always stressed the importance of adaptation in accounting for the differences between apes and men, and sometimes have used the idea in interpreting racial divergencies. But suggestions of adaptations are not enough. It is easy to guess that a form is adaptive, but the real problem is to determine the precise nature of a particular adaptation. . . . I would like to take this opportunity to present an outline, a beginning, of an analysis of the human body into complexes which may vary independently.

In this work, the guiding principle has been that the major force in evolution is selection of functional complexes. A variety of methods has been used to demonstrate the adaptive complexes. The four major methods for factoring complexes out of the body are: (1) comparison and evolution; (2) development; (3) variability; and (4) experiment. All these have been used by numerous investigators, but, to the best of my knowledge, they have not been combined into a working system. All must be used to gain an understanding of the human body.

The figure [see page 77] shows the body divided into the major regions, which seem to have had remarkable independence in recent evolutionary history. The complex to attain its present pattern first is that of the arms and thorax. This complex is associated with arm swinging in the trees, the way of life called "brachiation." It is association with a reduction in the deep back muscles and in the number of lumbar vertebrae and consequent shortening of the trunk and elongation of all parts of the upper extremity, adaptation of the joints and muscles to greater pronation, supination in the forearm, and flexion and abduction at the shoulder. Many changes in

the positions of viscera are associated with the shorter trunk. We share this complex with the living gibbons and apes. The bipedal complex was the next to develop and seems to have been fundamentally human in the South African man-apes. The major changes are in the ilium and in the gluteal muscles. Just as in the arm, the change is in a bone-muscle complex, which makes a different way of life possible. The head seems to have attained essentially its present form during the fourth glacial advance, perhaps 50,000 years ago. The brain continued to enlarge until the end of the last interglacial period, and the face decreased in size for some time after that. The great increase in the size of the brain and decrease in the face was after the use of tools.

Evolution, in a sense, has dissected the body for us, and has shown that great changes may occur in arms and trunk, pelvis and legs, and brain case, or face, accompanied by little change in the rest of the body. The first two complexes to change are related to brachiation and bipedal locomotion. The final changes in the head may well be related to changed selection after the use of tools.

To carry the analysis further, it is necessary to deal with one of the areas suggested by this preliminary dividing of the body. Let us consider the face, and especially the lower jaw. The figure [see page 79] shows a lower jaw divided into regions which can be shown to vary independently by all the methods of analysis suggested before. The coronoid process varies with the temporal muscle. The angle of the jaw varies with the masseter and internal pterygoid muscle. The tooth-supporting area varies with the teeth. The main core of the jaw is affected by hormones which do not affect the other parts, as shown in acromegaly. Alizarin dye, which stains the growing bone, reveals the pattern of growth. The split-line technique (Benninghoff) shows the mechanical arrangement.

After making an analysis of this kind, comparisons of a different sort are possible. The simple statement, that a trait is or is not there, is replaced by the attempt to understand under what conditions it might be present. For example, if the simian shelf is developed in monkeys and apes when the jaws are long and the anterior teeth large, then the South African man-apes and other fossil

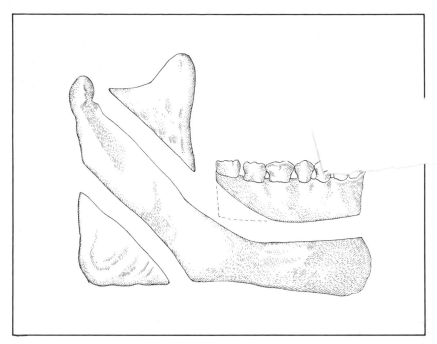

men would not be expected to have such a shelf. The dental characters necessary to bring out the expression of the shelf are absent in all except the Piltdown jaw. It can be argued that we have the potential for a simian shelf but that we do not have the necessary tooth and jaw size to make it evident. Trying to understand the process which produces a trait leads us to very different evaluations than does a listing of presence or absence.

In the light of this sort of information, let us look at the skull of an Eocene lemur, *Notharctus*. The jaw is long, in conformity with the length of the teeth. It is low, and there is a large angular region. This region has been described as lemuroid. If this angle has remained there for 50 million years, however, over countless generations of lemurs, it must have more of a function than to mark the jaw as primitive or to help us in identifying lemur jaws. If the mandible of a remarkably similar modern lemur (genus *Lemur*) is examined, it is found that the internal pterygoid muscle inserts at the end of the angle, but that the masseter muscle inserts only on the lateral side of the ascending ramus, leaving the angle bare of muscle. An internal pterygoid muscle inserting in this position is a protruder of the jaw. The function of the angle of the lemur jaw is to provide insertion for a large, func-tionally important muscle. The dependence of the angular process on the internal pterygoid and the exact function of the internal pterygoid need to be experimentally verified.

The only point to be stressed now is that the theory that such a process is of adaptive significance, and that it is maintained by selection, leads one to look for a functional complex. If such a process is regarded simply as a taxonomic aid, or as nonfunctional, no guide is available for research or future un-derstanding.

The post-orbital bar of this same lemur again illustrates the advantage of assuming, until it is proved otherwise, that a part is functionally important. Originally, the com-plete bony ring around the orbit may have been for protection or for some other unknown function. Once the ring is established, how-ever, the skeletal framework for radical modi-fication of the skull is present. The change from the lemur skull, with a wide interorbital region, to the monkey skull, with reduced olfactory mechanism and reduced interorbital space, is mechanically possible because pres-sure, tension, and buttressing of the sides of the face are provided by the complete ring of bone around the orbits. Structures which probably developed as part of a protective mechanism were pre-adaptive for a reorganiza-tion of the face.

Classic Neandertal man differs from other fossil men in that the angle of the lower jaw is poorly developed, the part of the malar bone associated with the origin of the largest part of the masseter muscle is small, and the lateral part of the brow-ridge is less sharply demarcated. All these differences may be related, and certainly the association of the small angle and malar suggest that the masseter muscle was small compared to the temporal muscle. Differences of this sort should be described in terms of the variation in the groups being compared. Since similar differences may be found in living men, the development of appropriate quantitative descriptive methods is merely a matter of time and technique. The procedure is: (1) diagnose the complex; (2) develop methods appropriate to describe variations in it; and (3) try to discover the genetic background of these variations.

So far, we are still engaged in finding the complexes, but even at this level it is possible to make suggestions about fossil men. Probably some Mongoloid groups will have the highest frequency of the big masseter complex, and some of the Negro groups the lowest. This is merely stating some traditional physical anthropology in a somewhat different way by relating statements about the face to those on the lower jaw and relating both to a large and important muscle. It differs from the traditional in the technique of analysis and avoids speculation of the sort which says that the characteristics of the Mongoloid face are due to adaptation to cold.

In this preliminary analysis of the lower jaw, the attempt has been made to divide a single bone into relatively independent systems and to show that the differences make sense in terms of differing adaptations. Eventually, it may be possible to understand the genetic mechanisms involved. If this type of analysis is at all correct, it is theoretically impossible to make any progress in genetic understanding by taking the traditional measurements on the mandible. They are all complex resultants of the interrelation of two or more of the variables. The measurements average the anatomy in such way that it is as futile to look for the mode of inheritance of the length of the jaw as it is to look for the genes of the cephalic index.

The implications for anthropology of this type of analysis may be made clearer by some comparisons of the skulls of monkeys. If the skulls of adult male and adult female vervets are compared, many differences may be seen. The male skull is larger in all dimensions, particularly those of the face. If, however, an adult female is compared to a juvenile male with the same cranial capacity and the same weight of temporal muscle, all the differences disappear, except that in the size of the canine tooth. What would appear to be a very large number of unrelated differences, if traditional methods were used, are only aspects of one fundamental difference in the size of the face. If a large-faced monkey is compared with a small-faced one, both of the genus *Cercopithecus*, there appear to be many differences. Yet again, if animals of the same cranial capacity and the same temporal muscle size are compared, almost all the measurements are the same. The species difference is in quantity of face, although this appears in many different forms. If these two skulls were fossil men, differing in the same way, and if they were treated by the usual anthropological methods, they would be found to differ in numerous observations, measurements, and indices. Yet one may be transformed into the other by a simple reduction in mass of face (including teeth, bones, muscles). Perhaps many fossils are far less different than we have supposed. The methods used created the number of differences, just as a metrical treatment of these monkeys would make the adults appear very distinct.

The purpose of this paper has been to call attention to the changes which are taking place in physical anthropology. Under the influence of modern genetic theory, the field is changing from the form it assumed in the latter part of the nineteenth century into a part of modern science. The change is essentially one of emphasis. If traditional physical anthropology was 80 per cent measurement and 20 per cent concerned with heredity, process, and anatomy, in the new physical anthropology the proportions may be approximately reversed. I have stressed the impact of genetics on anthropology, but the process need not be all one way. If the form of the human face can be thoroughly analyzed, this will open the way to the understanding of its development and the interpretation of abnormalities and malocclusion, and may lead to advanc[...] atomy, and medicine. Alth[...] fascinating in itself, the [...] of the functional anatomy wh[...] gained from it is of more than ph[...] al importance. The kind of systemic ana[...]y in which bones, muscles, ligaments, etc. are treated separately became obsolete with the publication of the "Origin of Species" in 1859. The anatomy of life, of integrated function, does not know the artificial boundaries which still govern the dissection of a corpse. The new physical anthropology has much to offer to anyone interested in the structure or evolution of man, but this is only a beginning. To build it, we must collaborate with social scientists, geneticists, anatomists, and paleontologists. We need new ideas, new methods, new workers. There is nothing we do today which will not be done better tomorrow.

*selection* 12

# Custom and Range of Human Response

### John P. Gillin

*From* Character and Personality, *Vol. 13, No. 2, December, 1944, pp. 101–134. By permission of the author and the publisher.*

## Formulation of the Problem

In considering the range of response in the repertoire of the human species we are interested in two aspects: limits of the range, and the variety within it. Once we knew accurately the outside limits of human performance, we should also know the limits of cultural activity (although not necessarily the limits of cultural complexity, of course), while more precise and organized knowledge of the learned or learnable responses of the species within the outside limits of the repertoire would increase the soundness and value of science in all types of social and personal planning and readjustment which involve the cultural factor. . . .

## Muscular Responses

From the point of view of a North American, some of the most unusual muscular responses to become customary in any group are the exercises of the Indian cult of Yoga. In the exercise of diaphragm-raising the practitioner stands with his feet a few inches apart, with trunk and knees bent a little forward, hands slightly over the knees. He exhales completely, then, raising the ribs in mock inhalation, he raises the diaphragm, causing a marked depression of the abdomen. Somewhat more difficult is voluntary vomiting. The exerciser drinks four or five glasses of water on an empty stomach, bends forward, spreads his legs, rests hands on knees, and then exhales deeply. Abdominal muscles are contracted backward and upward, then relaxed. This muscle contraction is repeated at the rate of seven to eight times per minute. With a little practice one vomits at will and cleanses the stomach of impurities. Another method of stomach-cleansing is to swallow a thick piece of cloth about twenty-two feet long and three inches wide. After the cloth is in the stomach, proceed to the diaphragm-raising exercise interspersed with isolation and rolling of the recti-abdominis muscles. After about twenty minutes the cloth is pulled out by the free end that remains between the teeth. In order to follow this procedure of cleansing the stomach, it is necessary to learn "the most important of the purificatory exercises . . . in which the two muscles, the recti-abdominis, are isolated: first together and then independently." After the diaphragm has been raised, while the practitioner is in the standing position, the portion of the abdomen above the pubic bone is dragged downward and forward by voluntary action of the abdominal muscles. If this is done, the two recti-abdominis muscles, long flat muscles extending vertically on either side along the ventral surfaces, will stand out, somewhat like cords on either side of the upper abdomen. The next stage is a rolling manipulation, consisting of rapid contraction and relaxation of the two muscles in succession from left to right and right to left. Having learned to do this, one is now able to learn not only stomach-cleansing, but also colon-washing. When the recti-abdominis muscles are isolated a partial vacuum is created in the colon, which enables water to be taken into the rectum, provided that one learns to open the anal sphincters voluntarily. For those who cannot establish voluntary control over the relaxation of the sphincters, a bamboo tube is used. A similar technique is used to wash the bladder. Apparently it is impossible to learn voluntarily

to open the urethral sphincters, so that the Yoga practitioner inserts a lead, silver, or rubber tube as far as the bladder with the outer end in a bowl of water. By performing the isolation of the recti-abdominis, he draws up a half-glass of water into the bladder and retains it for about twenty minutes. Yeats-Brown also claims that followers of Yoga are trained to open the pyloric valve of the stomach voluntarily in order to pass large quantities of water rapidly through the alimentary tract.

Control over the anal sphincters may be established so that they may be alternately contracted and relaxed for several minutes in succession. This exercise may be combined with diaphragm-raising by relaxing the sphincters with each inhalation and contracting them with exhalation. Once complete voluntary control is established, the sphincters are opened while the abdomen is withdrawn for the diaphragm-raising exercise, so that the gases may be forced out of the lower colon. When the abdominal muscles are relaxed, the same process is repeated in order to take in fresh air from the outside.

Still another Yoga muscular response strange to us is the tongue-rolling exercise, in which the tongue is voluntarily rolled backward and upward to cover the posterior nasal cavities leading into the pharynx at the base of the skull. This response is apparently almost beyond the range of normal human capabilities, although some learn it without surgery. The majority, however, cut the frenulum at the base of the tongue a little each week until the fibrous band is completely severed.

We see from this material that it is apparently within the range of human capability to learn voluntary control over the diaphragm, several muscles of the ventral wall of the abdomen, certain of the smooth muscles of the stomach and alimentary tract, the anal sphincters, and certain muscles of the tongue.

Although the skeletal architecture of the human foot is not adapted to opposability of the great toe, a considerable degree of lateral "spreading" and adduction is possible, providing voluntary control can be established over the muscles involved. Among civilized peoples wearing shoes, these muscles are almost entirely untrained. But reports of customs involving adduction of the great toe against the second toe as a grasping organ are so common in reference to primitive peoples as scarcely to require citation. For example, Man says of the Andaman Islanders that much use is made of the feet in holding and picking up light objects, and that the great toe is "opposable" (*i.e.*, adductable). The Maori of New Zealand "often used their toes to pick up any small article." Metraux notes with respect to the Chorotí, Chulupis and Matake of the Chaco region of South America that "the caraguata (Bromelia serra) plant is uprooted with a forked stick and the leaves are cut off with a wooden saw. The saw is held between the big and second toe and the leaf is rubbed against it." From the Guiana region of Venezuela Simpson reports of the Carib Kamarakoto Indians that "women usually sew their dresses holding the cloth with the toes and pushing the needle toward themselves." One of his illustrations shows a woman holding the crossbar of a small hand loom with the large and second toes of both feet. Covarrubias tells us how young girls of Bali are trained to take part in the *sanghyang dedari* dance of exorcism. At one point in the dance the girls, in a state of induced trance, climb on men's shoulders. Each girl maintains a standing position on the shoulders of her male partner by the grip of her "prehensile feet"; grasping the shoulders with the feet is a learned response taught to successive generations of girls. The position is maintained for two or three hours at a time during the dance.

Sitting and walking postures may involve a wide variety of muscle, tendons and joint responses, only a few of which are customary in any one culture. The painfulness of sitting on the heels in the kneeling position is familiar to Americans who have attempted to maintain this customary Japanese sitting posture for an extended period. Among the Maori the men usually sat in a cross-legged position, while women sat on the buttocks with the feet turned to one side in a position most uncomfortable for Europeans. The girls were taught to walk in an awkward-looking, loose-jointed manner, swaying from the hips, while men practiced a loose, shuffling walk. When working with anything on or close to the ground, the Maori customarily squatted on the heels, with the soles of the feet planted on the ground. Weeding of gardens was carried on in this position hour after hour, and even now, with the introduction of steel

spades, the posture is used, and the muscular patterns of the arms are adapted to it, resulting in the spade customarily being thrust into the soil at a low rather than a right angle. When camping out in wet weather, the Maori did not lie down and learned even to sleep in the sitting posture, or at least to doze. . . .

Let us now turn to a consideration of the range of customs which have been developed for the satisfaction of certain basic drives. We shall begin with a consideration of hunger.

## Hunger

In considering the relation of hunger and the other innate drives to the building of cultures we shall have to mention a few elementary facts from physiology, but such physiological considerations will be limited on the whole to data which appear to be of significance in habit and custom formation. It must be borne in mind that physiological knowledge of the needs and requirements of the human body is a relatively recent discovery in our own culture and that new findings in this field are constantly coming forth from research laboratories. Systematic field investigation based upon these findings in other societies has barely begun, so that we are at present far from being able to deal exhaustively with the nature of and reaction to physiological needs as they are manifested in the various cultures of mankind. The theoretical and practical importance of such an extension of knowledge is so great, however, that we shall discuss some of the data at hand for their suggestive value.

### Physiological needs for nourishment

The physiological objects of nourishment may be summarized under three heads. First, the fuel requirements of the body must be met to compensate for the constant oxidation and consequent loss of heat which mammalian living entails. . . .

The second requirement is for protein, which seems to be necessary for the repair of body structures as well as for maintaining the normal colloidal composition of the blood. . . .

Thirdly, the body requires a variety of minerals and vitamins in order to maintain full or adequate functioning. . . .

Vitamin intake is likewise essential to the normal performance of many bodily functions, and for proper assimilation of other food substances. For example, Vitamin D facilitates the absorption of calcium in the intestines and its storage in the trabeculae of the bones. Lack of Vitamin A results in impaired vision and night blindness. Exposure of the retina to light produces a chemical change involving the bleaching of the visual purple. Before sensitivity can be restored, this pigment, which is structually related to Vitamin A, must be replaced. Vitamin A is also essential in maintaining the structural integrity of the epithelial cells, for without it these cells are replaced by stratified keratinized epithelium; in other words, lesions and deteriorated areas appear on the skin and mucous membranes. . . .

It should be clear, however, that if requirements of this sort are physiologically required for the healthy functioning of the human animal, each society must inculcate customs which satisfy these needs, or pay the price of failure to do so in lost efficiency, lowered health, or eventual extinction.

### Physiological needs and hunger drive

Many of the required substances may be stored in some form in the body, but an average daily intake of the quantities indicated seems to be required to maintain normal functioning and homeostasis. Deficiency within certain limits of any or all of these requirements is not always, nor even often, directly fatal to the individual or the population, but deficiency always results in some impairment of structure or function which must be compensated in one way or another. Thus, prolonged deficiency in energy-producing foods results progressively in loss of weight, emaciation, and decline in strength and ability to carry on activity. It is interesting to note that the internal economy of the body is such that the tissues of the brain and nervous system seem to be "starved" last of all, and that they may continue functioning long after the muscular and bony structures have deteriorated because of malnutrition. Does this fact have any bearing upon the characteristic philosophical orientation of Hindu Indian culture, for example?

At all events, it appears that we may deduce from these facts of physiology the theorem that any culture which does not or cannot (perhaps because of environmental limitations) supply the nutritional requirements of its population will inevitably contain other patterns correlated with the nutritional patterns and compensating for them either in the form of decreased activity or of activity of a restricted type.

In building customs, however, the members of human societies are motivated by psychological drives rather than by physiological needs. . . .

### Cultural responses to hunger and appetite drives

The natural human response to hunger is, of course, the introduction of something into the stomach. But eating customs usually consist of introducing certain substances into the alimentary tract (*i.e.*, making specific responses to specific categories of stimuli). For eating habits there seem to be two types of satisfaction or reinforcement, immediate and long-run. Immediate satisfaction is obtained by remission of the uneasiness, craving, stomach cramps, and other symptoms of hunger. But to be actually satisfying in the long run, it would seem that eating habits or customs must also banish feelings of weakness, lassitude, and discomfort which are the ultimate aftermath of undernutrition. The establishment of eating customs and their maintenance, therefore, would seem to depend upon their ability to provide an immediate feeling of satiety, plus their action in reducing or preventing the rise of fatigue due to insufficient nourishment. It seems, however, that direct satisfaction of hunger or appetite is much more reinforcing than the effect of lowering fatigue drive, on the principle that delayed reinforcement is less effective than immediate reinforcement. It is possible that fatigue drive motivates customs involving energy intake, but it is doubtful that fatigue is directly or automatically motivating for customs involving certain mineral and vitamin intakes. Deficiencies in the latter eventually produce lassitude and fatigue, but their results are on the whole slow and cumulative in appearance and disappearance. Proper responses to mineral and vitamin deficiency are, therefore, not immediately rewarding in many cases. Hence the operation of fatigue drive as a psychological motivation in building physiologically proper mineral and vitamin habits and customs is usually quite indirect and must be mediated by intermediate, acquired motivations of one sort or another. The child, for example, may be motivated to drink his cod-liver oil by combining it with candy (which is directly rewarding to appetite), or by coddling, patting, or other immediate rewards. . . .

It seems that any substance which is mechanically capable of being swallowed (not too large, too rough, etc.) and which does not immediately arouse pain drive (as do strong acids, lacerating substances, and certain quick-acting poisons) will, in suitable quantities, lower the hunger drive (or some acquired drive based on it) if introduced into the stomach. All such substances, in other words, which are not lethally or painfully poisonous may become cultural equipment associated with eating customs, for almost anything else can be reduced to the proper size and consistency for passage into the stomach.

### Variety in food customs

To obtain some idea of how these principles actually affect culture, let us examine a few more or less extreme examples of customary foodstuffs, taken at random from the literature. The Vedda of Ceylon eat no less than five kinds of rotted wood, usually garnished with honey, bark, leaves, and fruits. Among some of the Guiana tribes, greenheart seeds, which are woody in consistency, were grated, soaked, and "mixed with rotted wood, pounded previously and sifted" at those times of the year when cassava bread was scarce. A number of cases are on record from the sixteenth and seventeenth centuries of peoples who had formed the habit of eating small pebbles after each meal, and, to quote "It has frequently been stated that the peasants of Styria are in the habit of taking from two to five grains of arsenious acid daily for the purpose of improving the health, avoiding infections, and raising the whole tone of the body. It is a well-substantiated fact that the quantities taken habitually are quite sufficient to produce immediate death ordinarily."

Clay- and earth-eating is customary among various peoples, sometimes, at least, motivated by an actively felt desire or drive. Among the Issa-Japura tribes of Amazonia (mainly the Boro and Witoto), for instance, the desire for clay, although regarded with disfavor in the culture, nevertheless is said to amount to an unconquerable craving, and if the clay cannot otherwise be obtained, it will be scraped from under the fireplace and eaten in secret. Possibly this is a response to a physiologic mineral need. Schoolboys in Morocco eat potter's earth regularly before breakfast in the belief that they thereby learn their lessons better. Dickens and Fort made a study of the widespread custom of clay-eating among the Negroes of Mississippi. The practice is also found among whites of this region, but is not so prevalent. By means of "hidden question" tests of statistical reliability, they found that 25 per cent of a random sample of 207 Negro school children had "eaten dirt" at least twice in a period of 16 days. Clay soils only were used, free from sand, and of a reddish brown color. "Reasons given for eating dirt were: it is good for you; tastes good, rather sour, like a lemon; helps women who are pregnant; and tastes good if put in the chimney and smoked first." The notion that people crave dirt is common. They get to the place where they feel that they must have clay to eat. . . . One hears, too, that dirt is carried long distances to people who can no longer get it themselves. The authors conclude that "dirt eating is simply a culture trait like dipping snuff or smoking," although they think it may be related to an iron-deficient diet. More investigation is needed, because simply calling a practice a culture trait does not explain it. . . . Also, it is significant that starch-eating may displace earth-eating, for it is apparent that the chemical composition of laundry starch has nothing in common with that of red clay and presumably would not satisfy the same physiologic need. The similarity between the two substances seems to reside in the tactile sensation produced in the mouth, and one is led to believe that the craving, in such a case at least, is predominantly acquired rather than innate. . . .

Earth-eating in one form or another has also been widely reported in the Amazonian and Guiana country.

Judging by the number of societies which do so, it seems to be well established that members of the human species can be trained to tolerate and even to prefer putrefied food. It has been suggested that this may be a means of obtaining vitamins, as it is well known that the bacteria of putrefaction manufacture Vitamin $B_1$, for example. So long as toxin-producing organisms are not present in the putrefaction, no harm is done to the consumer. . . .

Although human groups may live on meat and/or fish alone or on a combination of meat and dairy products, it appears that there are no societies which subsist upon a starch diet alone, which is apparently a response to the human requirement for protein. The researches of certain societies as to the edibility of various animal species have resulted in eating customs involving animals of a considerable variety. Let us briefly consider only insects, vermin, and reptiles. The Issa-Japura Indians eat monkeys (sometimes with the hair), frogs, iguanas, and head lice. With respect to the latter, "a scurf comb is a most important present, and to comb your neighbor's hair and eat the 'bag' an honour and a luxury. They will also eat the grubs of wasps and bees, and in fact any larvae."

Cannibalism may be based on a variety of motivation, but among certain tribes in South America, Melanesia, and Africa, the custom of man-eating seems to be a method of satisfying specific acquired appetite. Also, as Whiffen states for the Issa-Japura tribes, "It is possible that the salt in human blood may be one of the unrealized attractions that lead these people to anthropophagous habits."

That actual food cannibalism, regardless of religious or other types of cultural motivation, can become a cultural complex is supported by ample evidence, particularly from Melanesia and Africa. For example, in New Britain human flesh was eaten and sold in butcher shops or markets. Among the Bahuana of Africa cannibalism is said to be confined to men, but is general to the sex. It cannot be "ascribed to a craving for animal food, since game is plentiful in the Bahuana country. It is, in fact, due to a sincere liking for human flesh, of which the natives are in no way ashamed. . . . No special ceremonies are observed in connection with cannibalism, and the flesh is prepared and boiled in the same fashion as any other meat." Cannibalism can also be motivated by other acquired cultural drives, such as the desire to gain prestige by eating an enemy, desire to honor a relative by eating a part of his body or bones, desire to gain supernatural power through magical ingestion of human flesh, and the like, but, as we have seen, it is possible for a society to inculcate in its members an appetite (acquired drive) for human flesh as such.

From the point of view of species survival, the ability of man to obtain nourishment from so wide a variety of items and "to learn to like almost anything" has been a great advantage, for these abilities have enabled man to live in environments where more specialized animals starve.

The discovery that healthy human beings can subsist entirely on a diet of animal products has been made by several societies (*e.g.*, Eskimo: meat, fish; certain Mongol tribes of Central Asia: meat, products of horse milk). The arctic explorer Stefansson was perhaps the first to make this clear to our own society, on the basis of his observations among the Eskimo and on an experimental basis. He and another man of white stock lived on an exclusive meat diet for a year. Beyond a diminished tolerance for carbohydrate, attributed to lack of the usual dextrose stimulus, these men showed no significant changes in blood, urine, or kidney functions, and no evidence of vitamin deficiency. . . .

### How far can hunger be resisted?

Hunger, or appetite associated with it, seems to be a drive which rises periodically, in our society at least, and which seemingly must be satisfied to some extent three times per day. Is this characteristic of the species? It is obvious, even in ordinary experience, that one can fast for various longer periods of time without permanent damage. How long can a human being be trained to withstand hunger "as a regular thing" and still continue to function as a member of society? In many circumstances, such as traveling and nomadic life, it would obviously be an advantage if men could develop the custom of eating, say, only once in three days, for thereby they could feed at established settlements and save the energy and inconvenience of carrying supplies with them.

There is probably no absolute period of time at the end of which food deprivation becomes lethal. Survival depends to a large extent upon the amount of stored bodily energy the individual possesses at the start of the fast. One of the longest nonfatal fasts on record is that of Merlatte of Paris, who fasted for 50 days. Succi on the fortieth day of his fast had lost 25 per cent of his weight. Terence MacSwiney, Mayor of Cork, ended a hunger strike of 74 days in 1920 by death in a coma. Even in prolonged starvation, brain and heart lose only three to four per cent of their weight.

Although no cultural system includes patterns for such extreme fasts, customary fasting of rather extended length is not unknown.

For example, a warrior of the Papago Indians of the Southwest United States returning from a raid in which he had killed a man customarily fasted for 16 days after his return. Small quantities of corn meal and water were the only intake allowed. Really brave men would allow the corn meal to settle in the bowl of water and drink only the latter. . . .

Drugs are used culturally in some societies to inhibit the rise of hunger drive and fatigue. Even at the present time Indian porters of the Andean region are accustomed to chew coca leaves instead of eating, when traveling over the mountains with burdens. The cocaine contained in the leaves inhibits hunger and fatigue and obviates the necessity of carrying food supplies in addition to the "pay load" (personal observations of the author). Fasts of two to three days, sustained by coca, are a regular part of a cargo carrier's routine.

Except for specialists such as cargo carriers or in unusual circumstances, all societies of which I know seem to have patterns for feeding at least once a day. Is this because of an absolute physiological necessity? Is it because the human hunger drive cannot normally be repressed without malaise for more than 24 hours? Again, further investigation is required.

Within the 24-hour cycle, however, there is considerable cultural variability, even within the area of European civilization. Although each society prefers its own feeding schedule, it would be interesting to know what an optimum interval between feedings would be for the species. In North America the standard number of meals is three with an interval of from four to five hours between the first and second and from five to six hours between the second and third. Four meals per day was a standard in a number of peacetime European societies, *e.g.*, England, which inserted afternoon tea, and Germany, which inserted second breakfast into the three-meal schedule. In part of Scandinavia five and six meals per day were *de rigueur*. In each society individuals were trained "to feel hungry" at the appropriate feeding times.

Turning to preliterate cultures, we find a similar variety, although usually in the direction of fewer meals per day. . . . Among the Bemba, whose food customs have been so well studied by Richards, a single daily meal is the rule, and it occurs at very irregular times during the day, depending upon the type of work in progress. "Men and women are accustomed to go to their gardens in the early morning to do the bulk of their work on what we habitually describe as an 'empty stomach.' They return to the village about noon, when the whole community awaits the evening meal." The concentration on a single daily meal in this pattern seems to require considerable training. Richards says that children are allowed to eat snacks all day long, and only as they approach adolescence do they succeed in emulating their elders. Among adults it is considered "undignified" to be eating at all hours of the day. Thus we seem to have the timing aspect of the eating customs operating on an acquired drive of prestige anxiety which overrides the hunger drive. . . .

Perhaps these instances of varying meal schedules are sufficient to indicate something of the variety of the cultural control which is exerted over the hunger drive in the human species. We need more investigation of this subject if we are to be accurate in cultural planning in this field. What is the limit to which intervals between feedings could be stretched culturally? What is the optimum schedule for customary feeding? What auxiliary drives and what methods of training are most efficient in producing disciplined customary responses to hunger? . . .

## Summary

It has been suggested in the foregoing pages that a fruitful lead to a more adequate operational understanding of culture is to be found in the dynamic relationships existing between customs, the innate response abilities of the human species, physiological needs, and psychological drives or motivations. . . .

The following points have been partially documented. (1) Certain muscles and muscle-groups which are ignored or regarded as untrainable in many societies have been trained to perform customary responses in specific societies. A more refined and systematic study of the trainability of the muscles of the human body is needed. It is possible that human potentialities exist which have never been incorporated into any culture. (2) Customs involving muscular responses vary with respect to mechanical and physiological efficiency. Other things equal, the individual and his society pay a price for inefficient muscular customs in waste energy, lost motion, and their physical and social sequelae. (3) The customs of a society either satisfy the minimal physiological needs for nourishment or provide compensation for failure to do so in the form of patterns for decreased activity, etc. (4) The basic hunger drive or drives are not sufficient in themselves to motivate automatically the establishment of customs completely satisfying to all biological needs for nourishment. Although it is possible that certain "innate hungers" exist in the human species for vitamins, minerals, etc., in cultural situations the motivating power of these "drives" often seems to be obscured, disguised, or overlaid by acquired "appetites." Thus, it is possible for the basic physiological needs to remain only partially fulfilled by the customs of a society, although the customs themselves are reinforced by the effect of satisfaction which they give to conventionally felt desires (appetites) for certain food objects comparatively irrelevant biologically. It is also apparent that effects of satiety feeling can be produced by certain eating customs which fall far short of physiological adequacy.

(5) An acquired drive or "appetite" can apparently be developed in a human group for any ingestible substance which is not immediately painful or lethal. The interpretation of accompanying odors, state of decomposition, and appearance is apparently entirely a cultural matter and varies from society to society through a very wide range. Put the other way around, it appears that responses which may be made customarily to hunger drives, either innate or acquired, are limited only by the size of the human gullet and by the capacity of such responses to produce immediate pain or death. (6) Seemingly hunger drive is suppressed on a customary basis no longer than 24 hours in any society. Within this limit human beings can be trained to experience a rise of the drive at a considerable variety of stated intervals, depending upon the pattern of their culture and the training they have been given. (7) The upper limit of the amount of food which can be repeatedly eaten on a customary basis at regular feeding periods is not determined for man. . . .

*selection 13*

# Adaptive Changes in the Human Body

## Carleton S. Coon, Stanley M. Garn, Joseph B. Birdsell

Within the confines of a given zone of environment it may be some culturally determined factor, like the choice of food grown, or its importation from elsewhere, that determines body size, rather than the unaltered, or unprocessed, attributes of the environment itself.

*From* Races: A Study of the Race Formation in Man. *Charles C. Thomas, 1950, pp. 36–45. By permission of the authors and the publisher.*

## Dry Heat

One kind of environment, however, appears to produce special effects on all those who live in it for many generations. That is the extreme, the rigorous environment of the hot desert. The famous Tuareg of the Sahara reveal themselves, when shorn of their robes and veils by the anthropologist, to be tall, lean, skinny men, with long arms and legs, short, shallow bodies, narrow hands and feet. The average adult male European who tries to wield a Tuareg sword is unable to compress his hand into the space meant for it on the hilt. The Tuaregs have only been living on the desert for 1300 years, since the introduction of the camel from Asia. Their ancestors were Berbers from the Moroccan Middle Atlas, and facially they still look like Berbers, and they still have a large minority of blue and green iris color, like their mountain kinsmen. But the Middle Atlas Berbers who live in cool forests and grasslands have a normal body build, legs as short and hands and feet as wide as those of a normal European.

The Somalis of the desert regions of the Horn of Africa are built very much like the Tuareg; and so are the Australian aborigines

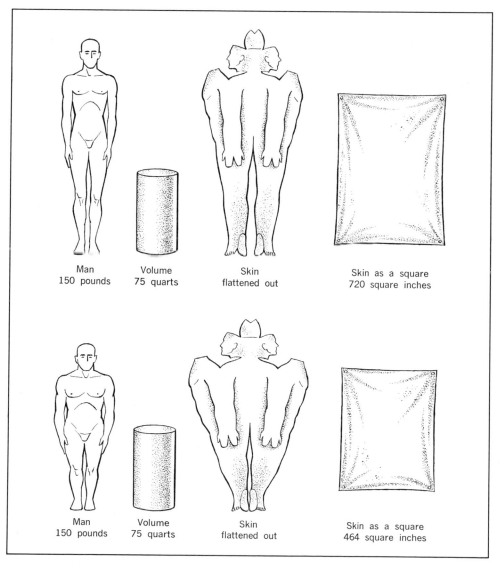

| Man<br>150 pounds | Volume<br>75 quarts | Skin<br>flattened out | Skin as a square<br>720 square inches |
| Man<br>150 pounds | Volume<br>75 quarts | Skin<br>flattened out | Skin as a square<br>464 square inches |

**Figure 1** Body volume and skin surface area. With constant volume, the more linear individual has the largest area.

who inhabit the desert regions of northern and central Australia. Precise evidence from desert-living American Indians is not at hand, but we understand that long limbs and narrow extremities characterize such peoples as the Seri. Zoologists and paleontologists know that animals that live in deserts tend to have long, slender, light-boned bodies, with the emphasis on length and slenderness of the limbs, while animals that live in lush, moist environments tend to be heavier boned. That this principle should apply to man is not surprising.

All the peoples just mentioned are literally *skinny*. Their skin surface area is great in proportion to their volume and weight. They are not tall; high stature does not necessarily go with this kind of build. The critical factor seems to be for the organism to present the maximum skin surface area in proportion to mass and weight to the external environment, thus permitting a maximum of cooling surface for evaporation [as shown in the figure on page 89]. Now 50 per cent, more or less, of the body's blood is inside of the legs at any given time. A long, pipe-like leg is an excellent radiator; it exposes much more cooling surface per unit of weight and volume than a short, barrel-like one, which may be more useful in other environments.

Looking at the information which we have at our command, environmental, cultural, and anatomical, for all continents, we can see that there is a three-way correlation between food, body form, and desert living and it is not possible to separate out the independent variables. Suffice it to say that desert dwellers are forced to live on concentrated low-bulk, high-protein, high-fat and high-sugar diets; for example, in Arabia and the Sahara, milk and milk products, dates, and some grains are the foods of the desert dwellers. Bulky, high-cellulose fruits and vegetables, which do not grow in deserts and are hard to transport, are off their menu. A long-gutted organism, like a gorilla, can operate efficiently on high-bulk, low-concentrated diets. A short-gutted, narrow organism like a weasel requires more concentrated food.

## Damp Heat

Peoples who live in moist heat, like the Pygmies and Forest Negroes of Africa, the Indonesians and Melanesians, and the Indians of the Amazon-Orinoco basin, do not exhibit this lanky desert form. Their bodies have less heat and more humidity to cope with. Heat loss cannot, it seems, be increased through an increase of relative surface area, owing to the difficulty of evaporation in a nearly saturated atmosphere. These people show no clear adaptation in body form to their special environment which, it must be remembered, was the original environment in which the ancestors of man lived before their descent from the trees. The living genera of anthropoid apes show a great range of body form in this environment. Their differences in shape seem related to means of locomotion rather than to the factors considered above.

## Extreme Cold

Another environment which leaves its mark on people is that of the Arctic. We must remember that human beings were not able to live in climates involving extreme seasonal cold until they had attained a level of technological skill necessary to make warm clothing. Otherwise they could not have left their houses or caves to go hunting in the middle of winter. Here again the time factor is short compared with the time span of human evolution, but still it gives us between 700 and 1000 generations. All of the people living around the Arctic Circle, from North Cape to Greenland, are short. They vary from 154 to 164 cm. in stature means, with few absolutely tall individuals. They include people whose ancestors have moved into this region in fairly recent times. In Norway the population of Finnmark is much shorter than that of the more southerly provinces, and the Norwegian settlers themselves are shorter than their relatives farther south. In Siberia the Yakuts, Turkish herdsmen forced north by the expansion of Genghis Khan's empire, are shorter than their kin on the grasslands to the south. It is probable that Russian colonists, several generations on the spot, have lost stature as well. In Greenland we have statistical evidence of the gradual reduction in stature among the colonists from Iceland, up to the time of their extinction. Iceland itself, warmed by the Gulf Stream, does not fall in the stature zone with which we are concerned, although there is evidence

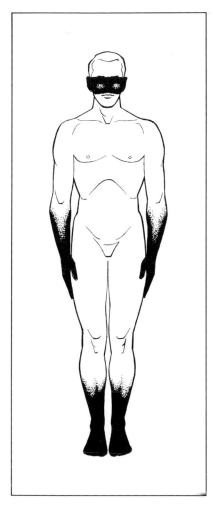

**Figure 2** Critical areas for cold—the extremities, the nose, the eyes, and the middle face.

that a temporary change of climate during the Middle Ages was accompanied by an equally temporary depression in stature.

The short peoples who live around the Arctic Sea are also uniform in another respect: they are thick set. Their bodies are chunky, their chests thick and wide, their legs short and thick, their fingers and toes short, and their wrists and ankles small and fat-covered. Even so, in Alaska surgeons on ships and in mission stations amputate many frozen toes from Eskimos; this is said to be their commonest operation. In contrast to the inhabitants of overheated deserts, Arctic peoples present the least possible skin surface area to the outside world, in proportion to volume and weight [as shown in the figure

on page 89]; and even that surface they keep covered, except for their faces, when outdoors in the cold. They are built to radiate as little heat as possible. As it is, much of the animal fat eaten by an Eskimo or Chukchi is expended in heat loss, for they have almost twice the caloric requirements of people living in our environment. Any eyewitness account written by explorers will mention the enormous quantities of fatty foods which these people eat. Some of it they store. When they are young and in their prime they tend to be fat-protected as well as muscular. Old age brings a loss of fat under the skin, wrinkling, and general inability to withstand the rigors of the environment. Death comes early; few live to be really old.

*Why* Arctic peoples are relatively globular is clear enough; *how* they became so is harder to answer. However, we know enough about the physiology of heat loss to venture an explanation. Individuals who exhibit the minimum surface area for their volume are those who have the least prominent surface projections, and the maximum development of visceral protection. This is like insulating the furnace to save heat. Sleep studies have shown that during slumber the temperature of the extremities approaches outside air temperature, while the viscera are maintained near the waking temperature. Short extremities are less likely to cool to a dangerous level than long ones, particularly if the bones and blood vessels are well covered with fat and muscle.

A second possible effect of cold is its influence on the growing organism: through stimulation of the adrenals and their secretion of cortical hormones, and the consequent storing of fat, building of muscle, and early closure of the epiphyses of the long bones. This may help make Arctic peoples short and relatively globular. This effect may be considered as a temporary or phenotypical change which might be altered dramatically by changing the environment of a child at an early age, and leaving the more-than-adequate diet constant.

Arctic-dwelling peoples sometimes go hungry, and many die of starvation. Selection would favor those who could store and utilize fat, as it would those who could escape freezing their extremities. In the siege of Leningrad, women suffered less from starvation than men, presumably because of their greater fat reserves per unit of body weight. Dickerson and Gowen have described a breed of mice which show a hereditary ability to utilize food more efficiently and thus develop "obesity" than other breeds fed on the same diets. Such a capacity, while unpopular in our society, is of unquestioned survival value in others where food is scarce.

Starvation is a powerful force in natural selection, in man as in other animals. This principle is a general one and must apply to other peoples outside the Arctic area who are of interest to anthropologists. Many "primitives" grow fat when they are taken off the range and put on reservations. Some who live on deserts and are at the same time exposed to starvation develop concentrations of fat in special areas, especially the buttocks, while the extremities are not affected. This combination is found among the South African Bushmen.

*selection 14*

# Early Man in East Africa

*Phillip V. Tobias*

Olduvai Gorge in Northern Tanganyika (Republic of Tanzania) has in recent years thrown a flood of light on an early chapter in the evolution of man. Between 1955 and 1963, L. S. B. Leakey, M. D. Leakey, and their sons and helpers uncovered fossil bones representing no fewer than 14 individuals from various levels in the Olduvai strata. Although detailed descriptions are yet to be published, it is clear that earlier and lower mid-Pleistocene deposits of East Africa contain the remains of at least two different kinds of fossil hominids (that is, members of the Hominidae, the family of man). The first group of fossils fits comfortably into a well-defined category, the australopithecines, which have long been recognized as a partially hominized group, that is, a group possessing some characteristics like those of *Homo*. The second assemblage has proved most difficult to place in any existing category. After exploring every other possibility, we have been forced to attribute this second group of fossils to a new and lowly species of *Homo*, namely *Homo habilis*: this species represents a more markedly hominized lineage than the autralopithecines and comprises a hitherto-unrecog-

*From* Science, *Vol. 149, No. 3679, 1965, pp. 22–33. Copyright 1965, American Association for the Advancement of Science. By permission of the author, and the publisher and copyright holder.*

nized and even unsuspected transitional or intermediate form of early man.

In this article I consider the history and some of the characteristics of the new fossils, as well as their cultural and evolutionary position, and propose modifications to some existing schemes of hominid phylogeny in the light of these new discoveries.

## The Olduvai Sequence

Before I review the new discoveries in detail, it may be useful to describe briefly the Olduvai stratigraphic succession (Fig. 1).

Olduvai Gorge has been cut by river action through a deep succession of old sediments, tuffs, and lavas. From the exposed strata, a remarkable series of fossils and implements has been recovered, ranging in age from Lower to Upper Pleistocene.

The strata exposed in the walls of Olduvai Gorge were divided by Hans Reck into five beds, numbered I to V, from the lowest upwards. This classification was adopted and the limits of the beds were more precisely defined by Leakey and, more recently, by Hay. It should be stressed, however, that these beds are not absolute stratigraphic units cor-

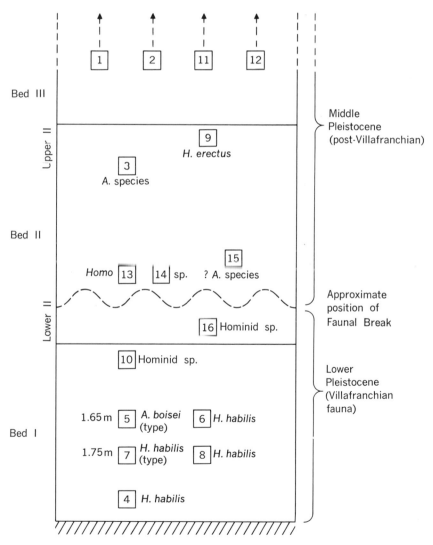

**Figure 1** Schematic representation of the lower half of the Olduvai sequence, showing the approximate vertical positions of hominid fossils (numerals enclosed in squares). The potassium-argon dates are indicated near the left margin (m = million years).

responding to sharp divisions in the Pleistocene sequence of events. Rather they are conveniently mappable units. Thus, as Hay has pointed out, two different marker beds have in various parts of the Gorge been regarded as the top of Bed I. Again, while Reck defined the base of Bed I as the basalt flows, Hay has preferred to include within Bed I the tuffs beneath the basalt. Hay thus regards the basalt flows as a constituent of Bed I in the eastern part of the Gorge.

Further, the newer analyses of fauna made by Leakey and his collaborators tend to relate the fauna of the lower part of Bed II to that of Bed I and to interpret both as belonging to a final Villafranchian faunal stage. On the other hand, the fauna of the middle and upper part of Bed II is considered post-Villafranchian and so to be associated with that of Beds III and IV. The complex of Middle and Upper II, III, and IV comprises a mid-Pleistocene stratigraphic sequence.

In this presentation, the subdivision into five beds will be used to provide a background against which to consider the hominid remains.

Potassium-argon dates are available for several levels within Bed I. The span of time represented by these Beds is suggested by ages 1.75 and 1.65 million years for two levels in the lower half of Bed I. In a word, the chapters of human evolution which are dealt with here cover the period from about 2 million to about hafe a million years ago.

### The Australopithecine Chapter

Exactly 40 years have elapsed since R. A. Dart published a description of a new kind of higher primate which had been recovered from a limestone fissure at Taung in South Africa. This discovery was one of the most remarkable, perhaps the most important, in the history of paleoanthropology. Earlier discoveries of fossilized human ancestors had shown unequivocally human affinities: this is true of the Neanderthal group and even of the earlier and morphologically more primitive Java ape-man, *Homo erectus* (or *Pithecanthropus*, as he has been called until fairly recently). But the Taung specimen differed from the others in being so much smaller-brained, bigger-toothed, and in other respects morphologically more archaic, that its precise affinities remained a cause of dispute for

Table 1   Dates of Discovery of Australopithecine Fossils

| | |
|---|---|
| 1924 | Taung (S. Afr.) |
| 1936–1949 | Sterkfontein Type Site (S. Afr.) |
| 1938–1954 | Kromdraai (S. Afr.) |
| 1939 | Garusi (E. Afr.) |
| 1947–1961 | Makapansgat (S. Afr.) |
| 1948–1952 | Swartkrans (S. Afr.) |
| 1955–1959 | Olduvai (E. Afr.) |
| 1957–1958 | Sterkfontein Extension Site (S. Afr.) |
| 1957–1958 | Sterkfontein Extension Site (S. Afr.) |
| 1964 | Peninj, Lake Natron (E. Afr.) |

decades. Initially, Dart claimed no more than that it was an ape with a number of features suggesting hominization, that is, an advance in a general human direction. He therefore called it *Australopithecus africanus*—simply the "southern ape of Africa."

With the wisdom of hindsight, we are today able to recognize in Dart's fossil the first real proof of the animal origins of man, the first concrete fossil evidence that Darwin's theory of the origin of species by small modifying steps and gradations from other pre-existing species is applicable to man. For here was an apelike creature which showed in its anatomical makeup a greater number of resemblances to hominids than are shown by any of the existing manlike apes of Africa or Asia.

It took time, as well as the discovery of many new specimens of *Australopithecus* (Table 1), the patient study of their anatomical features, and a closer look at the living great apes, to reach the now widely accepted conclusion that the australopithecines were an early branch of the Hominidae, the family of man, rather than of the Pongidae, the family of the apes. No fewer than eight sites in Africa have yielded australopithecine fossils (Fig. 2).

Most of the African australopithecines belong to deposits which have been classified, on comparative faunal evidence, as Lower Pleistocene. At least three sites have provided evidence that the australopithecines survived in Africa into the Middle Pleistocene—namely Swartkrans and Kromdraai in the Transvaal and Peninj (Natron) in Tanganyika.

Of all early hominid groups, the Australopithecinae are the best represented in our fossil storehouses. From the South African sites alone, no fewer than 315 australopithecine entries have been prepared for the forthcom-

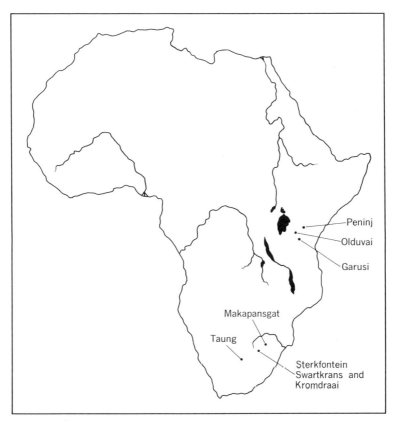

**Figure 2** The African sites which have yielded fossilized remains of *Australopithecus*, popularly known as ape-man, near-man, or half-man. The three northern sites are in the Republic of Tanzania; the five southern sites are in the Republic of South Africa.

ing new edition of the *International Catalogue of Fossil Man*: some comprise a single isolated tooth, some an almost complete cranium. If we accept that all the isolated teeth from Swartkrans and Sterkfontein do indeed belong to australopithecines, the total number of australopithecine teeth now available is over 600. The figure for Olduvai includes only the 16 maxillary teeth of the type specimen of *A. boisei*, although others may need to be added to this total on further study. Juvenile and adult specimens are known, as well as male and female. Apart from age and sex variations, more than one kind of australopithecine is represented; the diversity is such that some would classify them as different genera, while others have lumped them into one genus (*Australopithecus*) with several subgenera; yet others would see them as simply different species of a single genus.

Whatever the proper classification, there is an abundance of evidence bearing on the ana-

tomical structure and variation, the behavioral (or cultural) characteristics, and the ecological, geographical, and temporal background of the australopithecines. These lines of evidence concur in demonstrating that at least some of the known australopithecines, or of slightly earlier creatures of very similar aspect, fulfill the morphological requirements for a hypothetical human ancestor.

### East African Australopithecines

Australopithecines have been found at three East African sites, Garusi (1939), Olduvai (1955, 1959, and ?1963), and Peninj (1964), all situated in northern Tanganyika.

The first specimen was found by Kohl-Larsen at Garusi in 1939. It comprises a fragment of upper jawbone containing both premolars. In 1943 Kohl-Larsen stated that his specimen resembled *Australopithecus*, but Weinert later reclassified it as an African species of *Meganthropus*. However, Robinson has shown convincingly that the premolars fall within the range for the South African *Australopithecus* from Sterkfontein. This is the smaller-toothed *Australopithecus* which is usually classified today as *A. africanus*. As yet, the Garusi specimen is the only evidence we have suggesting the presence in East Africa of the gracile *africanus* species of australopithecine. The other East African australopithecines are of the larger-toothed *boisei* or *robustus* species.

The most important East African australopithecine is the specimen originally called by Leakey *Zinjanthropus boisei* and now reclassified by Leakey, Tobias, and Napier as a species of the genus *Australopithecus*, namely *A. boisei*. For the time being the name *Zinjanthropus* is being retained to designate a subgenus within the genus *Australopithecus*. The specimen comprises a very complete cranium, including all 16 upper teeth; the wisdom teeth or third molars were still in process of erupting, suggesting that the individual was in his late teens at the time of death. A brief preliminary description has been given by Leakey. Tobias has placed on record the cranial capacity as 530 cubic centimeters; that is, the specimen's brain was no larger than that of the small-toothed *A. africanus* child from Taung. A detailed monograph on *A. boisei* will appear as part of a series of volumes on Olduvai Gorge by Leakey and his collaborators. It may be mentioned here that *A. boisei* is the biggest-toothed and most robust of all the australopithecines, exceeding in most dental dimensions even the largest-toothed of the crassident *A. robustus* group from Swartkrans in the Transvaal.

It is probable that more large-toothed australopithecines are present in the Olduvai deposits. Three adult teeth, found at the site MNK II, in the lower middle part of Bed II, are for the most part of australopithecine form, shape, and dimensions (Fig. 1, hominid 15). According to Leakey, this part of Bed II is characterized by a post-Villafranchian fauna; it is early mid-Pleistocene. These teeth were referred to by Leakey and Leakey, but no attempt has yet been made to identify them specifically. Other australopithecine remains may well be present in Bed II, including the very large molar discovered in 1955, high in Bed II. Detailed studies of all these specimens are under way, and it will be some years before the complete series of full reports is published.

The third site in East Africa to yield an australopithecine is Peninj, on the west side of Lake Natron, about 80 kilometers northeast of Olduvai Gorge. Here, in January 1964, one of Leakey's assistants, Kamoya Kimeu, a member of the expedition led by Richard Leakey and Glynn Isaac, discovered a nearly complete and superbly preserved mandible of a large-toothed australopithecine. According to Leakey's provisional identification of the fauna from this new site, it is of early mid-Pleistocene age and thus much later than the original *A. boisei* from Olduvai. It would seem to be equivalent in age to the upper part of Bed II, or even to the overlying Beds III and IV, in the Olduvai sequence. Despite this age difference, it is of interest to note that the mandibular dental arcade fits that of the maxilla of the Olduvai *A. boisei* almost perfectly and may be provisionally identified as a mandible of *A. boisei*. Although age comparisons between East and South Africa are fraught with difficulties, it would seem likely that the Peninj australopithecine is comparable in age with those of Swartkrans and Kromdraai. The three sites give evidence that the large-toothed australopithecines survived in Africa well into the Mid-Pleistocene.

### Unlikely Claimants for Australopithecine Status

At least one other fossil from Africa has been claimed to be australopithecine, namely an incomplete cranium discovered in northern Chad and described by Coppens as an australopithecine. In 1963, we invited Coppens to visit South Africa and study the original australopithecine material. As a result of his study, Coppens has reached the same conclusion as Leakey and I reached independently, namely that the Chad fragment represented a more advanced hominid than *Australopithecus*. It may belong to the new species, *Homo habilis*, or even to the more advanced *Homo erectus*. The original diagnosis of the Chad fauna as very early Villafranchian is likewise being revised by Coppens; the site is apparently late Villafranchian. Unfortunately, the extremely weathered and distorted state of the Chad specimen may preclude exact comparison with

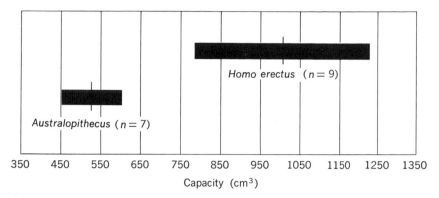

**Figure 3** The ranges and means of cranial capacity in two early hominids, *Australopithecus* (including both small- and large-toothed forms) and *Homo erectus* (formerly known as *Pithecanthropus*). The largest estimated australopithecine capacity is 600 cm³ and the smallest of *Homo erectus*, 775 cm³.

other hominine remains, but it is possible that further hominid material and stone tools may yet be discovered in the area.

The possibility has been raised that the teeth and cranial fragments found outside Africa, at Ubeidiya on the Jordan River in Israel, may have belonged to an australopithecine. From a preliminary study of the scanty human remnants, generously placed at my disposal by M. Stekelis, these remains are highly likely to have belonged to *Homo* rather than to *Australopithecus*, although it may be impossible, without the discovery of further mate-

rial, to attribute them to a particular species of *Homo*.

From Java has come another form of early hominid known as *Meganthropus palaeojavanicus*, of which three or possibly four mandibular fragments were found in the Djetis Beds dated to the beginning of the Middle Pleistocene. Robinson has suggested that this Javanese *Meganthropus* is simply an australopithecine. However, from a recent reexamination of the originals of *Meganthropus* I and II in comparison with original material from Africa, von Koenigswald and I concluded that, while *Meg-*

*Table 4   Some Fossil Hominids Which Have Been Claimed to Be Australopithecines*

| nature of specimen | original designation | revised attribution | latest interpretation |
|---|---|---|---|
| | | *Swartkrans* | |
| 1 mandible, 1 mandibular fragment, and 1 radial fragment | *Telanthropus capensis* | Australopithecine (Dart, Le Gros Clark) | *Pithecanthropus* (Simonetta), *Homo erectus* (Robinson) |
| | | *Chad* | |
| Craniofacial fragment | Australopithecine | *Homo* sp. | *Homo* sp. (unpublished) |
| | | *Ubeidiya* | |
| 2 teeth and 4 cranial fragments | Hominid | ?Australopithecine | *Homo* sp. (unpublished) |
| | | *Sangiran (Djetis Beds)* | |
| 3 mandibular fragments | *Meganthropus palaeojavanicus* | Australopithecine (Robinson) | More advanced than African Australopithecine (*?Homo* sp.) (Tobias and von Koenigswald) |
| | | *China* | |
| Isolated teeth | *Hemanthropus peii* (originally *Hemianthropus peii*) | Australopithecine (Simons) | Status not clear (*?Homo habilis*) |

*anthropus palaeojavanicus* has some strong resemblances to australopithecines, it shows
several features in which it is somewhat advanced beyond the australopithecine grade.
In this sense, it stands in the same relation
to *Australopithecus* as does *Homo habilis* in
Africa, except that *Homo habilis* has departed
further from *Australopithecus* in some respects.

Another group of Asian fossils has been
thought to possess australopithecine status,
namely a group of isolated teeth from China
attributed by von Koenigswald to *Hemanthropus
peii*. Simons has suggested that these teeth
are australopithecine. It is not impossible,
however, that they may represent a more advanced hominid, such as *Homo habilis*; but it
may be impossible to resolve the problem of
their status until more specimens are recovered, including teeth in a mandible or cranium.
The position of some claimants to australopithecine status is summarized in Table 4.

In sum, the case for the existence of an
australopithecine stage in Asia remains un-
proven; the only convincing australopithecine
sites remain the eight East and South African
sites listed in Table 1.

**The Gap between Australopithecus
and Homo**

Although *Australopithecus* fulfills the morphological requirements for an ancestor of man,
there remains a substantial gap between the
australopithecines and the most lowly representative of the hominines hitherto recognized
(that is, *Homo erectus*, formerly called *Pithecanthropus*, *Sinanthropus*, *Atlanthropus*, and so
on). The size of this morphological gap may
best be illustrated by reference to three parameters which have shown most marked
change during the process of hominization in
the Pleistocene: brain size, tooth size, and
tooth shape. Unfortunately, we cannot use the
evidence of hand and foot bones, since we have
insufficient evidence bearing on these features
in *Australopithecus* and in *Homo erectus*. On the
other hand, good samples of teeth and fair
samples of braincases and endocranial casts
exist for both of these groups . . . [and] there
is a clear and sizable gap between known
australopithecines and *Homo erectus*. Until recently, it has apparently been tacitly assumed
that *Australopithecus* graded more or less in-

sensibly into *Homo erectus* in the manner
postulated in general terms by Charles Darwin. It is therefore of no small interest to note
that so large a gap exists, not only with respect to one parameter, brain size, but, in the
same creatures, with respect to dental traits.

It is this gap that has been filled by *Homo
habilis*, the newly discovered hominid which,
with respect to the three parameters used to
characterize the gap, as well as with respect
to other morphological markers, lies in a
largely intermediate position.

**Homo habilis: the Early
Pleistocene Hominine**

The family Hominidae may be divided into two
subfamilies, the Australopithecinae and the
Homininae. The term "hominine" is the common or colloquial name connoting a member
of the subfamily Homininae.

From at least four levels in Bed I and the
lower (Villafranchian) and middle parts of
Bed II in the Olduvai succession have come
skeletal remains of another type of hominid.
(Fig. 1) This hominid differs widely from *A.
boisei*, the large-toothed australopithecine
found in the same beds. For instance, the
teeth are appreciably smaller than those of
*A. boisei*. While the sizes of the teeth of *A.
boisei* in general fall *above* the top of the range
for the South African australopithecines, the
teeth of this second hominid, especially the
premolars, fall at or below the lower end of
the australopithecine range. Such wide divergence between the two hominids from the same
site is far in excess of what can be attributed
to sexual dimorphism: in any event, it is accompanied by divergences in shape, proportions, and detailed morphology of the teeth,
in cranial shape and curvature, and in cranial
capacity. Clearly the second batch of fossils represents another type of hominid. In
almost all the departures of the second hominid from the australopithecine morphological
pattern, it approaches more closely to the
hominine pattern. In other words, the total
pattern is more markedly hominized than that
of *Australopithecus*. To the Bed I form characterized by these more hominized features we
have given the name *Homo habilis*. . . .

In accordance with international convention
in the naming of new species, one set of re-

mains was selected as the "type specimen" of *Homo habilis*. These were the remains of a juvenile (No. 7 in Fig. 1) whose bones—comprising a lower jaw with teeth, an upper molar tooth, the incomplete parietal bones of the cranial vault, and a set of hand bones—were found scattered on a single floor at the site FLK NNI in the Olduvai Gorge. In the 3 years that elapsed between his discovery and his naming, he was known as "pre-Zinjanthropus" because the living floor on which his bones were found lies some 35 cm *below* the living floor on which "Zinjanthropus" (or *A. boisei*) had been found. The youth of the individual represented was attested by the state of eruption of the teeth and by the signs of incomplete growth and ossification of the other bones, thus permitting the confident association of this group of bones as those of a single individual. . . .

The features which distinguish *H. habilis* remains from those of australopithecines and relate them rather to the more advanced Homininae include the capacity of the braincase, both absolutely and in relation to estimated body size, the size, proportions, and shape of the teeth, the shape and size of the jaws, and the curvature of the cranial bones. In addition, the postcranial bones help us to obtain a picture of the very hominine morphological pattern of *Homo habilis*, but they do not assist in the taxonomic problem of deciding whether, for instance, the hand of *H. habilis* was closer to that of *Australopithecus* or to that of the Homininae. This is because we do not know enough about the structure of the hand in either the australopithecines or *H. erectus*.

In all those parts for which we do possess adequate comparative material for both australopithecines and early hominines, most of the bones of *H. habilis* fall at the extreme or beyond the range of variation for the australopithecines. . . .

In sum, *H. habilis* was a pygmy-sized hominid with a relatively large cranial capacity, reduced and narrow teeth, and a number of markedly hominine features in his limb bones. His total structural pattern was that of a creature appreciably more hominized than any of the large group of australopithecines of South and East Africa. The advanced features, moreover, were not those of an individual extreme variant, but characterized all the individuals

represented over some considerable time. Clearly, this strain represents a distinct taxon intermediate between the most advanced *Australopithecus* and the most primitive *Homo*.

Since the original description was published in April 1964, a detailed comparison has been made between the original specimens from Tanganyika and those from Java. As a result, G. H. R. von Koenigswald and I have concluded that in the Bed II paratype of *H. habilis* (which lived some ¾ million years later than the type specimen), the hominizing trends have been carried still further; as a result, the jaws and teeth of the later specimen closely resemble those of *H. erectus* attributed to the early Middle Pleistocene Djetis Beds of Java. If these features represent sequential changes, we are virtually seeing here evolution in action, with subtle intergrades from one level of hominization to the next.

## Cultural Status of Homo habilis

It is accepted that cultural or ethological evidence may be added to morphological evidence in assessing the taxonomic status of a group. We may ask the question: Did *H. habilis* behave like an *Australopithecus* or like a *Homo?*

At each of the levels in Bed I where remains of *Homo habilis* have been found, primitive stone implements have been recovered. These artifacts are commonly made from pebbles or irregular fragments, and the cultural phase represented by the succession of stone industries constitutes the Oldowan Culture, formerly known as the Oldowan phase of the pre-Chelles-Acheul Culture. For long, the identity of the makers of the Oldowan Culture tools has been uncertain: some have maintained that the australopithecines were responsible, others have attributed the tools to early members of *Homo erectus*—but always on the basis of very indirect arguments. When in 1959 the cranium of the Olduvai australopithecine (*A. boisei*) was found on a living floor alongside Oldowan tools, at a time when no other adequate hominid remains were known to be associated with these tools, Leakey claimed that this australopithecine must have been the Oldowan toolmaker. This left a difficult problem: Why was the East African australopithecine associated with stone tools, whereas the Makapansgat australopithecine was associated with the bone, tooth, and horn tools described by Dart? Subsequently, however, remains of *H. habilis* were found on the same living floor as *A. boisei* and the tools. Furthermore, remains of *H. habilis* were found on the lower (earlier) living floors in Bed I, in each instance associated with Oldowan artifacts. While it is possible that both *A. boisei* and *H. habilis* made tools, it is probable that *H. habilis* was at least the more advanced toolmaker.

Furthermore, if we make a survey of all the evidence from South and East Africa, we see that *Australopithecus* alone has not yet been found with stone objects which are undoubtedly tools, except where advanced hominid remains were present as well. Six out of 12 deposits have yielded australopithecine remains with no stone tools; four sites which have australopithecines and stone tools contain, in addition, indications of a more advanced hominid. The remaining two deposits contain only the more advanced hominid and stone tools. At no site where australopithecine remains are the only hominid remains present are there any stone implements; conversely, at every site which has yielded stone implements and associated hominid remains, these hominid remains include those of a more advanced hominid, whether or not australopithecine remains are present in addition. Furthermore, at every site which has yielded the more advanced hominid, stone tools are present.

It has tentatively been concluded from these associations that no unequivocal evidence exists that *Australopithecus* made Oldowan stone tools to a set and regular pattern and according to a developing cultural trend. On the other hand, it seems very probable that *H. habilis* was the maker of the Oldowan stone tools, while *H. erectus* made the later (Chelles-Acheul) implements.

Dart has demonstrated that the australopithecines were capable of a wide range of cultural activities. It may, however, be argued that all of these activities fall into the categories which Napier has classified as *ad hoc* tool-using, purposeful tool-using, tool-modifying for an immediate or even for a future purpose, and possibly even *ad hoc* tool-making. But it may be questioned whether these australopithecine activities constitute cultural tool-making—that is, whether they exhibit a set and regular complex of patterns which, moreover, show developmental trends with the passage of time.

If this interpretation is correct, ethological or cultural evidence could be added to the anatomical evidence which tends to ally *H. habilis* with the hominines rather than with the australopithecines.

One further probable manifestation of the culture of the early Olduvai hominids is a rough circle of loosely piled stones discovered on a living floor at DK I in the lower part of Bed I. It suggests a crude shelter or windbreak and is on the same level as that on which the earliest remains of *H. habilis* were found (MK I). *H. habilis* may have been responsible for this rude structure.

## Significance of Homo habilis

Both its structure and its place in time impart a unique significance to *Homo habilis*, while, culturally, it seems to provide us for the first time with a knowledge of the makers of the Oldowan Culture.

Structurally, *H. habilis* may be regarded as a most effective link between the Australopithecinae and the Homininae, between which, as has been mentioned, there is a larger gap than has hitherto been recognized. Its very intermediacy is underlined by the fact that some workers would regard the newly discovered form as the most advanced australopithecine and others as the most primitive hominine. Thus, even in the short time since the new fossils were discovered, various workers have believed that the habilines were simply another australopithecine, a new genus between *Australopithecus* and *Homo*, a new lowliest species of *Homo*, namely *H. habilis*, and even a new subspecies of *H. erectus*, namely *H. erectus habilis*. The position adopted by my colleagues and myself would seem to be a compromise between the extreme views on either side. Although argument on the exact taxonomic position may continue for some time, it seems that there is already fairly general agreement on this virtually uniquely linking position of *H. habilis*. Perhaps only *Meganthropus palaeojavanicus* of Sangiran, Java, lies in a similarly intermediate position between the Australopithecinae and the Homininae, albeit a little nearer to the australopithecines than is *H. habilis*.

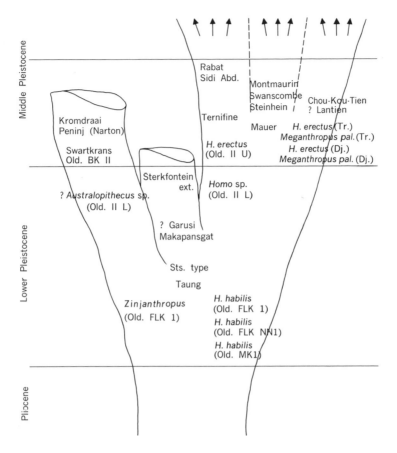

**Figure 4** Schema of Lower and Middle Pleistocene hominids, showing the position in time and space of the most important specimens discovered to date. The left trunk of the tree represents the large-toothed australopithecine line; and the right trunk, the hominine line leading to modern man. *Sts.*, Sterkfontein; *Sidi Abd.*, Sidi Abderrahman; *Old. II*, Olduvai Bed II; *U*, Upper; *L*, Lower; *Tr.*, Trinil beds; *Dj.*, Djetis beds.

Chronologically, the recognition of *H. habilis* means that a more hominized line of creatures was evolving alongside the somewhat less hominized australopithecines even in the Lower Pleistocene. Previously, the *H. erectus* remains of the Djetis Beds, agreed by most as belonging to the beginning of the Mid-Pleistocene, represented the earliest recognized hominine. It was still possible then to claim that, if indeed the Homininae stemmed off from an australopithecine ancestral group, this lineage of *Homo* need not have arisen any earlier than the end of the Lower Pleistocene. It now seems clear that, if the habilines are in fact members of the Homininae, then hominines were already present in Africa, and perhaps in Asia, during at least the second half of the Lower Pleistocene. The departure of the hom-

inine line from its presumed australopithecine ancestor must then have occurred as early as at least the Upper Pliocene or the first part of the Lower Pleistocene.

The early hominines must have been contemporaries of several diversified australopithecines—a megadont line (*A. boisei*), a macrodont line (*A. robustus*), and a mesodont line (*A. africanus*). In fact, at least in East Africa, and probably, too, in South Africa, *H. habilis* and *Australopithecus* spp. were sympatric and synchronic. More precisely, Olduvai I provides us with early evidence of the sympatric coexistence of the largest-toothed australopithecine (*A. boisei*) and *H. habilis*, while Swartkrans gives us later evidence for the sympatric compresence of the large-toothed *A. robustus* and a more advanced hominine, *H. erectus*

(*"Telanthropus"*). Doubtless, ecological differences permitted this situation to persist right through until the middle part of the mid-Pleistocene (Fig. 4).

## Bearings on Hominid Evolution

As a total morphological complex, *H. habilis* represents a more advanced grade of hominid organization than *Australopithecus*. Have the habilines arisen from the australopithecines? Since they are contemporary with *H. habilis*, the australopithecine populations represented by the actual fossils recovered to date are clearly too late—and possibly slightly too specialized—to have been on the actual human line, unless we are to postulate a polyphyletic origin of the Homininae at varying times from australopithecine stock. Morphologically, the gracile *A. africanus* is closest to *H. habilis* and seemingly least specialized. It would not be rash therefore to suggest that of the various australopithecines *A. africanus* has departed least from the common ancestor of *A. africanus* and *H. habilis*. On the other hand, the large-toothed, specialized *A. robustus* and *A. boisei* would seem to be far off the common *africanus-habilis* line. Two possible interpretations spring to mind:

1. The Pliocene ancestral australopithecine was large-toothed and perhaps adapted to a vegetarian diet; *A. boisei* and *A. robustus* would then represent a conservative line which maintained these qualities right through into the Middle Pleistocene, while *A. africanus* developed different ecological requirements which, perhaps through a more carnivorous or, at least, omnivorous diet, led to a relaxation of selective pressures maintaining large teeth. The gracile *H. habilis* stemmed off from this smaller-toothed line of australopithecines and became selected for increasingly hominine features.

2. The ancestral australopithecine was unspecialized, small-toothed, omnivorous. At some time in the Upper Pliocene, it diversified into macrodontic and megadontic lines (*A. robustus* and *A. boisei*), with specialized dentition, perhaps accompanying a specialized, essentially herbivorous diet. Another line remained little changed and unspecialized, eventually to dichotomize into a progressively more hominized line represented by *H. habilis*

in Africa and perhaps *Meganthropus* in Asia and a more conservative residual line (*A. africanus*) which, because of ecological similarities to *H. habilis*, did not long outlast the emergence of this hominine.

Which of the two interpretations is correct, or whether other alternatives should be considered, only the direct evidence of Pliocene fossils will determine. Pending their discovery, I incline to favor the second view, on indirect lines of evidence to be presented elsewhere. That is, I tend to regard the large teeth and supporting structures of *A. robustus* and *A. boisei* as secondary specializations, rather than as primitive or ancestral features which J. T. Robinson seems to believe.

Irrespective of which interpretation we adopt, it seems reasonable to infer that late in the Pliocene, or thereabouts, some populations of ancestral *Australopithecus*-like hominids moved forward to a further grade of hominization, thus generating the Homininae. We may tentatively conclude that *H. habilis* is on this direct hominine line. Such is the message of his morphology and his culture, while his position in space and time is compatible with this conclusion. As a Lower Pleistocene hominine, he bids fair to provide us with a population, one or more sections of which were ancestral to the mid-Pleistocene hominines (Fig. 5). Nothing in the structure or dating of the relevant fossils rules out the possibility that some populations of *H. habilis* underwent further hominizing changes by phyletic evolution late in the Lower Pleistocene, to attain the *H. erectus* grade of hominization.

Such a reconstruction permits us to recognize a series of grades of hominization, within which we may classify the available fossils. Despite wide variation within each grade—only a fraction of which is as yet known for most grades—we may recognize: (i) an australopithecine grade, represented convincingly only in South and East Africa; (ii) a habiline grade from Africa, perhaps corresponding to a meganthropine grade in Asia; (iii) an earlier *H. erectus* grade, represented in Africa possibly by remains from middle Bed II, Olduvai, and by *"Telanthropus"* from Swartkrans, and in Asia by the Djetis Beds hominines from Sangiran, Java; (iv) a later *H. erectus* grade, represented in Africa by "Chellean Man" from upper Bed II, Olduvai and by *"Atlanthropus"* of

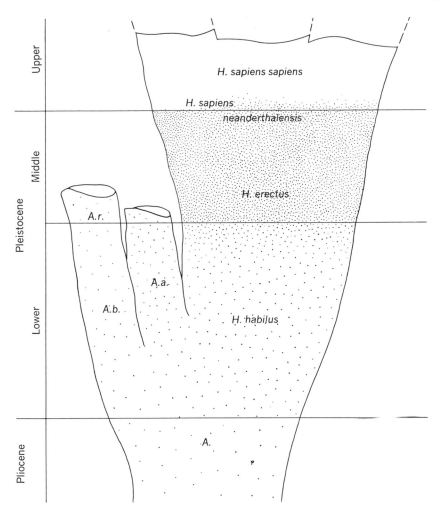

**Figure 5**   A provisional schema of hominid phylogeny from Upper Pliocene times to the Upper Pleistocene. Increasing intensity of shading represents increasing degrees of approach toward the structure and behavior of modern man. *A.*, the hypothetical ancestral australopithecine; *A.b.*, *Australopithecus* (Zinjanthropus) *boisei*; *A.r.*, *Australopithecus robustus*; *A.a.*, *Australopithecus africanus.* The schema indicates the synchronic coexistence of several different hominids in the Lower and Middle Pleistocene, the australopithecines surviving into the Middle Pleistocene alongside more advanced hominids of the genus *Homo.*

Northwest Africa; in Asia by the Trinil Beds and Chou-Kou-Tien hominines; and in Europe possibly by the remains of Mauer; (v) an earlier *H. sapiens* grade (Neanderthal) widely distributed in the Old World; and (vi) a later *H. sapiens* grade, ultimately worldwide in distribution. This sequence shows remarkable parallels between Africa and Asia from grade 2 onwards.

We see in conclusion that *H. habilis* has bridged the last remaining major gap in the Pleistocene part of the story of human evolution.

### Summary

Recent discoveries of early Pleistocene hominids in East Africa have revealed a new stage in human evolution. The remains of *Homo habilis*, discovered by L. S. B. Leakey and his family, bridge the hiatus between the most advanced australopithecines and the most primitive hominines. The new species was bigger-brained and smaller-toothed than *Australopithecus*, the fossil apeman from South and East Africa. It is very probable that *Homo habilis* was, as his name implies, a "handyman," maker of the earliest stone culture, the Oldowan.

These primitive hominines were already in existence in the Lower Pleistocene, living alongside a variety of more conservative hominids, the australopithecines. The closeness of morphology between *H. habilis* and *Australopithecus africanus* points strongly to a common ancestry in the Upper Pliocene or the very beginning of the Pleistocene. The large-toothed *A. robustus* and *A. boisei* were already diverging by specialization from the postu-

lated unspecialized ancestral australopithecine. The first hominines must thus have come into being by the beginning of the Pleistocene. Later, some populations of *H. habilis* seemingly underwent further hominizing changes to generate a new species, *Homo erectus*, bigger men with larger and more effective brains, smaller and more modern human teeth, probably more complete adjustment to upright stance and bipedal gait, a more precise manual grip, and an appreciably advanced material culture.

*Homo habilis* thus fills in the last remaining major gap in the Pleistocene story of human evolution.

*selection  15*

# Somatic Paths to Culture

## J. N. Spuhler

. . . In thinking about human phylogeny, I believe in using all, or nearly all, the hominoid fossils we know about, so long as they are not fragments. To argue that none of the known man-like fossils are in *the* human phylogenetic line seems to me obscurantist. To argue that the fossils we know about are "somewhat near" but not exactly on the main line seems unnecessarily cautious and hedging and may give the unknown greater weight than the known. Perhaps Weidenreich and Heberer went too far in using all known hominid specimens they considered authentic. But I prefer their use of all of them to Wood Jones' use of almost none.

There is not space here to give a review of new developments in human paleontology. In the last few years we have acquired a wealth of new specimens and new ideas and we have also been able to discard some old specimens and ideas with good cause. If additional fos-

*From J. N. Spuhler (arr.),*
*The Evolution of Man's*
*Capacity for Culture.*
*Wayne University Press,*
*1959, pp. 1–12,*
*as reprinted from*
*Human Biology,*
*Vol. 31, No. 1, 1959, pp.*
*1–13. Copyright © 1959,*
*Wayne State University*
*Press. By permission*
*of the author, and the*
*publishers and the*
*copyright holder.*

sils become available it may be necessary to make major revisions in what I am about to say. By taking an abstract level—the level of the taxonomic genus—I can avoid some undecided issues on the phylogenetic placement of individual specimens. For the moment I am going to assume a human evolutionary sequence of 4 or 5 genera:

1. Leaving out the periods before the Miocene, we start with *Proconsul*, the earliest ape whose skull is known. I assume *Proconsul* had precursors who developed the general features of a man-like thorax and arms as we know them today, but that these terrestrial apes were not highly specialized as brachiators. There is no reason to suppose that any human ancestors since the Miocene have been arboreal to the extent characteristic of living gibbons, orangutans, or chimpanzees.

2. We don't know what happened in the Pliocene.

3. At least by Early Pleistocene there is *Australopithecus*, now known from dozens of good, or as Broom would say, "beautiful," specimens, and the earliest evidence of man-like animals with bipedal locomotion.

4. By Early Pleistocene times, and lasting into Middle Pleistocene in parts of Asia, we have the genus *Pithecanthropus*. From the neck down they were very like the genus *Homo* and like him they were tool makers, fire users, and hunters. Their brain volume was intermediate between *Australopithecus* and *Homo*.

5. At least by Middle Pleistocene we have the genus *Homo*, represented by such forms as Swanscombe, Fontéchevade, the Neanderthals, and Upper Paleolithic man. Everyone agrees that some, if not all, members of the genus *Homo* have culture.

Now, in the context of this sequence of 4 known genera, and with comparisons from living monkeys and apes, I want to discuss 7 biological topics which are preconditions for the beginning of culture. They are:

1. Accommodative vision,
2. Bipedal locomotion,
3. Manipulation,
4. Carnivorous-omnivorous diet,
5. Cortical control of sexual behavior,
6. Vocal communication,
7. Expansion of the association areas in the cerebral cortex.

Of course, these 7 conditions alone did not make a population of apes lacking culture into a population of men with culture. The evolution of man was not predetermined by a few conditions in a population of Miocene apes. Mutations are the fundamental genetic events in the historical process of the acquisition of the capacity for culture. Mutations are random events that do not point in an orthogenetic direction. But mutations are limited by the structure of the gene which mutates and this structure is determined by the evolutionary forces, especially selection, active in the history of the gene. In this way populations that survive accumulate genes which are favorable in the prevailing environment of the population.

To illustrate the complexity of human evolution since the Miocene as seen at the mutational level, let me do some speculative arithmetic—using figures that have fair justification and are conservative. From the Miocene to now there must have been at least two million generations in the hominoid line. If the total breeding population in successful phyla was 10 thousand, we have 20 billion individuals as real or potential ancestors of modern man. If genes at the average locus mutate at a rate of 1 in 100,000, and if only 1 in 200,000 of these result in new and favorable steps (and that is a low estimate), we still could have about 20 thousand "visible," favorable mutational steps (in all loci) since the Miocene in the hominoid line.

Thus when we talk about 7 conditions we are perhaps oversimplifying the matter. But there is not time for further discussion, even if we knew what to say. And, I should add, the 7 conditions I list do not represent unit mutations, although mutation is the ultimate source of the genetic variation in each condition. Further, the order of listing is not strictly chronological. Evolutionary changes in the 7 conditions were interdependent and roughly synchronous.

1 ACCOMMODATIVE VISION  Vision has been the primary sense in vertebrates as far back as we know them. It makes possible their great mobility. The most complex vertebrates, birds and mammals, interact with their external environment predominantly *via* their eyes. Under the influence of the arboreal habitat, primate

vision was perfected into a leading sense. Visual behavior is one key difference between the nocturnal, mostly solitary Prosimians, and the diurnal, more social Anthropoidea. The difference between these two is perhaps the largest gap in non-human Primate social behavior. With upright, or sitting-up posture, vision in the Anthropoidea gained strict control of manipulation—it became super*vision*, a guide and control of fine manipulation.

The relationship between the evolution of keen vision and fine manipulation is two-directional. As Polyak says: ". . . vision itself [became] more refined and the intellectual absorption and mental utilization more complete and lasting, as the skilled movements became more complex and more efficient." We will find that this kind of bothway causation with two or more systems evolving simultaneously, where progress in each stimulates change in the other, is important to the understanding of many topics in this symposium.

Before taking up bipedal locomotion, let me mention one good thing that came out of the Piltdown affair. It was the insight given, for example in Hooton's excellent paper, on the asymmetrical character of human evolution. Hooton . . . was early to stress that different regions of the human body change at different rates. Many workers today would follow Washburn's separation of the human body into three regions distinct in phylogeny, with arms and thorax the oldest, the bipedal complex of pelvis and legs later, and the head and face latest of all to reach their modern form.

2  BIPEDAL LOCOMOTION  Although functional differentiation of the front and hind limbs started with the first tetrapods where the front legs reach out and the hind legs push, *Australopithecus* is the first primate with upright bipedal locomotion (the tarsiers are bipedal hoppers). The australopithecine pelvis, sacrum, and femur resemble modern man in those features which make his upright posture possible. There are some features of full bipedalism not found in *Australopithecus*—these are fully developed in *Pithecanthropus* from Java and Peking. Australopithecine locomotion was certainly more similar to that of *Pithecanthropus* and *Homo* than to any of the quadramanus primates. We must conclude that, by the early Pleistocene, hominoids were bipedal with free hands which could be used to handle

tools. We will see that this was a master adaptation that demanded other adaptations leading to man's capacity for culture.

3  MANIPULATION  A good start toward precise manipulation is seen in monkeys. When monkeys sit up their hands are temporarily free and are used to bring objects close to the organs of touch, vision, taste, and smell. But something like a quantum jump is made when the hands are continually free for such activity as they are in an upright, fully bipedal hominoid. Then the arms and hands—under the guidance of binocular vision with good accommodation—are principal organs for interaction with the immediate physical environment. Getting food, eating, grooming, fighting, making, using, and carrying tools, these manipulations, accompanied by a rich flow of sense data including those from the more developed proprioceptive arm-and-hand muscle sense, enlarge the flow of information to the brain which in turn fosters development of association areas for storage of past experience with the hands and guides and initiates new hand movements. The neural delay required when some extra-organic tool is interposed between stimulus and response probably had much to do with the first ability to use symbols and the start of language. The co-adaptation of the hands, senses, and association areas in precise manipulation seems a first basis for the subsequent development of human intelligence.

4  CARNIVOROUS-OMNIVOROUS DIET  Man and the tarsier are unusual among primates in being carnivores. Many monkeys are omnivores and take small animals as prey. Man is unique among living primates in taking large animals for food and these in large numbers.

Fortunately we have some fossil evidence on the problem of diet. It is still an open question whether the Australopithecines were hunters or the hunted. But by Middle Pleistocene times the *Pithecanthropus* of Peking were hunters of large mammals as well as gatherers of hackberries and other plant food.

The change to a partially carnivorous diet had extremely broad implications for the social organization of early hominoids. Carnivores get a large supply of calories at each kill. This concentrated food is more easily transported to a central, continually used shelter than is low-calorie plant food, especially before containers were available.

Whoever killed the baboons and bucks associated with the Australopithecines must have been tool carriers as well as tool users. Tool carrying implies a degree of conceptualization not required in the occasional use of tools. Before starting on the hunt there must be a minding which associates the tool with an event which is to occur in the future. This type of mentation has not been observed in captive chimpanzees or monkeys, and certainly not in wild non-human primates. The archaeological record shows it was a consistent part of *Pithecanthropus* behavior by Middle Pleistocene times.

Compact animal protein high in calories is a good basis for food sharing. Of non-human mammals it is only the carnivores that share gathered food. It is unlikely that the long dependency of human children—so important in the acquisition of culture by individuals—could develop in a society without food sharing. And the amount of information which needs to be transduced in a communication system for plant eaters like the gibbons is small compared to that needed in group-hunting of large animals. Gibbons share, by vocal communication, knowledge about the location of food collected and eaten individually on the site; hominoids share in the location, collection, and consumption of food.

5  CORTICAL CONTROL OF SEXUAL BEHAVIOR There seems little danger that modern anthropologists will overlook the importance of sex in the evolution of culture. Some of us fail to emphasize that, with regard to the physiology of sexual behavior, man is neither a) completely like most other beasts, nor b) completely different from non-human animals. Here, as in many other biological characters, the apes and man are alike and man and the apes are unlike other mammals. In the majority of mammals sexual behavior is seasonal and the sexual periods correspond to times when the female has high probability of ovulation and conception. In such mammals including the lower primates, copulation is evoked by an increase of gonadal hormones in the body fluids. In such animals we can bring about, or prevent, copulation by gonadectomy and hormonal injections. But in man and the chimpanzee, and probably also in other apes,

copulation is strongly under cortical control and is not prevented by gonadectomy.

An important adaptation for culture is the change from built-in nervous pathways to neural connections over association areas (where learning and symboling can be involved) in the physiological control of activities like sleep, play, and sex. Cortical rather than gonadal control of female sexual receptivity may not be essential to the hominoid family (observations on other animals suggest not), but cortical dominance in sexual activity may have contributed to the easy transition of the family from a social unit where sex and reproduction were more important than food economy to a unit where subsistence is the dominant familial function.

6  VOCAL COMMUNICATION Human speech is an overlaid physiological function. It uses a set of body parts of quite diverse primary action. Consider the muscles used in speaking. Most of our coordinated muscular movement involves corrections and adjustments from proprioceptors. But the laryngeal muscles lack proprioceptors, and feedback control of speech comes by way of the ear and the 8th cranial nerve. When we talk, the voice box, tongue, and lips must work together smoothly and precisely. The 10th nerve controls the adjustment of the vocal cords and the 5th nerve the movement of the lips. Both of these involve branchial muscle while the 12th nerve moves the tongue with somato-motor muscle. The neurological basis of speech is not clear, but it is clear that the only place where the motor organs and steering apparatus of speech are wired together is in the cerebral cortex. Perhaps hand-tool manipulation in group activities like hunting coordinated by vocalization may have helped to make the connections.

Although the larynx is homologous in all primates its position in the throat differs in man. The larynx of quadrapedal primates from the lemur to the chimpanzee is in close to slight contact with the soft palate. This is why chimpanzees cannot make long, resonant sounds. As a consequence of upright posture and flexion of the craniofacial base, the larynx in man is moved down the throat away from contact with the soft palate, and an oral chamber is formed which makes possible resonant human phonation.

This is not to deny a rich variety of vocal production to the chimpanzee and other primates. The position of the larynx, however, is one reason why attempts to teach chimpanzees English have failed. Unfortunately no one has tried seriously to teach a chimpanzee to learn to speak using chimpanzee "phonemes."

7 EXPANSION OF THE CEREBRAL CORTEX  Current statements in the anthropological literature regarding the size of man's brain often involve misinterpretations in one or the other of two directions. On one extreme, some investigators stress the fact that, compared with *mammals* in general, especially large mammals, man's brain is unusually large, both absolutely and relatively. For example, a 150 pound man has a three pound brain, while a 150 pound sheep has a one-quarter pound brain, and a 1500 pound cow has a one pound brain. On the other extreme, the stress is put on the conclusion that man's brain is indeed large, but not unexpectedly so. For example, when the log of brain weight in *primates* is plotted against the log of body weight, the slope of the regression line is steeper than it is among mammals in general (proportional to the 0.79th power of body weight in primates, the 0.66th power in mammals), and on visual inspection the plot shows—as log transformations often do—remarkably little scatter, suggesting that brain weight in modern man is just about what would be predicted given the general regression of brain on body weight in primates and a knowledge of man's body weight alone. But if we take 1345 gm as a brain weight typical for modern man, say of 60 or 70 kg body weight, we find man's brain is significantly larger than the value of 1095 gm of brain for 70 kg of body, predicted by van Bonin's regression formula: log brain weight $= 0.79$ log body weight $- 1.00$. A conclusion which avoids both extremes might stress at least two reasons for man's large brain weight: a) about 80% of man's brain weight may be explained because he is a primate of large body size, and b) about 20% of man's brain weight results from an evolutionary increase in the relative size of hominid brains—resulting in a total brain weight which is vast compared with mammals in general, and is significantly large compared with primates in general. One reason we have overstressed the size of man's brain, even among primates, is that the chimpanzee and gorilla have relatively small brains, especially for primates. Similar arguments suggest that the frontal lobes in man, while well developed, are not of extraordinary and unexpected volume compared with other higher primates. . . .

Man is not much different from other primates, especially the apes, in the general sequence of events from conception to birth. After birth, the ontogenetic pattern in man differs markedly from that of all non-human primates but differs in a direction forecast by the general trend of primate evolution. I would guess that this elongation of the life periods after birth is a consequence of physiological adaptation to the acquisition of culture. Culture is a biological adaptation with a nongenetic mode of inheritance depending on symbolic contact rather than fusion of gametes. It has greatly supplemented somatic evolution. In all known human societies, individuals participate in social systems whose members represent more than a single biological family in which all are connected (as the social insects are) by gametes from one parental set. No human family is a self-sufficient system of social action. Symbols rather than gametes make this so. It may be assumed that the genes controlling the growth cycle in man have been changed through selection to man's *human, cultural* environment.

# A Physical Anthropologist's View of the Peopling of the New World

## T. D. Stewart

*From* Southwestern Journal of Anthropology, *Vol. 16, No. 3, 1960, pp. 259–270.* © *1960, Department of Anthropology, University of New Mexico. By permission of the author, the publisher, and the copyright holder.*

. . . [In 1951] I pointed out that since Ulloa first said it in 1772 it has become an adage that he who has seen one Indian may be said to have seen them all, so much are they alike in color and bodily form. Admittedly this statement contains elements of hyperbolism. No one would deny that Indians vary, and especially in such things as stature and head shape, if not much in skin color, hair form, etc. The classifications of von Eickstedt and Imbelloni, and the typologies of Dixon, Hooton, Hrdlička, and Georg Neumann bear witness to this variability. However, recent studies have tended to ascribe less and less of this variability to changes in population heredity wrought in this hemisphere and to attribute it to environment. Thus Marshall Newman has demonstrated for the hemisphere at large that many elements of the Indian phenotype are primarily adaptive responses to environment and are distributed in accordance with Bergmann's and Allen's ecological rules; Hurtado and Monge have shown that in Peru the thin air of high altitude induces a distinctive physical type; and Lasker and Scrimshaw, working in Mexico and Central America-Panama, respectively, have observed that the attainment of growth maxima depends upon the quality of the diet during the ages when growth is in progress. In view of these demonstrations of physical plasticity in certain recent Indians— a trait which they share, of course, with all mankind—the long recognition of a basic phenotypic homogeneity throughout the hemisphere must be regarded as a necessary truth. Indeed, it is safe to say that no population of comparable size has remained so uniform after expanding, in whatever time has been involved, over such a large land area.

On the other hand, a generalization about the genotype akin to Ulloa's adage about the phenotype appears to be in the making. Here, of course, we have practically nothing to go on but blood groups. Leaving out of consideration some northern peoples known to be late comers to the hemisphere (see below), the blood groups of aboriginal Americans are monotonously limited to O, M, and Rh+, to mention only the better known categories. After having typed the bloods of several hundred Indians in the highlands of Guatemala ten years ago for ABO and MN, I was saying to myself, in effect, "Type one Indian and you have typed them all, so much are they alike in their blood groups." Boyd recognized this situation when he classified the American Indians genetically as a separate race, distinct even from the Asiatic monogoloids.

Before the middle of this century any such generalization about the American genotype was blocked by reports of high frequencies of blood group B at two points in South America and of even higher frequencies of blood group A in parts of North America. The latter is now accounted for on the basis that it represents a late thrust onto the northern continent of mongoloid groups, notably the Eskimos and Athapascans, with different blood group patterns. Blood group B in South America can now be dismissed on the basis either of White admixture or of faulty serological technique. . . .

So far I have said nothing about the Diego factor, a serological discovery only five years old. Most of the work on this factor has been done by Layrisse and associates in Venezuela. Partly for this reason, the circum-Caribbean area appears as a center of high frequencies in the distributional pattern thus far revealed. At first, when Diego could not be found in Whites or Negroes, the term "Indian factor" was suggested for it. Then, when Diego still could not be found in Whites or Negroes, including African Negroes, and was not found in Australians and Polynesians, but was found in Chinese and Japanese, it was dubbed "Mongolian factor." Aside from this, the main finding has been a great variability in frequency in closely associated groups, for example, 35% in the Caribs and only 5% in

the neighboring Arawak. Lack of uniformity over the area examined and limitation of the positive findings to the mongoloids suggests imperfect sampling and perhaps some unrecognized selection factor. Whether or not this is true, only time will tell. Certainly it is premature to erect on such an insecure basis any hypothesis regarding the peopling of America.

From this brief review it is evident that the genotype of American Indians as represented by the blood groups has come in for much attention lately. Much more could be said about this, and especially about the rarer blood types. However, enough has been said to show that the long-standing impression of genetic homogeneity throughout the hemisphere still has strong support. If this is accepted, along with what has been said about the homogeneity of the phenotype, it constitutes a remarkable phenomenon, which, in view of the sizes of the populations and land masses involved, must have significance as regards the time required for the peopling of the hemisphere.

### Explanation of Homogeneity

The explanation of this remarkable phenomenon depends, in the first place, on the obvious geographical peculiarities of the western hemisphere. It is generally conceded that in ancient times man could have entered this area only by way of what is now called Bering Strait. Also, the main obstacles to man's migration and multiplication within the hemisphere probably were close inside the entrance. Be this as it may, the peopling of America can be described as the filling of a humanly uninhabited and generally attractive cul-de-sac through a relatively inaccessible northern entrance. In other words, the American aborigines constitute a major isolate.

In the second place, the explanation of what happened subsequently to the descendants of the first invaders depends upon the relative actions of the following four agencies regarded by geneticists as being mainly responsible for changes in the genetic character of populations: mixture, mutation, natural selection, and random genetic drift. The fact that the ancestors of the American Indians were not preceded in the hemisphere by a different breed of men is the first point to be noted in this connection. Obviously the only mixture that took place here for many thousands of years was that between groups of much the same genetic make-up. It does not seem likely, therefore, that mixture played a significant role in the development of the American population.

The second agency for population change is gene mutation. Just how important a force this is in human evolution has not been fully established. Curt Stern says simply that "As a general phenomenon . . . it is very unlikely that the present polymorphism and, even less the polytypy, of man are the result of singular, nonrecurrent mutations." However, he goes on to say that "If mutation from one allele to another occurs recurrently and at numerous loci, most of the single mutations at any one locus will never be established and even none of the many recurrent mutations at any one locus may become established. Some mutations at some loci, however, will escape extinction and may, indeed, even become numerous." Since in any event mutations are simply a source of "newness" in heredity, the utilization of which depends upon the action of the remaining two agencies of population change, selection and drift, let us pass on to them.

"By selection," according to Boyd, "we mean that organisms possessing certain characteristics survive in relatively larger numbers, and leave relatively more offspring, than do other organisms of the same kind possessing other characteristics." In man differential survival—or better, differential fertility—is brought about by all sorts of things, most if not all of which collectively constitute the environment. Thus, for example, disease germs are conditioned as to numbers and varieties by the climate. In turn the disease rates in humans caused by germs depend on the susceptibilities of individuals. And the resulting mortality rates help determine the relative contribution to the next generation by a given set of individuals.

I have chosen this example deliberately because it has special pertinence to the Americas. The cold of the Far North has been characterized as a screen serving in past times to prevent the flow of many pathological germs along with the movements of their human hosts. There is much evidence to support this generalization even in this day of rapid transportation. Apparently the cold screen explains why at the time of the first European contact the Indians lacked many disease entities common to the Old World, and hence were so vulnerable to the diseases introduced by the Europeans and their African slaves. We have only to remember in this connection that smallpox and not Spanish armor was the decisive factor in the fall of Mexico in 1520.

On the other hand, the reduced number of diseases in the prehistoric New World means that disease was less important here as a selective agent than in the Old World. But if disease was not so important, the same cannot be said for most other environmental factors. Just about every kind of climate was present and each had its own peculiar assortment of plants and animals which man could use as foods, some being rich in nutritive values and others poor. In more familiar terms this means tundras, temperate forests, grassy plains, deserts, rain forests, jungles, seacoasts, mountains, etc. In occupying all such environmental niches the American Indians exposed themselves to the selective processes which these habitats exert upon mankind. Today "few serious workers in biology doubt the efficiency of selection in bringing about evolution."

The last of the agencies producing changes in population heredity, random genetic drift, "depends for its operation on the islation of one small population from other populations with which it could interbreed." According to Stern, "fluctuations in the size of [human] isolates must have been great as the result of famines, epidemics, and wars. During each of these lows in population number, the sample of alleles which passed through the narrow 'bottleneck' of the few parents which connected an earlier, relatively large, with a later, relatively large population, provided a striking opportunity for a demonstration of the effect of drift and often must have resulted in greatly different allelic ratios before and after the bottleneck generation. Similarly, migration of a fraction of a population to a new region constituted opportunities for drift. . . . In other words, the allelic ratios found in the migrants may have deviated considerably from those of the original groups, and, in any case, these ratios may often have undergone great changes during the early generations when the migrated population remained small. Drift in its various aspects," Stern concludes, "probably accounts for much of the polytypy of man."

From what has been said, it stands to reason that the vast and variable spaces which opened up before the first immigrants into the western hemisphere were made to order for the operation of the last two evolutionary agencies or forces we have been considering. Yet, as we have seen, the resulting population is remarkably homogeneous in phenotype and genotype. Even the diseases of this population, with one possible exception, did not proliferate. The exception is syphilis, which may have put in an explosive appearance quite late. Otherwise, the diseases regarded as unique to the hemisphere, such as uta, verruca, and oroya fever, are of quite limited distribution. All this suggests that the total time involved in the peopling of America was too limited to effect major evolutionary changes. From this point of view, if the first immigrants were not much the same as modern man, or in other words, if they were something like Neanderthal man, I think circumstances would have favored the perpetuation of this more primitive variety; or at least traces of such a variety would have persisted somewhere in the hemisphere. Nothing of the sort has been found.

**Eastern Asia**

Let us now move across Bering Strait and see what evidence has been turned up in eastern Asia regarding the antiquity of the modern form of man. Of course, over the past twenty years and until quite recently circumstances have not been propitious for archeological work in this area. Unfortunately, also, newer dating techniques, for example the flourine test, have not yet come into use here. For such reason attention can be called to only three recent putative early-man finds complete enough to be significant in the present connection. One of these, the so-called Tzeyang man, was found in 1951 in an open site just west of Chungking in Szechuan Province, some 7–800 miles in a direct line southwest of Peking. The fauna said to be associated with the human remains includes the woolly mammoth (*Mammonteus primigenius*) and very likely belongs to the late Pleistocene. Because of this and of the type of the skull, Ju-kang Woo claims that Tzeyang man ". . . represents an early form of *Homo sapiens*, more primitive than the European Cro-Magnon people and the Upper Cave people of Choukoutien [and thus] is the earliest fossil representative of the Neanthropic stage so far found in China." This claim already has been modified, as will appear. Also, judging from the illustrations, I would say that the skull, which lacks parts of the face and base, could be lost in certain high-vaulted Indian series, for example one from southern Florida.

The second find, so-called Liukiang man, was found in 1958 in a cave near Liuchow in the Kwangsi Chuang Autonomous Region of southern China. In this case the dating of the human remains by means of the associated fauna leaves something to be desired. Although extinct forms, such as *Rhinoceros sinensis* and *Stegodon orientalis* were recovered, more importance is attached to the finding of *Ailuropoda melanoleucus*, the giant panda which still exists in southern China. This is shown by the following statement by Ju-kang Woo: "As the skull of *Ailuropoda* was found in a site in close proximity to that of the human skull and both were adhered with reddish matrix which is different from the consolidated yellowish deposits yielding the other vertebrate fossils, it seems reasonable to assume that the fossil human skull together with that of *Ailuropoda* are later than Middle Pleistocene. As the fossil human skull is definitely fossilized and of *Homo sapiens* type, it can be assumed that it is of late Pleistocene age." Combining this argument with his observations on the skull, Woo concludes that ". . . Liukiang Man represents an early form of the evolving Mongoloid and is the earliest fossil representative of modern mankind so far found in China." In my opinion the skull type, which is moderately low vaulted with wide, short face, is not very different from that of some California Indians.

The third and most recently reported find, a fragmentary skull cap, is probably much older and certainly more primitive than the other two. This fragment was recovered in 1958 in a limestone cave near the village of Mapa in Kwangtung Province (the province east of the Kwangsi region) in southern China. The list of generic names of the associated fauna includes both recent and extinct forms, so it is difficult to evaluate the dating which is said to be late Middle Pleistocene or early Late Pleistocene. According to Woo and Peng "The most conspicuous features . . . are the supraorbital tori which, similar to the condition observed in *Sinanthropus*, almost form a continuous cross bar at the base of the forehead. They are separated only by a slight depression in the glabella region, that is to say, fairly distinct torus glabellaris or supranasalis unites the supra-orbital tori of either side. The supra-orbital tori are very thick and project markedly both forward and sidewise. Their upper surfaces merge gradually into the frontal squama with a slight sulcus supratoralis, but not so distinct as in *Sinanthropus*." Although the finding of artifacts is not mentioned, the authors conclude that the Mapa skull ". . . is the earliest human fossil so far found in China with the exception of *Sinanthropus*. This new discovery indicates that in the time of middle Pleistocene, not only North China but also South China are [sic] inhabited by early hominids. Thus it greatly extends the distribution of Paleolithic man in China." It is safe to add that nothing so primitive as this specimen has been found in the western hemisphere.

Accepting the first two of these new finds as reported and combining them with the three well-known Upper Cave skulls from Choukoutien in northern China, we have evidence of American Indian-like types over a wide area of eastern Asia in late Pleistocene times. In this connection it is important to call attention to Georg Neumann's thus far briefly reported reappraisal of the types of the Upper Cave skulls. Many will recall that Weidenreich thought one of these skulls resembled an Upper Paleolithic European, another a Melanesian, and the third an Eskimo. Typing of this sort, of course, is highly subjective and dependent on the viewer's orientation, so it is not surprising that where Weidenreich, an Old World anthropologist, saw Old World types, Neumann, a New World anthropologist, sees New World types. "All of the traits in question," Neumann says, "appear repeatedly in various early American Indian populations and should be regarded as expressive of the natural variability of the group." Also, it is to be remembered that Melanesians and Australians have been placed in America, quite illogically, on very little more evidence than skull typing. I feel that it is just as unreasonable on this same basis to place Melanesians in north China in late Pleistocene times.

If these newer views have validity . . . the existence in eastern Asia in late Pleistocene times of varieties of modern man akin to the later Indians may be accepted as reasonably well established. How long they had existed there we still do not know. That these varieties represent the population from which the first Americans were derived seems highly probable, although the point in time at which the separation occurred remains to be discovered.

## Summary

In summary, then, the putatively ancient New World skeletons thus far recovered show the presence of only modern man over a period of about 20,000 years. Already before that time related varieties existed in eastern Asia. When the first Asiatics crossed Bering Strait into America, they entered a huge cul-de-sac offering every variety of environment and no forerunners to mix with. A reconstruction of what happened thereafter takes into account that the resulting population at the time of discovery constituted a major isolate that was homogeneous, both phenotypically and genotypically. It is contended that such homogeneity is not consistent with the passage of a long period of time following the establishment of the first beachhead, because the hemisphere offered ideal conditions for the action of selection and drift, the two main agencies responsible for genetic changes in populations. It follows from this that the first beachhead was established by modern man.

*selection  17*

# The Study of Race

## S. L. Washburn

. . . Discussion of the races of man seems to generate endless emotion and confusion. I am under no illusion that this paper can do much to dispel the confusion; it may add to the emotion. The latest information available supports the traditional findings of anthropologists and other social scientists—that there is no scientific basis of any kind for racial discrimination. I think that the way this conclusion has been reached needs to be restated. The continuation of antiquated biological notions in anthropology and the over-simplification of facts weakens the anthropological position. We must realize that great changes have taken place in the study of race over the last 20 years and it is up to us to bring our profession into the forefront of the newer understandings, so that our statements will be authoritative and useful.

This paper will be concerned with three topics—the modern concept of race, the interpretation of racial differences, and the social significances of race. . . .

The races of man are the result of human evolution, of the evolution of our species. The races are open parts of the species, and the species is a closed system. If we look, then, upon long-term human evolution, our first problem must be the species and the things which have caused the evolution of all mankind, not the races, which are the results of local forces and which are minor in terms of the evolution of the whole species. . . .

The evolution of races is due, according to modern genetics, to mutation, selection, migration, and genetic drift. It is easy to shift from this statement of genetic theory to complications of hemoglobin, blood groups or other technical information. But the point I want to stress is that the primary implication of genetics for anthropology is that it affirms the relation of culture and biology in a far

*From* American Anthropologist, *Vol. 65, No. 3, Part 1, 1963, pp. 521–531. By permission of the author, and the publisher.*

firmer and more important way than ever in our history before. Selection is for reproductive success, and in man reproductive success is primarily determined by the social system and by culture. Effective behavior is the question, not something else.

Drift depends on the size of population, and population size, again, is dependent upon culture, not upon genetic factors as such. Obviously, migration depends on clothes, transportation, economy, and warfare and is reflected in the archeological record. Even mutation rates are now affected by technology.

Genetic theory forces the consideration of culture as the major factor in the evolution of man. It thus reaffirms the fundamental belief of anthropologists that we must study man both as a biological and as a social organism. This is no longer a question of something that might be desirable; it must be done if genetic theory is correct.

We have, then, on the one hand the history of genetic systems, and on the other hand the history of cultural systems, and, finally, the interrelation between these two. There is no evolution in the traditional anthropological sense. What Boas referred to as evolution was orthogenesis—which receives no support from modern genetic theory. What the geneticist sees as evolution is far closer to what Boas called history than to what he called evolution, and some anthropologists are still fighting a nineteenth-century battle in their presentation of evolution. We have, then, the history of cultural systems, which you may call history; and the history of genetic systems, which you may call evolution if you want to, but if you use this word remember that it means selection, migration, drift—it is real history that you are talking about and not some mystic force which constrains mankind to evolve according to some orthogenetic principle.

There is, then, no possibility of studying human raciation, the process of race formation, without studying human culture. Archeology is as important in the study of the origin of races as is genetics; all we can do is reconstruct as best we can the long-term past, and this is going to be very difficult. . . .

Genetics shows us that typology must be completely removed from our thinking if we are to progress. For example, let us take the

case of the Bushmen. The Bushmen have been described as the result of a mixture between Negro and Mongoloid. Such a statement could only be put in the literature without any possible consideration of migration routes, of numbers of people, of cultures, of any way that such a mixing could actually take place. The fact is that the Bushmen had a substantial record in South Africa and in East Africa and there is no evidence that they ever were anywhere else except in these areas. In other words, they are a race which belongs exactly where they are.

If we are concerned with history let us consider, on the one hand, the ancestors of these Bushmen 15,000 years ago and the area available to them, to their way of life, and, on the other hand, the ancestors of Europeans at the same time in the area available to them, with their way of life. We will find that the area available to the Bushmen was at least twice that available to the Europeans. The Bushmen were living in a land of optimum game; the Europeans were living close to an ice sheet. There were perhaps from three to five times as many Bushmen ancestors as there were European ancestors only 15,000 years ago.

If one were to name a major race, or a primary race, the Bushmen have a far better claim in terms of the archeological record than the Europeans. During the time of glacial advance more than half of the Old World available to man for life was in Africa. The numbers and distributions that we think of as normal and the races whose last results we see today are relics of an earlier and far different time in human history.

There are no three primary races, no three major groups. The idea of three primary races stems from nineteenth-century typology; it is totally misleading to put the black-skinned people of the world together—to put the Australian in the same grouping with the inhabitants of Africa. And there are certainly at least three independent origins of the small, dark people, the Pygmies, and probably more than that. There is no single Pygmy race. . . .

The concept of race is fundamentally changed if we actually look for selection, migration, and study people as they are (who they are, where they are, how many they are); and the majority of anthropological textbooks need substantial revision along these lines.

Since races are open systems which are intergrading, the number of races will depend on the purpose of the classification. This is, I think, a tremendously important point. It is significant that as I was reviewing classifications in preparing this lecture, I found that almost none of them mentioned any purpose for which people were being classified. Race isn't very important biologically. If we are classifying races in order to understand human history, there aren't many human races, and there is very substantial agreement as to what they are. There are from six to nine races, and this difference in number is very largely a matter of definition. These races occupied the major separate geographical areas in the Old World.

If one has no purpose for classification, the number of races can be multiplied almost indefinitely, and it seems to me that the erratically varying number of races is a source of confusion to student, to layman, and to specialist. I think we should require people who propose a classification of races to state in the first place why they wish to divide the human species and to give in detail the important reasons for subdividing our whole species. If important reasons for such classification are given, I think you will find that the number of races is always exceedingly small.

If we consider these six or nine geographical races and the factors which produced them, I think the first thing we want to stress is migration. . . .

Migration has always been important in human history and there is no such thing as human populations which are completely separated from other human populations. And migration necessarily brings in new genes, necessarily reduces the differences between the races. For raciation to take place, then, there must be other factors operating which create difference. Under certain circumstances, in very small populations, differences may be created by genetic drift, or because the founders are for chance reasons very different from other members of the species.

However, the primary factor in the creation of racial differences in the long term is selection. This means that the origin of races must depend on adaptation and that the differences between the races which we see must in times past have been adaptive. I stress the question of time here, because it is perfectly logical to maintain that in time past a shovel-shaped incisor, for example, was more efficient than an incisor of other forms and that selection would have been for this, and at the same time to assert that today this dental difference is of absolutely no social importance. It is important to make this point because people generally take the view that something is always adaptive or never adaptive, and this is a fundamental oversimplification of the facts.

Adaptation is always within a given situation. There is no such thing as a gene which has a particular adaptive value; it has this value only under set circumstances. For example, the sickle-cell gene, if Allison and others are right, protects against malaria. This is adaptive if there is malaria, but if there is not malaria it is not adaptive. The adaptive value of the gene, then, is dependent on the state of medicine and has no absolute value. The same is true of the other characteristics associated with race. . . .

I turn now to a brief statement on the influence of culture upon race. Beginning with agriculture and continuing at an ever-increasing rate, human customs have been interposed between the organism and the environment. The increase of our species from perhaps as few as five million before agriculture to three billion today is the result of new technology, not of biological evolution. The conditions under which the races evolved are mainly gone, and there are new causes of mutation, new kinds of selection, and vast migration. Today the numbers and distribution of the peoples of the world are due primarily to culture. Some people think the new conditions are so different that it is better no longer to use the word race or the word evolution, but I personally think this confuses more than it clarifies.

All this does not mean that evolution has stopped, because the new conditions will change gene frequencies, but the conditions which produced the old races are gone. In this crowded world of civilization and science, the claim has been made repeatedly that one or another of the races is superior to the others. Obviously, this argument cannot be based on the past; because something was useful in times past and was selected for under conditions which are now gone, does not mean that it will be useful in the present or in the future.

The essential point at issue is whether the abilities of large populations are so different that their capacity to participate in modern technical culture is affected. Remember in the first place that no race has evolved to fit the selective pressures of the modern world. Technical civilization is new and the races are old. Remember also that all the species of *Homo* have been adapting to the human way of life for many thousands of years. Tools even antedate our genus, and our human biological adaptation is the result of culture. Man and his capacity for culture have evolved together, as Dr. Dobzhansky has pointed out. All men are adapted to learn language—any language; to perform skillful tasks—a fabulous variety of tasks; to cooperate; to enjoy art; to practice religion, philosophy, and science.

Our species only survives in culture, and, in a profound sense, we are the product of the new selection pressures that came with culture.

Infinitely more is known about the language and culture of all the groups of mankind than is known about the biology of racial differences. We know that the members of every racial group have learned a vast variety of languages and ways of life. The interaction of genes and custom over the millenia has produced a species whose populations can learn to live in an amazing variety of complex cultural ways.

Racism is based on a profound misunderstanding of culture, of learning, and of the biology of the human species. The study of cultures should give a profound respect for the biology of man's capacity to learn. Much of the earlier discussion of racial inferiority centered on the discussion of intelligence; or, to put the matter more accurately, usually on that small part of biological intelligence which is measured by the IQ. In the earlier days of intelligence testing, there was a widespread belief that the tests revealed something which was genetically fixed within a rather narrow range. The whole climate of opinion that fostered this point of view has changed. At that time animals were regarded as primarily instinctive in their behavior, and the genes were supposed to exert their effects in an almost mechanical way, regardless of the environment. All this intellectual climate has changed. Learning has proved to be far more important in the behavior of many animal species, and the action of the complexes of genes is now known to be affected by the environment, as is, to a great degree, the performance that results from them. For example, Harlow has shown that monkeys learn to learn. Monkeys become test wise. They become skillful in the solution of tests—so monkeys in Dr. Harlow's laboratories are spoken of as naive or as experienced in the use of tests. To suppose that humans cannot learn to take tests is to suppose that humans are rather less intelligent than monkeys. . . .

We can generalize this point. All kinds of human performance—whether social, athletic, intellectual—are built on genetic and environmental elements. The level of all kinds of performance can be increased by improving the environmental situation so that every genetic constitution may be developed to its full capacity. Any kind of social discrimination against groups of people, whether these are races, castes, or classes, reduces the achievements of our species, of mankind.

The cost of discrimination is reflected in length of life. The Founding Fathers were wise to join life, liberty, and the pursuit of happiness, because these are intimately linked in the social and cultural system. Just as the restriction of social and economic opportunity reduces intelligence so it reduces length of life.

In 1900 the life expectancy of White males in the United States was 48 years, and in that same year the expectancy of a Negro male was 32 years; that is a difference of 50 per cent, or 16 years. By 1940 the difference had been reduced to ten years, and by 1958 to six. As the life expectancy of the Whites increased from 48 to 62 to 67 years, that of the Negroes increased from 32 to 52 to 61 years. They died of the same causes, but they died at different rates.

Discrimination, by denying equal social opportunity to the Negro, made his progress lag approximately 20 years behind that of the White. Somebody said to me, "Well, 61, 67, that's only six years." But it depends on whose six years it is. There are about 19 million people in this country sociologically classified as Negroes. If they die according to the death rate given above, approximately

100 million years of life will be lost owing to discrimination.

In 1958 the death rate for Negroes in the first year of life was 52 per thousand and for Whites 26. Thousands of Negro infants died unnecessarily. The social conscience is an extraordinary thing. A lynching stirs the whole community to action, yet only a single life is lost. Discrimination, through denying education, medical care, and economic progress, kills at a far higher rate. A ghetto of hatred kills more surely than a concentration camp, because it kills by accepted custom, and it kills every day in the year.

A few years ago in South Africa, the expectation of life for a Black man was 40 years, but it was 60 at the same time for a White man. At that same time a White woman could expect 25 more years of life than a Black woman. Among the Blacks the women lived no longer than the men. People speak of the greater longevity of women, but this is only because of modern medicine. High birth rates, high infant mortality, high maternal mortality—these are the hallmarks of the history of mankind.

Of course there are biological differences between male and female, but whether a woman is allowed to vote, or the rate that she must die in childbirth, these are a matter of medical knowledge and of custom. Biological difference only expresses itself through the social system.

Who may live longer in the future—Whites or Negroes? There's no way of telling. Who may live longer in the future—males or females? There is no way of telling. These things are dependent on the progress in medical science and on the degree to which this progress is made available to all races and to both sexes.

When environment is important, the only way genetic difference may be determined is by equalizing the environment. If you believe in mankind, then you will want mankind to live on in an enriched environment. No one can tell what may be the ultimate length of life, but we do know that many people could live much longer if given a chance.

Whether we consider intelligence, or length of life, or happiness the genetic potential of a population is only realized in a social system. It is that system which gives life or death to its members, and in so doing changes the gene frequencies. We know of no society which has begun to realize the genetic potential of its members. We are the primitives living by antiquated customs in the midst of scientific progress. Races are products of the past. They are relics of times and conditions which have long ceased to exist.

Racism is equally a relic supported by no phase of modern science. We may not know how to interpret the form of the Mongoloid face, or why Rh$^o$ is of high incidence in Africa, but we do know the benefits of education and of economic progress. We know the price of discrimination is death, frustration, and hatred. We know that the roots of happiness lie in the biology of the whole species and that the potential of the species can only be realized in a culture, in a social system. It is knowledge and the social system which give life or take it away, and in so doing change the gene frequencies and continue the million-year-old interaction of culture and biology. Human biology finds its realization in a culturally determined way of life, and the infinite variety of genetic combinations can only express themselves efficiently in a free and open society.

*part 4*

# *Primate Behavior*

# Japan's Contribution to Modern Anthropology

## John Frisch, S.J.

*From* Studies in Japanese Culture *edited by Joseph Roggendorf, S.J., 1963. Sophia University, Tokyo, Japan. By permission of the author, the publisher and the copyright holder.*

. . . Studies of the behavior of wild Japanese monkeys (*Macaca fuscat*) were initiated in 1949 by a group of young workers under the leadership of Professor Imanishi, now teaching at Kyoto University. The group eventually developed into the organization now known as the Japan Monkey Center, grouping professors of several public and private universities. Though active in widely different fields, they are united by a common interest in problems of primate behavior and evolution. Although this article will deal exclusively with studies on the social behavior of Japanese monkeys, as most representative of the work of the group, it is important to remember that field work is also currently being conducted on the behavior of wild chimpanzees (Tanganyika) and of langurs (India). Likewise, physiological aspects of the life of wild monkeys have been the object of important research, especially those that pertain to reproduction. These areas of research are of great potential significance for anthropology but are not dealt with here. The purpose of the present paper is merely to give a sample of the work done by the Center and to point out its relevance to anthropology.

The Japanese Macaques live among the mountains and more scarcely populated hills of the islands. The northern boundary of their range, the north tip of Honshū (the main island of the Japanese archipelago), is also the northern limit of non-human Primates the world over. The total population of *Macaca fuscata* throughout Japan is estimated to number between 40,000 to 60,000 animals. These live in groups of very unequal size, some counting as few as 15 individuals, while the largest one has increased to-day to more than 500 animals. Of these many groups, about 30 are the object of observations on the part of workers of the Primate Research Group. In most groups a new method has been used, designed to make observations possible at close range with a minimum of interference with the freedom of the group. This method consists in setting up a feeding station in an open space within the territory of the group. In most places, the troop now comes down regularly but after various lengths of time, to the feeding place which has become the focal point in the group's activities and where inter-individual relationships can be studied with comparative ease. One of the greatest advantages of this technique is that, by providing prolonged close-range contacts, it allows the individual identification of most members of the group, without the help of any artificial markings.

The first important data yielded by this method of observation concerns the social structure of the group. The observations made on the colony of Takasakiyama, a steep wooded mountain on the eastern coast of Kyūshū, between Oita and Beppu, are the most detailed and complete. They will, therefore, be used as the main source for the description of a typical group.

In 1959 the Takasakiyama group was composed of 104 males, 205 females and 250 young less than five years old. As the group gathered around the feeding ground, the division of the members into "classes" is accurately reflected by the spatial relationships between individuals. The central area is occupied by the six dominant adult males, females, infants and juveniles of both sexes. The remaining ten adult males, together with the sub-adult ones, sit in the trees or on the rocks surrounding the feeding ground, the adult males being somewhat closer to the central area but none being allowed within it. Infants and juveniles, on the other hand, circulate freely within the entire range of the group. Two adult males have only occasional and brief contacts with the group and are designated as "solitaries."

This concentric pattern of grouping is also reflected in the order followed by the group when leaving the feeding place at night. The leaders leave first, accompanied by some females and their children. The subdominant males are then free to enter the central area,

may be accepted by the females, and perform the same roles as the leaders. The sub-adult males, however, still remain at the periphery and enter the central area only after most of the subdominant males have also retired to the mountain. At that moment, all the remaining males band together to drive away the females and occupy the feeding ground for some time before retiring to the sleeping place.

Such observations, duplicated by many others, have suggested that the social structure of the group is based not only on a single rank order but on a system of classes, each one giving to the animal a definite status, recognized by all members, and including functions and privileges. The dominant males insure the good order among the females and their young who are feeding in the central area. Examples of disciplinary action are not rare. The leaders also prevent other males from entering this area and eventually protect the females from their attacks. The subdominant males, closer to the center, co-operate with the leaders in policing the group and also co-operate with the sub-adults at the periphery in defending the group against outside enemies. They often are seen perched in trees, watching for any oncoming danger.

The social structure, including the division into classes and a definite dominance hierarchy within each class, appears to be quite stable, at least in Takasakiyama. Seven years after the group was first studied, the basic hierarchy had remained largely unchanged in spite of a three-fold increase in population.

As can readily be seen from this brief description, the "social classes" correspond essentially to biological categories determined by age and sex. Infants and children of both sexes belong to the central area. Differentiation between males and females begins with the juveniles. The females remain in the central area, while male juveniles show a tendency to interact with the sub-adult males located at the periphery. Eventually they join this class and are then excluded from the center. As they approach full maturity the males again approach the center and acquire the status of subdominance. All leaders are fully adult individuals.

Within each class, however, there also exists a dominance or ranking order, determining attitudes of submission or superiority between any two individuals. This rank, it has been found, does not depend exclusively on biological factors, such as physical strength or age. Infants, for instance, being always under the protection of their mother, share indirectly in their mother's status. A three year-old individual has been observed to take advantage of its mother's high rank to lord it over all but the leaders of the group. More interesting still, the degree of dominance of this young monkey was found to vary in accordance with the social fortunes of the mother. Kawai has called this social status of infants "dependent rank."

The dependent rank enjoyed by children has a deep influence on their later status in the group. This is particularly true of females, since they remain in the center of the group from birth to death and grow into adulthood under the same influences which determined their dependent rank as infants. The latter tends therefore to become solidified into a permanent rank. The situation is different for male children who, as they become juveniles, retire towards the periphery of the group. This would seem to favor the development of independent behavior, based on the juvenile's own ability to acquire and maintain a particular rank in his class. This ability, of course, depends largely upon age and physical strength, but other factors should also be considered. It would be wrong to surmise, for instance, that the dependent rank enjoyed by a male child is without influence on his later permanent rank. As Imanishi points out, "children of dominant females involuntarily learn attitudes of the dominant and those of submissive females learn attitudes of the submissive."

The vantage position enjoyed by children of dominant females is best exemplified by what happens in Takasakiyama in late spring when the females are about to give birth to their next young. The year-old infants are then cared for by the dominant and subdominant males. The relationship thus established between a given infant and its "protector" seems to be of a lasting nature. It would seem reasonable to infer, although I have seen no reports on this matter, that the children of the more centrally located dominant females are also more likely to be adopted by the top-ranking leaders with whom they are already better acquainted. In

this way, all other things being equal, male offspring of dominant females are better prepared to co-operate with the leaders and will be accepted by them more readily.

It seems, therefore, probable that, quite apart from physiological and biological factors, the habits acquired in childhood play an important role in determining the place of each male in the dominance hierarchy.

The importance of these observations for anthropology lies in that they suggest strongly that the way a non-human primate society arranges itself is not determined solely by the law of the strongest. Family lineage also appears to play an important role. The classes that compose the structure of the group are therefore analogous to the social classes of human society not only by the respective functions they fulfill in the life of the group, but also in the way they are formed. Learned patterns of behavior, transmitted from parents to children, play perhaps as much of a role in structuring non-human primate society as mere biological competition.

A second important set of data concerns the marked variability of behavior observed between different troops of monkeys.

Differences in food-habits are among the best documented. An ecological study showed that the territory of the troop on Arashiyama, near Kyoto, contained as many as 600 kinds of edible plants. However, only 200 of these were actually eaten by the animals. That this limitation results from a choice by the group appears from the fact that the other groups eat foods that are here neglected. Moreover, an identical food can be eaten by two groups but in different ways. Study of the excrements has shown that some groups chew the seeds of a given fruit while others swallow the seeds without previous chewing. Again, some groups devastate crops and fields while others leave them untouched.

Inter-group behavioral variability extends, of course, to many other items, such as varying degrees of sexual tolerance, child care, aggressive behavior, etc. Some details can be found in a previously published article.

The importance of these observations lies in that they show the existence of behavior typical for each group. Individual variability, which has been known for a long time, is also present. But much more important, and probably new to most students of primate behavior, is the evidence that members of one group tend to be much more similar in habits to each other than to the members of another group. To that extent the set of behavioral patterns proper to a given group is not without analogy with the cultural patterns observed in human society.

Finally, a third sort of phenomena must be considered here that can best be described as "inventive behavior." Since, to the writer's knowledge, these data have not yet been made the object of official publication, they will be mentioned briefly.

The monkey colony on Kōshima island, off the south-eastern coast of Kyūshū, is perhaps to-day the group that has had the least contact with human beings. The island is uninhabited, except for a family of fishermen. A feeding station was established near the seashore eleven years ago but, fortunately, the colony has so far been spared the curiosity of tourists. Up until two years ago, the monkeys of Kōshima only rarely entered the sea. Then, one day, some of them began to try swimming. To-day, two years later, only 13 members of the group of 50, all of them adult, do not enter the sea. All the others have acquired the habit of swimming.

About one year after the setting up of the feeding station on the beach near the seashore, a sixteenth-month female monkey began to wash the sand from the sweet potatoes by plunging them into a small brook that was running through the sand towards the sea. This "washing behavior" spread gradually through the group, beginning with the younger animals, and replaced the mere rubbing of the potatoes with the hands which had been customary so far. The new habit had spread to one half of the animals after 4 years, to 71% after 9 years (1962). More significantly, the habit is now shared by 80 to 90% of all animals born since it was first observed. A further modification in the process of cleaning the sweet potatoes occurred when some monkeys started to wash them in the sea water. This new method seemed preferred by some to the former one, perhaps, it has been suggested, because of the salty taste of sea water. Even in cases where the food lay scattered on the sand near the brook, some animals took the potatoes all the way to the sea. In doing so they occasionally walked on their hind legs, as most monkeys do at times, carrying the food in their hands. Later, as the monkeys began to enter the sea more frequently, the posture of walking erect in the water and holding the potatoes in the hands became more and more common. Subsequently erect bipedal walking became more frequent on land also, and the most agile individuals are reported to walk distances of up to fifty meters. The development of the whole process requires close investigation. It seems already certain, however, that two factors played an important role in the acquisition of this new habit: the distribution of food near the sea and the increased familiarity with water. Given this new environment and the new opportunities it offered, a new behavior also arose correspondingly.

Perhaps the most striking invention by the troop at Kōshima has to do with the eating of wheat. Picking up the wheat scattered on the beach proved to be rather tiresome work, the more so since sand almost inevitably got mixed with the food. A solution to this problem has been found: carrying the wheat to the sea and plunging it into the water. By so doing, the sand falls to the bottom of the water thus separating from the wheat. Eating the remaining and purified wheat is easy. The workers of the Japan Monkey Center insist that this method of sifting the sand from the wheat has never been taught or shown to the monkeys. If this is true, we certainly witness here a sort of behavior which it is difficult to call by any other name than "invention."

The inception of new, though less striking, behavior has also been reported from several other groups, the most common one being the adoption of new food habits in connection with the setting up of feeding places. The acceptance of new foods can take a very long time. A wild group investigated by the author near the thermal station of Yūgahara refused the offered sweet potatoes for four years before taking on this new food-habit. Later on it accepted also tangerines and apples. All other food has so far been refused. Here also the differences between groups are pronounced: some accept new food readily, others so far have always refused it.

It will be noted that the adoption of new habits, as well as the occurrence of inventive behavior, has always followed the alteration of the environment and living conditions of the group resulting from the providing of food. It can therefore be interpreted as an adaptation of the group designed to take full advantage of the new ecological conditions. The importance of this inventive behavior lies in that it shows that non-human primates can adapt to changed conditions by spontaneously modifying their habits. Their adjustment therefore apparently does not depend on the occurrence of favorable genetic mutations. They are able not only to modify or enlarge already existing behavioral patterns (selecting new foods etc.) but also, most importantly, to create new ones (erect walking, sand sifting).

The relevance to modern anthropology of the three sets of observations briefly described above hardly needs to be stressed. Their bearing on the nature and the origins of culture will be briefly considered.

Japanese studies have made it plain that much of the behavior of natural societies of non-human, and even non-hominoid, primates is characteristic for the particular group rather than for the species. The inference follows that the amount of socially learned and transmitted behavior, as opposed to instinctive and genetically inherited behavior, may be considerable and doubtless appears much larger than was commonly thought until now. The behavior of a given young male, for instance, depends to a large extent on the nature of the group in which it has grown and on the position of its mother in this group.

The fact that such statements can be made explains why the publication of these data in Japan touched off a controversy as to whether inter-group variations of the type recorded above could be considered as the sign of so many distinct "cultures." Whatever the use of the concept of "protoculture" proposed by some, it seems evident that the data made available by recent Japanese studies should invite anthropologists to rephrase, or at least to refine, some of the current definitions of culture. If we define culture as "the sum total of things that people do as a result of having been so taught," or still as "an organized group of learned responses characteristic of a particular society," there seems to be little or no reason to deny the possession of culture to the natural societies of Japanese monkeys. If, on the other hand, as this writer believes, culture in its proper sense is the exclusive possession of man, then its

definition must be phrased in such a way as to stress characteristics that are proper to human society alone. It seems doubtful that definitions which strongly emphasize such concepts as social heredity, socially acquired response-patterns, learned traditional behavior and the like, can be accepted any longer. The observations made in Japan force upon us the realization that such an item of behavior usually considered as peculiar to man may not in fact be so limited. In human behavior, they help us to distinguish more clearly that which is typically human from that which is common to many other primates. It is this writer's belief that only those definitions of culture will be acceptable that stress the importance of common understandings and of a conceptual interpretation of the world of nature.

By stressing the culture-like characteristics of non-human primate behavior, the studies of Japanese workers also provide some valuable hints concerning one of the major problems that confront modern anthropology: the origin of culture, particularly at the early hominid stage.

Since the end of the Second World War numerous discoveries of fossil early hominids, especially in South and East Africa, have given anthropologists an abundance of material to study and speculate about. Besides fossil bones, increasing evidence regarding environmental conditions and the discovery of early hominid living sites has enabled anthropologists to reconstruct with considerable detail the ecology of the first known representatives of the family of man.

One of the main consequences of these finds has been to encourage anthropologists to think about human evolution along new lines, stressing particularly ecological and behavioral aspects. This new trend in the study of human origins has recently been introduced to the large public by the somewhat journalistic and not always well-inspired book of Ardrey, and by the much more commendable, though also controversial book of Professor Raymond Dart, *Adventures with the Missing Link*. On the scientific level, most significant is the symposium organized in 1961 by the Wenner-Gren Foundation for Anthropological Research on the *Social Life of Early Man*. A number of often quoted articles published in recent years show similar interest for a behavioral and ecological approach which, it will be remembered, was already that used with success by Darwin himself.

The point stressed by this new anthropological approach is that primate evolution in general and hominid evolution in particular consist first of all in the evolution of ways of life. All the evidence collected by the paleontologist, the ecologist or the comparative anatomist becomes meaningful in as much as it tells us something about the behavior of these animals. In order to make this induction possible it is of course of prime importance to know more about the behavior of living primates, especially of those more closely related to man.

The importance and significance of Japanese studies are thus enhanced by the fact that they occur at a time when their potential contribution to the understanding of the hominization process is becoming clear.

A case in point can be seen in the "inventions" reported from the Kōshima colony. These show that non-human primates can adjust their behavior to changed environmental conditions and make prompt use of new opportunities when these are offered. It is most likely that the same situation occurred around the time and in the environments where the hominization process took place. In fact, it is reasonable to assume that primates much more highly evolved than the Japanese macaque would have shown a flexibility of behavior and a readiness to exploit new opportunities much greater than those observed in Kōshima. It will also be noticed, and this may be of extreme importance, that such remarkable ability to adjust to a new environment and make the most of it can exist independently of the capacity to make tools.

The question thereby arises whether the selective advantages due to this inventive adaptability are not sufficient to offset the absence of biological specializations for food-getting, self-defense, etc., even before tool-making has appeared, or at least before it has become an important behavioral item. The importance of this consideration for the discussion of Australopithecine status is evident. It has often been argued that the absence of specializations for self-defense (no sharp canine etc.), together with life in an open habitat, made it imperative for these hominids to be tool-makers, or at least tool-users. The inventive behavior observed in Kōshima makes one wonder whether, espe-

cially when developed at an even greater degree, it could not make possible the survival of defenseless hominids even in the absence of true tool-making. On the other hand, it is also possible to see in this inventive behavior one of the stages that prepared the way to the first elementary making of tools. The willingness to experiment with new ways of doing things would obviously be of the greatest value in leading hominids to habitual tool-using and from there to the discovery of true tool-making.

If material culture is defined as the transformation of nature by man in order to better his living, then the inventive behavior exhibited by Japanese monkeys can probably be considered as an important step in that direction. In this sense the term proto-culture may prove quite useful, indicating a mid-term between the predominantly passive acceptance of the environment and the positive transformation of the same.

In a collection of essays, Professor Umezao, of Osaka Municipal University, has described the kind of research conducted by the members of the Primate Research Group and remarks that the approach used in these studies has something original, not found in similar studies made by Westerners. While most of the research in natural sciences in this country has followed the tracks laid by European and American scientists, research on primate behavior has been conducted with new methods and in a different spirit. Umezao goes on to say that this new approach may well reflect the traditional Japanese way of looking at nature, where the distinction between man and other living things is not stressed nearly as much as in Western culture. In this view of nature the emphasis lies rather on the affinity which all living things have with each other.

Going deeper into this matter may yield some insights on a topic seldom talked about: the cultural anthropology of scientific research. It may also point out in what direction Japanese anthropology can be expected to make some original contributions in the years ahead. Only a few comments, however, can be made in the present article.

One of the most important features of the Japanese approach to the study of monkey behavior is undoubtedly the practice of individual identification of each animal in the group. In order to understand what is going on in a society it is obviously indispensable to be able to identify the individuals that compose it. Only then can their respective roles be ascertained and the interactions of various individuals be observed over longer periods of time. The greatest difficulty in identifying individuals of a large group is that, to the inexperienced observer at least, they all look very much alike. Attempts at identification have, therefore, been made by catching the animals and marking them with a number. Japanese fieldworkers, however, have succeeded in identifying animals without the use of any marking, simply by becoming familiar with the face and the general appearance of each individual. This seems hard to imagine for Western scientists. I remember an American scholar, with a long experience in the study of wild monkey populations, telling me his amazement in finding out that the worker supervising the colony of Takasakiyama (several hundreds strong) knew most adult animals by face. He could have added "by name," for Japanese fieldworkers, after starting to give a number to each animal, soon replaced these by names expressing the particular personality of each individual. Umezao is probably right in seeing in this practice the expression of a feeling of personal attachment for each individual animal and it is equally probable that this feeling contributed largely to the success of the identification process. It can therefore be said that the abundance of valuable details found in monographs written by Japanese workers and the observations on the history of each group are made possible first of all by a quasi-personal acquaintance with all members of one group.

However, for this acquaintance to be made, frequent and prolonged contacts with the group are needed and these contacts, moreover, must take place at a close enough distance to allow individual identification. The difficulty to obtain such frequent contact has been one of the major obstacles in the method of behavioral studies under wild-life conditions. Japanese workers have solved this problem in an original way, by setting up feeding places, as described above. This method is responsible for the collecting of most of their data.

Many foreign scholars seem to have their doubts as to the advisability of the method thus developed by Japanese workers. They feel that interference with the natural environment of animals should be kept to a minimum so as to alter as little as possible the original behavior of the group. Establishing feeding stations, they feel, is likely to seriously disturb wild behavior and therefore tends to make objective observations nearly impossible.

Japanese workers recognize the problem but feel much less compunction about modifying the environment, at least to the limited extent of providing food. It is not impossible, as Umezao suggests, that the feeling of sympathy with the animals which they study makes them consider food provisioning as one element in the mutual relationship which has been established between the observers and the observed. In other words, while the Western scientist tends to regard the animals as objects situated in front of him, somewhat as bacteria under the microscope, his Japanese colleague tends to think in terms of a personal relationship with individuals who have a name and whose life stories are often familiar to him.

Evidence of this personal relationship can be found in the—to Western eyes—most unlikely places. Correcting the English abstract of a paper written by university professors on anatomical variations in a monkey, I was not a little surprised to find that, where Western scientists would have identified the specimen with a number, the writers referred to the monkey by the name the laboratory workers gave him when still alive. I tried to explain to the authors that mentioning the name was not quite usual in a paper on anatomy. To them, obviously, this was quite proper.

Reading the reports published by the Primate Research Group during the last ten years leaves no room for doubt that the unique approach adopted by the Japanese workers has yielded a rich harvest of data so far unavailable. To what extent the originality of their method reflects the feelings of closeness to nature and sympathy with animals characteristic of Japanese culture may be a question open to debate. One thing, however, seems certain: it is enough to have looked at the countenance of fieldworkers observing animals or dealing with them or to have listened to the way they describe their observations in order to realize that most of these people are personally involved in the history of the group which they are studying. Theirs is more than a scientific interest in the common sense of this word. The closest comparison that comes to mind is that with a cultural anthropologist participating in the daily life of the people he wants to understand. To somebody who has had personal contacts with these workers and who is at all familiar with Japanese cultural history there can be little doubt that the intellectual and spiritual tradition of this country constitutes a most favorable environment for the development of the science of non-human primate behavior.

Though there are some unique assets, in this cultural context, the misgivings of many a Western scholar may not be altogether without foundation. For one thing, the existence of quasi-personal relationships between the human observer and the observed animals strongly increases the danger of uncritical anthropomorphism in the interpretation of non-human primate behavior. Many an otherwise sympathetic Western scholar has been shocked by expressions used by the Japanese workers in describing the behavior of the Japanese monkey, expressions which, if taken out of context, would suggest that the writer is rather naive and unsophisticated in his subject.

While recognizing frankly this weakness in some of the writings of Japanese workers one should not lose sight of the fact that a certain amount of anthropomorphism and anthropocentrism cannot be avoided. In the first place, any sort of understanding of the outside world is necessarily reached through the categories of human reason. This is true in a special sense of our attempts to interpret animal behavior, particularly the behavior of animals closely related to us. In most instances the working hypotheses will be suggested by the analogies that this behavior presents to our own human experience. The difficulty consists in distinguishing a necessary from an uncritical anthropomorphism. As Teilhard de Chardin puts it,

Nothing is more ambiguous than the accusation of anthropomorphism. That anthropomorphism is harmful which transfers human properties down to animals or up to God without correction. But there is another sort of anthropomorphism, permissible and unavoidable, which appraises from our standpoint a Universe of which we are part. . . . The whole difficulty consists in making the corrections called by analogy.

In the light of this remark one better discerns perhaps the real weakness in some of the interpretations proposed by the Japanese workers. It lies not so much in their use of anthropomorphic concepts, probably unavoidable, but rather in their failure to perceive clearly the nature of the distinction between human and non-human behavior. A philosopher would say that they have no adequate grasp of the relationship of analogy that both unites and separates the human from the animal world. This is only another way of expressing, negatively, what Umezao observes when he says that the Japanese view of nature sets no clear distinction between man and animals. The lack of such distinction may, by evoking feelings of sympathy with and closeness to the animal world, provide valuable insights for the understanding of non-human behavior. But it also tends to obscure important differences and makes it more difficult to appraise the true originality of non-human and human behavior respectively.

It is interesting to notice that a similar remark has recently been made by a well-known Japanese historian of science commenting upon the adverse influence of the Japanese view of nature on the development of natural sciences in this country. The author points out that a person brought up in such a culture pays attention not to nature itself but rather to the reaction nature evokes in him. The object of his attention is not nature as distinct from man but the fusion and harmony of both. It follows that, where the perception of natural phenomena is so closely bound with one's personal feelings and impressions, it becomes well near impossible to consider these phenomena as particular cases of general and impersonal laws. Poetry will thrive on such ground, but science will wither.

The analysis of Yoshida is valuable in that it shows how a cultural trend can hinder the development of certain intellectual pursuits. It should be read, however, in conjunction with the essay of Umezao pointing out how the same cultural trend can foster a particular type of investigation.

The contributions made by Japanese workers to the science of primate behavior and to physical anthropology thereby provide a striking illustration of the positive and negative influence exerted by a cultural tradition on scientific endeavors. Reading their reports reveals how the feeling of closeness to and affinity with nature can indeed suggest valuable hints in analyzing and interpreting non-human primate behavior, but it also shows that these hints need be checked in a rigorous scientific way to which this attitude towards nature is less congenial.

To the credit of the Japanese primatologists it must be said that the best among them are keenly aware of this necessity. Itani, one of the leading figures of the group, asked one day by Umezao to what he attributed the success of the work accomplished in Japan, pointed to its scientific character. Umezao doubts this and, as was seen above, emphasizes rather the importance of the cultural context. Both he and Itani may be right. Interest and sympathy for animals certainly explain much of the devotion of the workers to their task. On the other hand, Itani rightly points out that it is the scientific character of the Japanese work which made it valuable and attracted world-wide recognition. Failing this, it would not have outgrown the stage of amateur work so often found in the natural history type of books. The work of the Japan Monkey Center is a good instance of a field where a peculiar inclination of the Japanese people gives new inspiration to a natural science and is in turn purified by the Western scientific tradition.

Raising our sights beyond the science of primate behavior and even beyond anthropology, we may see in this particular example an indication of the nature of the contribution which Japan can be expected to make, not only to anthropology, but to our wider understanding of nature in its relation to man. Bringing together the resources of knowledge by intuition and sympathy with the impersonal methods of science into one harmonious understanding is probably one of the major tasks lying ahead of us. Even in the West, more and more voices are being heard calling for a synthesis between personal and scientific knowledge.

Anthropology, connected as it is with so many diverse disciplines, certainly has an important role to play in this unifying process. In a modest but significant degree, the work done by the Japanese primate research group points out one of the ways in which this synthetic understanding of man and nature, and man in nature, can be reached.

*selection  19*

# Social Deprivation in Monkeys

## Harry F. Harlow and Margaret Kuenne Harlow

*From* Scientific American, *Vol. 207, No. 5, 1962, pp. 137–146. Copyright* © *1962, Scientific American, Inc. By permission of the authors, and the publisher and copyright holder.*

In *An Outline of Psychoanalysis*, published posthumously in 1940, Sigmund Freud was able to refer to "the common assertion that the child is psychologically the father of the man and that the events of his first years are of paramount importance for his whole subsequent life." It was, of course, Freud's own historic investigations, begun a half-century before, that first elucidated the role of infantile experiences in the development of the personality and its disorders. The "central experience of this period of childhood," he found, is the infant's relation to his mother. Freud's ideas have now shaped the thinking of two generations of psychologists, psychiatrists and psychoanalysts. Much evidence in support of his deep insights has been accumulated, particularly from clinical studies of the mentally ill. Contemporary writers stress inadequate or inconsistent mothering as a basic cause of later disorders such as withdrawal, hostility, anxiety, sexual maladjustment, alcoholism and, significantly, inadequate maternal behavior!

The evidence from clinical studies for this or any other view of human personality development is qualified, however, by an inherent defect. These studies are necessarily retrospective: they start with the disorder and work backward in time, retracing the experiences of the individual as he and his relatives and associates recall them. Inevitably details are lost or distorted, and the story is often so confounded as to require a generous exercise of intuition on the part of the investigator. Nor does evidence obtained in this manner exclude other possible causes of personality disorder. Against arguments in favor of a biochemical or neurological causation of mental illness, for example, there is no way to show that the patient began life with full potentiality for normal development. Given the decisive influence ascribed to the mother-infant relation, there may be a tendency in the reconstruction of the past to overlook or suppress evidence for the influence of other significant early relations, such as the bonds of interaction with other children. Little attention has been given, in fact, to child-to-child relations in the study of personality development. Yet it can be supposed that these play a significant part in determining the peer relations and the sexual role of the adult. Plainly there is a need to study the development of personality forward in time from infancy. Ideally the study should be conducted under controlled laboratory conditions so that the effects of single variables or combinations of variables can be traced.

Acceding to the moral and physical impossibility of conducting such an investigation

with human subjects, we have been observing the development of social behavior in large numbers of rhesus monkeys at the Primate Laboratory of the University of Wisconsin. Apart from this primate's kinship to man, it offers a reasonable experimental substitute because it undergoes a relatively long period of development analogous to that of the human child and involving intimate attachment to its mother and social interaction with its age-mates. With these animals we have been able to observe the consequences of the deprivation of all social contact for various lengths of time. We have also raised them without mothers but in the company of age-mates and with mothers but without age-mates.

We have thereby been able to make some estimate of the contribution of each of these primary affectional systems to the integrated adult personality. Our observations sustain the significance of the maternal relation, particularly in facilitating the interaction of the infant with other infants. But at the same time we have found compelling evidence that opportunity for infant-infant interaction under optimal conditions may fully compensate for lack of mothering, at least in so far as infant-infant social and heterosexual relations are concerned. It seems possible—even likely—that the infant-mother affectional system is dispensable, whereas the infant-infant system is the *sine qua non* for later adjustment in all spheres of monkey life. In line with the "paramount importance" that Freud assigned to experience in the first years of life, our experiments indicate that there is a critical period somewhere between the third and sixth months of life during which social deprivation, particularly deprivation of the company of its peers, irreversibly blights the animal's capacity for social adjustment.

Our investigations of the emotional development of our subjects grew out of the effort to produce and maintain a colony of sturdy, disease-free young animals for use in various research programs. By separating them from their mothers a few hours after birth and placing them in a more fully controlled regimen of nurture and physical care we were able both to achieve a higher rate of survival and to remove the animals for testing without maternal protest. Only later did we realize that our monkeys were emotionally disturbed as well as sturdy and disease-free. Some of our researches are therefore retrospective. Others are in part exploratory, representing attempts to set up new experimental situations or to find new techniques for measurement. Most are incomplete because investigations of social and behavioral development are long-term. In a sense, they can never end, because the problems of one generation must be traced into the next.

Having separated the infant from its mother, our procedure was to keep it alone in a bare wire cage in a large room with other infants so housed. Thus each little monkey could see and hear others of its kind, although it could not make direct physical contact with them. The 56 animals raised in this manner now range in age from five to eight years. As a group they exhibit abnormalities of behavior rarely seen in animals born in the wild and brought to the laboratory as preadolescents or adolescents, even after the latter have been housed in individual cages for many years. The laboratory-born monkeys sit in their cages and stare fixedly into space, circle their cages in a repetitive stereotype manner and clasp their heads in their hands or arms and rock for long periods of time. They often develop compulsive habits, such as pinching precisely the same patch of skin on the chest between the same fingers hundreds of times a day; occasionally such behavior may become punitive and the animal may chew and tear at its body until it bleeds. Often the approach of a human being becomes the stimulus to self-aggression. This behavior constitutes a complete breakdown and reversal of the normal defensive response; a monkey born in the wild will direct such threats and aggression at the approaching person, not at itself. Similar symptoms of emotional pathology are observed in deprived children in orphanages and in withdrawn adolescents and adults in mental hospitals.

William A. Mason, now at the Yerkes Laboratories of Primate Biology, compared the behavior of six of these animals, which were then two years old and had been housed all their lives in individual cages, with a matched group of rhesus monkeys that had been captured in the wild during their first year of life and house together in captivity for a while before being individually housed in the laboratory. The most striking difference was that all the animals that had been born in the wild—and not one of the laboratory-born animals—displayed normal sex behavior. That the laboratory-born animals were not lacking in sex drive was indicated by the fact that the males frequently approached the females and the females displayed part of the pattern of sexual presentation. But they did not orient themselves correctly and they did not succeed in mating. Moreover, the monkeys born in the wild had apparently learned to live with others in a stable hierarchy of dominance, or "pecking order"; consequently in the pairing test they fought one another less and engaged more often in social grooming. They would also release a companion from a locked cage more frequently than did the laboratory-born animals, which usually ignored their caged partner's plight.

The severity of the affliction that grips these monkeys raised in the partial isolation of individual wire cages has become more apparent as they have grown older. They pay little or no attention to animals in neighboring cages; those caged with companions sit in opposite corners with only rare interaction. No heterosexual behavior has ever been observed between male and female cage-mates, even between those that have lived together for as long as seven years. When efforts have been made to bring about matings, by pairing animals during the female's estrus, they have sometimes fought so viciously that they have had to be parted. Attempts to mate the socially deprived animals with sexually adequate and experienced monkeys from the breeding colony have been similarly frustrated.

In the summer of 1960 we undertook to devise a group-psychotherapy situation for 19 of these animals—nine males and 10 females —by using them to stock the monkey island in the municipal zoo in Madison, Wis. This was their first experience outside the laboratory, and they had much to learn in order to survive. They had to learn to drink water from an open trough instead of from a tube in the wall of a cage, to compete for food in a communal feeding situation, to huddle together or find shelter from inclement weather, to climb rocks and avoid the water surrounding the island. Most difficult of all, they had to learn to live together. Within the first few days they made all the necessary physical adjustments. The three casualties—a male that drowned and two females that were injured, and had to be returned to the laboratory—resulted from the stress of social adjustment. Fighting was severe at first; it decreased as effective dominance relations were established and friendship pairs formed. Grooming appeared in normal style and with almost normal frequency. A limited amount of sex behavior was observed, but it was infantile in form, with inadequate posturing by both females and males. In the hope of promoting therapy along this line we introduced our largest, strongest and most effective breeding-colony male to the island around the middle of summer. He immediately established himself at the head of the dominance order. But in spite of his considerable persistence and patience he did not succeed in starting a single pregnancy.

Back in the laboratory these animals ceased to groom and fought more frequently. In pairings with breeding-colony monkeys, not one male has achieved a normal mount or intromission and only one female has become pregnant. After two years we have had to conclude that the island experience was of no lasting value.

As the effects of the separation of these monkeys from their mothers in infancy were first becoming apparent in 1957 we were prompted to undertake a study of the mother-infant affectional bond. To each of one group of four animals separated from their mothers at birth we furnished a surrogate mother: a welded wire cylindrical form with the nipple of the feeding bottle protruding from its "breast" and with a wooden head surmounting it. The majority of the animals, 60 in all, were raised with cozier surrogate mothers covered by terry cloth. In connection with certain experiments some of these individuals have had both a bare-wire and a cloth-covered mother. The infants developed a strong attachment to the cloth mothers and little or none to the wire mothers, regardless of which one provided milk. In fright-inducing situations the infants showed that they derived a strong sense of security from the presence of their cloth mothers. Even after two years of separation they exhibit a persistent attachment to the effigies.

In almost all other respects, however, the behavior of these monkeys at ages ranging from three to five years is indistinguishable from that of monkeys raised in bare wire cages with no source of contact comfort other than a gauze diaper pad. They are without question socially and sexually aberrant. No normal sex behavior has been observed in the living cages of any of the animals that have been housed with a companion of the opposite sex. In exposure to monkeys from the breeding colony not one male and only one female has shown normal mating behavior and only four females have been successfully impregnated. Compared with the cage-raised monkeys, the surrogate-raised animals seem to be less aggressive, whether toward themselves or other monkeys. But they are also younger on the average, and their better dispositions can be attributed to their lesser age.

Thus the nourishment and contact comfort provided by the nursing cloth-covered mother in infancy does not produce a normal adolescent or adult. The surrogate cannot cradle the baby or communicate monkey sounds and gestures. It cannot punish for misbehavior or attempt to break the infant's bodily attachment before it becomes a fixation. The entire group of animals separated from their mothers at birth and raised in individual wire cages, with or without surrogate, must be written off as potential breeding stock. Apparently their early social deprivation permanently impairs their ability to form effective relations with other monkeys, whether the opportunity was offered to them in the second six months of life or in the second to the fifth year of life.

One may correctly assume that total social isolation, compared with the partial isolation in which these subjects were reared, would produce even more devastating effects on later personality development. Such disastrous effects have been reported in the rare cases of children who have been liberated after months or years of lonely confinement in a darkened room. We have submitted a few monkeys to total isolation. Our purpose was to establish the maximum of social deprivation that would allow survival and also to determine whether or not there is a critical period in which social deprivation may have irreversible effects.

In our first study a male and a female were housed alone from birth for a period of two years, each one in its own cubicle with solid walls. Their behavior could be observed through one-way vision screens and tested by remote control. The animals adapted to solid food slowly, but they had normal weight and good coats when they were removed from the isolation boxes at the end of two years. Throughout this period neither animal had seen any living being other than itself.

They responded to their liberation by the crouching posture with which monkeys typically react to extreme threat. When placed together, each one crouched and made no further response to the other. Paired with younger monkeys from the group raised in partial isolation, they froze or fled when approached and made no effort to defend themselves from aggressive assaults. After another two years, in which they were kept together in a single large cage in the colony room, they showed the same abnormal fear of the sight or sound of other monkeys.

We are now engaged in studying the effects of six months of total social isolation. The first pair of monkeys, both males, has been out of isolation for eight months. They are housed, each monkey in its own cage, in racks with other monkeys of their age that were raised in the partial isolation of individual wire cages. For 20 minutes a day, five days a week they are tested with a pair of these monkeys in the "playroom" of the laboratory. This room we designed to stimulate the young monkeys to a maximum of activity. It was not until the 12th and 27th week respectively that the two totally deprived monkeys began to move and climb about. They now circulate freely but not as actively as the control animals. Although frequently attacked by the controls, neither one has attempted to defend itself or fight back; they either accept abuse or flee. One must be characterized as extremely disturbed and almost devoid of social behavior. The other resembles a normal two-month-old rhesus infant in its play and social behavior, and the indications are that it will never be able to make mature contacts with its peers.

A considerably more hopeful prognosis is indicated for two groups of four monkeys raised in total isolation for the much shorter period of 80 days. In their cubicles these animals had the contact comfort of a cloth-covered surrogate. They were deficient in social behavior during the first test periods in the playroom. But they made rapid gains; now, eight months later, we rate them as "almost normal" in play, defense and sex behavior. At least seven of the eight seem to bear no permanent scars as the result of early isolation.

Our first few experiments in the total isolation of these animals would thus appear to have bracketed what may be the critical period of development during which social experience is necessary for normal behavior in later life. We have additional experiments in progress, involving a second pair that will have been isolated for six months and a first pair that will have been isolated for a full year. The indications are that six months of isolation will render the animals permanently inadequate. Since the rhesus monkey is more mature than the human infant at birth and grows four times more rapidly, this is equivalent to two or three years for the human child. On the other hand, there is reason to believe that the effects of shorter periods of early isolation, perhaps 60 to 90 days or even more, are clearly reversible. This would be equivalent to about six months in the development of the human infant. The time probably varies with the individual and with the experiences to which it is exposed once it is removed from isolation. Beyond a brief period of neonatal grace, however, the evidence suggests that every additional week or month of social deprivation increasingly imperils social development in the rhesus monkey. Case studies of children reared in impersonal institutions or in homes with indifferent mothers or nurses show a frightening comparability. The child may remain relatively unharmed through the first six months of life. But from this time on the damage is progressive and cumulative. By one year of age he may sustain enduring emotional scars and by two years many children have reached the point of no return.

In all of these experiments in partial and total isolation, whether unwitting or deliberate, our animals were deprived of the company of their peers as well as of their mothers. We accordingly undertook a series of experiments designed to distinguish and compare the roles of mother-infant and infant-infant relations in the maturation of rhesus monkey behavior. Our most privileged subjects are two groups of four monkeys each, now two years old, that were raised with their mothers during the first 18 and 21 months respectively and with peers from the first weeks. Each mother-infant pair occupied a large cage that gave the infant access to one cell of a four-unit playpen. By removing the screens between the playpens we enabled the infants to play together in pairs or as foursomes during scheduled observation periods each day. In parallel with these two groups we raised another group of four in a playpen setup without their mothers but with a terry cloth surrogate in each home cage.

From the time the mothers let them leave their home cages, after 20 or 30 days, the mothered infants entered into more lively and consistent relations with one another than did the four motherless ones. Their behavior evolved more rapidly through the sequence of increasingly complex play patterns that reflects the maturation and learning of the infant monkey and is observed in a community of normal infants. The older they grew and the more complex the play patterns became, the greater became the observable difference between the mothered and the motherless monkeys. Now, at the end of the second year, the 12 animals are living together in one playpen setup, with each original group occupying one living cage and its adjoining playpen. All are observed in daily interaction without the dividing panels. The early differences between them have all but disappeared. Seven of the eight mothered animals engage in normal sexual activity and assume correct posture. The deviant is a male, and this animal was the social reject in its all-male group of four. Of the two motherless males, one has recently achieved full adult sexual posture and the other is approaching it. The two motherless females appear normal, but it remains to be seen whether or not their maternal behavior will reflect their lack of mothering.

Observation of infants with their mothers suggests reasons for the differences in the early social and sexual behavior of these playpen groups. From early in life on the infant monkey shows a strong tendency to imitate its mother; this responding to another monkey's behavior carries over to interaction with its peers. It is apparent also that sexual activity is stimulated by the mother's grooming of the infant. Finally, as the mother begins

occasionally to reject its offspring in the third or fourth month, the infant is propelled into closer relations with its peers. These observations underlie the self-evident fact that the mother-infant relation plays a positive role in the normal development of the infant-infant and heterosexual relations of the young monkey.

That the mother-infant relation can also play a disruptive role was demonstrated in another experiment. Four females that had been raised in the partial isolation of individual wire cages—and successfully impregnated in spite of the inadequacy of their sexual behavior—delivered infants within three weeks of one another. This made it possible to set up a playpen group composed of these "motherless" mothers and their infants. The maternal behavior of all four mothers was completely abnormal, ranging from indifference to outright abuse. Whereas it usually requires more than one person to separate an infant from its mother, these mothers paid no attention when their infants were removed from the cages for the hand-feeding necessitated by the mothers' refusal to nurse. Two of the mothers did eventually permit fairly frequent nursing, but their apparently closer maternal relations were accompanied by more violent abuse. The infants were persistent in seeking contact with their mothers and climbed on their backs when they were repulsed at the breast. In play with one another during the first six months, the infants were close to the normally mothered animals in maturity of play, but they played less. In sexual activity, however, they were far more precocious. During the eight months since they have been separated from their mothers, they have exhibited more aggression and day-to-day variability in their behavior than have the members of other playpen groups. The two male offspring of the most abusive mothers have become disinterested in the female and occupy the subordinate position in all activities.

More study of more babies from motherless mothers is needed to determine whether or not the interrelations that characterize this pilot group will characterize others of the same composition. There is no question about the motherless mothers themselves. The aberration of their maternal behavior would have ensured the early demise of their infants outside the laboratory. As for the infants, the extremes of sexuality and aggressiveness observed in their behavior evoke all too vivid parallels in the behavior of disturbed human children and adolescents in psychiatric clinics and institutions for delinquents.

Another pilot experiment has shown that even normal mothering is not enough to produce socially adequate offspring. We isolated two infants in the exclusive company of their mothers to the age of seven months and then brought the mother-infant pairs together in a playpen unit. The female infant took full advantage of the play apparatus provided, but in three months the male was never seen to leave its home cage, and its mother would not permit the female to come within arm's reach. Social interaction of the infants was limited to an occasional exchange of tentative threats. For the past two months they have been separated from their mothers, housed in individual cages and brought together in the playroom for 15 minutes each day. In this normally stimulating environment they have so far shown no disposition to play together. Next to the infants that have been raised in total isolation, these are the most retarded of the infants tested in the playroom.

It is to the play-exciting stimulus of the playroom that we owe the unexpected outcome of our most suggestive experiment. The room is a relatively spacious one, with an eight-foot ceiling and 40 square feet of floor space. It is equipped with movable and stationary toys and a wealth of climbing devices, including an artificial tree, a ladder and a burlap-covered climbing ramp that leads to a platform. Our purpose in constructing the playroom was to provide the monkeys with opportunities to move about in the three-dimensional world to which, as arboreal animals, they are much more highly adapted than man. To assess the effects of different histories of early social experience we customarily turn the animals loose in the room in groups of four for regularly scheduled periods of observation each day.

The opportunities afforded by the playroom were most fully exploited by two groups of four infants that otherwise spent their days housed alone in their cages with a cloth surrogate. In terms of "mothering," therefore, these monkeys were most closely comparable to the four that were raised with surrogates in the playpen situation. These animals were released in the playroom for 20 minutes a day from the first month of life through the 11th, in the case of one group, and through the second year in the case of the other. In contrast with all the other groups observed in the playroom, therefore, they did their "growing up" in this environment. Even though their exposure to the room and to one another was limited to 20 minutes a day, they enacted with great spirit the entire growth pattern of rhesus-monkey play behavior.

They began by exploring the room and each other. Gradually over the next two or three months they developed a game of rough-and-tumble play, with jumping, scuffling, wrestling, hair-pulling and a little nipping, but with no real damage, and then an associated game of flight and pursuit in which the participants are alternately the threateners and the threatened. While these group activities evolved, so did the capacity for individual play exploits, with the animals running, leaping, swinging and climbing, heedless of one another and apparently caught up in the sheer joy of action. As their skill and strength grew, their social play involved shorter but brisker episodes of free-for-all action, with longer chases between bouts. Subsequently they developed an even more complex pattern of violent activity, performed with blinding speed and integrating all objects, animate and inanimate, in the room. Along with social play, and possibly as a result or by-product, they began to exhibit sexual posturing—immature and fleeting in the first six months and more frequent and adult in form by the end of the year. The differences in play activity that distinguish males and females became evident in the first two or three months, with the females threatening and initiating rough contact far less frequently than the males and withdrawing from threats and approaches far more frequently.

Thus in spite of the relatively limited opportunity for contact afforded by their daily schedule, all the individuals in these two groups developed effective infant-infant play relations. Those observed into the second year have shown the full repertory of adult sexual behavior. At the same chronological age these motherless monkeys have attained as full a maturity in these respects as the infants raised with their mothers in the playpen.

Another group of four motherless animals raised together in a single large cage from the age of two weeks is yielding similar evidence of the effectiveness of the infant-infant affectional bond. During their first two months these animals spent much of their time clinging together, each animal clutching the back of the one just ahead of it in "choo-choo" fashion. They moved about as a group of three or four; when one of them broke away, it was soon clutched by another to form the nucleus of a new line. In the playroom the choo-choo linkage gave way to individual exploratory expeditions. During periods of observation, whether in their home cage or in the playroom, these animals have consistently scored lower in play activity than the most playful groups. We think this is explained, however, by the fact that they are able to spread their play over a 24-hour period. At the age of one year they live amicably together. In sex behavior they are more mature than the mother-raised playpen babies. No member of the group shows any sign of damage by mother-deprivation.

Our observations of the three groups of motherless infants raised in close association with one another therefore indicate that opportunity for optimal infant-infant interaction may compensate for lack of mothering. This is true at least in so far as infant-infant and sexual relations are concerned. Whether or not maternal behavior or later social adjustment will be affected remains to be seen.

Of course research on nonhuman animals, even monkeys, will never resolve the baffling complex roles of various kinds of early experience in the development of human personality. It is clear, however, that important theoretical and practical questions in this realm of interest can be resolved by the use of monkeys. The close behavioral resemblance of our disturbed infants to disturbed human beings gives us the confidence that we are working with significant variables and the hope that we can point the way to reducing the toll of psychosocial trauma in human society.

# A Comparison of the Ecology and Behavior of Monkeys and Apes

*Irven DeVore*

*From Classification and Human Evolution.* Viking Fund Publications in Anthropology, *No. 7, pp. 301–319. Copyright* © *1963, Wenner-Gren Foundation for Anthropological Research, later transferred to Aldine Publishing Company. By permission of the author, the publisher, and the copyright holder.*

Comparisons of nonhuman primates have traditionally contrasted the behavior patterns of New World and Old World monkeys. The Platyrrhines of the New World are said to live in loosely organized social groups in which individuals are rarely aggressive and dominance behavior almost absent. The social group of the Old World Catarrhines is described as more rigidly organized by social hierarchies, based on dominance-oriented behavior and frequent fighting among adult males. To the extent that this distinction is valid, the behavioral differences being compared are not those between New and Old World monkeys, but between arboreal and terrestrial species. The only systematic field studies of New World monkeys have been on the howler monkey, *Alouatta palliata,* and Carpenter's brief observations on spider monkeys, *Ateles geoffroyi.* Both of these species are highly specialized, morphologically and behaviorally, for living in the tall trees of the South American jungle. They are seldom seen in the lower branches of trees and almost never come to the ground. On the other hand, behavioral studies of Old World monkeys, principally those of Zuckerman and Carpenter, had until recently included only species in the baboon-macaque group. In both morphology and behavior the baboon-macaques are more terrestrially adapted than any other monkey or ape.

Comparisons between monkey and ape behavior have also been difficult, since Carpenter's gibbon study is the only long term study of an ape that has previously been available. This Asiatic brachiator is as highly specialized

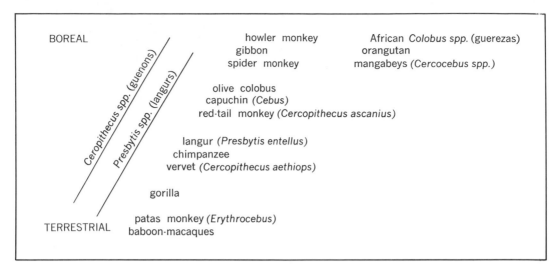

BOREAL

howler monkey
gibbon
spider monkey

African *Colobus spp.* (guerezas)
orangutan
mangabeys (*Cercocebus spp.*)

*Ceropithecus spp.* (guenons)

*Presbytis spp.* (langurs)

olive colobus
capuchin (*Cebus*)
red-tail monkey (*Cercopithecus ascanius*)

langur (*Presbytis entellus*)
chimpanzee
vervet (*Cercopithecus aethiops*)

gorilla

patas monkey (*Erythrocebus*)
baboon-macaques

TERRESTRIAL

**Figure 1** Schematic representation of selected species of monkeys and apes along a continuum of relative adaptation to terrestrial or arboreal life.

for arboreal life as the baboon-macaques are for life on the ground. If the monkeys and apes are arranged along a continuum with those that are terrestrially adapted at one pole and those with specialized arboreal adaptations at the other (Fig. 1), it is clear that long-term naturalistic observations have been confined almost entirely to species lying at the two extremes and that little has been known of the majority of species falling somewhere in between. The species shown in Figure 1 are those for which some field data are available, and the intention is to suggest only the broad outlines of adaptation to life on the ground or in the trees.

Napier has discussed the habitats of monkeys in detail. In brief, spider monkeys, howler monkeys, gibbons, orangutans, and most species of colobus and mangabeys live in the higher levels of mature, tropical forests. The olive colobus lives by preference in the lower forest level, seldom higher than twenty feet from the ground, yet not descending to the ground; South American capuchin and African red-tail monkeys, though primarily tree dwellers, may also come to the ground to feed. Langurs, vervets, *Cercopithecus l'hoesti*, and chimpanzees seem equally at home on the ground or in trees; and gorillas, patas monkeys, baboons, and macaques are clearly adapted to terrestrial life. Field studies of non-human primates are expanding at a rapid rate,

with more than fifty workers currently engaged in field research, and in a few years it will be possible to refine greatly the provisional conclusions discussed here. In the following pages the available evidence on home range, intergroup relations, population density, and social behavior is reviewed with respect to adaptation and taxonomy.

## Home Range

The size of the area which an organized group of animals customarily occupies, its "home range," varies widely among the primates. Current studies have revealed a high correlation between the size of home range and the degree to which a species is adapted to life on the ground—the more terrestrial the species, the larger its home range (Table 1). Arboreal gibbons occupy a range of only about one tenth of a square mile, and a group of howler monkeys range over about one half of a square mile or less of forest. Since the average gibbon group numbers only four and howler groups average about seventeen, the amount of range needed to support an equivalent amount of body weight in each species is comparable. These home ranges are small, however, by comparison to the home ranges of langur groups, *Presbytis entellus*, studied by Jay (unpub. ms.). Langurs, which frequently feed on the forest floor and raid open fields,

*Table 1 Summary of Available Data on Group Size, Population Density, and Home Range for Monkeys, Apes, Wolves, and Human Hunting Groups Living in Relatively Arid, Open Country*

| species | groups mean | groups extreme | sample population | sample no. of groups | population density, indiv. per sq. mile | group range, sq. miles | source |
|---|---|---|---|---|---|---|---|
| Orangutan | 3 | 2–5 | 28 | 10 | | | Schaller 1961 |
| Gibbon | 4 | 2–6 | 93 | 21 | 11 | .1 | Carpenter 1940 |
| Black & white colobus | 13 | | | 1 | | .06 | Ullrich 1961 |
| Olive colobus | 12 | 6–20 | | | | | Booth 1957 |
| Spider | 12 | 3–17 | 181 | 19 | | | Carpenter 1935 |
| *Cebidae* | 15? | 5–30 | | | | | Carpenter 1958 |
| Howler | | | | | | | |
|   1933 census | 17 | 4–35 | 489 | 28 | 82 | .5 | Carpenter 1934 |
|   1951 census | 8 | 2–17 | 239 | 30 | 40 | | Collias & Southwick 1952 |
|   1959 census | 18.5 | 3–45 | 814 | 44 | 136 | | Carpenter 1962 |
| Langur | 25 | 5–120 | 665 | 29 | 12 | 3 | Jay Unpub. Ms. |
| Mountain gorilla (Virunga Volcanoes) | 17 | 5–30 | 169 | 10 | 3 | 10–15 | Schaller 1963 |
| *Macaca mulata* | | | | | | | |
|   temples | 42 | 16–78 | 629 | 15 | | | Southwick 1961a |
|   forest | 50+ | 32–68 | 334 | 7 | | | Southwick 1961b |
| *M. radiata* | 32 | | 65 | 2 | | | Nolte 1955 |
| *M. assamensis* | 19 | | 38 | 2 | | | Carpenter 1958 |
| Baboon | | | | | | | |
|   Nairobi Park | 42 | 12–87 | 374 | 9 | 10 | 15 | DeVore & Washburn |
|   Amboseli | 80 | 13–185 | 1203 | 15 | | | (in press) |
| Human | | | | | | | Shapera 1930; D. |
|   bushman | 20 | | | | .03 | 440–1250 | Clark pers. comm. |
|   aborigine | 35 | | | | .08 | 100–750 | Steward 1936 |
| Wolf | 12 | 9–25+ | | | | 260–1900 | Stebler 1944; Murie 1944 |

range over an average area of three square miles in a year—even though their average group size (twenty-five) is much the same as howler monkeys.

Terrestrial species like the mountain gorilla and the baboon occupy much larger home ranges. Schaller and Emlen found that gorillas in the Virunga Volcanoes region of Albert National Park, Congo, have an average group size of seventeen, and customarily travel over an area of from ten to fifteen square miles during a year. An average troop of forty baboons, living on the East African savanna in the Royal Nairobi National Park, covers an area of about fifteen square miles during a year. In general, it is clear that a terrestrial adaptation implies a larger annual range; a baboon troop's range is 150 times as large as that of a gibbon group. Even if these figures are corrected to allow for the greater combined body weight of the individuals in a baboon troop, the baboon home range is still at least five times as large as that of gibbons. It is frequently stated that the habitat of arboreal monkeys is actually three-dimensional, and that a vertical dimension must be added to horizontal distances traveled before the true size of a group's range can be accurately determined. Many arboreal species, however, seldom come to the ground, or even to the lower levels of the forest. Howler monkeys are largely confined to the upper levels of primary forest, avoiding secondary growth and scrub forest; gibbons ordinarily stay just beneath the uppermost forest canopy; and most species of African colobus monkeys appear to stay above the shrub layer of primary forest. Limited to arboreal pathways through the forest, such species are far less free to exploit an area completely than are primates that do not hesitate to descend to the ground. In effect these arboreal species occupy a two-dimensional area above the forest floor. Some species which exploit both the arboreal and terrestrial areas of their range with facility, such as South American capuchin monkeys, Indian langurs, some African *Cercopithecus spp.*, and probably chimpanzees, may be accurately described as living in a "three-dimensional range." Even terrestrial species such as baboons and macaques spend much of their lives in trees, returning to them to sleep each evening and feeding frequently in them at certain seasons.

The ability to exploit both forested and open savanna habitats has had distinct advantages for the baboon-macaque group, enabling it to spread throughout the Old World tropics with very little speciation. Similarly, the most ground-living Indian langur, *Presbytis entellus*, and the most ground-living *Cercopithecus* monkey, *C. aethiops*, have wider distributions than the other species in their respective genera. In this sense the home range of an organized group of monkeys can be said to be proportional to the geographic distribution of the species. However, this is not always true. The gelada baboon, *Theropithecus gelada*, and the gorilla are geographically restricted, while the gibbon is found throughout Southern Asia. Adaptation of the species to local conditions, the interference of human activities, and competition from other species may explain these contrary examples. Even so, the terrestrial gorilla represents a single, widely separated species while gibbons are divided into a number of well-defined species.

The ability to cross natural barriers and occupy a diversity of environments is reflected in both the size of a group's home range and the amount of speciation that has occurred within its geographic range. This is particularly true when man is considered with the other primates. Speech, tools, and an emphasis on hunting have so altered man's adaptation that direct comparisons are difficult, but if hunter-gatherers living in savanna country with a stone-age technology are selected for comparison, an immense increase in the size of the home range is apparent. Although detailed studies are lacking, the home ranges of two African bushman groups were estimated as 440 and 1250 square miles. An average bushman band would number only about 20, or half the size of a baboon troop with a home range of 15 square miles. In Australia, depending on the food resources in a particular area, a band of aborigines has a home range of between 100 and 750 square miles; an average band numbers about 35. Many hunter-gatherer ranges average 100 to 150 square miles, and even the smallest are much larger than the biggest home ranges described for non-human primates. The land area it is necessary for human hunters to control is more comparable to that of group-living predators than it is to that of monkeys and apes. The home range of wolf packs, for example, is between 260 and 1900 square miles. Consistent hunting rapidly depletes the available game in a small area, and in the course of human evolution an immense increase in the size of home range would have had to develop concomitantly with the development of hunting.

## Core Area and Territoriality

Within the home range of some animal groups is a locus of intensive occupation, or several such loci separated from each other by areas that are infrequently traversed. These loci, which have been called "core areas," are connected by traditional pathways. A core area for a baboon or langur troop, for example, includes sleeping trees, water, refuge sites, and food sources. Troops of baboons or langurs concentrate their activities in one core area for several days or weeks, then shift to another. Most of a baboon troop's home range is seldom entered except during troop movement from one of these core areas to another; a troop in Nairobi Park with a home range of just over fifteen square miles primarily occupied only three core areas whose combined size was only three square miles. Except that baboon range and core areas are larger, this description would apply equally well to langurs or, for that matter, to the coati groups, *Nasua narica*, studied by Kaufmann.

The home ranges of neighboring baboon troops overlap extensively, but the *core areas* of a troop very rarely overlap with those of another troop. The distinction between a group's home range and the core areas within that range becomes important when the question of territorial defense is considered. Carpenter's review of territoriality in vetebrates concludes that ". . . on the basis of available data territoriality is as characteristic of primates' behavior as it is of other vertebrates." His description of "territory" in another review, however, confirms to what has here been described as "home range," following the distinction between "home range" and "territory" (as a defended part of the home range) made by Burt and others. Groups of baboons, langurs, and gorillas are frequently in intimate contact with neighboring groups of the same species; yet intergroup aggression was not observed in langurs, tension between baboon troops is rare, and gorilla males only occasionally show aggression toward a strange group. Clearly, no definite areal boundaries are defended against groups of conspecifics in these three species. On the other hand, organized groups of these species occupy distinct home ranges, and the fact that a strange baboon troop, for example, is rarely in the core area of another troop indicates that there are spacing mechanisms which ordinarily separate organized groups from each other. Different groups are kept apart, however, not so much by overt aggression and fighting at territorial boundaries, as by the daily routine of a monkey group in its own range, by the rigid social boundaries of organized groups in many monkey species, and, in some species, by loud vocalizations.

Intimate knowledge of the area encompassed in a group's home range is demonstrably advantageous to the group's survival. Knowledge of escape routes from predators, safe refuge sites and sleeping trees, and potential food sources combine to channel a group's activities into daily routines and seasonally patterned movements within a circumscribed area. Beyond the limits of a group's usual range lie unknown dangers and undiscovered food sources, and a baboon troop at the edge of its home range is nervous and ill at ease.

## Organization of Primate Groups

In addition to the spacing effect of relatively discrete home ranges, most monkeys and some apes live in organized groups which do not easily admit strangers. Gibbons, howler monkeys, langurs, baboons, and macaques all live in such "closed societies." Although Carpenter described numerous instances of individuals moving from one group to another in his study of the rhesus colony transplanted to Cayo Santiago, Altmann's later study revealed that almost no individuals changed troops during a two-year period. In retrospect it seems likely that when Carpenter first studied the rhesus colony the six heterosexual groups he described were composed of comparative strangers, and that organized troops had not yet had a chance to stabilize. During Altmann's study approximately the same number of animals were divided into two highly stable troops with almost no individuals' changing troop membership—despite the crowded conditions on the island, where natural spacing mechanisms probably could not operate normally.

Studies by the Japan Monkey Center on Japanese macaques, *Macaca fuscata*, confirm the fact that macaque societies are closed groups. During more than 1400 hours of observations on more than twenty-five baboon troops, only two individuals changed to new troops. Jay found that langur troops were similarly conservative, but among langurs individual males or small groups of males may live apart from organized troops. Not all monkey and ape groups have such impermeable social boundaries. Some gorilla groups, for example, can be described as somewhat open or "fluid."

Although different gorilla groups vary considerably in the extent to which they accept individuals into the group, some of them have a high turn-over of adult males. During a twelve-month study period, some dominant adult males remained with a group of females and young throughout, but other adult males frequently left one group, and either led a solitary existence or joined another group. Males who join a group have access to sexually receptive females, and group-living males usually make little or no attempt to repel them. This "relaxed attitude" toward nongroup members is reflected in intergroup relations. Schaller and Emlen report that "seven different groups were seen in one small section of forest during the period of study." In contrast, it is doubtful if any adult male baboon or macaque can join a new troop without some fighting with the dominant males of the troop.

At present there are not enough detailed studies of the social behavior of monkeys and apes to determine whether organized groups in most species are relatively closed, as in baboons, or relatively open, as in gorillas. A recent study of hamadryas baboons in Ethiopia by Kummer and Kurt, for example, revealed an altogether different kind of group structure. The hamadryas were organized into small groups of from one to four, rarely as many as nine, females and their offspring accompanying only one adult male. These "one-male groups" aggregated into sleeping parties each night which numbered as many as 750 individuals, but during the day the small, one-male units foraged independently, and membership in them remained constant during the observation period, while the number of individuals gathering at sleeping places fluctuated constantly. Kortlandt's observations of chimpanzees indicate still a different group structure, with anywhere from one to thirty individuals gathered together at one time.

### Intergroup Vocalizations

Loud vocalizations seem to aid in spacing groups of some species. Carpenter has suggested that "vocal battles" often substitute for physical aggression in howler monkeys and gibbons. Jay found that langurs also give resounding "whoops" which carry long distances and tend to keep langur troops apart; Ullrich found the same is true of black and white colobus. Since these loud cries invariably begin at dawn, when no other group is in sight, and often continue as the group leaves its sleeping place and moves to a feeding area, it seems likely that such vocalizations serve more often to identify the *location* of the troop than to issue a challenge to neighboring troops. Altmann's following observations of howling monkeys support this view:

The morning roar, despite, its spectacular auditory aspects, was not accompanied by any comparable burst of physical activity. While giving the vocalization, the male stood on four feet or sat. Occasionally, he fed between roars . . . The vocalizations that are given by the males at sunrise are essentially the same as those that are given during territorial disputes, suggesting that these morning howls serve as a "proclamation" of an occupied area.

By advertising its position the troop reduces the likelihood that it will meet a neighboring troop. Such location cries can thereby function as spacing mechanisms, but usually without the directly combative connotation which "vocal battle" suggests. When a gibbon or howler group approaches another group, loud vocalizations increase. Two groups of gibbons, however, will mingle without aggression after the period of vocalizing has passed, and Jay saw langur troops frequently come together without aggression.

Loud vocalizations of the sort found in gibbons, howlers, colobus and langurs are conspicuously absent in baboons and macaques. The situation on the African savanna, where visibility frequently extends for hundreds or even thousands of yards, is very different from the very limited visibility of dense forests. Baboon ranges are large in Nairobi Park, and troops seldom come near each other. Adjustments in the direction of troop movement can easily be made by sight alone. Even when baboon troops do come together, as they frequently did in that part of the Amboseli Reserve where food and water sources were restricted, no intergroup aggression was observed. In view of the relatively high degree of dominant and aggressive behavior typical of baboons, the fact that intertroop relations are pacific may seem contradictory. If defense of territory is not thought of as fundamental in the behavior pattern of primates, however, the peaceful coexistence of neighboring troops is not inconsistent with a high level of agonistic and dominance behavior between individuals within the group.

Loud vocalizations, as a means of keeping groups apart when they are not in visual contact, are also absent in the gorilla. When two groups come together, or in the presence of man, adult males may give dramatic intimidation gestures (abrupt charges, chest beating, etc.) While some of these gestures may be accompanied by loud vocalizations, their impact is primarily visual. As in the baboons and macaques, visual communication tends to substitute for loud vocalizations, and it is suggested that methods of intergroup communication correlate with the degree to which a species is arboreal or terrestrial. Vocal expression as a spacing mechanism is very important in gibbons and howler monkeys, less important among langurs, and virtually absent in the gorilla, the baboons, and the macaques. It is also reasonable to suppose that vocalizations are more important in intra-group behavior in arboreal species, where foliage interferes with coordination of group activity, than they ordinarily are in terrestrial species. Baboon studies to date have concentrated on troops living in open areas, where troop members are usually in constant visual contact. If baboons become separated from the troop, however, contact is reestablished by vocalizations, and when the troop is feeding in dense vegetation soft vocalizations (e.g., low grunting) are apparently more frequent, and may serve to maintain contact between troop members. Many baboons live in forests and a study of these forest-living baboons could definitely determine whether vocal behavior is more frequent in this habitat than it is on the open plains.

## Population Density

Pitelka has pointed out that the fundamental importance of territoriality lies not in the behavior, such as overt defense, by which an area becomes identified with an individual or group, but in the degree to which the area is used exclusively; that is, functionally, a territory is primarily an ecological, not a behavioral, phenomenon. Recent field studies indicate that if territoriality can be ascribed to most monkeys and apes it is in this more general, functional meaning of the term only. As a means of distributing the population in an available habitat, the core area of a nonhuman primate group's home range may serve the same function as literal, territorial defense does in some vertebrate species. At the human, hunter-gatherer level this is much less true. Although a hunting band may have core areas, around water holes for example, the band tends to consider most or all of its home range an exclusive possession. Human hunting activities require the use of large areas, and the hunting range is usually protected

from unwarranted use by strangers. One of the important differences between home ranges which overlap and the exclusive possession of a range is reflected in the population density of the species. Although a howler monkey group ranges over about .5 of a square mile, the 28 troops counted in 1933 could not have exclusively possessed more than an average of .2 of a square mile per group; in 1959 the average per group could have been no higher than .136 of a square mile. In Kenya, about 50 per cent of a baboon troop's home range overlaps with that of adjacent troops, and a troop would seldom possess more than one square mile of its range exclusively. One result of this extensive overlapping is that the population density of the nonhuman primates is far higher than would be expected from a description of home range sizes alone (Table 1).

The population density of howler monkeys on Barro Colorado Island in 1959 was 136 individuals per square mile. Terrestrial species like baboons and gorillas have much lower population densities (10 and 3 per square mile), but they are nevertheless far more densely populated than many hunter-gatherers, who average only .03 to .08 per square mile in savanna country. That hunting man, like other large, group-living carnivores, will inevitably have a lower population density than the other primates can be illustrated by the numbers of lions in Nairobi Park. This area of approximately 40 square miles supports a baboon population of nearly 400, but it supports an average of only 14 lions (extremes: 4–30—i.e., 4 to 30 lions).

In summary, all monkeys studied to date live in organized groups whose membership is conservative and from which strangers are repelled. These groups occupy home ranges which may overlap extensively with those of neighboring groups, but which contain core areas where neighboring groups seldom penetrate. Rather than territorial defense of definite boundaries, monkey groups are spaced by daily routine, tradition, membership in a discrete social group, and the location of adjacent groups. Among the apes these same generalizations would seem to hold for gibbons, but they are much less true of gorillas, and, probably, orangutans and chimpanzees. The trend toward increasing size of the home range, however, from the very small range of arboreal species to moderately large ranges in terrestrial species, would appear to be true of all monkeys and apes. Means of identifying the position of adjacent groups shifts from loud vocalizations in arboreal species to visual signals in terrestrial ones. Man exemplifies his terrestrial adaptation in his enormously increased home range, his lower population density, and in his reliance on vision in the identification of neighboring groups.

### Group Size

Mention has already been made of the average size of the social group in several species of primates; available data on group size are summarized in Table 1. When the size of the social group is compared to the degree of arboreal or terrestrial adaptation of the species, a trend toward larger groups in the terrestial species is apparent, in both Old and New World monkeys and among the apes. Although there are no adequate data for the orangutan, the largest group ever reported is five, and the average size of a gibbon troop is four. Schaller found that the average gorilla group was seventeen, temporarily as large as thirty, and Kortlandt saw as many as thirty chimpanzees together in his study area. The average size of monkey troops varies from 20 or less in the olive colobus, spider, howler, and *Cebidae* group to an average of 25 (but as large as 120) in langurs, and an average of from 40 to 80 in the baboons and macaques (with some troops as large as 200). Present observations suggest three central grouping tendencies in monkeys and apes: five or less for the gibbon and orangutan; from twelve to twenty in arboreal monkeys and the gorilla; and fifty or more in baboons and macaques. This small sample may be misleading, but it is clear at present that, in addition to having a larger home range and lower population density, terrestrial monkeys and apes live in larger organized groups.

### Sexual Dimorphism and Dominance

Field studies of monkeys indicate that dominance behavior, especially of the adult male, is both more frequent and more intense in ground-living monkeys than in other species. This increase in dominance behavior is accompanied by an increase in sexual dimor-

phism, particularly in those morphological features which equip the adult male for effective fighting—larger body size, heavier temporal muscles, larger canine teeth, etc. If the apes are compared with respect to sexual dimorphism, there is a clear trend toward increasing sexual dimorphism from the arboreal gibbon, where the sexes are practically indistinguishable, to the chimpanzee, in which the male is appreciably more robust, to the gorilla, where sexual dimorphism is greatest. Only the orangutan is an exception. The trend toward increased sexual dimorphism in terrestrial species of monkeys is also apparent. Some male characteristics, such as the hyoid bone in howler monkeys and the nose of the proboscis monkey, are more pronounced in arboreal species, but morphological adaptations for *fighting* and *defense* are clearly correlated with adaptation to the ground. The various baboons and macaques all illustrate this tendency. Among *Cercopithecus* species sexual dimorphism is pronounced in *C. aethiops* and the patas monkey (a species closely related to *Cercopithecus*) and decreases in the more arboreal forms.

The trend toward increased fighting ability in the male of terrestrial species is primarily an adaptation for defense of the group. Zuckerman's account of baboon behavior would indicate that the acquisition and defense of "harems," and concomitant fighting among the males, places a high premium on aggressiveness and fighting ability in intragroup behavior. Behavioral observations on confined animals can be very misleading, however, and no field study of baboons has found that sexual jealousy or fighting is frequent in free-ranging troops. Observations of many baboon troops in close association indicate that intertroop aggression is very rare and that males do not try to defend an area from encroachment by another troop (although baboons were seen trying to keep vervet monkeys away from a fruit tree). The fact that hundreds of hamadryas may gather at one sleeping site would indicate that interindividual tolerance is high in this baboon species as well. The intergroup fighting of rhesus which Carpenter observed on Cayo Santiago was probably aggravated by unsettled conditions on the island. One index of these conditions is that more infants were killed than were born during his period of study.

Life on the ground exposes a species to

far more predators than does life in the trees. Not only are there fewer potential predators in the trees, but also escape is relatively easy. By going beneath the canopy (to escape raptorial birds) or moving across small branches to an adjacent tree (to escape from felines), arboreal species can easily avoid most predators except man. The ultimate safety of all nonhuman primates is in trees, and even the ground-living baboons and macaques will take refuge in trees or on cliffs at the approach of a predator (except man, from whom they escape by running).

Much of the day, however, baboons may be as far as a mile from safe refuge, and on the open plains a troop's only protection is the fighting ability of its adult males. The structure of the baboon troop, particularly when the animals are moving across an open area, surrounds the weaker females and juveniles with adult males. At the approach of a predator, the adult males are quickly interposed between the troop and the source of danger. The structure of a Japanese macaque troop is apparently identical, even though no predators have threatened the Takasakiyama group in many years. The ecological basis for sexual dimorphism in baboons has been described elsewhere. Because only the adult males are morphologically adapted for defense, a baboon troop has twice the reproductive capacity it would have, for the same number of individuals, if males and females were equally large. Adaptation for defense is accompanied by increased agonistic behavior within the troop, but intratroop *fighting* is rare. Stable dominance hierarchies minimize aggression among adults, and male baboons and macaques actively interfere in fights among females and juveniles.

Field studies of other monkeys indicate that intragroup aggressive and agonistic behavior decrease by the degree to which a species is adapted to arboreal life. Among langurs, where sexual dimorphism is less pronounced, females may threaten or attack adult males— behavior that is unparalleled in the baboon-macaques. Langurs are usually in or under trees, where escape is rapid and the need for males to defend the group is much less important. The same argument, with suitable qualifications, holds for the other, more arboreal monkeys. The sexes in the olive colobus, for example, are almost identical in size and form; this species is never seen on the ground.

This does not imply that the male in other primate species has no protective role. Male colobus, vervets, and howlers have been seen taking direct action against potential predators, and the male in many species is prominent in giving defiant cries and/or alarm calls. With the possible exception of the gibbon, some measure of increased defensive action by adult males is a widespread primate pattern. The evidence does suggest, however, that increased predation pressure on the ground leads to increased morphological specialization in the male with accompanying changes in the behavior of individuals and the social organization of the troop. Although troops of arboreal monkeys may be widely scattered during feeding, a baboon or macaque troop is relatively compact. Some males may live apart from organized groups, either solitarily or in unisexual groups, in less terrestrial species (e.g., langurs), but we discovered no healthy baboons living outside a troop. Dominant adult males are the focal point for the other troop members in baboons, macaques, and gorillas. When the males eat, the troop eats; when the males move, the others follow. Compared to other monkey species: the baboon-macaques are most dominance-oriented; troop members are more dependent upon adult males and actively seek them out; and the social boundary of the troop is strong.

**Behavior and Taxonomy**

Species-specific behavior has been valuable in the classification of some vertebrate species, notably the distinct song patterns in birds. Spectrographic analyses of primate vocalizations will undoubtedly reveal specic differences in communication patterns, but these are only now being undertaken. Studies of social behavior in monkeys and apes have only begun, and no observations have yet been made in sufficient detail to permit close comparisons. Some general comparisons can be made, however, from studies recently completed.

The African baboons and the Asiatic macaques are very similar in both morphology and general adaptation. Both groups have forty-two chromosomes and their distribution does not overlap, suggesting that they are members of a single radiation of monkeys. Baboons, including drill, mandrill, hamadrayas, and savanna forms (but excluding gelada) are probably all species within one genus, *Papio*. Comparisons between the social behavior of East African baboons and macaques (rhesus and Japanese macaques) have been made elsewhere. At all levels of behavior, from discrete gestures and vocalizations to over-all social structure, baboons and macaques are very much alike. Both groups have an elaborate, and comparable, repertoire of aggressive gestures. In social interactions, the same behavioral sequences occur: an animal who is threatened may redirect the aggression to a third party, or may "enlist the support" of a third party against the aggressor. If support is successfully enlisted, two or more animals then simultaneously threaten the original aggressor. Relations between the adults and the young of both groups are similar.

Play patterns in juvenile groups and the ontogeny of behavior follow the same course. Relationships within the adult dominance hierarchies, and the social structure of the troop are comparable. Some details of gesture and vocalization are certainly distinct, and there is a striking difference, for example, in the form and duration of copulation. Copulation in rhesus monkeys usually involves a series of mounts before ejaculation, as does copulation in the South African baboons ("chacma") studied by Hall, while a single mounting of only a few seconds' duration is typical of East African baboons. Details of gesture and vocalization during copulation also vary between the three groups. On the other hand, most of the behavioral repertoire seems so similar that an infant baboon raised in a macaque troop, or vice versa, would probably have little difficulty in leading the adult life of its adopted group. Behavioral observations clearly confirm the evidence of morphological similarity in this widespread group of monkeys. No other primate, except man, has spread so far with as little morphological change as the baboon-macaque group. With man, these monkeys share the ability to travel long distances, cross water, and live in a wide range of environmental conditions.

On the basis of the present, random studies of monkeys and apes, generalizations regarding trends in behavior must remain speculative, particularly since the majority of the studies are concentrated in the baboon-macaque group. Much more useful statements with regard to the adaptive significance of different behavioral and morphological patterns will be possible when field studies of several species within one genus have been undertaken. The *Cercopithecus* group presents a wide range of ecological adaptations, from swamp-adapted species like *C. talapoin*, through the many forest forms, the savanna-living *C. aethiops*. Forms closely related to the *Cercopithecus* group, Allen's swamp monkey, patas, and gelada, would further extend the basis of comparison. A study of patas or gelada monkeys would be particularly useful for cross-generic comparison with baboon and macaque behavior. Although Ullrich has made initial observations, no long term study of an African colobus species is yet available for comparison to Jay's study of Indian langurs. Booth's report that olive colobus do not ascend to the upper levels of forests even when these are not occupied by black colobus and red colobus indicate that even brief field observations of the behavior of sympatric primate species would be an immense aid in settling some of the persistent questions in primate taxonomy.

## Summary

Field studies of monkeys and apes suggest a close correlation between ecological adaptation and the morphology and behavior of the species. All terrestrial forms occupy a larger home range, and, in monkeys, the geographic distribution of the species increases according to the degree of terrestrial adaptation. Many arboreal species use loud vocalizations in spacing troops; ground-living forms depend more on visual cues. A marked decrease in population density accompanies terrestrial adaptation. Man is part of this continuum, illustrating the extreme of terrestrial adaptation.

Morphological adaptation of the male for defense of the group is more prominent in ground-living species (except man, whose use of tools has removed the selective pressure for this kind of sexual dimorphism), and least prominent in most species that do not come to the ground. The dependence of the other troop members creates a male-focal social organization in terrestrial species. Dominance behavior is much more prominent in terrestrial monkeys, but actual fighting is rare. Terrestrial life and large adult males have not been accompanied by a comparable increase in dominance behavior in the gorilla, however, indicating that defense is more important than intragroup aggression in the development of sexual dimorphism in terrestrial primates.

Man's way of life has preserved the division between the male and female roles in adult primate life, but cultural traditions have replaced biological differences in the reinforcement of this distinction.

*selection 21*

# Baboon Ecology and Human Evolution

## Irven DeVore and S. L. Washburn

*From African Ecology and Human Evolution.* Viking Fund Publications in Anthropology, *No. 36, pp. 335–367. Copyright © 1963, Wenner-Gren Foundation for Anthropological Research, later transferred to Aldine Publishing Company. By permission of the authors, the publisher, and the copyright holder.*

The ecology of baboons is of particular interest to the student of human evolution. Aside from man, these monkeys are the most successful ground-living primates, and their way of life gives some insight into the problems which confronted early man. We have been concerned with an attempt to reconstruct the evolution of human behavior by comparing the social behavior and ecology of baboons with that of living hunter-gatherer groups, and applying these comparisons to the archaeological evidence. The following description of baboon behavior and ecology is based on field data collected during 200 hours of observation by Washburn in the game reserves of Southern Rhodesia in 1955, and on more than 1200 hours of observations by both of us in Kenya game reserves during 1959. . . .

### Classification

The African baboons are very similar to the Asiatic ground monkeys, the macaques. Both groups have forty-two chromosomes, and their distribution does not overlap. The newborn are usually black, changing to brown. Skulls, teeth, and general physical structures are much the same. In social life and basic habits the two groups are very similar. In contrast to all other monkeys (both New and Old

World), the macaques and baboons do most of their feeding on the ground. They can cross rivers and may live in dry areas, moving far from trees. Compared to other monkeys they are more aggressive and dominance-oriented, and their average troop size is considerably larger than any other species yet studied. These characteristics have enabled the baboon-macaques to occupy a much larger area than that of any other group of monkeys. It is an area very comparable to that utilized by *Homo* before the time of the last glaciation. Ground living, ability to cross water, an eclectic, varied diet, the protective troop, and aggressive males permitted the baboon-macaques to occupy this vast area with a minimum of speciation. The contrast in the number of species between ground-living and tree-living monkeys emphasizes this point. There are more species in the genus *Cerco-pithecus* in the African forests than among all the baboon-macaques from Cape Town to Gibraltar to Japan. There are more species of langurs in Southeast Asia alone than species of *Cercopithecus*. Further, the most ground-living of the langurs (*Presbytis entellus*) has the widest distribution, and the same is true for the most ground-living vervet (*C. aethiops*). The taxonomic contrast between tree and ground monkeys is clearly seen in Ceylon where the island is occupied by one macaque, one dry country langur, and four forest forms. Apparently in Ceylon the rivers have been a major factor in isolating the langurs, but they do not form barriers for the macaques. The general relation between ecology and taxonomy in the monkeys appears clear: the more ground-living, the less speciation. There are many more adaptive niches in the forests than in the drier regions.

The men of the Middle Pleistocene, genus *Homo*, occupied the same range as the baboon-macaques but without speciation. Their way of life (based on tools, intelligence, walking, and hunting) was sufficiently more adaptable and effective so that a single species could occupy an area which ground monkeys could occupy only by evolving into at least a dozen species. This comparison gives some measure of the effectiveness of the human way of life, even at the level of Pekin and Ternifine man. Obviously, there is nothing to be gained by being dogmatic about the number of species of Middle Pleistocene men. Perhaps when many more specimens have been found it will be convenient to recognize two or three species, but the general form of this argument will still hold. There is no suggestion that any of the known fossil men (genus *Homo*) differ in size or form as much as a chacma baboon and a drill, or a crab-eating macaque and a pig-tail macaque. Even in its most primitive form the human way of life radically alters the relation of the organisms to the environment. As early as Middle Pleistocene times man could migrate over three continents without major morphological adaptation.

*Australopithecus* may have occupied an adaptive position midway in effectiveness between the ground monkeys and early *Homo*. Small-brained, bipedal toolmakers probably occupied larger areas than baboons, and without speciation. It is most unlikely that the East African and South African forms of *Australopithecus* are more than racially distinct. Robinson's suggestion that the jaws from Java called "Meganthropus" are closely allied to the australopithecoid from Swartkrans supports the notion that *Australopithecus* was already able to disperse widely with minimum biological change. The presence of small and large Australopithecoids in South Africa at the same time suggests that their adaptation was much less effective than that of *Homo*. It may be possible to reconstruct more of this stage in human evolution with a more thorough study of the ecology of baboons, and by contrasting their mode of adaptation to that of man. With this hope in mind we will now consider the ecology of baboons in East Africa. . . .

## Troop Structure

Baboons are intensely social, and membership in a troop is a prerequisite for survival. Most of a baboon's life is spent within a few feet of other baboons. Baboon troops are closed social systems, individuals very rarely change to a new troop, and the troop regards any strange baboon with suspicion and hostility.

Within the troop, subgroups are based on age, sex, personal preferences, and dominance. When a troop is resting or feeding quietly, most of the adult members gather into small clusters, grooming each other or just sitting. Juveniles gather into groups of the same age and spend the day in these "play groups," eating, resting, and playing together. The most dominant adult males occupy the center of the troop, with the mothers and their young infants gathered around them, and the groups of young juveniles playing close by. These dominant males, and the small black infants near them, seem to be greatly attractive to the other troop members. During quiet periods the other troop members approach the adult males and the mothers, grooming them or sitting beside them. It is unnecessary for male baboons to herd the troop together; their presence alone insures that the other troop members will not be far away.

Around this nucleus of adult males, mothers, and young juveniles are the more peripheral members of the troop—the less dominant adult males, older juveniles, and pregnant or estrus females. Estrus females and their consorts usually stay at the periphery of the troop. Although the juvenile play groups will not wander far from the troop's center, peripheral adults may leave the troop for short periods. While the center of the troop moves slowly along, the adult and older juvenile (subadult) males and adult females sometimes move rapidly ahead to a new feeding spot. This may separate them from the rest of the troop by a quarter of a mile or more, and they may not rejoin the troop for thirty minutes or an hour. Although peripheral adult males may make such a side trip alone, or in small groups, other troop members will not leave the troop unless accompanied by the males. Healthy "solitary males" observed during the early part of our study later proved to be troop members who had left the troop for a short while.

A baboon troop that is in or under trees seems to have no particular organization, but when the troop moves out onto the open plains a clear order of progression appears. Out in front of the troop move the boldest troop members—the less dominant adult males and the older juvenile males. Following them are other members of the troop's periphery, pregnant and estrus adult females and juveniles. Next, in the center, comes the nucleus of dominant adult males, females with infants, and young juveniles. The rear of the troop is a mirror image of its front, with adults and older juveniles following the nucleus and more adult males at the end. This order of progression is invariably followed when the troop is moving rapidly from one feeding area to another during the day, and to its sleeping trees at dusk. A troop which is coming toward trees from the open plains approaches with particular caution. The tall trees in which baboons sleep are found only where the water table is near the surface, usually along a river or beside a pond. Vegetation is usually dense at the base of these trees, and it is in this undergrowth that predators often spend the day. The arrangement of the troop members when they are moving insures maximum protection for the infants and juveniles in the center of the troop. An approaching predator would first encounter the adult males on the troop's periphery, and then the adult males in the center, before it could reach defenseless troop members in the center.

Because they are in front of the troop by twenty to forty yards, the peripheral adult males are usually the first troop members to encounter a predator and give alarm calls. If a predator is sighted, all the adult males actively defend the troop. On one occasion we saw two dogs run up behind a troop, barking. The females and juveniles hurried ahead, but the males continued walking slowly. After a moment an irregular group of some twenty adult males was between the dogs and the rest of the troop. When a male turned on the dogs, they ran off. On another day we saw three cheetahs approach a troop of baboons. A single adult male stepped toward the cheetahs, gave a loud, defiant bark, and displayed his canine teeth; the cheetahs trotted away. If baboons come upon predators while en route to their sleeping trees, the troop stops and waits while the males in the center move ahead and find an alternate route (the young juveniles and mothers with infants stay behind with the peripheral adult males). Eventually the dominant males return, the original order of progression is re-established, and the troop proceeds along the new route. These behavior patterns assure that the females and young are protected in the troop's center.

The ultimate safety of a baboon troop is in

the trees. When the troop is away from trees, the adult males are very important in troop defense. We saw baboons near such predators as cheetahs, dogs, hyenas, and jackals, and usually the baboons seemed unconcerned— the other animals kept well away. Lions, however, will put a baboon troop to flight. From the safety of trees baboons bark and threaten lions but make no resistance to them on the ground. The behavior of baboons when near trees contrasts strikingly with their behavior on the open plains. If the troop is under trees, it will feed on the ground within thirty yards of predators, including lions.

### Ecology and Sex Differences

The role of the adult male baboons as defenders of the troop has been described. This behavior is vital to the survival of the troop, and especially to the survival of the most helpless animals—females with new babies, small juveniles, and temporarily sick or injured individuals. Selection has favored the evolution of males which weigh more than twice as much as females, and the advantage to the troop of these large animals is clear, but it is not obvious why it is advantageous for the females to be small. The answer to the degree of sex differences appears to be that this is the optimum distribution of the biomass of the species. If the average adult male weighs approximately 75 pounds and the average adult female 30 pounds, each adult male requires more than twice the food of a female. If the food supply is a major factor in limiting the number of baboons, and if survival is more likely if there are many individuals, and if the roles of male and female are different—then selection will favor a sex difference in average body size which allows the largest number of animals compatible with the different social roles in the troop.

If selection favors males averaging 75 pounds, then it will favor females which are as much smaller as is compatible with their social roles. Since the females must travel the same distances, carry young, engage in sexual and competitive activities, there are limits to the degree of sexual differentiation, but the adaptive value of the difference is clear. For example, a troop of 36 baboons composed of 6 adult males and 12 adult females and their young (18 juveniles and

infants) has a biomass of some 1,000 pounds. If the females also weighed 75 pounds each, 6 adult males and 6 adult females would alone total 900 pounds and have only one-half the reproductive potential of 6 adult males and 12 adult females. Because this would halve the number of young, it would greatly reduce the troop's chances of survival. Our data are not sufficiently detailed to analyze the actual distribution of biomass in the troops we observed, but our observations are compatible with the limited data on weights and the numbers of adult animals we saw. Viewing sexual differentiation in size as a function of the optimum distribution of biomass of the troop offers a way of understanding sexual dimorphism fundamentally different from the view which considers only sexual selection, dominance, and intratroop factors. Obviously, all factors should be considered. Adaptation is a complex process and results in compromises between the different selective pressures, but a distribution of biomass which doubles the reproductive potential of a species is so important that other factors may be mimimized.

The importance of sex difference in body size is reinforced by social behavior and the structure of the troop. As described earlier, some subadult and adult males are peripheral in the structure of the troop. They tend to be first, or last, when the troop moves. They are the most exposed to predators and are, biologically, the most expendable members of the troop. Interadult male antagonism results in a social order which both protects females and young and reduces feeding competition with females and young. Without altruism, the dominance behavior of a small number of males keeps a feeding space available to subordinate animals.

Juvenile play prepare the adults for their differential roles. Older juvenile females do not engage in the serious mock fighting which characterizes the play of older juvenile males. In this "play" the males learn to fight, and by the time the canine teeth have erupted and the temporal muscles grown to adult size they have had years of fighting practice. Play, social arrangement, and structural sexual dimorphism all supplement each other, producing a pattern in which the females and young are relatively more protected than the large males. Sexual differentiation must be seen as a part of this whole complex social pattern which leads to the survival of troops of baboons. . . .

## Vegetable Foods

The diet of baboons living in the savanna of Nairobi Park can be divided into: the vegetable foods which provide forage for them throughout the year, seasonal fruits, insects, and the live animals which they occasionally catch and eat. Grass is the baboon's single most important food. In ten months of observations, not a single day passed in which baboons were not observed eating grass, and for many weeks during the dry season, grasses composed an estimated 90 per cent of their diet. The portion of the grass eaten varies with the season. When the tassels contain seeds, these are "harvested" by pulling the tassel through the closed palm or clenched teeth. Most often, however, baboons pull up the grass shoots in order to eat the thick, lower stem at the base of the culm. Before eating the shoot, the dirt in the root system is carefully brushed away, and the roots themselves bitten off and discarded. By the middle of the day season, when grass shoots are rare, baboons concentrate on digging up rhizomes—the thick, rootlike runners of the grasses which lie from two to four inches beneath the surface. Even after many weeks or months without rain, these rhizomes are still juicy, providing baboons with considerable water. The ability of baboons to shift to subsurface rhizomes and roots when surface vegetation is dry and sparse is one of their most important adaptations to the grasslands. It enables them to feed in an area which has been denuded of surface vegetation by the many ungulates with whom they share this habitat, and to find sufficient forage during long dry seasons. Digging these rhizomes out of the hard, dry soil with the fingers is a laborious task, and in the dry season baboons spend longer hours getting their food than they do during the rest of the year. The use of a simple digging stick or sharp stone would enormously increase their efficiency in extracting this food from the ground, but no baboon was even seen trying to use a tool in this or any other way.

There are numerous plants on the Nairobi plains which have large, tuberous roots or bulbs, and the baboons are very adept at finding the tiny stem or leaf which indicates that such a root lies below. It may take as long as twenty minutes for a baboon to uncover a large root, and require a hole as large as 25 inches long, 8 inches wide, and 15 inches deep. Where the water table is high, along the rivers in Nairobi Park and around the water holes at Amboseli Reserve, the lush grasses attract many animal species, including baboons. Not only is the grass more plentiful here during the dry season, but also the earth is softer and more easily dug and many water plants are found which grow nowhere else in the area. Baboons spend the majority of their time feeding in the grass near the water, but they will also wade into the shallow water to eat such plants as rushes and the buds of water lilies.

The baboon's usual diet is further extended by the various bushes, flowering plants, and shrubs of the savanna. In Nairobi Park they were seen eating the berries, buds, blossoms, and seed pods of such plants. Another very important source of food throughout the year is provided by the acacia trees. Probably the buds, blossoms, and beanlike seed pods of all acacias are eaten, but those of the fever trees (*A. xanthophloea*) are particularly important. Not only is this species used almost exclusively as sleeping trees, but when they are in the height of their bloom the baboons also usually feed in them for one or more hours before starting their morning round, returning in the afternoon for another heavy feeding period at dusk. Out on the plains the ant galls on the short whistling-thorn trees (*A. drepanolobium*) are constantly plucked for the ants inside, and extrusions of its sap are eaten as well. Some edible portion—bud, flower, seed pod, sap—of one of the types of acacia tree will be available within a troop's range at almost any time of year, and acacias are second only to grasses in the quantity of food they provide for Nairobi Park baboons. In addition to the plants and trees which provide forage for baboons all year, certain seasonal foods may constitute the bulk of their diet for short periods. The most important source of these seasonal foods in Nairobi Park are fig trees. When large fig trees are in fruit, the baboons may also use them as sleeping trees.

The most important food sources in the

park are the grasses, acacia, and fig trees, but despite the frequency with which they feed in these trees, baboons were never seen eating tree leaves. On the southeastern slope of Mt. Kilimanjaro, baboons were observed feeding on the forest floor, while vervets (*Cercopithecus aethiops* and *C. mitis*) fed in the lower adjacent trees. Leaf-eating *Colobus* monkeys occupied the canopy of the same forest. Their ability to find food both on the open plain and in the trees is a distinct advantage for the baboons. Although they compete with a wide variety of ungulates for their food on the plains at Nairobi Park, their only close competitors in the trees are the vervets. Vervets and baboons are commonly seen feeding in adjoining trees in the park and occasionally they occupy the same tree—the baboons on the lower branches and the vervets in the canopy.

In addition to the staple diet, other vegetable foods were frequently eaten when they were available. These included "kei-apples," croton nuts, sisal plants, mushrooms, and the produce of native gardens (potatoes, yams, bananas, beans, maize, peanuts, sugar cane, etc.). Since almost all cultivated plants in this area have been imported from the New World, it is clear that baboons are very eclectic in their food habits.

### Insects

Baboons eat many types of insects when they can find them, but the climate of Nairobi Park with its dry season, its hot days and cool nights does not support a very heavy insect population. The most common insect eaten in the park is the ant living in the galls of the *Acacia drepanolobium* trees. The amount of ants eaten in this way, however, is very small compared to the grasses and plants eaten during the same feeding period. If the troop is walking slowly through an area strewn with large stones, some of these may be turned over and the ground beneath them examined carefully. Under such stones an occasional beetle, slug, or cricket will be found and is quickly eaten. Rarely, an ant nest is uncovered, and the baboon bends over and licks up the contents of the nest from the earth, licking additional ants from its hand and arms afterward. But the baboons' attitude toward insects is one of mild interest, and no troop

was ever seen moving from its pathway to systematically turn over the stones in an area.

Besides the ants in acacia galls, a baboon most frequently eats the grasshoppers which it finds on the branches of the bushes or blades of grass where it is feeding. Young baboons are seldom able to capture grasshoppers, but an adult will move the hand cautiously and deliberately to within one or two feet of the insect, then grasp it very quickly in a movement which is usually successful. Not all insects encountered are eaten. When a rock is overturned, some beetles and centipedes are ignored while others are carefully selected. Too few instances were observed to be able to say whether such selection was by individual preference, or whether these insects were avoided by all baboons in the park.

Although insect food is minor in the overall baboon diet, a very heavy infestation of "army worm" caterpillars in the park showed that for short periods insects can become the baboons' most important food. Beginning in early April, during the rainy season, army worms appeared in the park in large numbers. For about ten days the baboons ate little else. Feeding on the worms in a small area were: three baboon troops, totaling 188 animals; several troops of vervet monkeys, perhaps 75 in all; and a group of about 300 Marabou stork (*Leptoptilos crumeniferus*). The different baboon troops fed very near each other, and the other animals, without incident. All were gorging themselves on the caterpillars; several baboons were timed picking up 100 army worms per minute, and continuing at this rate for from 10 to 15 minutes without a break. The eating of insects, in addition to the extensive inventory of vegetable foods, further increases the dietary adaptability of the baboon.

### Live Animals

On six, perhaps seven, occasions during the twelve months of study in Kenya and the Rhodesias, we saw baboons eating freshly killed animals. Twice they caught and ate half-grown African hares (*Lepus capensis crawshayi*). On the first occasion the male in possession of the hare was being harried not only by two more dominant males in this troop, but by a pair of tawny eagles (*Aquila repax raptor*) as well. The male in possession eluded his harassers and managed to consume most of the hare, the eagles retrieving scraps of viscera and skin. In his haste the baboon dropped the rib cage and a foreleg of the hare, with most of the flesh still attached, *but these pieces were ignored* by the other two baboons chasing him, despite their desire to obtain his catch.

Two or three times baboons were seen eating fledgling birds of some ground-nesting species, probably the crowned plover (*Stephanibyx coronatus*). On several occasions they chased fledglings some yards through the grass without catching them. We never saw baboons finding and eating eggs, but when offered a dozen guinea fowl eggs, they ate these without hesitation. Entire eggs were stuffed into the cheek pouches and the shell broken by the hand pressing the cheek against the teeth and jaws. More significant than the few instances of baboons' eating fledglings are the numerous times when baboons were seen feeding across a plain covered by bird nests without discovering the contents of a single nest. The same animals which are able to detect an underground root from only a tiny dried shoot on the surface will walk beside a bird nest six inches in diameter without noticing it. Furthermore, four species of weaver bird inhabit the park, and their nests are frequently clustered in the acacia branches where the baboons are eating, but no baboon was ever seen investigating such a nest, much less eating its contents. The baboon's attitude toward food is clearly vegetarian. It is common to see a baboon troop completely mingled with a flock of guinea fowl without incident. The only eggs or fledglings which they seem to recognize as food are those which are literally stepped on as the troop searches for vegetable foods on the plains.

On December 14, near the close of the study, two very young Thomson gazelle (*Gazella t. thomsonii*) were caught and eaten by the adult males of a troop. The actual capture of the second gazelle was seen. An adult male baboon grabbed it, brought it above his head, and slammed it to the ground. He immediately tore into the stomach of the gazelle and began eating. Beginning with the most dominant males, five of the six adult males in the troop participated in eating this gazelle, and two

hours later only skin, teeth and large bones remained. The viscera were eaten first, followed by the flesh, and finally the thin brain case was bitten open and the contents carefully scooped out with the fingers—bits of skull being pulled through the teeth and licked clean. The incisors, not the canines, were used in biting and tearing at the flesh.

These two Thomson's gazelle were apparently only a few days old, and were hiding in the grass some 150 yards from the herd of 38 with which they were no doubt associated. After the baboon troop moved on, two females from the herd of gazelle (of 35 females, 2 young, and one adult male) came over and paced nervously around the remains of the carcasses. It seems reasonable to assume that the discovery of these two young gazelle took place under circumstances very similar to those involved in the eating of the young hares, that is, that they were discovered accidentally in the grass. In fact, after the first gazelle had been found, and four of the males were pressing its possessor closely, the males passed within five yards of an African hare sitting in plain view. They clearly saw the hare but did not even walk over toward it.

All these cases of flesh eating have one thing in common—they involve the eating of immature animals whose defense is to hide "frozen" in the grass, and in each case their discovery by the baboons seemed fortuitous. Nothing resembling a systematic search of an area or the stalking of prey was ever observed, nor was fresh meat eaten except when it was found alive or taken up immediately by a waiting baboon. Since baboons avoid lion kills when they are away from trees and other carrion is not eaten, the lack of interest shown by the male in the portion of hare which had been dropped (described above) may be due to their avoidance of carrion. It is also possible that baboons do not recognize as edible any meat which is not alive and easily caught. In either case it seems clear that their attitude toward other animals is not that of a predator, nor do the scores of other species with which they live peacefully so regard them.

The final instance of meat eating was observed in Amboseli Reserve. While watching baboons in an open area, we heard loud screeches and chattering in a tree where baboons and vervets had been feeding peacefully for the previous hour. When we approached the tree we saw an adult male baboon walking through the branches with a juvenile vervet dangling from his mouth, and the vervet troop had left the tree. The baboon consumed most of the vervet, carrying the carcass in his mouth as he walked toward the troop's sleeping tree at dusk. This observation is in striking contrast to the many occasions when the two types of monkey were seen feeding peacefully together. During a brief aggressive interaction between the two species in Nairobi Park, DeVore saw an angry adult male baboon put a troop of vervets to rapid flight, and this case of meat eating may have been the incidental result of such a situation in the tree at Amboseli. Although Washburn saw baboons chase vervets quite frequently near Victoria Falls, he only once saw a baboon catch one. This was held in the mouth by the female who caught it. She was apparently bewildered by the situation and soon released it unharmed. In much the same way one of the fledglings DeVore saw eaten was actually caught by a juvenile baboon, which seemed puzzled by the object and quickly relinquished it to an adult male (who promptly ate it).

In summary, baboons may be described as very inefficient predators. Meat eating, to judge by the bewildered state of the female baboon who caught a vervet and of the young juvenile who caught a bird, would appear to be learned by each generation, and meat never becomes an important source of food for the whole troop. Only one baboon other than adult males (an adult female) participated in the eating of meat in any of the instances observed during the study. Accounts of meat-eating in captive baboons are contradictory. Kenya baboons kept near Nairobi Park ate meat readily, but Bolwig found that his captives refused it. In South Africa, where most reports of carnivorous baboons have originated, baboons are only now being systematically studied, and we feel that the importance of meat in the baboon diet has been considerably overstressed. The usual reason given for the habit of meat-eating in South African baboons is that the hardship of drought creates the conditions under which it flourishes, but when the two Thomson's gazelle were eaten in December the park was well into the rainy season, and the vegetable foods baboons ordinarily eat were more abundant than at any other time of year.

It would seem more reasonable to us, on the present evidence, to assume that meat has been a consistent but very minor part of the baboon diet throughout their evolutionary history. In localities where sources of animal protein can be obtained without danger, baboons apparently include these in their regular diet. At Murchison Falls, baboons are often seen digging out and eating crocodile eggs. Hall's description of the foods eaten by baboons along the coast of South Africa is very similar to the inventory of vegetable and insect foods discussed here, except that the South African baboons also eat marine foods such as mussels, crabs, and sand hoppers found along the beach. But baboons are ill fitted anatomically to be carnivores, and too great a dependence on meat eating could have been detrimental to their wide exploitation of the vegetable foods they depend upon today. By their utilization of a wide variety of plant and tree products, baboons have been able to spread over the African continent, and, together with the macaques, to cover most of the tropical Old World.

In the evolution of the human species, meat-eating played a very different role. We have suggested that the earliest hominids may have been living on a diet very like that of the baboons, that is, vegetable foods supplemented by an occasional small animal. The freedom to carry a simple digging implement in the hands would greatly enhance this adaptation. During the dry season in Africa, human hunter-gatherers are also very dependent on the subsurface roots and tubers sought by baboons. A digging stick greatly improves the humans' chance for survival during this period of food shortage, and it may be that the presence of baboon skeletons at Olorgesaille indicates the result of competition between baboons and humans over a limited food supply. It would be an easy step from killing baboons to protect a source of vegetable foods, to killing them for meat.

## Scavenging

Scavenging has been regarded as an important phase in the evolution of man's carnivorous habits. It seems reasonable that a primate liking eggs, nestling birds, insects, and an occasional small mammal might add to this diet and develop more carnivorous tastes and habits by gleaning meat from kills. This theory seemed reasonable, and we made a particular effort to examine kills and to observe the relations of the baboons to them. Although we saw over a dozen recent kills (including gnu, giraffe, zebra, waterbuck, impala, Grant's gazelle, warthog, Masai cattle, and goat) and have thorough records on some, we were primarily looking at baboons. The subject of scavenging is so important, especially in the interpretation of the deposits in which *Australopithecus* is found, that a much more comprehensive study is needed. However, here are our tentative conclusions.

The scavenging theory is not supported by the evidence, and primates with habits similar to those of baboons could get meat by hunting far more easily than by scavenging. There are several reasons for this. The first is that most kills are made at night and are rapidly and thoroughly eaten. When the hyenas leave at dawn, the vultures locate the remains and clean the last meat from the bones. Some kills are made by day. We saw the remains of a gnu which a pride of ten lions finished in an hour. A pride of four lions (two not fully grown) killed a gnu one afternoon and ate almost all of it in one night. The vultures finished the rest, and the bones were undisturbed for three days. Many bones disappeared on the fourth night. Similarly, we saw two lions eat a warthog, three lions eat a Grant's gazelle, and five cheetahs kill and eat an impala. Only the meat of very large animals is left for long, and Africa is well supplied with highly efficient scavengers which leave little meat to tempt a primate.

Actually there are far fewer kills than might be expected from discussions of scavenging. In the part of the Amboseli Reserve which we studied intensively there were on the order of 100 baboons to one lion. The lions move over large areas, and the chances of a troop coming on a "kill" are very few. We saw a troop around a kill left from the previous night only once in Amboseli. It had been largely eaten, and the baboons appeared to take no interest in it. During nine months of observation in Nairobi Park, baboons were seen to pass near four kills and paid no attention to the few scraps of meat left on them. A Grant's gazelle carcass, presumably a leopard kill,

hung in a fig tree where baboons ate and slept, but the baboons apparently ignored it. In addition, they did not attempt to eat fresh carrion when this was found. A further complicating factor is that when there is much meat left, the lions usually stay nearby, and the neighborhood of the kill is very dangerous.

In summary, the chances of a kill within the range of a baboon troop are very small; little meat is likely to be left; and the vicinity of the kill is dangerous. Most of the killing and eating is at night, and primates have neither the sense of smell of the hyenas nor the eyes of the vultures to locate the kill. As noted earlier, the baboons seem uninterested in dead animals. A slight increase in predatory activity against young animals would yield a far greater reward than scavenging, would be much less dangerous, and would represent a smaller change in habit. The use of a stick or stone for digging would increase the baboons' food supply more than any other simple invention. Perhaps in *Australopithecus* we see a form which had such a tool to exploit vegetable foods and which also used this tool as a weapon. If tools were being used at all, their use in the deliberate killing of small animals would be only a small change from the behavior observed in baboons. Once man had become a skilled tool-user in these ways, he could extend tool use to the hunting of large animals, to defense, and to driving carnivores from their kills. Scavenging may have become a source of meat when man had become sufficiently skilled to take the meat away from carnivores, but the hunting of small animals and defenseless young is much more likely to lie at the root of the human hunting habit.

**Discussion**

In this paper we have tried to stress those aspects of baboon ecology which are of the greatest help in understanding human evolution. Obviously, man is not descended from a baboon, and the behavior of our ancestors may have been very different from that of living baboons. But we think that in a general way the problems faced by the baboon troop may be very similar to those which confronted our ancestors. At the least, comparison of human behavior with that of baboons emphasizes the differences. At the most, such a comparison may give new insights. Many topics have been summarized above, and in this discussion we will call attention only to a few major points.

The size of baboon troops may exceed that of hunter-gatherers, and their population density far exceeds that of primitive man. The human group differs in being exogamous, so that many local groups form the breeding population. We believe that this radically different breeding structure has exerted a profound effect on the later phases of human evolution and has long been a factor in preventing speciation in man.

The social structure of the baboon troop is important to the survival of the species. Survival depends on the adult males being constantly close to the other troop members. Roles in the troop are divided between the sexes, but these are in the context of a compact troop. With man, the hunters leave the local group, sometimes for days, and then return to their home base. Such a pattern is radically different from anything known in monkeys or apes. Hunting with tools basically changed the social structure of the band, the interrelations of bands, the size and utilization of range, and the relation of man to other animals.

Diet has already been discussed and we will not repeat here, except to point out that our opinion of the importance of scavenging has changed through observation of the actual situation at the kills. It is not enough to speculate that scavenging might have been important. One must estimate how much meat is actually available to a vegetarian, and how dangerous it is to get meat by scavenging.

Finally, we would stress that survival is a complex process, and that all the factors which lead to reproductive success must ultimately be considered. Varied diet, social structure, and anatomy, all are important, but their meaning only becomes clear as they are seen making possible the behavior of a population. Sex differences, peripheral animals, and range—each of these has meaning only in terms of the survival of groups. With the coming of man, every major category is fundamentally altered and evolution begins to be dominated by new selection pressures. Some measure of how different the new directions are may be gained from the study of the ecology of baboons.

# part 5

# Primitive Technology

# The Making of
# Stone Implements

## Kenneth P. Oakley

*From* Man the Tool-maker. *British Museum (Natural History), London, 1950, pp. 23–29. By permission of the author and the publisher.*

Before describing the succession of Stone Age industries in relation to man's evolutionary development, which is the central theme of this guide, it is useful to consider the various ways in which stone can be worked into tools and weapons. The simplest way of producing a stone which will cut (the primary type of artifact) is simply to break it in half and to use the resulting fresh sharp edge; but to produce a stone tool which is even slightly more specialized, one of two courses must be followed. The lump of stone, whether pebble, nodule or angular fragment, can be brought to the desired shape by flaking, or knapping. The flakes removed from the lump are then primarily waste-products, while the core of the lump becomes the implement. Such is a *core-tool*. Alternatively, flakes struck from the lump can be used as implements, with or without further trimming (known as dressing, retouch or secondary work). In this case the core is the source of *flake-tools*, and will serve to yield flakes until too small, when it is discarded as waste. Before a core will yield flakes of the required shape it may have to be prepared, and in the course of this preliminary work a number of waste flakes are produced. In practice, too, the flakes removed in the production of a core-tool may be selected subsequently for use as implements. The simple classification into core-tool industries and flake-tool industries is further complicated by the possibility that large flakes may be selected to serve as cores. Moreover, even in a flake-tool industry, discarded cores would be used as occasional tools.

Industries producing long parallel-sided flakes are distinguished as *blade-tool* indus-

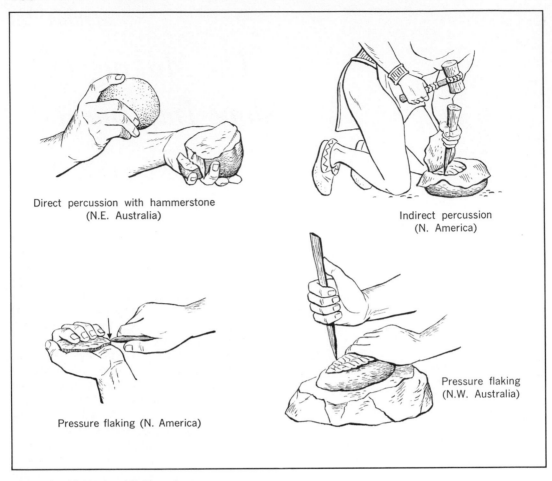

Direct percussion with hammerstone
(N.E. Australia)

Indirect percussion
(N. America)

Pressure flaking (N. America)

Pressure flaking
(N.W. Australia)

**Figure 1** Methods of flaking stone.

tries. (It is difficult to produce blades in rocks other than flint, chert or obsidian.)

There are several methods of flaking stone, each probably used at some time or other during the Stone Age. Flaking by direct blows with a hammerstone (or other tool for striking) has been the method most widely used, but even this is subject to considerable variation. The stone to be flaked can be held in the hand [as shown in the accompanying figure], or rested on a block, or held against the knee. If, while it is being struck, the stone is rested on a slab of rock (a technique reminiscent of the simple method of cracking nuts with a pebble), the resulting flakes are liable to show a bulb of percussion at both ends, owing to rebound from the anvil. This so-called biopolar technique was practiced by Pekin Man. The normal primitive method of knapping, however, is to hold the lump of

stone to be flaked in the hand, and to strike it repeatedly at selected spots with a pebble of suitable size. Each blow is delivered obliquely downwards near the edge of some conveniently placed flattish area (the striking platform), usually the scar of a flake previously struck off. Whether the flakes are short and thick, producing step-like bites along the edge of the piece of stone, or whether they are thin and extensive, skimming the surface, depends largely on the placing of the blows and on the angle at which they are delivered. The run of the flake can be controlled by preparation of the face of the core, and also by pressure of the finger. When a piece of stone is held in the hand and struck at the edge by blows directed obliquely downwards, the flakes come off the *lower* surface, against which the fingers or palm are easily pressed. In the shaping of a core-tool such as a hand-axe, which requires to be trimmed equally on two sides, it is turned over from time to time as the paring proceeds.

Experiments by the French master mason, Léon Coutier, have shown that flint and similar rocks can be flaked by direct blows with a stone or bar of hardwood. This "wood-technique" is an effective way of reproducing the smooth skimming flake-scars which form the surfaces of the finer palaeoliths. However, similar flake-scars, with subdued or soft bulbs of percussion, can be produced also by a cylindrical or soft hammerstone, especially if used in conjunction with skillful finger control.

Probably one of the most primitive methods of producing flakes for use as tools is to dash or swing the core against the edge of a larger stone, or anvil. This "block-on-block" technique is liable to produce thick flakes (and deep flake-scars on the core) as in coarse flaking by a hammerstone, but with more protuberant cones and bulbs of percussion, and with a wider flaking angle (the angle between the striking-platform and the surface of the bulb of percussion). Flakes belonging to the primitive Palaeolithic flake industry known as Clactonian show these features.

A common attitude of a stone knapper is a sitting or squatting one, and in the production of flake-tools by percussion with a hammerstone the core is generally held on the left thigh or knee. The knapper starts as a rule with a lump of stone far larger than the core or tool required. Experiments have shown that the preliminary trimming down and the production of large primary flakes are most easily accomplished with a hammerstone weighing about 3 lb., whereas for the subsequent dressing of flakes a hammerstone weighing 2 or 3 oz. gives the best results. . . .

Stone Age knappers relied wholly on craftsman's skill, and when they required flakes of standard type or long blades, they had to take great care in the preparation of the core. Studies of the flaking techniques employed by primitive peoples in recent times show that there are many different ways of producing the same results. The American Indians used various methods of indirect percussion. To produce blades, for instance, a wooden or bone punch was interposed between the hammerstone and the core. Owing to the reduction of shatter, flakes can be split off thus with greater precision than when the hammerstone

is used directly. The Aztecs of Mexico and a few North American Indians produced long blades by what is called impulsive pressure. The core was stuck in the ground and gripped by the feet of the flaker, who either stood or sat, and grasped a wooden staff, which had a cross-piece for resting against the chest, and a spike of horn or hardwood at the other end which was set on the prepared edge of the core. The flaker would thrust forward with his chest, thus using the leverage of the body to split a flake from the core. According to one seventeenth century observer, a Mexican flaker, using this method, could produce as many as 100 knife blades of obsidian in an hour.

Much has been learned about the more primitive flaking techniques by studying the methods of Australian aborigines. As a general rule the shaping of a core-tool takes only a few minutes, but the preparation of a core for the production of flake- or blade-tools is sometimes a lengthy proceeding. Moreover, a number of artifacts are rejected before completion. It has been stated that in North Queensland, for example, a native requiring a new knife will visit a traditional quarry and will perhaps strike as many as 300 flakes before he obtains what he considers to be a suitable blade. The rejects and waste-flakes are left on the working "floor," while the single satisfactory blade is taken away, mounted in a handle of resin and used until it is broken. The dressing, or secondary working of a stone tool to make the edge straighter or more serviceable, or to re-edge it when it has been blunted by use, is usually done by rapping it on a pebble, or with a piece of bone or hardwood. Some of the tribes, especially in the Kimberley region of Western Australia, dress spearheads by pressure-flaking.

According to first-hand accounts of the fashioning of a spearhead by this method, a flake of stone (or glass, or porcelain) is taken and its edges chipped with a hammerstone into a roughly symmetrical leaf form. The margins are then rasped with a piece of sandstone, which breaks away small chips so that a narrow platform or bevel is formed on each side of the edge. The completion of the spearhead by pressure-flaking requires much patience and skill. The native squats on one heel, with the other leg stretched out, and with an anvil stone on the ground between his legs. In his left hand he holds the unfinished spearhead on a cushion of paperbark, placed on top of the anvil stone. In his right hand he holds a pointed stick (or piece of kangaroo bone), in such a way that the sharpened end is close to the wrist and points towards his body. After adjusting the point of the stick against the bevel of the far edge of the flake, he brings the weight of his body to bear on his right arm, and at the same time levers his wrist downwards and outwards. A chip snaps off the lower surface of the flake, while the "jar" of the downward thrust is absorbed by the cushion. The process is repeated time after time, as he works along the edge towards the butt; then the flake is reversed and the same method applied to the other side. A skillful flaker can make a spearhead of bottle-glass in about ten minutes.

*selection 23*

# The First Tipi

## Alice Marriott

It wasn't really very different, Spear Girl* thought, being married and not being married. You worked just about as hard, and the great difference that you had expected—not having your mother boss you—hadn't happened at all. They were all at home in the old tipi: her mother and sister, and Hunting Horse and herself, and they just went on doing the same old things the same old way. It wasn't much fun.

Bow Girl came and sat beside her, to pack the pounded meat into rawhide cases. They were quiet for a long time, because, being sisters, they didn't need to talk with their voices. After while their uncle came and sat down with them.

"Where is your husband, niece?" he asked Spear Girl.

"At Sitting Bear's camp. They are making a feast for the Herders Society because that is Young Sitting Bear's society."

"That is your husband's, too."

"Yes, it is his."

Their uncle took out his pipe. It was old, a little short section of the big leg-bone of a deer. He didn't smoke it in the evenings, when

*From* The Ten Grandmothers. *University of Oklahoma Press, 1948, pp. 64–71. By permission of the author and the publisher.*

* This chapter is from the life story of the young Kiowa Indian woman, Spear Girl.

all the men gathered around, smoking, because he had a big red pipe that he liked to show off with. But when he really wanted to think, he got out the little old bone pipe.

"Your husband goes to society meetings as if he were not married."

"He likes to be with other young men, uncle."

"That's all right. Men like to be with each other part of the time. But part of the time they should be with their wives, too."

"My husband is with me a lot when he isn't working."

"He would be with you more if you had your own tipi."

Spear Girl felt ashamed. They were poor, and they had always been poor, because, until she married, they had no man to work for them all the time. Her uncle was rich, and he helped a lot, but that didn't take the place of someone working all the time. She didn't like to say so to her uncle, because he was good and generous, and helped them more than he was obliged to, as it was.

He shook out his pipe, now, and turned to face her directly. "I've been thinking a lot. Hunting Horse has nobody to help him get started. You have your mother and sister, and that's all. Somebody has to help you two. I guess I'd better do it."

Spear Girl just sat and stared at him. It was like her uncle, but still she hadn't expected it. She didn't even thank him. She just stopped pounding down the dried meat and sat and stared, and Bow Girl stared, too.

"I don't want to give you everything to get you started." Her uncle was putting his pipe away now, because his thinking was over. "I'll give you what you need to make things out of. We won't make a give-away out of it, or have any ceremony. But you'll have what you need to work with. You two will have to do the working yourselves." Then he got up and walked off, and Spear Girl and Bow Girl just watched him go.

It was very late when Hunting Horse got home. The Herders Society members had danced a long time, and then they had eaten a big feast, and he was tired. He just flopped down and started breathing deep, and Spear Girl knew there was no use trying to tell him anything then.

She waked early, with her skin prickling all over, wondering what it was that was going to happen that was so big and good and exciting. Then she remembered. This was the day that they were to get their things to start living with. She punched Hunting Horse in the ribs with her elbow, and he grunted and turned over, and started breathing again. For a minute she started to get angry with him, but the day was too good to spoil, so she got up quietly. She dressed and combed her hair. For a minute she thought about painting her face, and then decided that since it wasn't like getting regular wedding presents, she would look foolish if she did it. Instead, she went out and helped her mother get breakfast.

They had all had breakfast, even Hunting Horse, and the newness had rubbed off the day and most of the excitement was gone, when she saw her uncle coming across the camp. He was leading a horse, piled high with all sorts of things, and behind him came his two wives, each of them leading a horse with a big load. They stopped in front of the tipi.

"There you are, sister."

"Get down, brother."

Her uncle tied the horse, and stepped back into the shade beside the tipi. His wives tied their horses, and began to unload them. Spear Girl started to help them, but her mother called her back.

"You don't unload your own wedding presents, daughter."

She wanted very much to see what they were. But she would have to wait until every single thing was off all three horses before she could look. She got a dipper of water for her uncle, and he drank the water and handed the dipper back to her.

"I'm glad you like to use gourd dippers, niece. I have brought plenty of gourds for you to make them out of."

Well, that was fine. The gourds had got all sun-scorched that summer, and there weren't enough to make dippers for everybody. Even people who had got tin cups from the traders still kept some gourds around, and used old-time dippers for themselves. They just got the tin cups out when they had company and wanted to show off. Spear Girl knew how to make good dippers.

"Thank you, uncle," she said.

"There is everything there that you need to work with," her uncle said. "We have brought hides for a tipi, and willows for beds, and robes and deerskins to make bedding out of. All the hides are dried and rolled up.

You'll have to tan them and cut them yourself, but there are a lot there. How many buffalo hides are there?'' he asked his first wife.

''Thirty-two,'' she answered. ''Enough for a big tipi. We have logs for tipi-poles over at our camp. Your husband will have to trim them down and bring them over himself.''

Spear Girl wasn't paying much attention to the tipi-poles. She was thinking about the cover. Thirty-two hides were a lot, when they had to be tanned, and she had never cut or sewn a tipi-cover. Not very many people tried to cut their own. There were some women who were good at it, and they did that kind of work for everybody. But they wouldn't do the tanning.

Her mother was looking off across the camp, as if there were something she wanted to see on the other side. ''My daughter's husband hasn't much to do,'' she said. ''I guess he can start work on the tipi-poles right away.''

Spear Girl heard that, and it turned her mind away from the tipi-cover. Her mother shouldn't speak like that, even about her son-in-law. It made her feel queer, and without looking at Hunting Horse she knew it made him feel queer, too. But he didn't say anything. He took his axe and started across to her uncle's tipi.

Everything was all unloaded now. It made a big pile in front of the tipi. People were coming up to see what was happening.

''That's a lot of hides,'' said Grass Woman. ''Who's going to tan all those hides?'' Spear Girl straightened up and stopped thinking about what a lot of work it was going to be.

''I am,'' she answered. ''I want to tan the hides for my own tipi.''

Bow Girl was standing beside her. ''I'm going to help my sister,'' she added. ''We always do everything together.''

Nobody said anything, but Spear Girl felt better. The people around her felt better towards her. They must have been afraid she was going to let her mother do all the tanning.

Bow Girl brought water to her uncle's two wives. ''That was hot work for you, all that loading and unloading,'' she told them, and her aunts said, ''Yes, it was hot work, all right. Now you can get to work and get hot, too.''

That was all right. You ought to get hot, working on your own home. Spear Girl didn't mind it. Grass Woman spoke again. She al-

ways had something to say. ''That many hides takes a lot of brains for tanning. A hide needs all its own brains to tan itself. I have some brains. My man killed three buffalo this month, and I dried the brains and saved them. I'm going to make rawhide. I don't need them. You can have them.''

Spear Girl was feeling better all the time. The newness seemed to be coming back to the day. ''Thank you for the brains,'' she told Grass Woman.

''I have brains, too.'' That was Pond Woman. ''I don't need them. Four buffalo brains.''

It was like a give-away, then. It seemed as if every woman in camp had been saving brains. They all wanted to give some away, and they all gave them to Spear Girl. Grass Woman and Pond Woman got their brains, and then the others went for theirs, too. Spear Girl stood and watched flat cakes of dried brains pile up beside the buffalo hides, and felt more and more excited. It was going to be all right. Now she could get to work right away, without waiting for Hunting Horse to finish the poles and then go buffalo hunting and bring her back the brains, one at a time. This way they would finish their work on the tipi almost at the same time. That was right, too. They ought to work together, making their own home.

She said ''thank you'' to everybody, and when all had seen all the hides and the gourds and the willows for the beds, they went off to their own tipis, and Spear Girl could begin to put things away.

That was harder. There was just the one tipi for four of them, and they had it full already. While she was trying to bring in all the things that rain could spoil, her mother was sitting inside the tipi thinking. Spear Girl felt a little strange about her mother. Everybody else had given her things and had been encouraging, and wanted to see her get ahead, but her mother had hardly spoken all morning. Spear Girl didn't like it. It tied up a knot in her insides. She knew, suddenly, how her mother had felt the night that Spear Girl ran away with Hunting Horse, but knowing didn't make her feel any better now.

Finally her mother got up and came outside the tipi. Spear Girl and Bow Girl had everything picked up or covered up, and the camp looked nice again, with everything where it ought to be. Her mother looked at it all for a moment, with her eyes as if she didn't see.

"That's all right," she said, then. "I guess everything's the way it ought to be."

She was talking about the way the camp looked, but she was talking about something else, too. Spear Girl didn't exactly understand, but she knew that what her mother said went deep; down under the neatness and rightness of having everything where it ought to be.

Her mother sat down beside the tipi, with her legs folded sideways under her.

"I've been thinking a lot," she said. "I think I ought to do something for you, too."

"You don't have to," Spear Girl told her.

"I have the right to," said her mother. "I need to do something. That way I show respect for my daughter and the man she married. If I don't show respect for them, soon nobody's going to respect them. They'll just give things because they're sorry. That's not right. Nobody ought to have people feeling sorry for her."

"That's right," said Spear Girl. "That's what my uncle has said, lots of times."

"I can't do much," her mother went on. "We never did have much. But we have some things. What I'm going to do, I'm going to have the woman come to cut out your tipi. Then I'm going to have more women come to help sew. Lots of women. We'll give them a feast, just the women. That way, your tipi will be made right, just like everybody else's. But you got to tan your hides yourself. Just your sister can help you."

Spear Girl felt better than she ever had in her life, but what was odd about it was that feeling good made her cry. It was good crying, and she didn't mind it, but it was strange to cry just when you felt better than you ever had before. She turned to ask her mother about it, and her mother was crying too, but she was smiling at the same time.

"That's all right, daughter," she said, "You're just a young girl yet. You don't understand things. But feeling good just does make you cry sometimes. You'll know about it all when you get more grown up." She stopped crying and smiled all over. "When you get a home of your own," she added. That was funny, too, because while Spear Girl and Bow Girl talked without words more than they talked with them, neither of them had ever been able to do it with their mother before.

It was a lot of work, getting ready to cut and sew the tipi. Spear Girl and Bow Girl worked and worked with the hides. They wanted them all smooth, scraped down to the same thickness all over, and white; and it took them a long time to get thirty-two hides just the way they ought to be.

All the time that they were working with the hides, Hunting Horse was away all day. One day he worked on the tipi-poles, and the next day he went hunting. Their mother needed a lot of meat for the feast, and as he was the man of the family, it was up to him to get it.

When everything was all ready, Spear Girl laid the hides out smooth, one on top of the other. Everything they had was full of pounded meat, some of it pounded with berries, and some of it plain; and her mother had borrowed extra kettles from their uncle's wives. Even then, there weren't enough to cook in, and she had cooked some of the meat over coals, on sticks, and some of it she had boiled the old-time way, in the skin of a buffalo's stomach. Bow Girl thought that was very funny. "Just like men eating out on a war party," she said, and giggled.

Spear Girl dressed. She put on her best white buckskin dress, with beadwork instead of painting on it; and she braided her hair and painted the parting red, and put a red circle on each cheek. It was too bad to dress all up like that just to sew hides, but as everybody did it, she had to do it, too. Stepping carefully, so as not to get grass stains on her high white moccasins, she went over to Navajo's Eye Woman's tipi to tell her to come and start cutting the cover.

Navajo's Eye Woman knew she was coming and was all dressed up in her best clothes waiting for her. "Get down," she said. Spear Girl sat down beside her and drank the water Navajo's Eye Woman gave her in a tin cup. All her gourd dippers were ready, she remembered. She'd made them by the firelight in the tipi, when it was too dark to tan outdoors.

Navajo's Eye Woman listened to Spear Girl's invitation without saying anything. Then she put her robe around her, got up, and led the way out of the tipi. She had worked so much with hides that many people called her Hide Woman, even if that wasn't her name, and she was bent all over and walked with a stick, from stooping over so much, scraping. Spear Girl hoped she wasn't stooping herself, from tanning thirty-two hides, and straightened up as stiff as she could, following Navajo's Eye Woman back to the old tipi.

Navajo's Eye Woman looked over all the hides very carefully. She turned them over from one side to the other, and she felt over the whole surface to make sure they were all even. Spear Girl was glad they had worked so hard with them. She would have hated to have Navajo's Eye Woman find a poor one. Finally Navajo's Eye Woman finished.

"Spread them all out smooth on the grass," she said. "They are all good. I can use every one."

Spear Girl and Bow Girl tried not to show how proud they felt, spreading the hides out flat on the grass. While they were doing it, Navajo's Eye Woman gave each woman a handful of sinew thread, and she asked each one if she had her awl. Every woman did, and Navajo's Eye Woman nodded. "That's good," she told them. "Bad luck if somebody forgets her awl."

Then she walked around and looked at all the hides carefully, to make sure she got the right one to start with. When she had picked it, she moved it off to itself, took her knife from its sheath at her belt, and began to cut. She cut the ears at the top of the tipi first, and gave them to the two oldest women to sew, because they were the hardest part.

Spear Girl and Bow Girl were the last to get their sewing. It was just part of the bottom, next to the ground, because they were the youngest there, and that was the easiest part, but they worked hard, because they wanted it to be as right as all the rest of the cover.

They all sewed all day. None of the men came near them. Most of the men were in Sitting Bear's camp talking, because all the women were working on the tipi-cover, and there wasn't anything much for the men to do, or anybody around to tell them to do it.

There was a clear space between the rim of the sun and the ground when they finished, but not a wide one. All the pieces were sewed together, smooth and even, and Spear Girl wondered if she would be able afterwards to remember what woman worked on what piece; the work all looked so much alike. Navajo's Eye Woman looked around for her, and Spear Girl got up and went over to the old woman.

"Where are the poles for this tipi?" asked Navajo's Eye Woman.

Spear Girl stood up straight. She and Hunting Horse had made their plan that morning, early, before anybody else was awake. Now she stood up and faced toward Sitting Bear's tipi, and raised her arm straight up in the air.

Hunting Horse saw her. He had his horses all ready, all three of them. Two of them were loaded with tipi-poles, but the other one had presents on it, the best they had, out of the things Spear Girl's uncle had given them. A buffalo-hide robe with the hair on, a deerskin tanned white, a heavy smoked buckskin, bags of paints, and a gourd dipper—all women's things, that Spear Girl had made herself. Women's things to give to the woman who made the biggest woman's thing.

Hunting Horse led the horses up to the group of women. He dropped the lines, and let the pack-horses stand with the tipi-poles, while he gave the other horse's lines to Spear Girl. She led the horse to Navajo's Eye Woman, and Hunting Horse stood on the edge of the group of women to watch her.

"My husband and I want you to have these things," Spear Girl said, politely.

"That is good. That is kind," Navajo's Eye Woman said. She took the lines, and tied the horse to a tree behind her. "Thank you."

Spear Girl's mother began to set up the tipi-poles. Her brother's two wives came to help her, and they got the job done quickly. You could still see half of the red sun above the red earth.

Navajo's Eye Woman went and stood between the door-posts and raised her arms and prayed. She prayed for long life and good health for the people who would live in that tipi, and she prayed thankfully for the buffalo and the hides that made the tipi. Then she dropped her arms, and some of the women raised the tipi-cover and spread it over the poles. It just fitted.

They had the feast in the new tipi, after Spear Girl had lighted her first fire with coals from her mother's. All the women sat inside in the firelight while the dark grew around the outside, and their shadows grew bigger and bigger on the new white walls. Then they took what food was left—all a big lot of it— and tied it up in bundles to take home and make a feast for their husbands. Each one, as she went out, said, "Thank you for feasting," and every time Spear Girl replied, "Thank you for working."

When everybody else had gone, Bow Girl came and stood beside her, and they looked around at the new, clean, white walls. "I know what you're thinking," said Bow Girl, at last. "You're thinking that now when Hunting Horse comes home, you can put the beds in and have everything ready to start living here."

And that was odd, because Spear Girl wasn't thinking that at all. She was wondering if her mother ever had felt just the way she did right then. Now being married was beginning to feel really different.

*selection 24*

# How the Bemba Make Their Living

## Max Gluckman

*From How the Bemba Make Their Living: An Appreciation of Richards' "Land, Labour and Diet in Northern Rhodesia."* Rhodes-Livingstone Institute Journal, *June, 1945, pp. 55–67. By permission of the author and the publisher.*

Central Africa is dominantly poor. Over vast areas it has barren soils, the rainfall and water supplies are uncertain, and its people and stock are riddled with disease. Hunger and sickness are the common lot of the African. In this, they are typical of the inhabitants of most Colonies where there is a high incidence of such deficiency diseases as beriberi, pellagra, anemia, nightblindness, tropical ulcer, dental caries, and a high rate of tuberculosis and pulmonary infections in general. Besides these deficiency diseases, the population suffers from a very high infection of malaria, hookworm, bilharzia, venereal disease, leprosy, etc. Many tribes are unable to keep cattle because of lack of pastoral country and the presence of tsetse fly, and where the fly is absent tickborne and other diseases, as well as seasonal shrinkings of pasturage, make stockraising hazardous.

Most Central African peasants have to struggle with hard natural difficulties to maintain themselves at all. The problem of raising their standard of living is evidently an immensely difficult one to solve, considering these alone. In addition, we have to deal with human beings, whose health and energy are low because of tropical heat, malnutrition and disease, and whose habits of custom and belief have been conditioned by a cultural tradition which maintained a precarious balance between life and death. Ignorance and traditional knowledge set limits to the use of potential resources. This balance has been upset by the arrival of Europeans. . . .

The Bemba live in a well-watered bushed plateau and are "men of the trees." To grow their main crop, finger millet, on the poor soils of their plateau home they pollard trees over 8–13 acres, and pile and burn the branches to provide an acre's seed bed. This garden is commonly used for 4–5 years, on a single rotation; but every year they open up new gardens. For the Bemba, rich land is land with many trees, since these ultimately provide his main food-supply. In addition, huts, granaries, fences, beds, stools, drums, canoes, string and the nets and snares made of it, magical substances for curing disease, for increasing the durability of the season's crops, for all purposes, are made from trees. The Bemba, in a tsetse area, have no cattle, and their tools are simple: an axe, a hoe, a spear and a bow. With his axe the Bemba can do much: in a few minutes he makes chairs and tables for the touring European, he strips bark to tie his loads, he shapes poles to build his huts. As he walks through what seems to us to be miles of monotonous bush, his eyes are always on the trees, noting that here grows this species or that, suitable for some specialized profane or ritual use. He watches trees to see where bees are hiving, where caterpillar grubs are swarming, etc. The Bemba live in, with, and by, their trees. This concentration of interest is reflected in their mythology and ritual. The most important national ceremonies performed each year are at the tree-cutting season, when the chiefs pray to their ancestral-spirits to provide plenty of food and to watch over the safety of the young men who swarm up to the tops of the highest trees to cut off the branches, and shout in triumph as these crash to the ground. Richards suggests that the Bemba's pride in their agility and daring in pollarding has heightened their tendency to neglect soil differences, covered by the ash seed-bed, and to take only a minor interest in their subsidiary gardens made in hoed mounds. "The Bemba consider their own system of clearing the bush as characteristic, and therefore superior to that of other tribes. The method of shearing the trees of their branches is exceedingly skillful. It is the man's task *par excellence* in the whole economic routine. The Bemba are daring climbers. . . . No tree is considered too high or too dangerous to climb" (p. 289).* "In this form of cultivation the people's emotions seem entirely centered round one process—a particular method of tree-cutting which is their pride and delight, and closely associated with an elaborate form of ritual" (p. 300). When Richards described the merits of the English system of agriculture, she heard one young man behind her "observe to his friend with a snort of derision, 'Hm! Afraid to climb, I suppose.' " This form of agriculture has been constantly discouraged by Government officials, since the early days of the British South Africa Company, though agricultural research has recently impressed that it is well-suited to local conditions. "In 1907, a definite order prohibiting tree-cutting was promulgated, with the result that the people grew practically no millet, and in at least one district they had to be fed by Government for fear they should starve. The effort was then abandoned. It is true that these orders were issued to the Natives without any suggestion, apparently, as to an alternative method of cultivation. The research at present (1938–9) undertaken may result in the necessary discovery. But it is doubtful whether any system of 'cultivating on the ground' will have —at any rate for some years—the glamour of the old, and it seems likely, ironically enough, that those very factors which were formerly important incentives to production—the cultural emphasis on the value of tree-cutting and the religious rites associated with it—will act at the present day as barriers in the way of change" (p. 300).

This concentration of interest and prideful emotion on tree-cutting may partly explain why the Bemba do not use the richer soils of *ifipya* sites, tall grass-bush country, which the ecological survey says could be opened up profitably. In fact, the Bemba speak of "bad *ifipya*." But in addition the Bemba, to use the sites, would have to change his staple diet, probably to kaffir corn or cassava, and according to his dietetic theories cassava does not give energy as millet does (this is correct). In addition, the Bemba likes to feel the heavy

---

* This page reference, and all subsequent ones, refer to pages in Richards' book which is the subject of Gluckman's comments here.

millet porridge inside him; he "probably becomes accustomed to a particular sensation of tension inside. To the European this would amount almost to a pain but it is evident that the Bemba want to feel full in just this particular way, and do not feel satisfied unless they have reached this state." Cassava and maize flours are softer and "melt quicker inside." Richards describes how from infancy Bemba are conditioned to and desire this heavy porridge and how they miss it in the towns. This porridge is fed as gruel even to month-old babies, for the Bemba do not clearly see that mother's milk nourishes; the breast gives only comfort. The plight of a Bemba child born in town and sent to his relatives in the country is pitiful, because the porridge "was tasteless, but also because it was rough and gave him pain." However, the same may be said of every tribe and its staple food: Lubale cassava-eaters complain of stomach-ache when on a mealie meal diet, and Lozi maize- and sorghum-eaters dislike too much of the heavier millet porridge or the lighter cassava-meal.

A meal to the Bemba is millet-porridge. This has to be "eased" down by a relish, rarely meat or fish, usually vegetable. Essential though the relish is, it is millet porridge, eaten in heavy, quickly-cooked lumps, which is the Bemba's "daily bread." In proverb and folktale the word *ubwali* stands for food itself. When discussing his kinship obligations a Native will say, "how can a man refuse to help his mother's brother who has given him *ubwali* all these years?" or, "Is he not her son? How should she refuse him *ubwali*?" In fact, he uses the word as we do "bread" in such phrases as "daily bread" or "working for our bread and butter," but more constantly, and really with better reason.

"In Bemba ceremonial *ubwali* stands for food and indirectly for ordinary daily intercourse." It figures in important national ritual, in female initiation, at marriages, and is abstained from by those who become possessed by spirits. Thus physiologically and emotionally the Bemba are conditioned to eat this millet, and are likely to oppose a change in staple, though in the towns they have to eat other food.

Bemba physiological and emotional concentration on this one food runs throughout Richards' account. In this tsetse area, where fish are obtained perennially only in the Bang-weulu region on the far east and along the Chambeshi River which cuts diagonally across the kingdom, and where there is a single season of rain on predominantly poor soils, the people rely on this one main crop. Even of it they produce only sufficient for about nine months of the year, and the other three are distinguished as "hunger months." At the end of the rainy months they regularly expect a shortage, whether it is severe or not. "When the scarcity becomes marked the whole appearance of village life is changed. For adults meals are reduced from two to one a day, and beer is rarely if ever brewed. Children who seem to munch extras all day long in the plentiful season (April–October) are reduced to a single dish late in the day. In one bad year I saw cases of elderly people who ate nothing during the course of a day, and though this is not common, most adult Natives can remember occasions when they went two days without food, and 'sat in the hut and drank water and took snuff'" (pp. 35–36). Little wonder that when the harvest is reaped Bemba use "magic of durability" to increase the strength of the crops and counter witches who would steal its goodness, for "nothing but supernatural aid can carry a woman safely through the hazards of catering." She has to cater for an unknown number of eaters and the demands of relatives, and she lacks accurate methods of measurement: there is no incentive to have big numbers or standards of measurement, for the Bemba have neither cattle nor exchange. Also "the purely possessive attitude to property with all its concomitant virtues, such as thrift, foresight, or self-reliance, are not inculcated in the Bemba child and would probably unfit him for life in his society." Nevertheless, there is a golden mean between the stingy housekeeper and the inefficient housekeeper described graphically as "a fool in the rainy season" (pp. 200–201). . . .

Richards' comparative tables of calories per day show:

| Bemba village diet | typical European or American diet | government scale | Rhokana Corporation proposed scale |
|---|---|---|---|
| 1706 | 3000 | 4313 | 3663 |

This figure for the Bemba is averaged over a period, and obscures not only the great seasonal variation in intake (in Richards' samples the lowest intake was 286 calories per day in one family in the hunger months, the highest 3164 in another family in the hot season), but also an enormous variation in daily intake. One of the best analyses in the book is that of the Bemba housewife's catering problems. She lacks exact methods of measurement, she has to fit in garden-work, gathering firewood and the long process of preparing food, and she does not know how many mouths she will have to feed at each meal. Relatives may suddenly arrive, or, if she is the village headman's wife, she may suddenly have to feed passing travelers. Even before cooking, it takes hours to pound and grind the hard millet. Her solution is to prepare on the average the same quantity of food, whether five or fifteen are to eat it: and one day her food fills people from a distance, the next day her own dependents may eat elsewhere. . . . If the housewife is the center of several households, she has to provide several baskets of food, but none goes to the boys of nine and over, who have to hang around eating-groups waiting for scraps, and who live in perpetual hunger. . . .

The Bemba accept hunger as part of the regular course of life. "The physical effects of a seasonal shortage of food on the health of people, infant mortality and growth rate of their children has not yet been investigated, but from a sociological point of view there are other effects to be considered besides the lowering of energy due to actual underfeeding which the Natives themselves recognize and describe. In a society in which people regularly expect to be hungry annually, and in which traditions and proverbs accustom them to expect such a period of privation, their whole attitude towards economic effort is affected. In some primitive tribes [as, for example, the Trobrianders of Melanesia] it is considered shameful for an individual or a whole community to go hungry. It is something unexpected, and to be resisted with energy. [Indeed these tribes direct their effort to the accumulation of surplus plenty and its public competitive display, consumption, or distribution.] Among the Bemba scarcity is within the ordinary run of experience, and accepted as such. This fact has a subtle but very powerful effect on their ideas of wealth and their incentives to work." These ideas and

incentives, as will be seen, are rooted in the social organization.

The Bemba's monotonous diet produces cravings and sudden responses to unexpected plenty. Salt was in small supply, and in the old days natural salt from the Mpika pans (one Paramount Chief abandoned his throne to return to the Mpika chieftainship for salt) was one of the few goods traded about the country, and was given as tribute to the chiefs who rewarded with it their faithful followers. To some extent this was still done when Richards was there. The people recognize the craving for salt as most pronounced. Richards describes how at a village in the hunger-season "some children, who had been living for some weeks chiefly on gourds, picked up grains of salt from the floor of my tent with moistened fingers. Their avid faces were striking." Salt figures in folktales, in proverbs, and in ceremonial, and nowadays stands for the wealth of European goods. Two old women said they came to live near the administrative center at Kasama, where they could shop easily: "We came to lick a little of the White man's salt." Salt is still used for barter. The Bemba have a similar craving for meat, and lovingly store small shreds of dried flesh in their huts, and eat the most rotted flesh: so short is meat an educated Bemba "defended the use of putrefying meat by saying, 'Yes, it will give me diarrhoea, but that will be better than throwing the meat away.' " The "attitude to meat shows in a striking fashion the way in which a physiological craving easily accounted for in an area of pronounced shortage of animal protein and salt, becomes associated with all sorts of social and psychological desires. Meat is not only good to eat but it is so rare as to make a break in the daily monotony of food and life. It is a sudden unexpected stroke of good fortune and therefore means that the spirits are on the mortals' side. It means plenty and the royal way of living at the chief's court. It is an occasion for a feast." Therefore when a village obtains a sudden supply of meat it reacts in a way that is quite out of keeping with the purely physiological value of the accession of diet. "It is probably their excitement at the sudden change of diet, their pleasure at the sight of so much food in one community, and their relief at the unexpected appearance of relish got without the usual effort and calculation of ways and means that causes . . . dramatic outbursts of energy."

"For instance, at Kasaka village (September 1933) I shot a large roan antelope which was divided among twenty-two adults and forty-seven children in a community where there had not been much meat available recently. There was probably more than 2 lb. of meat a head on this occasion. Now meat takes some hours to digest, but the energy (or *amaka, i.e.* strength) which the Native claimed that the food gave him was shown not only before the food was digested, but before it was cooked! During the division of the animal the excitement was tense. Men and women gathered round shouting and talking. Before the meal there was a buzz of expectation. Women ground extra flour with enthusiasm, 'Because we have so much meat to eat with it.' Everyone sang at their work. Young men ran skylarking round the village, like a set of English schoolboys in a playground. Directly after the meal, the women gathered near me talking in loud voices. They kept describing with ecstasy how full they felt. 'Our stomachs are rammed tight' (*Munda uauma ndi! ndi! ndi!*), said one with enthusiasm, showing with a gesture a closed first ramming down material hard. 'Yes,' said another, 'we shall all fall asleep at once (*ukulalafye nku!*), not toss or or wake at night as we usually do.' A mother, pointing to a baby of two sprawling, legs wide, replete by the fire, exclaimed, 'Yes look at him, he is so full he cannot sit up straight.' Others pulled down their cloths from their breasts to display their bellies with delight, and indeed there seemed to be quite a visible swelling of the stomach. Part of the excitement seemed connected with the fact that there was not only enough meat for that day, but that it would last till the morrow. The food was so ample that all usual rules of courtesy were put aside. 'There is so much meat that you need not wait for an invitation to join a group of your friends round a basket,' said a young woman, 'you can just swoop down like a vulture and snatch what you want and no one will care.' An old couple sitting together on the veranda of their hut, repeated with quiet satisfaction over and over again, 'Yes, and there is just as much left for tomorrow.' Another old lady cried light-heartedly, hitting her stomach, 'I have been turned into a young girl, my heart is so light.'

"In an hour or so men and women gathered on the village square and burst into spontaneous dancing of a type I had never seen in ordinary life. Young men charged arm in arm up and down in lines singing Bemba and European songs. They imitated mission drilling and play-acting. Young girls played singing games amid screams of laughter. Drums beat, and the older women and babies clapped and shouted. It was like some wild Dionysiac rabble, and indeed these people might have been taken for drunkards, except that they were better tempered, more energetic, and showed more initiative in inventing new games. The next day, they went to work early, declaring that their arms were strong. The excitement on this particular occasion was admittedly unusual, but I have described it as an example of the extreme delight of the Bemba in the sight of meat, and of meat such profusion that it could be used for once in an utterly reckless way. . . ."

I pass now to examine the relation of these facts to Bemba social organization. This part of the argument has more than academic importance. We have seen that owing to the seasonal variation in amount of food available, and specific diet deficiencies, the Bemba in their home environment lack the energy for sustained effort to break out of the circle of dearth, and that this is emphasized by the psychological effects of recurrent hunger. The effect of these conditions on incentives and ability to produce more is obvious; but these incentives, or as Richards says "rather lack of incentives," are further conditioned by the whole economic and social setting of food production and consumption, and finally have been deleteriously affected by modern changes.

In two publications in the Rhodes-Livingstone Institute series of papers I have argued, with the support of other sociologists, that a dominant economic condition in primitive life is that there is very little variation in standard of living between individuals. This theme also runs through Richards' analysis. We meet it early in her book (at p. 34): "All Bemba individuals can be reckoned as eating, roughly speaking, the same type and quantity of food. Class distinctions practically do not exist in this respect. Chiefs certainly have a much more regular supply of food than commoners and drink very much more beer. In fact they often subsist entirely on the latter to the complete exclusion of solids. Their wives, children, and courtiers also eat on the average more than the ordinary family, so much so that Natives describe especially lavish hospitality as 'housekeeping after the fashion of the capital.' But the difference is one of certainty of supply rather than of greatly increased consumption per day, and a small class of individuals only is affected. Otherwise the rich man and his poorer neighbors eat very much the same throughout the year.''

The Bemba, with no cattle, have practically no material possessions and this emphasizes their egalitarian standard of living. There were no material possessions to accumulate, and ''the Bemba method of storage allows them to keep their staple crop for a period of about a year, but is hardly efficient enough to make it possible to accumulate for longer periods'' (p. 90). Therefore they could not have stored food beyond one season and in addition ''actual possession of great quantities of foodstuffs does not seem to have been a particularly cherished ambition of the Bemba. They valued a reputation for giving, not for having, and the distribution of food brought by villagers as tribute or levied as toll on the conquered peoples was a measure of wealth. . . . I never heard a chief boast to another about the size of his granaries, but often about the amount of food brought to him and distributed by him. . . . The Bemba say, 'We will shake the tree until it gives up its fruit,' that is to say we will nag the big man until he divides his supplies. If a chief attempted to dry meat and keep it for subsequent division his followers would sit and stare at it and talk about it until he was forced to give them some'' (p. 214). The ambition of the Bemba, from the chief down, was to be a host, not a hoarder— and though distribution of food gave a man the service of others, this service only produced food to distribute. Hungry men had the right to ''steal from the tribute garden of a chief'' (p. 261), and ''close relatives of the family may step into a garden and help themselves if really hungry'' to maize, sweet potatoes, and cassava, but not gourds or pumpkin. Children especially ''grub up roots from the garden of any near relative on either side of the family, saying indignantly if questioned, 'No, we are not stealing, this is our place here' '' (p. 186). Visiting relatives must be fed, and during the hunger months men go to where there is food. When a community has been raided by locusts or elephants, ''the householder will move himself and his family to live with other kinsmen in an area where food is less scarce.'' With transport difficulties and lack of exchange ''it is simpler for the needy individuals to move to a district of plenty than for the food itself to be transferred to them. Hospitality of this sort is commonly practised in the hunger seasons when families go all over the country 'looking for porridge,' or 'running from hunger'—the rather dramatic Bemba phrase to describe the custom of paying long visits to better off relatives'' (p. 109).

From birth the child is conditioned to share his food with his fellows. Bemba ''mothers who are such lax disciplinarians in other respects, speak quite sharply to their children on this one issue. I have seen a woman seize a lump of pumpkin out of a baby's hand and say in most vehement protest: 'You give some to your friends, you child, you! You sit and eat alone! That is bad what you do' '' (p. 197). The child learns that there are certain relatives who have a right to expect goods from him, and an obligation to help him. ''Food is something over which his older brothers and sisters have definite rights. . . . He is taught that they may pounce on any delicacy that he may be eating.'' Richards contrasts this system under which rights of precedence are impressed with ours, where the rule is ''give it to Baby first.'' Where the Bemba child is taught to share, our children, growing up in a society where individual initiative is on the whole encouraged, are taught to take a pride in their personal possessions.

The Bemba beliefs are supernaturally sanctioned: the wrath of a person who dies feeling that his rights have been denied him, is feared, and charges of sorcery are levied against the person who by persistent efforts produces more than he ought to have, in his station. ''Fear of the accusation of pride or that reputation for personal ambition, which is so often associated with charges of witchcraft'' limits disputes over land, with the young usually giving way lest they be called sorcerers (pp. 271–272), and while ''an occasional stroke of good luck is not resented . . . to be permanently more prosperous than the rest of the village would almost certainly lead to accusations of sorcery'' (p. 215).

On the whole, ambitions are still the same, but the desire for European goods produces inequalities in standards of living, a commoner can possess more clothes than an aristocrat—witchcraft charges increase. "We are dealing with an economic system in which the accumulation of large quantities of any type of material goods was neither very possible nor considered desirable. The accumulation of food was not an end in itself for the chief or notable, but rather a means to enable him to build up a large following of people which was to him the highest aim in life. His economic assets consisted in rights over food produced by others as well as in the cultivation of millet himself. For the commoner, the possession of excessive food supplies was definitely considered unsuitable, and people were afraid to admit they had such a store. In short the surplus crop was not a Bemba ideal. Under modern conditions the desire for European goods, and in particular clothes, leads the people to squander even their available food supplies on objects which have become more important to them" (p. 218). These dominant economic conditions form the background for the whole analysis.

We can now return, for the moment, to the problem of incentives to production. In these economic conditions it is difficult for the Bemba woman to budget, for her food is not only for the use of her own family, but has also to feed an indefinite number of relatives in a system of mutual help. "The economic conditions under which she lives necessitate reciprocal sharing of foodstuffs, rather than their accumulation, and extend the individual's responsibility outside her own household. Plainly, therefore, it does not pay a Bemba woman to have much more grain than her fellows. She would merely have to distribute it, and during the recent locust scourge the villagers whose gardens escaped destruction complained that they were not really better off than their fellows for 'our people come and live with us or beg us for baskets of millet' " (pp. 201–202).

Though there is this tremendous stress on sharing and hospitality, and the Bemba woman has to maintain a delicate adjustment between the rights of her relatives by blood and marriage and her own needs in her crops, it is wrong to describe the system as purely communistic or communal. The basis is highly individualistic. The Bemba had little difficulty in getting land to work and cut their gardens where they pleased, though naturally near their villages. But once a man has cut his garden it is his and not even a chief will interfere with him: "it would not pay him to do so," since the more his subjects the more the food produced in his country and the more the tribute he gets. "In fact, in the case of a new garden the Natives seem to believe that there is some particularly close connection of an almost magical nature, between the owner and the patch of ground he has just cleared of bush. Although a man can lend his garden to another in the second or third year, or even sell the crops on it, he should do neither of these things in the case of the first year patch" (p. 185). Despite this sharing, individual ownership of field crops, of bush-goods, caterpillar swarms, hives of wild bees, of meat and fish, "is very clearly defined among the Bemba" (p. 188). The "system of food consumption is determined by rules of individual ownership subject to the claims of elder relatives" (p. 195). . . .

Richards thus shows clearly that in the Bemba economic situation, with its conceptions of wealth, of the purposes for which food should be used, of the values attached to hospitality and to kinship, etc., there is a definite bias against individuals increasing their production. We thus come to one of the "balances" which experts always stress and the dangers of upsetting which they seem always to emphasize. Richards makes a careful, detailed analysis of the actual distribution of food and performance of labor tasks as she observed them in a typical village and she concludes that the establishing of isolated individual families, in which this "lack of incentives" might theoretically be overcome, would be unwise without provision to meet the new difficulties that would be created. For her analysis shows clearly "how the addition of each additional supporting household strengthens the position of the whole family" (p. 171), and a comparison with modern villagers near European centers shows that "the families in these communities are at present in an intermediate position—they do not have to share their supplies as do their fellows in the bush, yet they are much worse off during the hunger months, since they cannot rely on their kinsmen for support. Although it appears that most Africans must ultimately adopt the European system of economy, the encouragement of the single family household, before a system of trade has been established, might well lead to disaster" (p. 153). It must be recognized that joint housekeeping makes for greater security in a society with no system of exchange or purchase of food. To be attached to a "big house" is to share its fortunes——to have the chance of delicacies like beer and meat as often as possible, and to be certain of support in case of a shortage. A comparison between conditions in a modern village where the kinship groups are smaller makes this clear. Where the unit of consumption is only one or two households the people may be better off at good seasons of the year but practically destitute in a bad one.

"Joint cooking also eases the housewife's labor very largely." Richards by analyzing household tasks shows how difficult it is for a woman to fit in the lengthy process of cooking, how grinding and pounding go more quickly in company, and how where there are several women in a team some find relish and bring wood and water while another cooks. The isolated housewife cannot do this, and Richards' notes on typical families show this clearly (p. 132).

Richards traces food, the clearing of land, cooking, storing, and learning of household craft, through these economic conditions in a meticulous analysis, enlivened with the observations of a witty and sympathetic mind. The Bemba stand out as individuals, like Namukonda, "an incisive personality. She was a good organizer, who met each domestic emergency with calm decision and who kept her large family in wholesome awe of her sharp tongue. Her withering comments on the follies of the present generation were a constant delight to me. They were uttered with a shrug, a lifted eyebrow, and a glance of understanding as though between two adults alone in a nursery of tiresome children" (p. 171). We feel the dismay in the family of a young woman who refused to live with her hot-tempered husband and could not persuade her brother to provide his fourteen-year-old daughter as a substitute according to the old Bemba custom. "The injured husband retired to his own family's village to await events. After a few weeks a file of six women with empty baskets on their heads appeared from that direction. The wife's relatives stood aghast at the doors of their huts muttering, '*Yangwe*. They have come to take the grain.' They could only watch while the husband's kinswomen lifted the roof of the granary, emptied its contents, and left with their baskets full, after a brisk exchange of obscene abuse between both parties" (p. 190). We sympathize with the lot of a wife, one of six sisters, who lived happily with them in her village through the years of her husband's service to her father, but who when he gained the right to move to his own village could not bear "the contrast between the cheerful female group in her own village and her relative isolation in her husband's community." She ran away three times, and ultimately was divorced (p. 131). We see the modern chief struggling to maintain his court and status with income tremendously reduced, yet who knows all that is going on [in] his country, so that when a Bisa chief comes to ask for his daughter's hand he can send messengers to get beer and food at villages where he knows they will be found.

*part 6*

*Primitive Society*

# *Tupinamba — War and Cannibalism*

## *Alfred Metraux*

*From Handbook of South American Indians.* Bureau of American Ethnology Bulletin *143, Vol. 3, 1948, pp. 119–126. By permission of the author and the publisher.*

Religious and social values of high importance clustered around war and the closely connected practice of cannibalism. Prestige and political power were derived mainly from the ritual slaughtering of prisoners, which was so far reaching in its influence that it even affected sexual life. The Tupinamba's excessive interest in ritual cannibalism contributed toward keeping the different tribes and even local communities in a constant state of warfare and was one of the chief causes of their ready subjection by Europeans. Their mutual hatred of one another, born of a desire to avenge the insult of cannibalism, was so great that the Tupinamba groups always willingly marched with the White invaders against their local rivals. Their bellicose disposition and craving for human flesh loom large in many aspects of their culture, such as education, oratory, poetry, and religion. The rites and festivities that marked the execution of a prisoner and the consumption of his body were joyful events which provided these Indians with the opportunity for merrymaking, esthetic displays, and other emotional outlets.

The Tupinamba went to war only with the certainty of victory, which they derived from the interpretation of dreams and from ritualistic performances such as dancing and reciting charms. When marching toward the enemy, they paid special attention to any omen and to dreams. The slightest bad omen was sufficient to stop the expedition: once a party of warriors that had almost taken a village retreated because of a few words uttered by a parrot.

Besides arrows and bows, Tupinamba weapons included a hardwood club with a shape unique in South America. It consisted of two parts: a long, rounded handle and a flattened, round, or oval blade with sharp edges. The only defensive weapon was a shield of tapir hide. Warriors donned their best feather ornaments and painted their bodies. Men of importance were followed by their wives, who carried hammocks and food for them. The advancing army was accompanied by musical instruments. Whenever possible, they used canoes to avoid long marches. The chief always headed the column, which was disposed in one line. Scouts reconnoitered the country. At night the warriors camped near a river and built small huts in a row along a path.

The proper time to assault the enemy village was chosen cautiously. As a rule, they stormed it at night or at dawn, when least expected. When prevented by a stockade from entering a village immediately, they built another palisade of thorny bushes around the village and started a siege. One tactic was to set fire to the enemy houses with incendiary arrows. Sometimes they slowly moved their fence close to the opposite wall so that they could fight at close range.

The Tupinamba fought with courage and determination but without much order as they did not obey any command during the battle. They opened the attack by shooting arrows, hopping about with great agility from one spot to another to prevent the enemy from aiming or shooting at any definite individual. Amid ferocious howls, they rushed against their opponents to strike them with their clubs, trying to take prisoners, one of the main purposes of the war. Because it was difficult to seize an enemy without the assistance of several persons, it was an established rule that the prisoner belonged to the first man to touch him. When a man was disarmed, the victor touched him on the shoulder and said, "You are my prisoner." Thereafter, the man was his slave. Those who remained in possession of the battlefield would roast the corpses and bring back the heads and the sexual organs of the dead.

The long set of cannibalistic rites and practices began immediately after the capture of a prisoner. On the way home, the victorious party exhibited their captives in friendly villages, where they were subjected to "gross insults and vituperation." The latter retaliated by expressing their contempt for their victors and their pride at being eaten as befitted the brave.

Before entering their masters' village, the prisoners were dressed as Tupinamba, with foreheads shaven, feathers glued to their bodies, and a decoration of feather ornaments. They were taken to the graves of the recently deceased of the community and compelled to "renew," that is, clean them. Later they received the hammocks, ornaments, and weapons of the dead, which had to be used before they could be reappropriated by the heirs. The reason for this custom was that touching the belongings of a dead relative was fraught with danger, unless they were first defiled by a captive.

When the prisoners were taken into the village, women flocked around them, snatched them from the hands of the men, and accompanied them, celebrating their capture with songs, dances, and references to the day of their execution. They forced the prisoners to dance in front of the hut where the sacred rattles were kept.

After this hostile reception, the prisoners' condition changed for the better. Their victors often gave them to a son or some other relative, who had the privilege of slaughtering them and acquiring new names—one of the greatest distinctions which a Tupinamba coveted. The prisoners were also traded for feathers or other ornaments. In many cases, the only outward sign of the prisoner's status was a cotton rope tied around his neck, which according to some sources, was a symbolical necklace strung with as many beads as he had months to live until his execution. The captives were in no way hampered in their movements; they knew perfectly well that there was no place to which they could escape, for their own groups, far from welcoming them, would even have killed any member who attempted to return. On the other hand, to be killed ceremonially and then eaten was the fate for which any brave longed once he had lost his liberty. Nothing would have reminded a prisoner of his impending death if, on certain occasions, he had not been exhibited in public and again exposed to jeers and provocations. At drinking bouts, portions of his body were allotted beforehand to the carousers, each of whom—in the victim's presence—learned the part he was to receive at the ceremonial execution.

The village council chose the date of execution and sent invitations to friendly communities. Preparations for the sacrifice started a long time in advance. Certain accessories, like the plaited rope with which the victim was fastened, required a long time to make. Great quantities of beer also had to be brewed for the occasion.

The prisoner feigned indifference toward these signs of his threatening fate. In certain villages he was tied up, but then he indulged freely in all sorts of mischief to revenge his death. The rites observed in these cases started after the arrival of the guests and lasted 3 to 5 days.

On the first day the cord was bleached and artfully knotted, the prisoner was painted black, green eggshells were pasted on his face, and red feathers were glued on his body. The executioners also decorated their own persons with feathers and paint. Old women spent the first night in the hut of the captive singing songs depicting his fate. On the second day they made a bonfire in the middle of the plaza, and men and women danced around the flames while the prisoner pelted them with anything he could reach. The only ceremony of the third day was a dance accompanied by trumpets. The day before the execution the prisoner was given a chance to escape but was immediately pursued. The person who overtook and overpowered him in a wrestling combat adopted a new name, as did the ceremonial executioner. The ritual rope was passed round the prisoner's neck, the end being held by a woman. The prisoner was then given fruits or other missiles to throw at passers-by. Festivities began that night. The prisoner was often requested to dance. Apparently he did so without reluctance and took part in the general rejoicing as if he were merely a guest. He even regarded his position as enviable, for "it was an honor to die as a great warrior during dancing and drinking." The prisoner spent the remainder of his last night in a special hut under the surveillance of women, singing a song in which he foretold the ruin of his enemies and proclaimed his pride at dying as a warrior. His only food was a nut that prevented his bleeding too much. The same night the club to be used for the sacrifice received special treatment. It was decorated, like the prisoner himself, with green eggshells glued on the wood, the handle was trimmed with tassels and feathers and finally, it was suspended from the roof of a hut, women dancing and singing around it during the entire night.

The following morning the prisoner was dragged to the plaza by some old women amid cries, songs, and music. The rope was taken from his neck, passed round his waist, and held at both ends by two or more men. Again he was allowed to give vent to his feelings by throwing fruits or potsherds at his enemies. He was surrounded by women who vied in their insults. Old women, painted black and red, with necklaces of human teeth, darted out of their huts carrying newly painted vases to receive the victim's blood and entrails. A fire was lit and the ceremonial club was shown to the captive. Every man present handled the club for a while, thus acquiring the power to catch a prisoner in the future. Then the executioner appeared in full array, painted and covered with a long feather cloak. He was followed by relatives who sang and beat drums. Their bodies, like that of the executioner, were smeared with white ashes. The club was handed to the executioner by a famous old warrior, who performed a few ritual gestures with it. Then the executioner and his victim harangued each other. The executioner derided the prisoner for his imminent death, while the latter foretold the vengeance that his relatives would take and boasted of his past deeds. The captive showed despondency only if his executioner, instead of being an experienced warrior, was merely a young man who had never been on the battlefield. The execution itself was a cruel game. Enough liberty was allowed the prisoner to dodge the blows, and sometimes a club was put in his hands so that he could parry them without being able to strike. When at last he fell down, his skull shattered, everybody shouted and whistled. The position of the body was interpreted as an omen for the executioner. The prisoner's wife shed a few tears over his body and then joined in the cannibalistic banquet.

Old women rushed to drink the warm blood, and children were invited to dip their hands in it. Mothers would smear their nipples with blood so that even babies could have a taste of it. The body, cut into quarters, was roasted on a barbecue, and the old women, who were the most eager for human flesh, licked the grease running along the sticks. Some portions, reputed to be delicacies or sacred, such as the fingers or the grease around the liver or heart, were allotted to distinguished guests.

As soon as the executioner had killed the

victim, he had to run quickly to his hut, which he entered passing between the string and the stave of a stretched bow. Indoors he continued running to and fro as if escaping from his victim's ghost. Meanwhile his sisters and cousins went through the village proclaiming his new name. On this occasion, the male and female relatives of his generation also had to take new names. The members of the community then rushed into the killer's hut and looted all his goods, while the killer himself stood on wooden pestles, where the eye of his victim was shown to him and rubbed against his wrist. The lips of the dead man were sometimes given to him to wear as a bracelet. However, his flesh was strictly taboo to the killer. After this the executioner had to recline in a hammock until the hair on his shaved forehead had grown again. During seclusion, he entertained himself by shooting miniature arrows at a wax figure. For 3 days he might not walk but was carried whenever he needed to leave the hut. He also avoided several foods, especially condiments. His return to normal life was celebrated by a big drinking bout, at which the killer tattooed himself by slashing his body in different patterns with an agouti tooth—the more tattooing marks a man could exhibit the higher was his prestige. Even after the feast he was subject to a few more restrictions before he was again a full-fledged member of the community.

The same rites were practiced if, instead of a man, a jaguar had been killed. Later, when the Tupinamba could no longer sacrifice their war prisoners, they would open the graves of their enemies and break the skulls with the same ceremonies. The heads of dead enemies were pinned to the ends of the stockade posts.

*selection 26*

# Where Did the Plains Indians Get Their Horses?

*Francis Haines*

Although horses were unknown to the Indians of North America before the advent of the Spaniards, many of the tribes living in the great plains area were already in possession of these animals before the first explorers and traders reached them. This rapid diffusion of the horse well in advance of the on-coming white men proved an important factor in the subsequent history of the West and has caused a great deal of speculation concerning the details of such spread.

Because of the supposedly favorable environment for horses throughout most of the area west of the Mississippi, there has been

*From* American Anthropologist, *Vol. 40, No. 1, 1938, pp. 112–117. By permission of the author and the publisher.*

little question that the natural increase of a comparatively small starting herd could have furnished an ample supply for the whole area in the course of a century or two, much as the herd of twelve in South America spread over the pampas there in a much shorter time. The chief difficulty has been to determine the place of origin of the original stock, and with it the date of starting. Once this had been determined, it would be easier to trace the resulting lines of distribution and to approximate the rate of spread.

Possibly the most detailed work on this topic has been done by Clark Wissler, who has written on the influence of the horse on the culture of the Plains Indian. He indicates that animals lost or abandoned by the DeSoto and Coronado expeditions in the period 1540–1542 probably furnished the parent stock. With such an early introduction, horses could have reached the limits of their natural range by 1600. He says ". . . for all we know, the Crow and Blackfoot, for instance, may have had horses for 150 years before their first mention in 1742 and 1751." While few writers agree that the horses could have reached their northern limits so soon, many favor this theory that the strays from either or both of the expeditions multiplied rapidly on the plains and were adopted by the Indians before their next contacts with the whites.

Since this theory was so commonly accepted, it seemed that a careful search of source material should disclose a few items bearing on the subject which would, even though indirectly, substantiate such an explanation. The search for such items surprised me greatly. The evidence and deductions all indicated that the theory was highly improbable. The following argument is offered in support of this statement.

How many horses must have been lost or abandoned at one spot in order to have established a herd? Obviously the minimum number under the most ideal conditions would have been two, and the chances of survival would have increased rapidly with an increase in numbers. The maximum number that could have been lost is not so easily determined. The limiting factor here is how many animals could be lost at one spot and the loss still remain too small to be noted by the chroniclers? When we consider how important horses were to the early Spaniards, how frequently they are mentioned in the various accounts, and how losses of two or three animals at a time were noted, we may be quite sure that no substantial loss of animals would have gone unrecorded.

It must be emphasized that the animals must have been lost at one spot. Strays separated by even one day's march would have slight chance of finding each other. If they were searching for companions they would have been much more likely to rejoin the main herd. These considerations would limit the possible starting size of such a herd of strays to eight or ten at the very most.

What are the chances for the survival of such a small herd? Mathematically, under ideal conditions, two animals could produce more than three hundred offspring in twenty years, but actually such a result would be impossible. Each mare would not obligingly have a colt each year, nor could all the colts reach maturity. They would be subject to drought, northers, starvation. During the first few years when they could least afford the losses is precisely the period in which the percentage of loss would be the greatest because they would be adjusting themselves to a new environment. This adjustment would be all the harder to make because they would be located in the poorer sections of the country. In fact, the probability of horses straying from the herd, or of horses being abandoned because they are worn out increases directly with the unsuitability of country for their needs, through lack of feed and water.

More important than this, though, is a factor frequently overlooked. In the sixteenth and seventeenth centuries the prairies and plains were not suitable for raising of stock because of large numbers of predators—buffalo or gray wolves, coyotes, pumas. It was not until the hunter and trapper had slaughtered most of these that either range horses or cattle could increase rapidly. Here is a case where a restrictive environmental factor has been overlooked because it is no longer present; but stockmen of even the present day, or the government hunters, will testify to the deadliness of such predators toward colts or bewildered strays.

Nor could the Indian of that period furnish the necessary care and protection to nullify this danger. With very few exceptions Indian tribes did not develop into stock raisers until after they had been placed on reservations and had been instructed by the whites. They depended on horse stealing rather than horse raising for their supply of animals. It is hard to conceive of their spontaneously developing a method of horse raising only to abandon it before the approach of the whites, and when the horses were still too few for their wants. The tendency of the Indian to eat spare animals from the herd would also have hindered the growth of their herds.

Here let me offer a suggestion which might repay a little further study. Possibly much of this failure on the part of the Indian to raise stock can be attributed to his packs of fierce dogs, particularly deadly to the colts. Consider the case of the Nez Percé, one of the few tribes noted as horse raisers at the time of their first contact with the whites. They had few dogs, yet when their Indian Agent, Dr. White, in 1842 discussed with them the advisability of adopting a code of laws against common offenses, the one addition which the tribe made to the proposed code read:

"Those only may keep dogs who travel or live among the game. If a dog kill a lamb, calf or any domestic animal, the owner shall pay the damage and kill the dog."

It is evident that the dogs were more of a nuisance because of the added herds of domestic animals, but it also indicates how such dogs, accustomed to help in running game, might easily develop into colt killers before they could be trained to let the new animals alone. And if dogs could be a serious problem in this tribe where there were comparatively few of the animals, think how much greater the problem would be in a camp of the Plains Indians with a dog pack of five hundred or more.

If the horses escaped all these dangers, where would they be found after a period of sixty years? Surely in the vicinity of the line of march of the expeditions. In the case of the DeSoto expedition, we need not consider the horses lost or abandoned east of the Mississippi, nor those lost in the river bottom on the west bank. Since the hostile Indians of the region killed horses at every opportunity, such strays would have perished long before they could have wandered by chance to the plains.

Could Francisco de Guzman, who left De Soto to live with the Indians, have cared for his own mounts and yet have lost these strays, thus establishing a herd? No, because he had no horses at the time of his desertion. He had just gambled away the last, a spirited black, a day or two before his departure with his Indian concubine to prevent the latter being claimed in payment of his final debt. Nor could he have rounded up the four or five turned loose many miles down the river when the survivors of the expedition butchered their mounts to secure a supply of meat for their voyage to Mexico, because the Indians of the vicinity shot them full of arrows even before the boats of the Spanish were out of sight, and it is doubtful that any of them could have survived even to the next day.

No, if the DeSoto expedition furnished any horses to found the later Indian herds, it must have lost them on the march to the west, after DeSoto's death, in an attempt to reach New Spain overland. In such case the strays would have been left in north Texas somewhere near the Red River. The narrative of the trip mentions no horses lost except two killed by Indians.

In the case of Coronado, we need not concern ourselves about any horses lost between Culiacan and Tiguex on either the outward or the return journey, for such strays would have been cut off from reaching the plains. Also we do not need to consider losses by Coronado and his body of picked troops on their way to Quivira and return. Since he took thirty picked horses for forty-two men, any losses would have been important enough for the record. There is no hint that even one horse was lost on the trip.

It is true that Coronado suffered a serious loss of horses at Tiguex. There the Indians made a raid on the horse herd in retaliation for an attempted violation of an Indian woman by a Spaniard. While they were successful in securing a large number of animals, the evidence is against any of these being used later for breeding stock. "The next day Don Garcia Lopez de Cardenas went to see the villages and talk with the natives. He found the villages closed by palisades and a great noise inside, the horses being chased as in a bull fight and shot with arrows." As the Spaniards captured the village soon after, it is evident that any horses surviving this merry little game were recovered.

This limits the possible loss of horses by

Coronado to the territory covered by his army in its march east from the Pecos and return. It is interesting to note that this is the same area in which DeSoto's men might have lost horses the same year. If, then, either or both expeditions lost horses sufficient to found a herd but too few to be noted by the chroniclers of the expeditions, and if these horses succeeded in surviving and multiplying, for a good many years their center of distribution must have been a strip of land between the Canadian and Brazos Rivers. If such a herd increased rapidly enough to furnish an appreciable supply of horses to the Plains Indians, then this area should have been well stocked after a lapse of half a century.

Note that we are not interested here in the question, did any of the horses survive? The possible presence of an isolated band in a remote canyon has no bearing on the question, since we are discussing the probability of these horses furnishing a supply for the Plains Indians.

By 1600, then, when the Spaniards again explored this region, the horses would have had nearly sixty years to establish themselves. Their signs should have been visible at every watering hole, and bands of horses should have been sighted daily by the travellers, as they were throughout this same area at later times. Since the Indians in this vicinity had seen the Spaniards using horses, and since they had the finest opportunity of any of the tribes to capture horses, surely if any of the tribes had adopted horses by 1600 it would be those in this vicinity. But what are the actual conditions? Oñate's men traversed the area four times. They hunted game, surveyed the country, and observed the various kinds of plants and animals. They visited with and observed the Indians, reporting on their various methods of camping, hunting, use of dogs, and the like; yet in all this there is not a single mention of any horse, except the mounts of the Spaniards. When one considers the important part in the Spaniards' lives played by horses, and the many details of these animals included in the various accounts, he must conclude that the omission of Indian or wild horses from the reports can mean only that they did not see any horses or horse signs.

For a more definite statement we may turn to the famous *Memorial* of Fray Alonzo de Benavides. He states specifically that Oñate found no horses in New Mexico on his arrival there. Writing in 1630, Benavides described in detail the Vaquero Apaches from the east who came in to the settlements of New Mexico to trade, carrying all their belongings and trade goods on travois drawn by dogs. The detailed description of their hunting buffalo shows that these Indians did not use horses for that purpose either. Yet this is eighty-eight years after Coronado, and thirty years after horses might have reached the Crow and Blackfoot.

When the missionaries crossed to east Texas to minister to the Humanos Indians, they reported on various Indian customs and told of the various animals and plants in the country, but here again there is no mention of horses, either wild or tame, being found in any of the area traversed. In fact, it is not until the Mendoza-Lopez expedition to these same Indians in 1683–1684 that I find a specific mention of the Indians of Texas using horses. From this account, too, it would appear that horses were still scarce in the Texas country, indicating that they were rather recently introduced.

Is it not evident, then, that the chances of strays from the horse herds of either DeSoto or Coronado having furnished the horses of the Plains Indians is so remote that it should be discarded? Rather should we look for some white settlement with an increasing supply of stock which would furnish both the animals and the example of how they should be used. In contact with such a settlement the Indians would adopt the horse rather rapidly, and his equipment would be like that of the white man. The other theory would have us believe that after the Indians had seen one group of Spaniards for a few days, they would have been so versed in horse training and making of equipment that, years later, finding a few wild horses on the plains, they set about to capture and train these steeds, making equipment just like that of the whites. Then, after an interval of about a half-century they had surrendered all their horses to tribes further away, and had also disposed of all the wild herds.

Oñate's settlements, particularly Sante Fé, would furnish just the items necessary to encourage the adoption of horses by the Indians to the east—friendly contact through trade, ample supply of horses, and examples of the advantages of the new servants. From here the horses spread south, east, and north like a giant fan, reaching the southern and eastern limits rather rapidly because of the shorter distance to be covered. At the same time they were also spreading along the western slopes of the continental divide, but with a smaller area to fill; since much of the country was desert, they reached farther in a given time— but this topic is another problem.

The available evidence indicates then that the Plains Indians began acquiring horses some time after 1600, the center of distribution being Sante Fé. This development proceeded rather slowly; none of the tribes becoming horse Indians before 1630, and probably not until 1650.

*selection  27*

# The Northward Spread of Horses among the Plains Indians

## Francis Haines

The problem of the spread of the horse to the western tribes of North America, outlined by Clark Wissler some twenty-four years ago, has been rather neglected since that time, although many people working with individual tribes have included some local material on the horse. In the first paper of this series an attempt was made to determine the probability of stray horses from either the Coronado or DeSoto expeditions furnishing the basic stock for the Indian herds, with the conclusion that the available evidence was against it. This paper continues the discussion, taking up the subject at about the year 1600, and dealing with the northward spread of the horse from the Spanish settlements, with attention to the rate of spread, the lines of distribution, and the approximate dates when the various tribes secured their first animals. Special attention has been paid to the geography of the West, including such features as mountain masses,

*From* American Anthropologist, *Vol. 40, No. 3, 1938, pp. 429–437. By permission of the author and the publisher.*

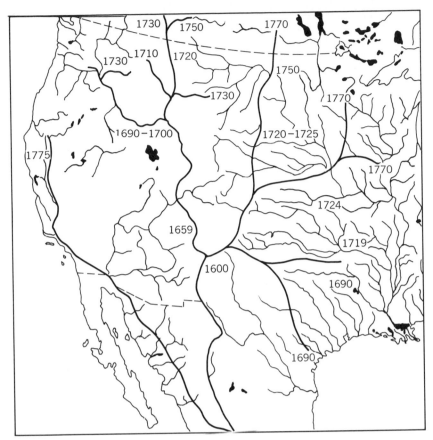

**Figure 1** Map showing the northward spread of the horse in the Western United States. Lines indicate the approximate routes followed by horses; the dates, the approximate time the horse reached each area.

Indian trails and trade routes, rivers, and deserts.

While it is possible that the Pueblo villages along the Rio Grande had a few horses before Oñate established his settlements there at the opening of the seventeenth century, they must have been quite unimportant, since no mention is made of them. None of the Plains tribes had been able to acquire the animals which later became such an important factor in their daily lives. The center from which the horses spread to the Indian tribes was the stock-raising area about Sante Fé, and from here they spread very slowly at first but later more rapidly until the entire plains and plateau country had been supplied.

The initial obstacle to be overcome in converting the Indian to the use of the horse was his ignorance in the care and use of the strange animal. This was overcome by the constant contact between the Indians and the horse-using Spaniard, rather than by the chance acquisition of a stray animal by some tribe. To such a tribe the stray would have suggested a dinner rather than a servant. While the Spaniards did not intend to make horse-users of the Indians of New Mexico, and were actually opposed to such a result, as is shown by the laws against Indians riding horses, their method of farming soon achieved that end. On the various farms run by the missions or by private individuals the Indians were the servants who did all the work, including the care of various kinds of livestock. Under such circumstances the herdsmen soon learned the methods of training and using horses, with the mission farm offering him the greater opportunity of learning to ride.

Once the mission Indian had learned to use the new servant he was but little better off than before. Only by seeking refuge among the nomadic tribes could he escape from the constant labor imposed upon him and be assured of safety from the soldiers whose duty it was to return him to his task and to fitting punishment. What would be more natural than for a herdsman to make his escape with some of the horses entrusted to his care? Frontier history abounds in such incidents.

If the fugitive was able to join one of the nomadic tribes before disaster overtook him, he might become an important man among his adopted people because of his knowledge of the white ways and his possession of the strange animal. Sometimes, however, he became a slave, worse off than before. In either case, the wild tribe would have horses and someone to teach them how to use the new servants. Warriors, who previously would have had no incentive to steal a horse except possibly for food, would now be interested in securing mounts and pack animals of their own. The tribe would gradually acquire more horses by barter or theft, but it would take many years before an adequate supply could be procured. Benavides, who has given a rather detailed description of the various tribes of New Mexico and the adjoining regions, made no mention of horses being used by the Indians, although he wrote thirty years after the first settlement.

By 1659 the Navaho Apaches to the northwest of the settlements are reported as making raids on the ranch stock. Five years later an account states that this has become a constant practice, and that the Apaches to the east bring in Indian captives from other tribes to trade for horses.

While it is evident that the gradual process outlined above would eventually have distributed horses throughout the entire west, the movement was greatly speeded up by the Pueblo revolt in 1680. When the Spaniards were driven out, many thousand horses, cattle, sheep, and hogs were captured by the rebels. Of these, the horses would be traded off to the Plains tribes since they would bring higher prices in trade and were of less value to the Pueblos. Most of the horses would probably go to the east in exchange for buffalo robes and dried meat, standard articles of trade in the region when the white men first appeared. The resulting distribution of horses probably was heavier to the southeast into Texas because of the close trade relations with the tribes in that direction.

This supposition is supported by the distribution of horses found in Texas by 1690. When Fernando del Bosque had explored along the Rio Grande from the mouth of the Conches to the Pecos River and some distance eastward into Texas in 1675, he found no trace of horses or of horse-using Indians. Eight years later the Mendoza-Lopez expedition also found the banks of the Rio Grande barren of horses, but as it progressed to the northeast it soon encountered Indians with a few horses. The farther north the expedition proceeded the more animals they found, indicating that the horse frontier was moving from north to south in Texas and had not quite reached the Rio Grande at that time.

This is quite different from the movement of horses in the next century, when the Plains Indians, particularly the Comanche, raided deep into Mexico, driving thousands of animals north each year. The Spanish missions and presidios also brought their stock in by the road from Monclova, while the road to Santa Fé was blocked by the wild tribes.

When the Spanish, in 1690, went to Matagordos Bay to expel the French left there by La Salle, they found a few horses near the mouth of the Colorado River of Texas, under conditions suggesting that the animals were a rather recent importation. Few of the Indians had horses to ride, and dogs were still used to carry the meat.

To the north the situation was quite similar. Tonty, in 1690, found about thirty horses among the Cadadoquis along the Red River near the Arkansas-Texas boundary. A few days' travel to the south-west he met the Naouadiche, who had many horses, each lodge possessing four or five. This indicates that the horses were spreading from west to east in that section, and that the Cadadoquis marked the extreme limit of their advance. It would seem, then, that by 1690 all the Plains tribes of Texas had horses, but that the animals were quite scarce to the south and east, indicating that they had but recently reached those areas.

North of Texas there is less data. Tonty's report of his first trip down the Mississippi, as given by Margry, indicates that he knew of horses on the Missouri in 1682. However, his manuscript as translated by Falconer does not indicate any such observation. The passage was probably written after 1695, and was based on Tonty's findings in 1690.

Du Tisne gives the first reliable account

of horses among the Pawnee. When he reached two of their villages in Oklahoma near the Arkansas River in 1719, it is evident he was in contact with the horse frontier. He found that the two villages possessed a total of three hundred horses, which to Du Tisne, accustomed to the Indians of the wooded regions who had none of the animals, seemed like a great number, and he so reported it. His statement that the Pawnee villages had a great number of horses has often been quoted without comment, leaving the impression with the casual reader that horses were as common there at that time as they were later when the Pawnee were the noted horse traders of that section of the country. Actually Du Tisne's figures show that the three hundred horses had to supply more than four hundred warriors, or less than one horse per man, while normal figures for such villages in later times would have been five to ten horses per man, or a total of from two to five thousand horses in all. Another indication that horses actually were scarce is Du Tisne's statement that they were highly valued and not for sale.

Bourgmont, on his trip up the Missouri River to the plains in 1724, likewise crossed the border of the horse area as is shown by his account. The Kansas Indians who accompanied him to the plains did not take horses on the trip, the detailed account listing fourteen war chiefs, three hundred warriors, three hundred women, five hundred children, and three hundred dogs, but no horses. Later, Bourgmont met some of the Kansas tribe farther west who did have a few horses, and he managed to buy seven animals at a high price. This would indicate that the edge of the horse area had just reached the neighborhood of the junction of the Kansas and Missouri Rivers at that time.

The next definite account of white men coming in contact with the northward moving border of the horse area is found in the writings of the Vérendryes. From their various journals covering the period 1735–1743, it is clear that there were no horses north and east of the Missouri River in the Dakotas until one of the sons brought two of the animals from the vicinity of the Black Hills to the Canadian posts. Horses had as yet appeared only occasionally on the southern bank of the Missouri opposite the Mandan villages. The real limit of horse using Indians was the

Black Hills country, the Mandans having acquired no horses yet although they had been trading with horse Indians for several years.

The Missouri should not be considered as a serious barrier to the spread of the horse in this region. During the low water of late summer it would have been comparatively easy to swim horses across the stream, especially with the aid of the "bull boats." May not the Mandans and some of the Sioux have delayed in acquiring horses because the animals did not fit into their plan of living? At any rate, Carver found a few horses at Prairie du Chien in 1766, but the Sioux whom he met in central Minnesota that same year were using canoes rather than horses. This is important for the purpose of this paper because Peter Pond, trading in the same area six years later, found horses in common use among the Sioux who, he says, are the same ones visited by Carver. David Thompson, writing in 1796, reported that the Sioux were then using horses instead of canoes, indicating that they had made the change in comparatively recent times or it would not have been worth the emphasis he gave it.

All the evidence considered above, in combination with the previous article dealing with the earlier period, would indicate that Santa Fé and the ranches in its vicinity was the center of distribution for the horses of the plains area. East of the mountains the horses spread in a fan shaped area, with the movement into Texas being the more rapid. The less rapid movement to the north and the northeast may have been due to the greater number of Indians to be supplied, or to the southward movement of the tribes, which nullified to some extent this northward movement of the horse, but these are merely guesses on the part of the writer. The spread of the horse to the plains area began about 1630 and reached its northern limits, except for a small extension into the timbered area, by 1770. Very few horses could have been owned north of central Kansas before 1700.

The presence of horses in the Blackfoot country, mentioned by St Pierre in 1751, confronts us with a new phase of the problem since it is highly improbable that the Blackfoot secured their horses by the way of the plains. By 1754 horses were in general use in this tribe both for pack animals and for riding. Although bands of wild horses were common in the Blackfoot country fifty years later, it is probable that the two seen on the range by Hendry in 1754 were strays escaped from some camp. The Assiniboin just to the east of the Blackfoot had a few horses which they used for packing but they had not yet learned to ride. Those farther to the east had no horses at all, indicating that the spread was from the eastern slope of the Rockies to the east, rather than from south to north.

We have much more definite information concerning the first horse in the Blackfoot country than we have for any other of the tribes discussed, since David Thompson was a friend of the chief who saw the first horse, and who helped introduce the animal to the tribe. In 1787 Thompson spent a long time visiting the tribe. An old war chief, whom he estimated to be between seventy-five and eighty years old at the time, gave him a detailed account of the first horse he had seen, and stated that the tribe had acquired their first animals from the Shoshone or Snake while the chief was a young man, but some years after his marriage. This event took place almost simultaneously with the acquisition of firearms by the Blackfoot. Since the chief was estimated to be seventy-five or eighty in 1787, he was probably born between 1700 and 1720 (allowing a great deal on each end for an error in Thompson's estimate). He heard of horses among the Snake for the first time when he was sixteen, but his tribe did not acquire any until after he had been married several years. Thompson gives the usual age for marriage as twenty-two for men in the tribe. Accepting Thompson as accurate in his estimates, this would place the acquisition of the horse between 1732 and 1737. I favor the earlier date because of the progress made in the use of the animal, and the numbers owned by the tribe in 1754. From all the evidence, it would seem more probable that the chief was older rather than younger than the estimated age. Note that the Snake were using the horse in war against the Blackfoot when the chief was sixteen, or about 1722. At this time the animal had not spread north of the Black Hills, some seven hundred miles away and on the line of distribution from the southern plains to the Blackfoot country.

Flathead tribal tradition holds that they had horses before the Blackfoot secured any, and that the Blackfoot got theirs from the Shoshone. The Flathead also say that their own horses came from the south and southeast. Keeping in mind that this account was given near Flathead Lake in western Montana, it is clear that the horses are indicated as coming from the headwaters of the Missouri River above Three Forks, Montana, or from the upper valley of the Snake River. The Flathead corroborate the Blackfoot story of their great fight against the Shoshone when the latter had horses but the former did not. Since the old chief told Thompson that the first horses came from west of the mountains, the story must be substantially correct, having been obtained from two independent sources.

Although the Flathead account placed the date of their acquisition of the horse at about 1600, it was probably about 1710–1720, or at about the time the Blackfoot first saw any. Working back, this would indicate horses among the Shoshone in Idaho about 1690–1700. Comparing this with our dates east of the mountains, the Shoshone had horses by the time the animals had reached the Oklahoma-Arkansas border, and twenty years before they reached the forks of the Kansas and Missouri Rivers. Now it is hard to believe that horses could have spread north along the eastern slopes of the Rockies to the North Platte, and thence by South Pass to the upper Snake country as quickly as they spread from southeastern Colorado to the mouth of the Kansas River.

Another indication that horses were in western Montana before they reached its southeastern corner is the Crow tradition that their first horses came from the west, from the Nez Percé, before they could get any horses from the east or south. From the North Platte-South Pass route to the Crow country is less than two hundred miles—another indication that there could hardly have been horses that near the Crows for thirty or forty years without their having secured some.

This discussion all indicates that there were two great lines by which the horses from Santa Fé were distributed to the north. One of these, well known for many years, was by way of the great plains. The other was to the west of the continental divide, and followed the same route later used so much by the mountain men. It went from Santa Fé to the Snake River by way of the headwaters of the Colorado, the Grand and Green Rivers. Along this path the Navaho Apaches, the Ute, and the Shoshone took horses to the Pacific Northwest. Thus the Shoshone of southern Idaho were the means of furnishing horses to the Cayuse, Walla Walla, Yakima, Palouse, Nez Percé, Coeur d'Alêne, Flathead, Blackfoot, Crow, and many other tribes before horses were common among the Sioux and the northeastern Assiniboin. It is interesting to note that the horse thieves of later years usually stole from the tribes from whom they traditionally secured their first animals.

# Bontok Social Organization

## Felix M. Keesing

*From Some Notes on Bontok Social Organization, Northern Philippines.* American Anthropologist, *Vol. 51, No. 4, 1949, pp. 578–601. By permission of the author and the publisher.*

The Bontok comprise one of approximately ten ethnic groups into which the "Igorot" (mountain peoples) of the Cordillera Central in North Luzon have been classified. Estimates of the total number in the Bontok group range from about 30,000 to 40,000. They live in 32 villages scattered over wild steep country where the headwaters of the Chico river bisect this great mountain mass. Here, at about the three to five thousand foot level, the malarial forests of the lowlands are replaced by scrub and grass, with occasional stands of pine and oak. Wherever water for irrigation, and soil and rock for building agricultural terraces, can be brought together in sufficient amount, even though enormous labor is involved, a settlement is likely to be established. A close correlation exists between the size of each village and the flow of water which it controls in its ancestral streams. The annual cycle of agricultural production, so ably recorded by Jenks, dominates Bontok life: a drama in which supernatural forces must conjoin with human activity for successful consummation.

The inaccessibility and poverty of this section of the mountain country, its sparseness of population, and the warlike character of its peoples caused the Spanish conquerors of the Philippines to leave it practically untouched for three centuries. Initiating a more active policy from 1860 on, they exercised a precarious control with the aid of garrisons, cutting trails, collecting tribute, enforcing peace, and putting down frequent "revolts." After 1902, when Americans established a special-protective type of government for the "non-Christian" peoples of Mountain Province, a group of American and Filipino administrators were able to develop an equilibrium of relationships among Bontok villages and between the Bontok and their neighbors through a series of "peace pacts" for which leading elders were made responsible. Headtaking became an occasional occurrence only, quickly dealt with by constabulary units mainly enlisted locally. Regional and local self-government was fostered, and welfare measures advanced. Protestant and Catholic missions also started work. . . .

Bontok villages are sometimes spoken of in the literature as "towns" or *pueblos*. The Bontok language itself appears to have no generic word for such a community unit, so that the people have adopted the term *ili* from Iloko speech, that is, the language of the coastal Ilocano which has long since become the *lingua franca* of the mountain region. As suggested by the demographic data given above, the average number of people to a Bontok village appears to be somewhat under a thousand. As of 1933, however, there was a range of variation from over 2,000 in the capital, Bontoc, not including a considerable immigrant fringe, to perhaps 300 in small villages high up in poor country.

The village sites have undoubtedly been occupied for centuries, as shown by the extensive group of step-like terraces which surround each. The names of a number of them appear in the records of the first Spanish explorers. Every topographic feature has ancestral associations, while all types of land have their precise definitions of ownership and use. No one lives outside the village, and no system of scattered farming is possible short of a revolution in social organization and belief, of which there are scanty signs.

Each village is zoned into a number of units which are referred to in the literature by such names as "sections," "wards," or "precincts." Out of an elaborate terminology connected with such a unit, the most comprehensive Bontok name for it is *ato*, a term made familiar through Jenks' work. The number of *ato* sections varies from community to community, and in villages actually analyzed with local informants a range showed from as few as six to as many as eighteen.

Each *ato* has a permanent name and its boundaries are clearly defined geographically and historically—though to the eye of the stranger there may be little if any indication as to its limits since the thatched dwellings, stone house platforms, granaries, pigpens, and other structures, including low stone dividing walls and walks, appear to be continuous over the hillside. The ceremonial center of an *ato* is a stone platform of varying shape, having a paved top ringed with large stones for sitting or leaning, a fireplace, one or more carved or pointed posts for displaying heads of slain enemies, and a low rectangular hut at the back end. This platform and the hut provide a formal and informal "clubhouse" for the males of the households attached to the *ato* section; it is ordinarily taboo to females, other than very young children in their fathers' care who sometimes may be there. The older men assemble there in "council" (*intugtukan*) to deliberate on matters of justice, politics and other *ato* concerns. Formerly ceremonies of war and headhunting were consummated at this center, and it was and may still be the repository of skulls; at the time of the writer's visit the *ato* was still thought of as dominantly connected with this type of activity. Rituals including animal sacrifices appropriate to the *ato* are conducted upon the platform, often accompanied by dancing in a space adjacent to it. At night the stones, often mat covered, together with wooden planks in the hut, are a sleeping place for unmarried boys and youths, and for divorced or widowed men of the households. The *ato* group also forms a unit for particular types of economic activity, especially of a ceremonial nature, calling for co-operation among members. Its adherents refer to themselves as *sinpangato*, literally "united with (the group) belonging to the *ato*." . . .

The unity of the village is perhaps most clearly seen in an elaborate system of community rituals (*kanyau*) connected variously with the annual cycle of agriculture, safety from storms, epidemics or fires in the village, droughts affecting the water supply, and other matters of common welfare. These, organized and conducted by recognized experts or priests who variously hold their positions by hereditary right or by nomination according to the nature of the activity, involve common religious holidays (*tengao*), hog sacrifices at sacred groves (*papatay*) on the outskirts of the village, consultation of omens, and other ritual procedures. Above all, the villagers are held together by an elaborate network of kinship connections and neighborly associations, by the needs until recently of common defense, and by the sense of identity so real in a little community with a common tradition and the intimacies of daily contact and gossip. The identity of the village is expressed in the term *sinpangili*, "the united community." . . .

Writers on Bontok also feature as the other characteristic institution the *olag* or girls' house. Each *ato* section has usually one or possibly two low huts of thatch, mud and stones, often built alongside a pig-pit, to which the girls of its constituent households go at night to sleep. A small *ato*, however, may be at times without an *olag*, so that the girls of its households use one in an adjacent *ato*. In other words it is a usual, but not a permanent and inevitable part of the *ato* organization.

The *olag* huts are a nightly gathering place, not only for the unmarried girls and unattached women, but also for unmarried youths and more occasionally unattached older men. Boys and young men are likely to go from their *ato* structures in congenial parties, visiting one *olag* after another, crooning, joking, teasing, and engaging in sex play with the girls. Those who have developed liaisons may, with full public sanction, sleep with their current partners in the hut. Nearly all Bontok marriages are the product of experimental pairing in the *olag*. the test of congeniality usually being that a child is on the way— hence the term "trial marriage" found in the literature. It is necessary, however, clearly to distinguish personal sex play and experimentation under these conditions from marriage proper, as the latter involves public ceremonies, rights and obligations that involve not only the couple, but also their kin groups.

How do these institutions really "function" in the total context of Bontok life? What relation do they have to other elements of the culture such as the household and wider kinship units already mentioned in passing? Is the *ato* membership based on local contiguity,

kinship, or the needs of economic, political or other forms of co-operation? What kinship and other considerations regulate the contacts of young people in the *olag*? Such questions as these have not been given adequate consideration in writings to date. Within the limits of the writer's own field notes, supplemented by other source materials available, the following is a tentative analysis.

The Bontok household can provide the most useful starting point. Its essential nucleus is an "individual family" of husband, wife, and children, almost always monogamous. It has, however, a somewhat elastic membership in terms of the different activities centered around the house—sleeping, eating, doing chores, conducting rituals, and so on. Unattached older relatives, for example, may come for meals, and young men courting the daughters may join in household work. Such a house group is called *pangafong*, literally "(those) belonging to the house." Terms for marriage, too, usually translate as variants of "becoming a householder," *e.g., iafongko*, "marry," *paafongek*, "perform wedding ceremony." An *ato* section will have from about ten to fifty such households within its boundaries.

The better class of Bontok house (*faoy*) is a substantial pyramidal structure on piles, described by Cole as like a "sharply pointed haystack." The ground space beneath has sections for husking rice, cooking, and storage There is also a box-like compartment (*angan*) in which the husband and wife sleep, together with very young children. Under the eaves, the house has a second story room more less walled in, and a loft used as a storehouse for *palay* (rice on the stalk), and other goods. A far less pretentious structure (*katufong*), rectangular shaped and on the ground, is used by very poor families and sometimes by widows. A feature of a marriage settlement is nearly always the provision of a house by one or other of the relationship groups concerned, customarily the bridegroom's kinsmen in accordance with a dominant principle of patrilocal *ato* residence. The building of a new house consumes much time, labor and wealth, and its erection is an affair in which many kinsmen and neighbors take part, not to mention ancestral and other spirits which are ritually invoked. At particular times in the yearly cycle of activities, and on special occasions such as births, marriages, cases of sickness, and deaths, it becomes a gathering place for appropriate groupings of kinsmen and friends.

During much of the day, the house may be deserted. The men and boys, if not away from the village, are usually at the *ato* platforms. The women and girls are likely to be in the fields, often leaving the young children to the care of their somewhat older siblings, to the fathers if they are handy, or to old men and women of the kin group. Females who remain at home because of taboos, childbirth, or to rest from the exacting agricultural tasks gather to work or gossip under their own house eaves or those of relatives and friends. For the two daily meals, or at least for the evening meal, the whole household normally assembles. Perhaps the family pigs should receive mention, too, for in their well-constructed stone pits near the house they are in a real sense members of the group; fed by the girls with leafage gathered after much hard climbing, eating up all the household rubbish including human excreta, providing in turn fertilizer for the fields, and coming at last to a distinguished end in the course of some all-important ritual sacrifice and feast. When darkness falls over the village, the stone pathways that traverse it are alight with moving pine torches as old people, boys and girls go from the households to their sleeping places, and amorous youths commence their visiting. Behind them are left the husband, wife and very young children who will crawl into the sleeping box, stoke up the embers of a fire within, and shut tight the door to keep out the chill mountain air and its wandering ghosts.

Such a household is the main unit for everyday economic, social and religious life. As part of a Bontok marriage, a series of consultations take place between the kin groups involved, as a result of which the couple receive agricultural land and other property to be held in common so long as they remain together. Unmarried persons rarely own important property of their own, so that such arrangements exercise a strong stabilizing force upon the household life. In case of divorce, which can take place by mutual consent or by pressure brought to bear by one or the other set of relatives—the usual cause being infertility or the repeated death

of children—there are elaborate legal prescriptions as to the disposal of such common property. Both husband and wife may also accumulate property separately in their own names through inheritance, gift, manufacture, or in other ways. A woman's rights, and back of them the related rights of her kin group, are meticulously observed.

What is the working relation of the household unit, as pictured here, to the *ato* unit? Normally the households which lie spatially within the *ato* boundaries provide its membership as a social, political and ceremonial grouping. Since *ato* affiliation is based typically on a patrilineal principle, and marriage on the patrilocal principle as noted above, males ordinarily adhere throughout life to the *ato* sections of their fathers' lines. Informants, in speaking of this, usually expressed it by reference to the grandparent generation: "I keep on in the *ato* of my (paternal) grandfather."

As with so much of Bontok usage, however, individuals are not compelled to adhere strictly to the norm, but have latitude to make personal choices. Cases occur when men live within an *ato* section other than that of their male ancestors, as where a newly married youth may stay for a time with his wife's people, or even transfer his allegiance to that *ato* group because of circumstances involved in the marriage settlement, or because of quarrels or personal tastes. A decision to shift is particularly likely to occur at marriage where the wife's relatives are of higher status or possess more rice lands. Again, in cases where a new *ato* has been founded near the village, those initiating such a move have drawn in various kinsmen and perhaps friends. Jenks says in his study that the *ato* "formally releases and adopts men who change their residence from one to another," and refers to a ceremonial feast to mark such adoption. Informants stated that this would be a minor ritual only, though a small animal sacrifice would be in order. Primarily, it was stated, a man signifies his change of allegiance by his "public words," together with his absence from the rituals and enterprises of his former *ato* and his presence at those of the new *ato*.

Allowing for these exceptions, the extent of which could not be ascertained precisely, ancestral tradition and public opinion nevertheless operate strongly to keep a man in the *ato* of his male progenitors. The boys growing up within each *ato* group become steeped in its special lore, and develop rights and duties in relation to it. A term *pangatona*, "*ato* comrades," expresses the warm relation especially between age mates in the group. To leave one's *ato*, or to be absent unnecessarily from its ceremonial activities, would mean risking not only the weakening of important social ties, but also incurring the displeasure of the ancestors and of family and *ato* spirits. An older man would rarely if ever shift to a new *ato*. Even if a young man moves, as through circumstances connected with his marriage, it is said that his sons tend to return to the *ato* of their grandfather.

The *ato* may therefore be visualized as comprising, in ideal terms, both a territorial and a social unit made up of a set of patrilineal and patrilocal households. It provides the main focus for political organization, and also involves important religious, ceremonial, economic, and other ties. Until the last two generations, it has been notably associated with war and head-hunting activities.

The steps that lead to marriage and the formation of the household bring into focus cusomary relationships between the sexes, including the role of the *olag* or girl's house. Principles of sexual segregation operate strongly in Bontok public behavior, and boys and girls tend to work and play apart from each other from their earliest years. Siblings of opposite sex meet within the home during the day, yet restraints are fostered that from the age of perhaps nine or ten become a definite rule of avoidance. This "brother-sister taboo" extends equally to step-children and adopted children. There are also restraints in conversation and in other behavior regarding sex matters between all males and females who are close relatives.

Young people of opposite sex have two main opportunities for getting together: on ceremonial occasions, many of which include dancing, and in the *olag* or girls' house. Even in the dance formations, however, the sexes characteristically line up apart. The *olag* affords the principal place where informal and intimate associations between unmarried and unattached persons of opposite sex can occur. The boys, as has been noted, visit the *olag* huts, and as sexual maturity is reached by boys and girls their casual sex play tends to give place to more serious and permanent liaisons. In the adolescent years, the young people are likely to make *olag* sexual adventures their principal preoccupation. Older unattached men may also visit the *olags*, but married men rarely do so; an elderly Don Juan would be considered rather ridiculous, as a man is expected to have had his playboy days in youth.

Because the girls belonging to the households of each *ato* normally spend their nights in the *olag* of that *ato*, the boys of those households are likely to have sisters, first cousins, or other close female relatives there. The rules of avoidance referred to above tend, therefore, to force boys to go to other *ato* units for their sexual contacts, either in their own village or nowadays even in other villages. If one desires to bring in the word, this operates to provide a kind of informal *ato* "exogamy." On the other hand, there is no explicit prohibition of sex contacts or of marriage between members of any *ato* group as such, other than as regards close relatives, although Jenks gives a table of Bontok marriages forbidden a man thus: mother or stepmother or their sisters, daughter, step-daughter, adopted daughter, sister, brother's widow, and first cousins by blood and adoption. Especially in larger *ato* groups, liaisons seems not infrequent, and these would be facilitated in the rare cases where an *ato* has more than one *olag*. Again, if a boy and girl in the same *ato* are eager to effect a liaison their fellows may help them, either by close female relatives shifting out temporarily to another *olag*, or else by the girl making such a shift. The pattern can be described as an avoidance of close relatives, which often extends on account of *olag* customs to cover approximately the immediate *ato* of the youth or man, and in a similar way to other *ato* groups where there are close female relatives in the *olag*.

The norm of youthful conduct could be stated thus. A boy cannot enter an *olag* in which there are immediate relatives such as his sister or stepsister. He either stays behind in the *olag* to which his amorous party has just been, or passes ahead to the one next on the visiting list. Should he have a somewhat less close female relative, such as a first cousin, aunt, or niece, he may enter, but should "hold back" instead of joining in the fun. Such rules are the more effective in that boys and girls rarely have opportunities for close association outside the *olag*, and public opinion frowns on sex intimacies elsewhere. Sex experiences are so much a matter of mutual interest and co-operation among the boys' and girls' groups, that the deviant would meet with ridicule if not ostracism.

Bontok marriage has two facets. The first is that of choice and compatibility. The great majority of first unions take place within approximately the same age-groups as the result of *olag* romances and experimentation, regulated by the above rules. Subsequent marriages, which are not infrequent because of the death of one of the partners or else of divorce, often cross age lines, especially through older men taking unmarried girls as wives. Genuine attachments often come from *olag* alliances, but the most frequent test of compatibility is that a child is forthcoming. A girl is therefore approved only if she has one lover at a time, ensuring, as the Bontok say, that paternity can be recognized.

The other facet to marriage is where the kin groups concerned, together with the ancestors and supernatural forces, have their say. This takes the form of a complex set of observances, varying with the class status and seniority of the parties, and including performance of symbolic services towards the prospective parents-in-law, consultations within and between the relatives, the reading of omens through animal sacrifices and other means, successfully maintaining a sacred fire during a ritual period and in other ways getting the sanction of the unseen world, and finally the passing of property by the two groups to the couple. Should the marriage be cancelled through family disapproval or bad auguries, an appropriate settlement is made. A pregnant girl may be given a rice field in trust for her expected child, or else some *carabao* (water buffalo). Neither she nor the child would suffer any social stigma. Possibly because women have to work under such trying environmental conditions as in the wet rice fields, and also because there is high infant mortality, children are all too few; the infant would therefore be readily adopted into the kin group of its mother, while the girl would perhaps even be the more sought after for having proved her fertility.

A consummated marriage links the two households concerned and the kin groups back of them with a series of mutual and reciprocal associations, privileges and responsibilities. These are especially elaborate where they involve persons and kin groups of the aristocratic class. Parents-in-law play a role of great importance, receiving every respect and in turn standing by to assist in all difficulties. Again, a husband and wife have relations of propriety and respect towards their brothers- and sisters-in-law, especially the eldest ones. The wife's kin keep an eye on the husband to see that his wife and children are well treated, and vice versa.

A marriage has at first a somewhat tentative character, and the relationships created between "in-laws" are correspondingly tentative. Subsequent participation in ceremonial and other activities, and above all the arrival of children on the scene, "build up" the marriage and cement affinal ties. In relation to the children, the kin groups of the husband and wife become in turn conjoined into a single kin group, which will stand back of such children as they grow up and in turn are married. Each marriage, especially if fertile, thus initiates fresh alignments of kin within the community. Each man, too, is the focal point for a network of lineal and affinal relationships extending not only within his own *ato* but also into the *atos* of his mother, his parents' sisters, his wife, his parents-in-law, his married sisters, his sisters-in-law, his daughters-in-law, and so on. A woman has corresponding ramifications of kinship. These linkages as indicated may even extend to other villages, especially in modern times and in the case of aristocratic lines.

This leads to broader consideration of the principles of kinship which operate beyond the household grouping. The written and photographic materials presented by Jenks show tantalizing glimpses of kin ties at work—groups of relatives building a house, mourning and burying the dead, dividing property among heirs, conducting feasts and animal sacrifices and so on. But apart from a few very general references and a meager list of kinship terms, he fails to trace the many ways in which kinship is actively exercised in interpersonal relationships pertaining to economic, social, political, ceremonial and other activities both within and outside the *ato* units.

An individual in such a close-set community constantly sees in the daily round persons who stand in various relationships to him, and may speak respectfully, stop to gossip, pass a joke, share a task, step aside modestly, or otherwise actively exercise prescribed or permitted kin behaviors. More formally, he is likely to take part relatively frequently in gatherings of kinsmen at his own house or those of others. As noted earlier, even certain types of political and judicial activity may be handled by elders of the kin instead of in the *ato* "councils"; for example, property disputes among relatives or troubles between different kin groups. Weddings and funerals are among the many other occasions in the social round which bring kinsmen together, and also their ramifications such as ceremonies to overcome sterility in a childless couple or holding memorial sacrifices for an illustrious ancestor. Again, bad luck or illness call for rituals at which relatives come together. Assemblies of kinsmen will be organized and directed by the senior elders present in the group.

The size and membership of such kin gatherings, including the extent to which they involve both lineal and affinal relatives, vary with the occasion, and generally according to the class status and seniority of the persons upon whom the occasion is focused. The Bontok do not have any precise delimitation of such larger kinship associations that would justify speaking of an "extended family" system over and above the household. Terms used to refer to kinsmen *in extenso* are very general. The one by which the identity of a group sharing common descent is expressed in the large is *pangapo*, literally "having unity with the same elders (ancestors)." A consanguineal group looked at from the viewpoint of youth may be called *sinpangapo*, *i.e.*, belonging to the parent and other ascendant generations; similarly from the viewpoint of age it would be *sinpanganak*, *i.e.*, belonging to the descendant generations. *Anak* is a classificatory kinship term more strictly for those one generation below that of the speaker. *Apo* is used as a respectful term for elders and those of high rank, and may also be given the more specific connotation of kinsman, living and dead, above the parental generation.

A detailed analysis of the Bontok kinship structure has never been made. Most of its

formal terminology is extant in the vocabularies published by Jenks, Clapp, Scheerer, and Seidenadel. Usually, however, terms are translated with little reference to the social context in which they are used, as for example, the marked classificatory character of nearly all terms of reference. Kroeber's important general study of Philippine kinship brings out, however, the major features of this as of other "Malayan type" systems, including marked bilateral emphasis; the merging of collateral with lineal kin; the use of reciprocal terminology; the primary importance of the generation principle; the strong classificatory tendency; and the rarity of sex differentiation in general terms of reference.

Space does not permit full analysis of how these principles work out as regards Bontok kinship structure. It may be noted, however, that the terminology of kinship reference is compounded for the most part from a few basic terms by the use of prefixes, suffixes, and descriptive addenda, including *ay lalaki* to indicate "male" and *ay fafai* to indicate "female." The following are the main terms: grandparent generation and above, *apo*; grandparent, more specifically, *ikid*; father, *ama*; other males of parental generation, *alitau*; mother, *inu*; own sibling, *itad*; child generation and below, *anak*; spouse, *asawa*; parent-in-law, *katukangan*; brother-, sister-in-law, *kasud*. Illustrating further the reciprocal character of kinship terminology, the following are examples of terms indicating relationships to one another: sibling, *agi*; spouses, *sinasawa*; "in-laws" generally, *aliwid*; brothers-in-law, *sinkasud*; brothers-in-law and sisters-in-law, *sininget*; grandparents and grandchildren, *sinpangapo*.

The markedly bilateral character of Bontok kinship has already been stressed in discussing marriage. Though a selective stress to the patrilineal side is discernible, as in the norm of *ato* affiliation, in succession among the aristocracy and sometimes in choosing personal names, an individual takes status and receives property by way of both parental kin groups. In household ceremonies, all ascendant generations on both sides, living and dead, will be honored.

The range of effective kinship appears to be rather elastic. In general, memories of specific genealogical data do not appear to go far back, perhaps at the most for seven or eight generations in the direct male line, and for the average person not more than two or three generations beyond the living. Members of aristocratic kin groups appear the more meticulous in this respect for the obvious reason to be shown that ancestry is of so much greater importance to them. Outstanding personalities, too, especially great warrior heroes of the past, are immortalized in the lore and story of kin and *ato* groups, and their lines of descendants may be kept, as Jenks says, "carefully in memory." Among the living, kin reckoning tends to be significant in close lines only. Usually little importance is attached to collateral ties beyond first cousins. Relationships in more distant lines may, however, be remembered and exercised if they are socially useful; that is, if they involve links to important kin groups and outstanding individuals, especially those of aristocratic status.

Three additional principles of Bontok social structure, already seen above to some extent as importantly at work in defining status, may be discussed more systematically here: age and generation, seniority among siblings, and rank and class distinctions.

The Bontok child learns from earliest years to obey those of the generations above him within the kin, and to respect older age in general. This principle holds throughout life, and as each individual becomes older there is a corresponding shift from being directed and dictated to by a circle of seniors, toward having rights and responsibilities as regards an enlarging circle of juniors. Correspondingly strong social bonds tend to exist between agemates, even though no formal age-grade system is involved. Within the hierarchy of generations are included the remembered dead as well as the living, for Bontok religion has as an important element a cult of ancestral spirits (*anito*) who are supposed to continue living around the village margins.

A clear distinction is made between siblings according to their order of birth. The terms *pangolo*, "head" or "senior," *yunan*, "older," *anodi* (*anochi*), "younger," and *yugtan*, "the last" are not only conversationally prominent, but express a hierarchy of privilege and responsibility. In some respects distinctions of generation and primogeniture transcend distinctions of sex, and this shows especially where the eldest survivor of a kin group or among siblings is a female. Except in the distinctively male functions, as in the *ato* affairs,

the eldest women members of a kin group exercise important authority, and this is enhanced if a woman is the eldest among siblings in the senior line. An examination of the *ato* "council" described by Jenks shows it to be essentially a gathering of the male elders from the constituent *ato* households, deriving their right to a voice in *ato* affairs primarily from their age and seniority.

Jenks speaks of such an *ato* "council" as "thoroughly democratic." Informants with which the writer discussed this matter and the distribution of authority within kin groups, indicated that underlying the outwardly free-and-easy discussion of problems a marked difference exists in the extent to which participating elders have an effective say. Though "all old people are consulted," an old man "must have influence in the community" for his voice to count strongly. An unimportant or "poor" person, no matter how old "doesn't have much say." In earlier times, one of the major ways in which an individual became influential was to be an outstanding warrior and taker of heads—and, of course, to survive to older age. The other major way, still current, is to be a member of what has been called at a number of points an aristocracy. . . .

At the top of the social scale in Bontok is a class known as *kadangyan* (*kachangyan*), or nowadays sometimes by the general name used in the mountain region for such an elite, and of *Iloko* origin: *baknang*. The main basis from which *kadangyan* status is derived is hereditary rank, or more strictly descent through senior lines within the class; secondarily it is possession of wealth and performance of major *kanyau* (ritual) observances, involving animal sacrifices and public feasts. In its narrower sense the term *kadangyan* is applied to the current titleholder or head in the senior family line, whose succession at the death of his father has been validated by required *kanyau* ceremonies. More widely it is extended to cover the household and immediate kin lines, so that people speak of the *kadangyan* as a class. Faculo and others spoke somewhat vaguely of three grades of *kadangyan* status. At the top were those counted *pangolo* ("head," or "first") or "royal" as Faculo translated it, and estimated by him at about 10 per cent of the *kadangyan* group; next came those classed as *misned* ("second"), and comprising about 15 per cent; and finally those *yugtan* ("last"), comprising about 75 per cent. It seems more realistic, however, to look at differentiations in *kadangyan* status not in terms of distinct subclasses, but rather as expressing degrees to which different households and their heads are linked more or less closely to senior *kadangyan* lines.

The individuals and kin groups counting themselves as more or less of *kadangyan* status were estimated by some as perhaps a quarter of the total population. Others regarded this figure as too high. Clearly it would require a detailed social "census" to make this matter definite, and in any case it would undoubtedly vary by villages. Below this group are the main body of the villagers who hold lands of their own, a kind of middle or commoner class. The households in this group may nevertheless have links through blood and marriage with *kadangyan* lines, which as indicated earlier they find it useful to remember and exercise. Probably few of them would not count themselves as of *kadangyan* derivation in some minor degree. In each generation the descendants in junior *kadangyan* lines (*i.e.*, the offspring of younger sons and daughters in the senior lines) tend to shift downward into this middle group.

At the bottom of the social scale are a class of people in a state of peonage, because of debts and other obligations to their richer fellows. They own little or no rice lands or livestock, and work on a share-cropping or tenancy basis, usually in the service of the top *kadangyan*. The traditional rates of interest and of crop division here as in so many other sections of east and south Asia make escape from this group, once in it, almost impossible so that the obligations tend to carry over indefinitely from generation to generation. The usual name for such people is *pusi* (often translated "poor," and said to be of Spanish derivation); another appellation is *kokitak* ("to be least, last, poorest"). Just as with the *kadangyan* group, this status interpenetrates with the main middle class group by way of blood and marriage ties, and so it is relative to the particular kin connections of the individual and household concerned. Links may even join between *kadangyan* and *pusi* groups through marriages of past or present, though this is more rare.

"The Bontok," Faculo writes, "feel that wealth, influence, and dignity do not count

without children to inherit and to care for the parents. Life to them is a matter of succession." He describes the absorption of the Bontok with marriage and death ceremonies, with emphasis upon marked contrasts existing between the types for those of high and low class status. "Each class," he says, "has its own marriage and burial customs." These differ to some extent in kind as well as in degree, an example being that outstanding *kadangyan* may be buried in special places away from those of lesser status. He, as well as other informants, described additional rituals emphasized in the *kadangyan* class, including "wedding anniversary feasts" held every three or four years to consolidate their marriages and make them fertile, and mourning ceremonies held periodically to honor their dead ancestors. In 1932, just before the writer reached the Bontok area, a wedding feast held at Dalican village involved the slaughter of 41 carabaos, along with numerous pigs.

Marriage operates as a major factor shaping the status of individuals within this class structure, and fosters counter tendencies of rigidity and mobility. Every marriage creates some new alignment of status. Each child in turn gets an ascribed status according to the position of his father and mother and their lines of kin within the class hierarchy.

At the top, the superior status of the senior *kadangyan* lines is maintained and reinforced through strategic marital alliances. It is quite usual for a *kadangyan* to betroth his children even in infancy, especially eldest sons and daughters, rather than waiting for *olag* liaisons to develop. In some cases those of the highest level marry within close degrees of relationship to maintain status and retain land and other property within their group. They may also marry across village lines, especially under modern conditions of peace, so as to link together lines of the highest status for mutual advantage. A betrothal arrangement made for an eldest son or daughter is likely to be insisted on. With younger children, however, earlier betrothals may be broken in favor of mates of their own choice. Even so, the *kadangyan* class discriminate against those of their members who marry beneath them. This was shown at the time of the writer's visit when an educated young man of high birth married a girl schoolteacher equally educated but of low class origin. His kinsmen refused to accept her into their circle: "She is just poor," they said.

Correspondingly at the bottom of the scale the tendency is for persons of the *pusi* group to marry among themselves for want of other partners. Granting the free-and-easy sex relations of the *olag* system, youths and girls are well aware, both by way of admonitions of kinsmen and their own ambitions to have rice fields and other possessions come to them via the marriage settlement, that the class status of a prospective lover should be taken into account. Faculo, recording in his manuscript on marriage customs the specific case of an *olag* attachment between a youth Kala and a girl Udchao, tells how "Kala's parents, satified of the prestige, means and standing of Udchao's parents, called a man from the neighborhood to act as a message-bearer, [and] sent to Udchao's parents to ask if they would agree to the marriage proposal." As a norm it would appear that unions, to be acceptable to the kin groups concerned, should take place within approximately the same class level, especially so in the case of eldest sons and daughters. But many exceptions occur, disrupting any tendency toward sharp class differentiation.

As might be expected in such a hard physical environment, aristocracy has become closely associated with wealth and economic dominance, a tendency which furthermore has been stimulated by the increasing penetration of the modern commercial economy in recent years. Asked as to the origin of the *kadangyan*, informants referred to stories telling how "in olden times rich people had a chance to buy the lands of the poor" and so consolidate their position. The leading *kadangyan* usually own the bulk of rice lands and claim rights over unoccupied lands; they are also likely to have the most hogs, and perhaps large water buffalo herds. A circle of poorer people are always in debt to them, and hence are partially or wholly their tenants and laborers. Over against this, however, the aristocrats carry responsibilities as financiers, storers of food, and organizers of community work. Tradition also demands of them the giving of elaborate feasts and sacrifices on varied ceremonial occasions, these participated in by a wide circle of the community, and even (at least nowadays) by invited guests from other Bontok villages. In this way, they exercise a function of village leadership which Jenks failed to record. In reality they accumulate prestige and, if their services are well performed, popularity, rather than much permanent wealth other than in land.

At times, individuals of *kadangyan* rank have become pauperized. This does not affect their hereditary standing in any immediate way, though it would tend to be impaired if prolonged, especially over several generations, as animal sacrifices believed necessary to bulwark social and supernatural status could probably not be performed. In modern times a few poorer people have risen to wealth and high position through commercial activities or as government officials and employees. While this gives them a status in terms of the new set of values inevitably filtering into the mountains today, and perhaps allows them to make strategic marriages, they remain in the eyes of conservatives—that is, of almost everyone—lowly. The persistence of the class system has become a source of personal difficulty among a small group of educated young people who have come under the influence of democratic American ideas, and at the time the writer was in the area there was presage of growing disturbance. Meantime, as in the past, wealth and other personal factors have remained subordinate to rank by birth.

The *kadangyan* households seem to be scattered fairly evenly through the *ato* sections. Though their houses are not markedly differentiated in construction from those of others, more elaborate material possessions such as rice granaries, a greater number of pig pens, and ceremonial porcelain jars of high value are usually an index to their status. Within *ato* councils as well as kin groupings, the voice of the *kadangyan* tends to carry a dominant weight. This is especially so now that the old men having fame as fighters and takers of heads are dying off. Such personal exploits gave even low-ranking persons an important place in the public eye, for war was essentially a man's career. With peace and commerce, however, the prestige and influence of the *kadangyan* tends to be enhanced, the more so as the government has generally used people of this class as local officials in the villages. An informant said, "The *kandangyan* now have all the real power."

Both the *ato* and the *olag* systems are also undergoing inevitable changes in modern times. The cessation of headhunting, and the transfer of political and judicial affairs increasingly to the government officials, have tended to thin out the *ato* activities considerably. The *olag* has been a main point of attack for missions and schools as being "immoral." While so far the institutions seem visibly little impaired among the Bontok, a study of their working, and of the attitudes of numbers of younger people toward them, revealed a trend toward disintegration. Already among the neighboring Lepanto, this is well under way. In all Lepanto villages one *ato* has tended to emerge to importance as the center to which officials come, and the others have correspondingly lessened in significance, especially as the people become Christianized and their ritual functions thin out. Again in some villages the girls' house system appears practically at an end.

No attempt has yet been made in the literature relating to such mountain peoples as the Bontok to analyze their cultures from the newer viewpoints of "personality" or "character structure." A number of observers, however, have offered broad characterizations, including Bontok officials in their reports. There is general agreement that the Bontok are the most "aggressive," "pugnacious," "stubborn," "proud," "conservative" and "unrepressed" of the mountain groups; as one writer put it, where members of other groups acting as carriers would stop outside or merely come inside the door, the Bontok would stride unconcernedly into your bedroom. A Bontok man usually looks a person deliberately in the eye, and gives an impression of self-confidence, even superiority, and of being good-humored and relaxed while yet having a very positive attitude to life; women, however, are likely to be more shy in the presence of strangers. Even Bontok conservatism has a certain resiliency, the people having adapted their usages freely where new experience fitted in with their own values. Of the former headhunting, Jenks writes, "(It is) his most-enjoyed and highly prized recreation."

Bontok "personality" ("character") formation offers tempting vistas for analysis: the baby usually slung precariously on the hip of mother or older sister, or being cared for by father or the elders; the traumatic shift from parents and the home sleeping box to the *ato* or *olag*; the little disciplined childhood mainly among age mates; the *kanyau* sacrifices to meet all insecurities; the steep barren habitat and precarious livelihood. A striking feature here is that most of these patterns are shared closely with neighboring ethnic groups, especially the Lepanto. Yet the end results are far from the same, as noted in the previous paragraph.

A search for the key to the distinctive aspects of Bontok character is likely to lead back in part to Bontok history. The Bontok know well that in the eyes of neighbors they have long been feared as the most dangerous and expert fighters in the region, always threatening, always likely to be on top, and their self-evaluations reflect this knowledge. Again, habitat factors may be involved. The Bontok country is in general the steepest and least hospitable zone of the mountains, and floods from the Chico river and its tributaries periodically wash out sections of the rice terraces, calling for adaptability and toughness of fiber as well as the labor of reconstruction. Again, as implied in a report written in 1931 by a Bontok official which states, "It is the things learned in (the *ato* and *olag*) that renders them so hostile to change," more would have to be known specifically of the role of these institutions in conditioning the distinctive Bontok character.

Summarizing this sketch of Bontok social organization, the household is seen as the basic economic and social unit, taking form typically out of *olag* attachments. Households are aligned, normally on patrilineal and patrilocal principles, into *ato* sections. These are territorial-social groupings having their own traditions and varied political, economic, ceremonial and other functions, particularly connected formerly with war and headhunting. Avoiding Jenks' unduly *ato*-centric focus, it can be seen that the households are also linked by wider kinship ties, lineal and affinal, which transcend *ato* lines, and in which age and generation, seniority, and class status are important principles of organization. The class system is based particularly on degree of relationship to the *kadangyan*, or hereditary aristocrat, whose position is based on succession and inheritance from senior lines, and validated by possession of wealth and by ritual activities. Though political and judicial authority tends to center in the *ato* units, the village as a whole has a real identity, fostered by common interests and ideology, the extensive network of kinship, and a round of common social and religious activities.

*selection 29*

# Kinship Systems

## A. M. Hocart

When we explore a new language, we infer the meaning of words from the objects to which they are applied. The first object gives us a preliminary definition. That may chance to be right, but further experience may compel us to revise it. Thus I may first hear the word "table" used of a list of facts in a book, and so translate it "page." By degrees I shall learn better.

This caution is generally borne in mind by students of literary languages, but it is too often lost sight of in the study of non-literary languages. Many investigators never get beyond the first use of the word that happens to come their way . . . [As an example,] an investigator heard the Uganda word *obuko* applied to palsy. He entered it in his dictionary as "palsy." It really refers to marriage rules, to a breach of which palsy is the consequence.

One of the most flagrant cases is the translation of the so-called classificatory kinship terms. The person most commonly called *tama* in Melanesia, the one most in evidence, is a man's father. He is the man who will be named if you ask, "Who is your *tama*?" So *tama* has been duly set down as "father." The same has been done with other kinship terms in Melanesia and elsewhere. It was soon noticed, however, that other men besides the father are called *tama*. By all rules the first translation should have been dropped,

*From* The Life-giving Myth, and Other Essays, *Grove Press, n.d., pp. 173–179. By permission of the publisher.*

and a new one found to cover all the different *tamas*, and thus express the essence of *tama*-ship. Unfortunately, no single word can do so, and it has remained in the literature of the South Seas as "father," with the proviso that it is "extended" to cover father's brother, father's father's brothers' sons, and so on. Ever since we have been racking our brains to explain how Melanesians can call their uncles, and even remote cousins, "fathers."

The effect on theory has been disastrous. The order in which we have learned the uses of *tama* and similar words has been confused with the order of development in actual history. Because we first took it to mean father we slip unwittingly into the assumption that it meant father originally.

This fallacy has now received official expression in the term "kinship extensions." That expression implies that the meaning father is primary and that all other uses result from extending the term to an ever-widening circle of kinsmen.

It is curious that this doctrine, which is historical since it describes a process of development in the past, is championed most stoutly by those who are forever gibing at origins, evolutions, historical reconstruction. This is a historical reconstruction, or what is?

The only way of proving that a process has taken place in the past is by recognized historical methods: either produce documents or resort to the comparative method. It is perhaps fortunate in this case that we have little documentary evidence and so must rely on the much more reliable comparative method.

Before we can apply it we must get our facts right. To that end let us forget all we have ever been told about the meaning of classificatory terms and rediscover the language, taking Fijian as an example. Evidently *tama* cannot mean father since it includes cousins to the $n$th degree, even cousins too young to have children; in fact, a man is born a *tama*. We notice, however, that all those cousins have one thing in common: they are once removed; in other words, they are of the generation next to Ego, and, to be more precise, of the one immediately before. Not all the members of this generation, however, are *tama*. There are two sides to that generation, the father's and the mother's; only those on the father's side are *tama*. That is

evidently the meaning of *tama*, so our final definition will run:

*tama* = all males of the previous generation on the father's side. Repeating the process, we go on:

*vungo* = all males of the generation immediately above and below Ego on the mother's side;

*tavale* = all males of the same generation on the mother's side.

And so on. When our list is complete we find that all the terms fall into two sets, one set belonging to the father's side, the other to the mother's. Each term refers to a particular generation within one side. In short, these terms do not express consanguinity, as we have unfortunately been accustomed by Morgan to believe, but they fix the place of any relative according to generation and side. If I call a man *tuaka* it is clear that he is of my generation on my father's side, and senior to me; a *wati* is a woman of my generation on the side from which my mother comes.

This last term affords an excellent illustration how a particular use is mistaken for the true one, and the true one comes to be looked upon as an improper one. A Fijian introduces his wife as *wati*, so the word is noted as *"wife."* When it is found there are hundreds of *watis* who are not his wives, the first translation is not abandoned, but all other uses are explained as extensions; these women, it is explained, are called wives because he might marry any of them if the family so decided; they are wives by anticipation, "potential wives." Upon this muddled lexicography has been built up a whole edifice of primitive promiscuity.

Exactly the same usage exists in Arabic. Arabic-speaking husbands can often be heard addressing their wives as *bint 'amm*; but they also call their paternal uncles' daughters *bint 'amm*. We do not translate "wife," "potential wife," because we know that *bint* is daughter, and *'amm* is paternal uncle; therefore *bint 'amm* means "cousin on the father's side." When a man marries his cousin, as it is best to do, he goes on calling her "cousin" as he has been accustomed to since childhood. The Fijian and the Ashanti do exactly the same.

We can remember the time when an English

youth would refer jocosely to his father as "The Governor." No one has ever suggested that this was primary and that the word has been extended to colonial administrators.

All our difficulties spring from a preconceived idea that kinship terms everywhere try to express the same thing as they do in Aryan and Semitic languages, and that in those languages they show the place on the family tree. The result is that in a certain African language the term *nana* is rendered father's father, father's father's brother, and so on through thirty four European relationships, and then it does not exhaust all the possibilities. And what is the outcome of all this painstaking? We have a list of cases, but we have not got the meaning. It is as if a dictionary under "hot" told us "the sun is hot, pepper is hot, *A*'s temper is hot, the discussion is hot," and left it at that. If we go to the trouble of extracting the meaning of *nana* from the cases we find it simply means "any relative two generations above or below."

At this point we may be asked what evidence have we that the people themselves understand kinship terms in this sense. The same evidence as we have for the meaning of any word, what is common to the cases in which it is used.

As regards the Chinese system we have more, we have the definite statement of a Chinaman. H. Y. Feng produces documentary evidence that the Chinese system was once a cross-cousin system, and so it is akin to the Fijian. As in cross-cousin systems, the kinsfolk are still divided into two: those of the same patronymic, and those of another. These sides he chooses to call "sibs." Besides this vertical division, there is a horizontal one into generations. "These two factors, sib and generation," he sums up, "not only pervade the whole system but regulate marriage." A man marries a woman of another patronym of the first generation.

The hill tribes of Viti Levu, Fiji, indicate very clearly what their kinship terms mean to them. Every hillsman assumes all other hillsmen to be his kinsmen. He is not concerned how near or how far related a stranger may be; he does not search the pedigrees to find out how they are related. All he wants to know is their respective generations. That is easy, because the whole population is divided into two alternate generations called *tako* and

*lavo*. If both are *tako* or both *lavo* they are of the same generation, and then the senior is *tuka*, and junior *tadhi*, terms which have unfortunately been translated (by myself among others), as elder and younger brother. Evidently they mean nothing of the kind, since a man's grandfather is his *tuka* as well as his elder brother. The words simply mean "of the same one of the two generations, on the same side, senior," or "junior," as the case may be. If one man is *tako*, the other *lavo*, then they are related as *tama* and *luve*—that is as one generation to the other. In the case of relatives who are known, and whose side is therefore known, two sets of terms exist, just as in all cross-cousin systems. The line and the generation is what the Fijian looks for in his kinship system, not propinquity.

Why should he be so interested in the generation and so little in the nearness of kin? Because nearness is of little importance in public affairs; generation and line are all important. If a chief, chieftain, or priest dies it is not the next of kin that succeeds, as with us, but the next senior of his generation, no matter how distant; if the deceased was the last of his generation, then it goes to the most senior of the next. A Lauan expresses the rule thus: "X was not made chief, because his *tama* was living." We are not rendering the meaning at all by translating *tama* "father," because X's father was dead. What is meant is that X could not succeed because there was still a member of the previous generation on his father's side to come before him.

We now understand why members of the same generation and side are so carefully distinguished as senior and junior (commonly rendered "elder brother and young brother, classificatory"). The order of seniority is all important. With us only one of a group of brothers has to have his status made clear in royal and titled families; so among such families he bears a special title "heir" which singles him out; the rest are lumped together as brothers, for their seniority is normally of little importance, since they drop out of the succession. It is only when the holder has no issue that the seniority of his younger brothers need be remembered.

It is not the whole of a generation that succeeds, but only those in the male line. Therefore the female line has to be distinguished from the male by special terms. Since the female line is completely excluded, seniority does not come into consideration at all in their case, so no distinction is made between senior and junior. Generation, line, and seniority decide not only succession, but everyday behavior. The duties in the ritual are fixed in the same way.

In short, what we seek most is the next of kin, and so we run up and down the family tree. The Fijians (and the Australian aborigines, and the rest) do not, because there is no point in doing so. All they want is such information as will enable them to place each man on the correct side in the right generation. An inquiry proceeds thus: "How are you related?" "Of the same side and generation." "Why?" "Because our fathers were of the same side and generation." Or else: "We belong to successive generations on opposite sides, because he is of my mother's side and generation."

*selection 30*

# Brother-Sister Avoidance among the Trobriand Islanders

## Bronislaw Malinowski

*From* The Sexual Life of Savages in North-western Melanesia. *Halcyon House, 1929, pp. 519–524. By permission of the author's estate.*

The relation between brother and sister is denoted by the term *luguta*. This term means "sister" when uttered by a male, and "brother" when spoken by a female. In its wider meaning it designates a person of the opposite sex and of the forbidden class, that is, of the same sub-clan or clan as Ego. In its widest and metaphorical sense it is used for any tabooed person or thing. As a metaphor the word "sister" (*luguta*) is frequently used in magical formulae when such things as a blight or a disease are to be exorcized.

The term *luguta* is used only with regard to the tabooed relationship, since children of the same parents and of the same sex use different kinship designations (*tuwagu, bwadagu*) to describe each other; *tuwagu* meaning "my elder brother" (man speaking) and "my elder sister" (woman speaking); and *bwadagu* "my younger brother" (man speaking) and "my younger sister" (woman speaking).

Round the word *luguta* a new order of ideas and moral rules begins to grow up at an early stage of the individual's life history. The child, accustomed to little or no interference with most of its whims or wishes, receives a real shock when suddenly it is roughly handled, seriously reprimanded and punished whenever it makes any friendly, affectionate, or even playful advances to the other small being constantly about in the same household. Above all, the child experiences an emotional shock when it becomes aware of the expression of horror and anguish on the faces of its elders when they correct it. This emotional contagion, this perception of moral reactions in the social environment is perhaps the most powerful factor in a native community by which norms and values are imposed on an individual's character.

The circumstantial arrangements and set customs which preclude any possibility of intimate contact between brother and sister are also, of course, very important. Brother and sister are definitely forbidden to take part at the same time in any childish sexual games, or even in any form of play. And this is not only a rule laid down by elders, but it is also a convention rigorously observed by the children themselves.

We know already that when a boy grows up and when there is a sister of his living in the parental house, he has to sleep in the bachelors' hut (*bukumatula*). In her love affairs, the girl must most rigorously avoid any possibility of being seen by the brother. When, on certain occasions, brothers and sister have to appear in the same company—when they travel in the same canoe, for instance, or participate in a domestic meeting—a rigidity of behavior and a sobriety in conversation falls upon all those present. No cheerful company, no festive entertainment, therefore, is allowed to include brother and sister, since their simultaneous presence would throw a blight on pleasure and would chill gaiety.

Although, in a matrilineal society, the brother is the guardian of his sister, although she has to bend down when he approaches, to obey his commands and to regard him as the head of the family, he never has any concern in his sister's love affairs, nor in her prospective marriage. After she is married,

however, he becomes the head of her family in more than a metaphorical sense. He is called by her sister's children *kadagu* (my material uncle), and as such exercises great influence, especially over the boys.

The careful avoidance by a man of any knowledge about his sister's amorous prospects is, I am certain, not only an ideal but also a fact. I was over and over again assured that no man has the slightest inkling as to whom his sister is going to marry, although this is the common knowledge of everyone else. And I know that nothing remotely touching upon the subject would be uttered within earshot of him. I was told that if a man came by chance upon his sister and her sweetheart while they were making love, all three would have to commit *lo'u* (suicide by jumping from a coco-nut palm). This is obviously an exaggeration which expresses the ideal and not the reality: if such a mishap occurred the brother would most likely pretend to himself, and to them, that he had seen nothing, and would discreetly disappear. But I know that considerable care is taken to preclude any such possibility, and no one would dream of mentioning the subject in the presence of the brother.

Brother and sister thus grow up in a strange sort of domestic proximity: in close contact, and yet without any personal or intimate communication; near to each other in space, near by rules of kinship and common interest; and yet, as regards personality, always hidden and mysterious. They must not even look at each other, they must never exchange any light remarks, never share their feelings and ideas. And as age advances and the other sex becomes more and more associated with love-making, the brother and sister taboo becomes increasingly stringent. Thus, to repeat, the sister remains for her brother the center of all that is sexually forbidden—its very symbol; the prototype of all unlawful sexual tendencies within the same generation and the foundation of prohibited degrees of kinship and relationship, though the taboo loses force as its application is extended.

The nearest female of the previous generation, the mother, is also surrounded by a taboo, which is colored, however, by a somewhat different emotional reaction. Incest with her is regarded with real horror, but both the mechanism by which this taboo is brought home and the way in which it is regarded are essentially distinct from the brother-sister taboo. The mother stands in a close bodily relation to her child in its earliest years, and from this position she recedes, though only gradually, as he grows up. As we know, weaning takes place late, and children, both male and female, are allowed to cuddle in their mother's arms and to embrace her whenever they like.

When a small boy begins his playful sexual approaches to small girls, this does not in any way disturb his relationship to the mother, nor has he to keep any special secrecy on the subject. He does not, by preference, discuss these matters with his parents, but there is no taboo against his doing so. When he is older and carries on more serious intrigues, he might, in certain circumstances, even be allowed to sleep with his sweetheart in his parents' house. Thus the relation to the mother and the sexual relation are kept distinct and allowed to run side by side. The ideas and feelings centering round sex on the one hand, and maternal tenderness on the other, are differentiated naturally and easily, without being separated by a rigid taboo.

Again, since normal erotic impulses find an easy outlet, tenderness towards the mother and bodily attachment to her are naturally drained of their stronger sensuous elements. Incestuous inclinations towards the mother are regarded as highly reprehensible, as unnatural and immoral, but there is not the same feeling of horror and fear as towards brother-and-sister incest. When speaking with the natives of maternal incest, the inquirer finds neither the rigid suspense nor the emotional reactions which are alway evoked by any allusion to brother and sister relations. They would discuss the possibility without being shocked, but it was clear that they regarded incest with the mother as almost impossible. I would not affirm that such incest has never occurred, but certainly I have obtained no concrete data, and the very fact that no case survives in memory or in tradition shows that the natives take relatively little interest in it. . . .

*selection 31*

# The Teachings of My Father

## Crashing Thunder

*From Paul Radin (ed.),*
Crashing Thunder: The
Autobiography of an
American Indian.
*D. Appleton and Co.,
1926, pp. 56–73.
By permission of the
publisher.*

My father used to keep up the old habit of teaching us the customs of the Winnebago. He would wake us up early in the morning and, seated around the fireplace, speak to us. The girls would be taught separately. Now this is what my father told me:

I

My son, when you grow up, see to it that you are of some benefit to your fellow men. There is only one way in which you can aid them and that is by fasting. Our grandfather, the Fire, he who stands at all times in the center of our dwelling, sends forth all kinds of blessings. Be sure that you make an attempt to obtain his.

My son, do you remember to have our grandfathers, the war chiefs, bless you. See to it that they have compassion upon you. Then some day as you travel along the road of life, you will know what to do and encounter no obstacles. Without any effort will you then be able to gain the prize you desire. The honor will be yours to glory in, yours without exertion. All the disposable war-blessings belong to our grandfathers, the war-controllers, and if reverently you fast and thirst yourself to death, then these will be bestowed upon you. Yet if you do not wear out your feet in frequent journeyings to and fro, if you do not blacken your face with charcoal, it will be all for naught that you inflict this suffering upon yourself. Not without constant effort are these blessings procurable. Try to have one of the spirits created by Earth-maker take pity on you. Whatever he says will come about. If you do not posess one of the spirits from whom to obtain strength and power, you will be of no consequence socially and those around you will show you little respect. Indeed they will jeer at you.

My son, it is not good to die in the village; in your homes. Above all, do not let women journey to the spirit land ahead of you. It is not done. To prevent this from happening do we speak to our sons and encourage them to fast. Some day in life you will find yourself traveling along a road filled with obstacles and then you will wish you had fasted. When such an event confronts you, that you may not find it necessary to reproach yourself, I counsel you to fast. If you have not obtained any knowledge from the spirits, why it may happen that some day, in later life, warriors will be returning from the warpath and as they distribute the war prizes to their sisters, your own sisters will stand there empty-handed envying the rest. [Among the Winnebago a man's sisters, especially his elder sisters, were very highly respected and all war prizes, such as wampum-belts, wampum necklaces, etc., were always given to them whenever a man returned from a successful war-party in which he had secured some honor. These war honors were of various kinds. The greatest

was considered to be the feat of having struck the body of a dead enemy first.] But if you obtain blessings from the war-controllers, your sisters will be happy. How proud they will be to receive the prizes, to wear them, and to dance the victory dance! Your sisters too will be strengthened thereby and you will be content and happy.

Now all this it would be well for you to obtain. Try to be a leader of men. To become one, however, is very difficult, the old people used to say. It may happen that you merely pretend to be a leader of men, that you are but a mere warrior in the ranks and yet take it upon yourself to lead a war-party and thus cause a needless waste of life, that you do what is called "throwing away a life." That is the most shameful of all acts. The relatives of the person whom you have thus sacrificed would then have the right to make you suffer, to torture you with burning embers. And then your relatives would have to stand by, sad and humiliated. Not with the blessing of one, not with the blessings of twenty spirits, can you go on the warpath. For that the blessings of all the spirits are necessary—those on this earth, those under it and those who lie pinned through it, the Island Weights; those in the waters and those on the side of the earth, the winds, all four of them. You need the blessings of the spirit who dispenses life from one side of his body and death from the other, the blessings of the Sun, the Moon, the Daylight, and the Earth. All these Earthmaker has make controllers of war and by all these must you be blessed in order to lead a war-party.

My son, if you cast off your dress for many people, that is, if you give to the needy, your people will be benefited by your deeds. It is good thus to be honored by many people. And even more will they honor you if you return victorious from the warpath with one of the four limbs, that is, one of the four war honors. But if you obtain two, or three, or perhaps even four limbs, then all the greater will be the honor. Then whenever a war feast is given you will receive part of the deer that is boiled, either part of its body or part of the head. [The meat of a deer at such a feast is given only to great warriors. The head is regarded as the choicest piece.] When on some other occasion, such as the Four Nights' Wake, you are called upon to recount your war exploits in behalf of the departed souls, be careful, however, not to claim more than you actually accomplished. If you do, you will cause the soul of the man in whose behalf you are telling it, to stumble in his journey to spirit land. [According to Winnebago belief the soul of a deceased individual in his journey to spirit land must cross a very slippery, swinging bridge and it is thought that if, during the wake following the man's burial, any of the invited warriors exaggerate their achievements the unfortunate soul will not be able to cross this bridge and will stumble and fall into the abyss of fire over which it is thrown.] If you tell a falsehood then and exaggerate, you will die before your time, for the spirits, the war-controllers, will hear you. It is indeed a sacred duty to tell the truth on such an occasion. Tell less than you did. The old men say it is wiser.

My son, it is good to die on the warpath. If you die on the warpath, you will not lose consciousness at death. You will be able to do what you please with your soul and it will always remain in a happy condition. If afterwards you wish to become reincarnated as human being, you may do so, or you may take the form of those-who-walk-upon-the-light, the birds, or the form of any animal you please, in short. All these benefits will you obtain if you die on the warpath.

## II

My son, if you cannot obtain war-blessings, fast at least for position in life. If you fast then, when you get married you will get along well. You will then not have to worry about your having children and your life will be a happy one. If you fast and have the spirits bless you with all that concerns the happiness of your home, then throughout life you will never be in need of anything. Fast for the food you are to receive. If you fast frequently enough for these things then some day when your children ask for food they will be able to obtain a piece of deer meat without difficulty; they may indeed be able to obtain a piece of moose meat. It lies within your power to prevent your children from ever going hungry.

Now again, my son, let me enjoin you. Do not abuse your wife. Women are sacred. If you make your wife suffer, then you will die in a short time. Our grandmother Earth is a woman, and in abusing your wife you are abusing her. Most certainly will you be abusing your grandmother if you act thus. Since after all it is she who is taking care of us, by your action you will be practically killing yourself.

When you have your home, see to it that whoever enters your lodge obtains something to eat, no matter how little you yourself may have. Such food will be a source of death to you if withheld. If you are stingy about giving food, some one might kill you in consequence; some one may poison you. If you ever hear of a stranger passing through your country and you want to see him, prepare food for him and have him brought to you. In this manner you will be doing good and it is always good to do good, it is said.

If you see a helpless old person, help him if you have anything at all. If you happen to possess a home take him there, and feed him, for he may suddenly make uncomplimentary remarks about you. You will be strengthened thereby. Or perhaps when he comes, he may bring with him under his arms a medicine bundle, something he cherishes very much and which he will offer you. If it is a bulb-medicine keep it to protect your house. Your home will never then be molested by anything evil and nothing evil will enter your house, neither bad spirits, ghosts, disease, nor unhappiness. Now such will be your life if you do as I tell you. Witches will keep away from you. Thus by fasting will you benefit yourself and your fellow men.

You know that Earthmaker created all the spirits, those that live above the earth, those who live on the earth, those who live under the earth, those who live in the water—all these he created and placed in control of powers. Even the minor spirits Earthmaker placed in control of something. In this fashion he created them and after that, he created us and because we were created last and no further powers were left, he could not put us in control of anything. Then, however, did Earthmaker create a week and this he placed us in control of. He further told us that none of the spirits he had created would have the power to take this weed away from us without giving us something in exchange. He told us that if we offered him a pipeful of this weed, which we call tobacco, he too would grant us whatever we asked for. Now it so happened that all the spirits came to long for this weed as intensely as they longed for anything in creation and for that reason if, at any time, with tobacco in our hands we make our prayer to the spirits, they will take pity upon us and bestow upon us the blessings which Earthmaker gave them. Indeed so it is, for Earthmaker created it thus.

Fast, my son. If you are blessed by the spirits and then blow your breath upon people who are ill, they will become well. Thus will you help your fellow men. If you can cure any of your fellow men of disease, then you will be of even more than ordinary help to them. If you can draw disease from out the body, people will greatly respect you. If then you happen to be without work, all that you need for your support they will give you. For as long a time as you live they will do this for you. After your death people will speak about your deeds for all time. During your lifetime they will say, "Yes, he really has power."

If you are not able to fast, do at least try to obtain some power from those individuals, who know the virtues and powers of certain plants. It is sad enough, of course, if you will have to admit to yourself that you could not obtain blessings during fasting; but if you could not, at least try to have those who possess the plants I have mentioned, take pity on you. If they take pity on you, they will present you with one of the good plants that give life to man. Now it will not suffice for you to possess merely one plant. You should try to obtain all those plants that grow among the hairy covering of our grandmother, the Earth—all those that give us life—until you have a complete medicine bundle. Then will you truly have reason to feel encouraged.

Some of the medicine men, the shamans, were blessed by the waterspirits. [Waterspirits are mythical animals generally described as having the shape of a lynx or wild-cat and provided with long tails that completely encircle their bodies. Their gifts to man are ambivalent and it depends upon the man whether he cares to make good or bad medicines from their bodies. Their so-called "bones" generally consist of semi- or completely fossilized objects.] If you wish to obtain really powerful blessings and gain the power of curing many people, you will have to fast a long time and sincerely. If four, or

say ten, of the truly powerful spirits bless you, then some day when you have children and anything happens to one of them, you will not have to look around for a medicine man, but all you will have to do will be to look into your own medicine bundle. Search there and you will undoubtedly be able to find the medicines necessary for curing your children. Indeed after a while you will be called upon to cure your fellow men. Then you can open your medicine bundle without embarrassment, for you will have the knowledge necessary for treating the sick. You will know where the disease is lodged and your treatment will be successful, for it was only after the greatest efforts on your part that you succeeded in obtaining the requisite blessings. If you declare to the patient that he will live, then he will live. If you make proper offerings to the medicine and speak to your medicine in the proper manner, it will exert all the power it possesses to cure the patient. Now you must make good offerings to these medicines; you must give many feasts in their honor and then if, in addition, you address them as if they were human beings, they assuredly will help you and do what you ask. You may accordingly accept the payments offered to you by your patients in good conscience and your children will wear these payments in the form of wampum necklaces and thus gain renewed strength. They will be well and happy. These are the reasons why I want you to be extremely careful in your attitude. Medicines are good for all purposes; that is why they were given to us. Earthmaker gave them to us so that we could cure ourselves from disease.

If any one tries to obtain these staffs of life, these medicines and inflicts sufferings upon himself in acquiring them, then assuredly will our grandmother Earth have cognizance of it. She knows all that you have lost in obtaining them and in the long run what you have lost, will be returned to you. You made your offerings for the future ard it is good for people to look forward to their future.

Say, you wish to obtain the paint medicine. For that you would have to put yourself in the most abject condition before the spirits. If you smear yourself with your paint medicine it will irresistibly attract the enemy; it will paralyze him, deprive him of all power of movement and utterly overpower him. Keep it in your home and then you will never be in want of riches. People will give you their most valued possessions owing to the influence of this paint medicine. The paint medicine is made from the blood of the water-spirits and that is why it is so holy. People obtain it by fasting and thirsting themselves to death and then receiving a blessing from the waterspirit. Earthmaker placed the water-spirits in possession of these powers so that they could then, in turn, bestow them on us.

Some people succeeded in obtaining a medicine that will enable a person to outdistance another in running. It might perhaps be well for you to learn something about this. There are medicines to be used in courting; medicines to prevent married people from separating; medicines for getting rich; medicines for causing people to become crazy. Should you, for instance, wish to make a person feel very sad at heart, then you can poison him with this last-named medicine and even make him crazy. It is also possible to make a woman who has refused you become a harlot, for this medicine will make her fall in love with every man she sees. Indeed any kind of medicine you desire can you obtain from certain individuals. Some are acquainted with medicines that put one to sleep, others with those that keep one awake and give one insomnia. Some have medicines enabling one to overcome the viciousness of dogs who are put to watch over women; others again have medicines that make people single out the possessor in a crowd. Every one will look at him and consider him a great man. There are medicines to prevent people from getting tired when walking and medicines to cause a dog fight to take place. In short there are medicines for everything.

Every one must take care of himself and try to obtain that knowledge which will enable him to live in comfort and happiness. Try therefore to learn about the things you will need. If you know them, then as you travel along in life, you will not have to go to the expense of buying them from others, but you will have your own medicines. If you act in this way and if, in addition, you fast properly, you will never be caught off guard in life. Should you possess a home, it will look beautiful and you will never be in want. That is why I know you will never regret this that I am

telling you. So you shall travel on your journey through life, along the virtuous road taken by all your fellow men, and your actions and behavior will never become the butt of your neighbor's sarcasm.

Help yourself as you travel along the road of life. The earth has many narrow passages scattered over it. If you have something with which to strengthen yourself, then when you get to these narrow turns you will be able to pass through them safely and your fellow men will respect you. See to it that people like you. Be on friendly terms with every one and then every one will like you. You will be happy and prosperous.

Never do any wrong to your children. Whatever your children ask of you, do it for them. If you act thus people will then say that you are good natured.

If any one in the village loses a friend through death, should you at all be wealthy, cover the expenses of the funeral of the deceased, if you can. Help the mourners likewise in defraying the expenses of feeding the departed. If you act thus, you will do well. All the people you have helped will then really know what kind of a man you are. For the good you do people will love you.

It is not good to win at gambling. You may possibly become rich thereby but that is no life to lead. If you are blessed with luck in cards, if you are blessed with luck at gambling, you will perhaps win things and have plenty of wealth, but none of your children will live.

Now if you do all that I have told you, you will lead a happy and prosperous life. That is why we Winnebago preach to a child we love so that it should never become acquainted with the things that are not right, and never do anything wrong. Then if, in later life, a person does anything wrong, he will do it with a clear knowledge of the consequences of his actions.

### III

My son, when you get married, do not make an idol of the woman you marry; do not worship her. If you worship a woman she will insist upon greater and greater worship as times goes on. This is what the old people used to say. They always preached against those men who hearken too strongly to the words of women; who are the slaves of women. Now it may happen that a man has received many warnings as to his behavior in this regard and that he pays no attention to them. It may go so far that when he is asked to attend a war-bundle feast he will refuse to go. [The war-bundle feast was the great war ceremony of the Winnebago. It was given by all those individuals who possessed a war-bundle and since theoretically there was only one war-bundle in each clan, the basis of the organization of the ceremony was the clan. The ceremony consisted largely of prayers, songs and speeches in honor of the spirits more definitely associated with war. For each of these spirits, a buckskin decorated with the symbol sacred to the spirit was prepared and then at the most dramatic moment of the ceremony these buckskins were thrown out of the ceremonial lodge and it was believed that the spirits came down in person to fetch them. The war-bundle feast was specifically a man's ceremony.] It may be that when he is married he will listen to the voice of his wife and refuse to go on a warpath. He might as well have been brought up as a girl. Men who are real men perform the deeds of men, but such a man will never perform a real man's deed. If he should actually attend a war-bundle feast he will be given the leanest piece of meat, only given to a man of no account. Why should any one run the risk of being thus jeered at? Now when a really brave man attends a war-bundle feast he is given a deer's head. This other man gets a lean piece! It will dry up in his throat, so humiliated and disgraced will he feel. After a while he will not be allowed to go to any feast; his wife will not let him. He will listen to the voice of his wife. His relatives will scold him, his sisters will think nothing of him. They will tell people never to go to visit him. Finally when he has become a real slave of his wife he will even hit his relatives if she asks him to. It is for these reasons that I warn you not to listen to women. You will be considered different from others. It is not good.

Remember this too, that women cannot be watched. If you try to watch them and are jealous about them, then your female relatives will also be jealous of them. Finally when your jealousy has developed to the highest pitch, your wife will leave you and run away with some one else. You have allowed her to see by your actions that you worship a woman, and one alone, and, in addition, you have been watching her all the time. Because of this incessant annoyance she will run away from you. If you think that your wife is the only one to love, you have humbled yourself and she will be taken from you. You have likewise made the woman suffer; you have made her unhappy. The whole world will hear about it. No other woman will want to marry you and you will have the reputation of being a bad man.

Now you may act in the following way: You see people starting on a warpath and you join them knowing that it is an honor to die on the warpath. But you will join them because you feel unhappy at your wife's flight. Now this is not the proper way to act. You are throwing away your life; you are causing the leader of the war-party to throw away a life. If you want to go on the warpath, do not go because your wife has been taken away from you, go because you feel courageous enough to do so.

It is on the warpath that a man has fun! Do not go, however, unless you have fasted adequately. You must fast for each specific warpath. If you do not and yet join a war-party, then in the midst of the fight, a bullet will come your way and kill you. That will happen because you did not fast. If you have performed any deeds of valor, recount them to your sisters and to your sister's children. Those in charge of war-bundles are good to listen to in such matters. Those to whom such people give advice will eat an excellent dish; they will have the honor of sitting near a great warrior in the middle of the lodge.

These are the things of which the old people spoke and this also is the advice I give you. I myself never asked for these things, but my father did. Your grandfather did. He asked for the information relating to the manner in which people are to behave. Never, when you are older, should you allow yourself to get in the predicament of not knowing what is the right thing to do. Ask for this instruction, my son. It is not a matter requiring a few moments; it is something that must be thoroughly learned. You, too, must learn it.

# Rank, Wealth, and Kinship in Northwest Coast Society

## Philip Drucker

*From* American Anthropologist, *Vol. 41, No. 1, 1939, pp. 55–65. By permission of the author and the publisher.*

Northwest Coast society was organized on no idealistic premises of the equality of man. Each individual had his place in the arbitrarily calibrated social structure of his community. However, the casual designation so often encountered of this social pattern of ranked statuses as a "class" or "caste" system with nobles, commoners, and slaves, is a crude over-simplification, except as regards the division of society into freemen and slaves. It will be the aim of this paper first to show that there were no social classes among the freemen, but rather an unbroken series of graduated statuses, and second, to investigate the principles underlying this gradation of rank.

For a working definition of a social class we may take the dictionary formulation: "Class: A group of persons, things, qualities, or activities having common characteristics or attributes"; or, "a group of individuals ranked together as possessing common characteristics or as having the same status." Thus, the fundamental requirement of a class, socially speaking, is the sharing by its members of some trait or traits which set them off as a distinct entity within their society. This common attribute, we may expect, will direct specific attitudes and behavior by them and toward them as a group. Where such attributes distinctive of social *groups* were lacking, we are not justified in speaking of a class system.

If we survey Northwest Coast society as a whole, we find that two great social classes existed everywhere: freemen and slaves. The distinguishing criterion, condition of servitude (whether by capture, birth, or debt does not matter here) placed every individual in one or the other group. As a member of his group he enjoyed certain rights or was subject to certain disabilities—depending on which group he was in—and by virtue of his membership was the object of esteem or scorn, and was entitled to scorn or esteem those of the other class. That slaves were sometimes treated with kindness and given certain concessions made no difference in their class membership; they were still slaves, and as such belonged in a sphere apart from the free.

As a matter of fact, the slaves had so little societal importance in the area that they scarcely need be considered in problems relating to the social structure. "Society," in the native view, consisted of the freemen of a particular group. Slaves, like the natives' dogs, or better still, like canoes and sea-otter skins and blankets, were elements of the social configuration but had no active part to play in group life. Their participation was purely passive, like that of a stage-prop carried on and off the boards by the real actors. Their principal significance was to serve as foils for the high and mighty, impressing the inequality of status on native consciousness.

If we seek groupings among the freemen comparable to the division into free and slaves we fail utterly to find them. I do not, of course, mean that all freemen were equals among themselves; but there was no class of nobility set off distinct from a class of "commoners," much less a three- or four-fold class system. We search in vain for any diagnostic traits defining groups within the society of freemen. There were individuals reckoned high and there were those considered lowly, true enough. Those of high rank abstained from menial tasks such as fetching wood and water, they wore costly ornaments and finer garb, and strutted in the spotlight on every ritual occasion. But these were not class prerogatives. They were not restricted to a certain group; there was no point in the social scale above which they were permitted and below which prohibited.

To compare the role of the highest ranking member of a Northwest Coast social group with that of the lowliest member gives an impression of a remarkably vast difference in cultural participation. The significant point is that the difference lay in extent of participation, not kind. One less high than the highest

in rank, participated less fully in ostentatious activities. A person a grade above the lowest participated in these a bit more than the one on the bottom rung. And thus the manifestations of statuses of high and low degree shaded into each other.

What actually occurred was that each society consisted not of two or more social classes, but of a complete series of statuses graded relatively, one for each individual of the group. No two individuals were precisely equal in rank, in fact, equivalences would pose insuperable difficulties. This is brought out most clearly in the potlatch. Barnett's keen analysis has brought out the prime function of the potlatch in validating status; all I want to do here is to point out the mechanics of the procedure. In the distribution of the potlatch gifts, it was manifestly necessary to give them out one by one, else a mad scramble would result. Invariably the giving was in order of rank. The highest ranking individual of the recipient group was named first, and given his allotted share; then the second highest, and so on down the line. This order of giving was, from southeast Alaska to the mouth of the Columbia, the most important expression of the concept of rank. For two recipients to be of equal status would throw the whole affair out of gear, obviously, for neither would submit to being called after the other. An event in recent Nootkan history reveals the difficulties involved in such a situation.

"During the latter half of the last century, apparently about eighty years ago, the Tlupana Arm tribe, consisting of several local groups who wintered at o'is, moved down to Friendly Cove, joining the Moachat ('Nootka'). The head man of o'is stood first in the tribe; he had married a close kinswoman of the Moachat chief, and because of his relationship the latter offered him and his tribe a place at Friendly Cove. (The Tlupana Arm groups had been seriously reduced in numbers both through wars and the usual historic-period causes.) In addition, the Moachat chief 'shared' his potlatch-seat with his kinsman. For a time, when one potlatched the joint tribe, he had to give simultaneously to the Moachat and Tlupana first chiefs, and by analogy, to both second chiefs, and so on down the line. This was extremely confusing; both names and both gifts had to be called out simultaneously. No one was satisfied.

Finally the Moachat chief in second place gave a potlatch at which he gave to all the Moachat chiefs, from first to last, then began with the Tlupana Arm chiefs. The first chief of the Moachat then tried to establish another order: himself and the Tlupana first chief; the second of Moachat, then the second of Tlupana; the third of Moachat, then the third of Tlupana, etc.

"This did not meet with favor; the Moachat second chief was really receiving third, the third fifth, and so on. Nor would the Moachat chiefs approve of a plan to give simultaneously to both first chiefs, then to all the Moachat chiefs and after them the Tlupana men. They insisted on following the lead of the second chief, each giving to his own first chief (Moachat) and his fellows first, then to the Tlupana chiefs. The Moachat chiews were rich, and did most of the potlatching; whether the Tlupana chiefs desisted because of poverty or from tact I do not know. There came to be considerable feeling over the situation. Finally the first chief of Tlupana potlatched, announcing that henceforth he would receive after the Moachat chiefs (and of course his subordinates received after him), so everything was settled. The whole difficulty was, in the informant's view, that the Moachat first chief 'had been trying to violate all the rules of the potlatch' in interfering with the established order of receiving."

In short, there were no classes of statuses in Northwest Coast society. Each individual had his own particular status in the graduated series from high to low; each person's status had its own attributes which were not quite like those of anyone else. To insist upon the use of the term "class system" for Northwest Coast society means that we must say that each individual was in a class by himself.

Before undertaking an analysis of the factors contributing to rank, it will be necessary to define briefly the social units within which rank was regulated. First of all, a survey of the source material indicates very clearly that the primary social unit was the local group, a group of people sharing rights to the utilization of economically important places and occupying a common village. Even among the Northern Nootkans, Southern Kwakiutl, and some Coast Tsimshian, where confederacies of these local groups formed larger units at the winter villages, the smaller divisions retained their economic autonomy and moreover manifested it in rituals, for the local groups were the usual participating units.

When we come to examine the constitution of the typical local group of the area, a more striking fact appears: everywhere this social division was no more and no less than an extended family (slaves of course excluded) and was so considered by its members. The individual of highest rank in the social unit was related to the lowliest, distantly, it is true, but nevertheless related. So ties of blood as well as common residence and common economic resources welded the group together.

Now while the economic resources—fishing, hunting, and gathering grounds—pertained to the local group as a whole, titularly they belonged to individuals. We have to do here with two overlapping and apparently not well differentiated concepts of property-right. Characteristically, a man is said to have "owned" an economically important tract. This "ownership" was expressed by his "giving permission," as natives usually put it, to his fellows to exploit the locality each season. At the same time fellow-members of his local group —his relatives—had an inalienable right to exploit the tract. The present writer time and again has heard statements by informants from northwest California to Tlingit country to the effect that a certain man "owned" a particular place, for example, a fishing-site, and that his permission was required before other members of his society could use it. Nonetheless no instance was ever heard of an "owner" refusing to gives the necessary permission. Such a thing is inconceivable to the natives. The situation is perfectly clear to the Indians, if not to us. Actually, individual ownership in these cases does not mean exclusive right of use, but a sort of stewardship, and the right to *direct* the exploitation of the economic tract by the local group. The latter it was who held exclusive right.

"Nootkan custom illustrated the nature of such rights very clearly. Almost every inch of Nootkan territory, the rarely visited mountainous back-country, the rich long-shore fishing and hunting grounds, and the sea as far out as the eye could reach, was 'owned' by someone or other. An owner's right consisted in the right to the first yield of his place each season—the first catch or two of salmon, the first picking of salmon-berries, etc. When the season came the owner called on his group to aid him in building the weir or picking the berries, then he used the yield of the first harvest for a feast given to his group, at which he stated his hereditary right (of custodianship) to the place, then bade the people to avail themselves of its products. Any and all of them might do so. (Outsiders were prohibited from exploiting these owned places, except where they could claim kinship to the owner, *i.e.*, for the time identify themselves with his local group.) The essence of the individual 'ownership,' was thus simply a recognition of the custodian's right."

The individual "ownership" or stewardship of economic areas was regarded as highly important, giving, as it did, a measure of authority to the incumbent of the position—political authority of a sort, and thus prestige. The rights were inherited according to local rules of inheritance (by the sister's son among Tlingit, Haida, Tsimshian, and Xaisla; by the son elsewhere in the area), so that it came about that in every Northwest Coast society economic wealth was in the hands of the direct descendants of a single line. Due to a disinclination to divide these holdings equally among a group of brothers, the bulk of the economic tracts of a local group was under the custodianship of a single individual at any one time: the eldest heir of the past "owner." This was as true in northwest California as in the regions north of the Columbia where the principle of primogeniture was so explicitly phrased. Thus, the economic possessions of a Northwest Coast society were chiefly in the custody of, or nominally "owned" by, a line of eldest sons of eldest sons (or the matrilineal counterpart of such a line). By virtue of their stewardship these men were elevated to prominence. Directing utilization of the natural resources as they did, they were the acknowledged heads of the groups—the heads of the extended families.

The extended family heads are the individuals referred to commonly as the "chiefs." The close relatives of the chiefs were not lacking in prestige, however, not only because they were intimately associated with the head of the social group, but in addition they customarily held various minor properties, in lands and other things as well. They were ranked according to their nearness to the chief. In the course of a few generations, as the sec-

ondary lines of descent diverged more and more from the direct line, and as patrimonies dwindled, descendants of the chief's brothers could claim but a low rank. Nonetheless by virtue of their kinship to the head of the village they retained certain rights and privileges. The rights of utilization of economic tracts by all group members may be reckoned an expression of this recognition of blood-relationship, as was, in the north, the right to receive at potlatches even though in a low place. The significance of these last-named facts is that status in its minimum terms—membership in society—was derived from kinship and expressed in terms of wealth. . . .

In peripheral northwestern California, where we might expect to find areal patterns expressed in simplest terms, we find that rank was determined primarily by possession of wealth. The reckoning of status according to one's mother's bride-price savors of the hereditary principle, but the cultural accent was on wealth-holding rather than on blood. Nevertheless social position in this region was hereditary, for the simple reason that the status-giving fortunes were inherited, not earned anew each generation. It must be owned that these statuses were only loosely seriated within the group; the elaborate gradation found in the north was unknown. The outstanding figure in each local society was the head of an extended family who by virtue of his capital directed many activities. His custodianship of economically important sites made him preeminent in matters relating to the food quest; his capital of token goods gave him a voice in ritual affairs, for he had to equip the dancers in the wealth display performances, and in the social life, where he contributed to marriage payments and weregild. Next to this proud figure stood close kinsmen, brothers, cousins, and the like, who basked in reflected glory, as they, according to nearness of kinship, could draw on the resources of the head of the group when necessary. Grading into this group were lesser men who depended on what scraps of riches they might possess, the amount of bride-price paid for their mothers, and their favor in the eyes of their "big friend." (These are not, of course, categories representing distinct social classes, for they shaded imperceptibly into each other.)

From the Columbia to the Straits of Georgia the basis of status was the same as in the south—hereditary wealth—although the fact of heredity was stressed more and more as one proceeds northward. Similarly, more precise systems of ranking within each society are suggested, as we enter the domain of the potlatch where order of precedence becomes a matter of great concern.

It was in the societies north of the Salishan-Wakashan linguistic boundary, however, that the concept of formal status had its most luxuriant growth. The principles underlying this gradation may be brought out most clearly if we begin with a type individual to see how he attained his place in his social system. The first thing that set our individual off from his fellows was his name. Names, on the northern coasts, were very definitely hereditary property, and what is more, each name carried with it a particular social evaluation based on its traditional origin and the honor or disrepute of its bearer subsequently. That is to say, the names themselves were ranked from high to low. Each name had a particular status associated with it, a status which was expressed on formal occasions of feasting and potlatching, where the order of receiving was determined by the sequence of the names. So firmly rooted was this association of name and rank that the process of assuming a particular status, social, political, or ritual, consisted in taking (or having bestowed upon one) a certain name. The Kwakiutl, among whom the system of naming reached its most profuse elaboration, had separate names for feasts, for potlatches, and for their secret society performances. A personal name was thus a key to its bearer's status and embodied all the rights, economic and ceremonial, to which he was entitled.

Our friend, then, by taking his real name, defined at a blow his formal status in his society. To assume his name and status two things were requisite. First of all, he had to have a right to the name in question, usually through heredity, though in some regions transfers outside of the direct line of descent might be made: in a repayment of a bride-price, for example, or the name might be captured in war, or seized if a debt was not paid. The sole purpose of the interminable discourses at naming ceremonies was to declare the right of the claimant, through heredity or other legitimate transfer, to the name in question.

The second requisite for name-taking was that it be done formally and publicly, accompanied by a distribution of goods, that is to say, a potlatch. Not only was the name itself considered wealth, and connoted wealth, but wealth in token goods was mandatory for assuming it. If our type individual was heir of the head of his social group, there was, of course, no problem. But were his name of lesser status, he would be unable to potlatch in his own right. This is one of the most significant features of the Northwest Coast wealth system; the national wealth of each society was definitely limited, and there was no way in which a poor man could make a fortune for himself—at least, not in the days before European trade inflated and completely altered the financial system. Formerly, the token wealth of the entire group was concentrated in the hands of the head of the unit just as was the custodianship of economic rights. Not only did he have a certain right to surplus products (those beyond the needs of subsistence) of the lands in his trust, but members of his group gave him the fruits of their industry: canoes, blankets, furs. The head of the group was, in a sense, custodian of the token wealth of the family just as he was custodian of the economic resources. Barnett has pointed out this significant fact in connection with the potlatch: the entire group of the nominal giver united to support the affair out of motives of group loyalty and in return for the patronage and social favors bestowed by the head of the group. It was in this patronage that we find the means by which those of lower rank assumed whatever status they had right to. Names of lower rank were formally bestowed by the chief on those who had the right to them during the course of a potlatch. Among the Nootkans (and perhaps among other groups) the correlation between the group assistance and the chief's patronage was made obvious, for it was etiquette for the chief, in announcing the new name and rank of a member of his group, to tell how much property the latter (or the latter's parents) had contributed to the total amount to be given out. Nothing is clearer than the intimate relationship between hereditary status and wealth in the northern region. Not only were the hereditary fixed rankings in society based on economic wealth, and themselves considered a form of wealth, but material wealth was necessary for their formal assumption.

In fine, throughout the Northwest Coast, possession of riches was the basis of social gradation. This wealth was inheritable, and thus status was hereditary. The northern and southern regions differed only in whether overt emphasis was put on wealth-holding or inheritance of wealth. In the south, possession counted for most; the fact that wealth was inherited was little stressed. In the north, the fact of inheritance dominated native consciousness, but wealth was an inevitable concomitant of high rank. Wealth and birth everywhere were absolutely inseparable factors in the determination of status. Whatever schismatic tendencies such a system of social inequality theoretically might have had were negated by the unbroken graduation of statuses from high to low, and the bonds of blood kinship which linked the head of each social unit with his humblest subordinate.

*selection 33*

# The Role of a Fijian Chief

## Clellan S. Ford

The chief is the leader of his people. He organizes the activities in his district, directing work in the gardens, in house building, and in fishing. He receives in return the best produce of the land. The labor of the men in the district is at his command, though by tradition the chief is liberal, and most of the supplies which he exacts return ultimately to the subjects by whose labor they were produced. No decision of importance in the district may be reached without his approval. Funeral services, for example, may not begin until he has given the word. Visitors must present themselves to the chief before they undertake to carry out the purpose of their visit. At any ceremonial function the chief receives the first bowl of *kava* and determines the order in which others are served. The chief is also the arbiter of disputes within the district. When any trouble arises, the persons involved must be brought before him. He is expected to be fair, judging carefully according to the dictates of custom. He holds the power of life and death over his subjects. Offenses against the chief are not tolerated; it is here that stresses and strains in the status relationship are most

*From* American Sociological Review, *Vol. 3, 1938, pp. 542–550. By permission of the author and the publisher.*

clearly apparent. Treason is severely punished. In the old days, for a person to step out of his role as subject and attempt to assume the status of a chief was tantamount to committing suicide. The penalty for plotting against a chief was inevitably death. The examples given in the literature reveal that the subject doomed to execution made little or no effort to avoid his punishment. When discussing this point with a member of the community I was told: "Whatever the chief says shall be carried out. He knows what is best for us. Who would want to destroy the Tui? . . . he is the leader of our community and no one could take his place. If he were not here, we would be lost." This power, now prohibited by the British, is the traditional heritage of a Fijian chief.

Except for the examples referred to, the picture thus far presented has been abstracted from behavior; we have not seen chiefs and their subjects actually living their roles. The formal description of a role necessarily involves a selection of certain aspects of the total behavior and is not always done with eyes open to the exact meaning of the descriptive terms employed, with the result that depth and content of the relationship often disappear. The above statement of the relationship between chief and subject leaves the impression that behavior accords rigidly with the description. The individuals occupying the statuses and roles seem little more than puppets. The personality of the individual is completely lacking.

The actual role of a real person gives a very different picture. When my wife and I arrived at Naviti, I was accepted as an American chief sanctioned by the British government. Our relationship to the chief was formally and rigidly defined. He treated us with respect coupled with an aloofness which was at first disturbing. Since he would be responsible for our treatment, we did our best to break down this barrier of formality and reserve. Although the language handicap, which only gradually was overcome, retarded our efforts, constant association and interest in the things he enjoyed soon led the chief to accept us as something more than mere representatives from another country. After seven months of closest association, spending most of our waking hours in his company, eating with him, and participating in his activities, we became firm friends. The affection which developed between us makes it difficult not to color accounts of his behavior, but I have attempted to give an objective description.

Ratu Kama is a typical Fijian chief in appearance and carries himself with dignity. He is a large, powerful man with broad shoulders, narrow hips, and rather small feet and hands. His piercing eyes, strong chin, and intelligent forehead distinguish a handsome face which, though genial, can be very stern. Despite his fifty odd years, he is in good physical condition and can walk fifteen to twenty miles a day over rugged hills without apparent discomfort. Customarily retiring at midnight, he is at work in the gardens every morning before five. His crowning glory is a mass of bushy black hair about six inches long encircling his head. This he keeps scrupulously clean and well groomed, washing it daily, anointing it with coconut oil, and combing it to perfection. Once a month it is dyed to prevent the appearance of a single white hair. He bathes at least once a day, carefully manicures his finger and toe nails, and keeps his skin in condition through frequent oil massages. His reasons for this extreme cleanliness and care are twofold. First, he attributes the tropical ulcers and boils so prevalent among Fijians to lack of cleanly habits. Second, he relates the prevalence of colds and pneumonia among the natives to their negligence in the use of oil. In the old days, he says, the natives used to remove their barkcloth when it had become wet. Oil served instead of clothing on wet and rainy days. Now that clothing has supplanted bark-cloth, the Fijian no longer uses coconut oil to keep him warm and dry, and, morever, he seldom changes his cloth *sulu* when it becomes damp. Many now become sick, the chief maintains, because the Fijian physique is not accustomed to this treatment.

Chief Kama enjoys his food immensely, especially when it is highly spiced with chili peppers, and he is extremely proud of the amount he can consume at one meal, regarding the ability to eat great quantities of yam, pork, and fish as an estimable accomplishment. He drinks *kava* to excess and chews or smokes tobacco constantly. He is extremely voluble and seems to enjoy shouting his orders and bellowing his jokes. His best loved pastime is to sit in a meeting house drinking *kava*, smoking a banana leaf cigar, joking and laughing heartily with the men who gather around him.

Whenever he has finished overseeing work in the gardens or the building of a house, for example, he takes time off to meet the men informally.

On certain occasions he manifests in striking manner his zest for pleasure and social enjoyment. On his fifty-first birthday he seemed afraid lest he lose a precious minute or two of the festive occasion. Before midnight he was supervising preparations for his birthday feast. He superintended the building of a huge earth oven, the heating of the stones, the slaughtering of the pigs, the special wrapping of a hundred or more yams and other vegetables and fish, and the all important preparation of fancy arrowroot and coconut puddings. When these were cooked, about six o'clock in the morning, he directed the men to make a bundle of all this food, so that it could be suspended from two poles and carried by the village youths. Throughout the preparations, his attitude seemed one of suppressed excitement and anticipation, somewhat like that prevailing among ourselves on Christmas Eve. At the same time he was insistent that everything be done in the traditional manner. The emphasis on custom was reflected in the elaborate adornment of the villagers, who bedecked themselves in brightly colored strips of pandanus leaf, powdered their hair with sandalwood, and painted their faces as though for a victory feast.

We formed a procession, with the food and its bearers following behind, to march several miles to a neighboring town. The shell trumpets of our party announced our approach, and we were met on the outskirts of the village by an escort of two men, one brandishing a spear and the other carrying a club. With due form, we entered the meeting house to attend the *kava* ceremony. The chief, fully attired in *tapa*, his face painted, and his body glistening with coconut oil, seated himself at the far end of the meeting house and at once became grave. Quietly he stated that the ceremony was to be carried out in all details as the *kava* rites had been conducted in the past. Nothing must disturb the majesty of the ceremony. After the mixing of the *kava* had begun, not a sound was heard in the meeting house except the swish and drip of the strainer in the bowl. At intervals old men seated behind the bowl accompanied the movements of the mixer with a weird, high-pitched chorus. The chief looked on with an immobile face, while everyone else scarcely dared to move. After some twenty minutes the mixing was complete, and a cup-bearer danced down with a bowl of *kava* for the chief. When all had been served and the ceremony was over, Ratu Kama quickly relaxed and became almost maniacal with joy. He supervised the feast and spread special mats for each person to sit on. These mats were his presents to the people. He laughed and joked with the men who ate with us and insisted that everyone eat as much as possible. After more than two hours of feasting, he watched formal dances by the women of the village, cheering them on; he danced with the girls, sang, slapped the men on their backs, and did his best to make this a joyous occasion for everyone. During the entire afternoon he acted like a child whose birthday party seems the most important thing in the world. After dark we walked back to our village, went to his house, and drank *kava* until late evening. He was still his happy, jolly birthday self. Suddenly drumbeats sounded, signifying that envoys from an island nearby had arrived. At once he became the cold, stern man who had officiated at the *kava* ceremony in the morning, and for several hours he carried on a dignified conference with the messengers. It seemed impossible that the next morning he could do anything but sleep, yet he was up at five to superintend the gardening. He seemed to be compensating for his good time of the day before, driven by conscience to perform his customary duties.

One of the most significant roles of a Fijian chief is to direct the food gathering activities of his village. One night Chief Kama called the men together and announced that next day we were to go fishing. This called for extensive preparations. Early in the morning the men began to make the *rau*, or fish barrier, and to prepare their spears, while the women mended their nets. When the tide had turned, we went to a place on the reefs selected by the chief. One man took an end of the *rau* and waded out into the water. Another, picking up the vine about ten feet away from the first, followed him out, and so on until, with forty or fifty men carrying the vine barrier, it was transported out on the reef and arranged in a huge circle. The chief stood on the shore shouting directions. The men had to go precisely where he indicated. Once when a carrier stumbled with the vine the chief reproved him, saying: "Get up, you crazy fellow; are you an old, old woman who can't walk?" When the circle was finally completed, the chief waded out so that he could better give his orders. He made the men stand motionless until he thought the tide suitable and then ordered them to close in on the fish. The men at one end carried the vine clockwise and those at the other counterclockwise, thus making the circle smaller and at the same time doubling the vine and increasing the effectiveness of the barrier. They closed in slowly and more slowly until the circle was about twenty feet in diameter. The chief then ordered the women to crowd around the edge of the vine with their nets and told the men to prepare their spears. Apparently the hard work was over; now it was going to be good sport. Hitherto the chief had been very matter of fact, spending much time judging the wind and tide and studying the contours of the reef. His was the responsibility for a good catch and he took it seriously. No one questioned his decisions nor did he seek advice. Now his attitude changed. He began to spend most of his time joking with the men and teasing the women. He would poke a woman in the seat and laugh heartily, as he saw a big fish leap out of the water, saying: "That is the fish I am going to spear. Shall I give it to you?" It is the chief's privilege to spear the first fish, and it is a matter of pride with him to score a hit on the first throw and also spear the largest fish in the pool. Chief Kama did not seem much concerned. After briefly scanning the water, he poised his spear and flung it almost half way across the enclosure, transfixing a huge forty-pound fish. Recovering his spear and raising his catch aloft, he gave a shout and cried: "That's the way to do it!" thus giving the signal for the men to spear the fish and the women to catch them in their nets. He then turned to us and became very solicitous. He showed me how to poise a spear, throw it, and judge where the fish would be by the time the spear hit the water. He pointed out the various species, teling us which were poisonous, where in the body of the fish the poison was located, and how by careful cleaning one could remove the harmful substance. Now and then he broke off to laugh and joke with the others, entering into the sport with infectious enthusiasm.

The behavior of Ratu Kama during this day

of fishing typifies the way he leads his people in food gathering and industrial activities. He always couples extreme enthusiasm with an insistence that everything be done correctly. Part of the time, he is a reserved, commanding leader whose instructions are promptly and accurately carried out, but at other times he delights in becoming one of the group, acts as though he had no responsibilities, and allows the men to joke at his expense as though he had no authority to maintain. On the day in question, there were times when all appeared to stand on the same level; deference to the chief was suspended so that a casual observer could not have distinguished him from his subjects. By his enthusiastic participation, he made the occasion a lark for the men and women of the village; a day of fishing with the chief is regarded by all the people as one of the best days in their lives. His concern for us was typical. Whenever we were present, no matter how busy or excited he was, he found time to explain things to us as if he thought no one else could do so.

Another incident will illustrate the way in which Chief Kama plays the role of judge and arbiter of disputes. Early one morning I was awakened by loud shouts. The chief was outside my house entreating me to come quickly and help him. One of the women of the village had been severely hurt. During the night the roof of her house had leaked and the water had dripped through to the mats which she used for a bed, but her husband continued to sleep soundly through the rain. Intensely annoyed, she seized a large cane knife, the only iron instrument at her disposal, rudely awakened her husband and threatened to kill him. However, according to her story, she carefully held the blade with the blunt edge toward him. Dazed from sleep, he thought she was really planning to make an end of him and fled for his life. She chased him around the room, shrieking and calling him names. Finally, as she aimed a blow at his head, he seized a mat from the floor and held it up as a shield. On striking the mat, the knife flew out of her hand and rebounded upon her head, cutting a long gash. She immediately set up such a shriek that the whole village congregated and the chief was called. After I had been summoned and had bandaged the poor woman's head, the chief called a meeting in which he attempted to get to the bottom of the trouble. The husband claimed that he could get no one to help him repair the house and that he was unable to do it alone. He also asserted that his wife spent all of her time making mats, that she seldom cooked for him, and that she neglected the duties of a good housewife. The chief listened with great seriousness and seemed quite disturbed. His problem in such a situation is to clear up the trouble and make peace within the village. This he could have done very easily by ordering the men of the community either to build a new house or to patch the roof of the old one and by fining the man and his wife for causing so much trouble. Kama, however, does not take things so lightly. He was determined to get at the root of the matter and to remove, if possible, whatever causes for trouble might exist. Hence, showing no regard for the pain which the woman was apparently suffering, he summoned her to the meeting. She insisted that her husband was a lazy good-for-nothing, that he spent all his time drinking *kava* and neglected his gardens, that he had made no attempt to repair the house, and that he did none of the things which a good husband should do. As the meeting continued, with first the husband speaking and then the wife, the chief found that he had reached an impasse; each, it seemed, had valid cause for complaint. He then called upon the other members of the village for their testimony. It transpired that the woman thought herself a bit too good for her husband and that he resented this. With this information out in the open, the chief induced the couple to admit to each other that this was one of the main reasons for their quarreling. He ordered the woman thenceforth to be a better housewife to her spouse. The husband he sent off to the gardens to work, warning him that should any future trouble arise between them through his fault, he would be exiled from the village. He then took from his own house a whale's tooth and presented it to the men of the village, asking them please to repair the house completely, thus eliminating further complaint from that source.

Justice having been dispensed, a mighty weight seemed to fall from the chief's shoulders. He ordered *kava* to be mixed, and as the sun came up he sat and drank with the men, laughing and jesting about the night's experience. He even ordered a feast to be held that day. Everyone attended.

The way he played his part in this incident exemplifies his behavior in similar cases. He always takes his position seriously and is not satisfied until he has been the kind, just father of his people and has settled the dispute as completely as possible. Instead of being vexed, he tries to impress his points in a kindly manner. The proclamation of a feast and his evident good humor were his ways of obliterating the unhappy after effects of such an episode and indicating to the offenders that the incident was closed. The attitude of Chief Kama in cases of this sort contrasts sharply with that of another district chief with whom we had a brief acquaintance. Chief S——— plays the role of judge in a quite different fashion, of which only the most obvious points of contrast can be presented here. In the first place, he is a much smaller man physically than Chief Kama, a fact which may have had something to do with his attitude. On the occasion when we were in his village some trouble had arisen among his subjects. In dealing with the offenders, he was extremely angry and disagreeable. He fined the man and wife who had been quarreling and harangued them at length. He further punished them by forbidding the woman to take part in the formal dance that afternoon and by not permitting the man to attend the *kava* ceremony. Even then he did not allow the village to forget the incident. His surly countenance was a continual reminder of his anger, and his acid remarks made the rest of the day very unpleasant for his subjects.

A Fijian chief is expected to display extreme tact. This does not apply, however, to those instances when he is justified in being angry. Most Fijian chiefs, therefore, exhibit their tact principally in dealing with other chiefs. In their dealings with common people, where the relationship is formally one of command and obedience, adroitness is not customary. In this respect, Chief Kama varied from the norm. Very seldom did he neglect to use tact when handling either men or women. If the situation could not be handled in any other way, he made a joke of it and made his point indirectly. He never used his position to exhibit anger or vexation as did Chief S———.

In his relationship with us, his use of tact was elaborated because we were considered chiefs from another land. One example will suffice to show how he would reprimand us. During our first few months in Naviti, we knew little of Fijian customs. We therefore unwittingly did a number of things which violated native ideas of propriety, but he never would correct us. Many times we asked, "Are we doing the things expected of us?" but he always made some joke or other about a chief from America not being able to do anything wrong, and let it pass. One day, however, as we were talking about the white officials of the British government, with a twinkle in his eye he proceeded to tell us various things certain officials had done in violation of Fijian custom. Everything he mentioned either my wife or myself had done inadvertently in our ignorance of the native folkways. To make certain I was right in my surmise that he was telling us indirectly what we should not do, I said that we had done a number of these very things and that no one had said anything to us about them. Slapping me on the back, he said that we were newcomers to Fiji and would require a long time to learn how to act in true Fijian fashion but that, since we were interested in the people's habits, we would soon learn.

Briefly reviewing these incidents, what can we say about the way Chief Kama plays his social role? First of all, it is apparent that he is a real chief. He maintains his position of authority with little difficulty, feels secure in his position, and has no anxiety over the possibility of losing his status. Not afraid to be liked by his people as an individual, he is able to descend to their level on occasion and to have a good time. When something occurs which makes it necessary for him to reassume his position of authority, there comes an instantaneous and automatic change in his demeanor to which his subjects immediately respond. He gives the impression of a mature person who has worked out his adjustment in life to the point where he is able to accomplish the things expected of him with a minimum of anxiety and fear. He is effective in his social role. On each occasion when he has fulfilled his duty, there is apparently a release of energy which he expends in ways enjoyable both to him and to the members of his village. Furthermore, he seldom takes advantage of his position to inflict pent up aggression on his subjects, and one of his main techniques of binding the people to him is his elaborated and extended use of tactfulness. His authority in reality is based as much upon the good will of his subjects as upon the traditional heritage of power which he holds by right of birth. Within a formal system of status based upon fear, Chief Kama has developed a status relationship founded primarily upon affection. This is a variation within the social patterning directly in contrast to the behavior of Chief S——, whose insecurity was so evident.

*selection 34*

# *Ibo Law*

## *Charles K. Meek*

*From* Essays Presented to C. G. Seligman. *London: Kegan Paul, Trench, Trubner & Co., Ltd., 1934, pp. 209–226. By permission of the author and the publisher.*

In the space allowed for this paper it will only be possible to refer to a few of those concepts of the Ibo which may be conveniently described as "legal," more particularly as it will be necessary to include an account of the social and religious organization, with which the whole of the legal system is closely interwoven. For

Ibo law is not a well-defined institution by itself, but is rather the expression, when such is called for, of the innumerable latent rules governing all the tribal institutions.

The Ibo-speaking peoples number about 3,185,000 people, and are centered mainly in the Onitsha, Owerri, Benin, and Ogoja Provinces of Nigeria. It is with the North-Western groups inhabiting the political divisions of Onitsha Province, known as Nsukka and Awgu, that this paper is principally concerned. . . .

The Ibo consist of a number of sub-tribes such as the Awhawzara and Awhawfia. But these terms are primarily geographical, and the most striking feature of Ibo society as a whole is the absence of any strong tribal or sub-tribal organization. In the Nsukka and Awgu divisions there is no higher social or political unit than the "village-area," *i.e.*, the group of villages united by the possession of a common name and territory, the belief in descent from a common ancestor, the sharing of common customs and cults, and sometimes of a comon *chi* or soul.

The village-area may thus constitute a clan (but there is no clan exogamy). But it is frequently a local rather than a kinship grouping; for, though the component villages may vaguely claim a common ancestor, it can often be proved that there was no original relationship, and in many cases, indeed, no relationship is claimed. Such unity as they possess is due to economic and political circumstances and to intermarriage.

A village-area is known as an *obodo* or *mba* or *ala*, and includes a number of subdivisions known as *ńkporo* or *ogbwe*. The *ńkporo* in turn is subdivided into smaller groups or hamlets known as *ónuma* or *nchi*. The hamlet may coincide with the single kinship grouping known as *umunna* or may embrace several *umunna*. An *umunna* may be composed of a single group of related families, each of which consists of such close relatives as a man and his wife, brothers or first cousins and their wives and children; or it may consist of two or more related groups of such families. Where the *umunna* consists of a single group of related families it may, for the purposes of this article, be described as an "extended-family," and where it consists of two or more groups of related families it may be described as a "kindred."

The *umunna* is the basic social unit. Where it consists of a single extended-family it is invariably an exogamous unit. (The exception is the Ache district in which marriage with close consanguineous relatives, *e.g.*, first cousins, is permissible.) Where it embraces a number of related extended-families it may or may not be an exogamous unit. Intermarriage between related extended-families is sometimes allowed and sometimes forbidden. The exogamous unit may therefore be as small as a dozen people or as large as five or six hundred. A large *umunna* differs little from a small clan (unless we are to regard exogamy as a *sine qua non* of clanship). Descent is reckoned patrilineally.

With regard to the religious conceptions of the people it may be said shortly that the Ibo believe in the existence of a Supreme Spirit known as Chuku. In his creative aspect Chuku is described as Chineke or Chukwoke or Chi Okike. He sends rain, makes the crops grow, and is the source from which men derive their *chi* or soul. He is sometimes equated with and sometimes regarded as the father of Anyańu (the Sun). He is also the father of Igwe (the Sky), Amadi Ọha (Lightning), and Ale (the Earth-deity). Sacrifices are not usually offered to Chuku, but he is regarded as the ultimate recipient of all sacrifices. In the Nsukka Division every householder offers regular sacrice Anyanu the Sun), but in the Awgu Division there are no sun-shrines, though a man may occasionally hang up a chicken in a piece of cleft bamboo with a prayer to Anyańu that he will receive it and convey it to Chuku. Incidentally the peoples of Awka are known to those Awgu as "the children of the Sun."

The most important deity in the religious and social life of the people is Ale or Ala or Ane, the Earth-deity. Ale is regarded as the owner of men, whether alive or dead. The cult of ancestors is therefore closely associated with Ale, who is queen of the Underworld (but is also sometimes regarded as a male deity). Ale is the source of human morality, and is in consequence the principal legal sanction. Homicide, kidnapping, poisoning, stealing farm-products, adultery, giving birth to twins or abnormal children, are all offenses against Ale, and must be purged by sacrifice to her. Laws are made in her name, and by her oaths are sworn. Ale is, in fact, the unseen president of the community, and no group is complete which has not its shrine and priest of Ale.

Under the control of Ale are numerous god-lings or spirits, of whom the most important is Njoku, the giver and protector of yams. The ancestors of the people also live under the control and act as the agents of Ale. They profoundly influence the lives of their descend-ants. They are the guardians of morality, and regard any departure from custom as a breach of morality. It is for this reason that priests of cults and heads of families, who are the living representatives of the ancestors, have frequently eschewed association with the new-fangled laws of the Government.

The head of each family-group, or *okpara* as he is called, owes his authority (or such authority as he possesses) largely to the fact that he is the representative and mouthpiece of the family ancestors, symbolized by the sacred stick known as *ofo*. This stick, which is a section of a branch of a species of tree be-lieved to have been set aside by Chuku as a symbol and guarantee of truth, is inherited and carefully preserved by all heads of fam-ilies.

All priests of cults have an *ofo*, which is the recognized means of communication with the deity or spirit of the cult. But it represents also the ancestors who formerly ministered to the cult. It is the symbol of authority of the living priests, and the guarantee and means of transmission of his "Holy Orders." And just as the priest himself tends to become identi-fied with the god he serves, so the *ofo* be-comes identified with the deity or spirit in whose service it is used. In many groups *ofos* are even specifically identified with the god or spirit of Truth and Justice. Oaths are sworn on *ofos*, and no *ofo*-holder would swear falsely by his *ofo*, unless he had become a renegade.

There is a final aspect of ancestor-worship which is of prime importance in the adminis-tration of justice, *viz.*, the societies (secret from women) in which the ancestors or ancestral leaders are [im]personated by maskers known as Mo. These societies act as policemen of the community, and are used particularly as a means of disciplining the female members of the community. The Mo might, on their own initiative, drive an adulterous woman out of the kindred, and banish anyone suspected of practicing witchcraft, or compel him or her to submit to the ordeal of drinking sasswood.

With this brief summary we may now pro-ceed to give some details of the manner in which law functions among the Ibo, and as law begins within the family-group or *umunna*, we shall consider first the mode by which the *umunna* is governed.

An *umunna* is composed of groups of com-pounds, each of which contains one or several small or biological families closely related to each other. Each of these families is in most respects an economic unit, as each farms and trades on its own account. But each com-pound or household recognizes its senior member as its moral and political controller. Similarly, each group of households constitut-ing a distinct extended-family within the *umunna*, is subject to the control of the var-ious heads of households, presided over by the *okpara* or senior householder, who holds the family *ofo*, and represents the family in all its external relations. Where the *umunna* contains a number of extended-families, the control is vested in the whole body of elders, presided over by the head of the senior ex-tended-family, who is the holder of the senior *ofo*. The authority of the *okpara* is based on the fact that he is regarded as living in close as-sociation with the ancestors, and is thus the chief repository of custom. He has charge of the shrine of the founder of the *umunna*, to whom he offers regular sacrifice once a year on behalf of the whole kindred, and irregular sacrifice on behalf of individuals who may be directed by the diviner to offer sacrifice. He can bring any recalcitrant member to heel by the mere threat of invoking his *ofo* against that man. To insult him is to insult the ances-tors, who are regarded as ever present in his *ofo*. One guilty of such an offense would be brought before him and the other elders, and ordered to hand over a chicken, some kola-nuts, and a pot of palm-wine, that sacrifice might be offered to the ancestors, lest in their anger they should kill the offender. The ad-vice of the senior elder cannot usually be dis-regarded, unless he is so old and decrepit that another has to act on his behalf. He takes immediate steps to stop inter-family fights, and, assisted by the other elders, investigates all disputes, warning those who have misbe-haved themselves that if they repeat their conduct they need not look to him for assist-ance. If the matter were serious, such as theft from a fellow-member of the kindred, he would warn the thief that a repetition of his offense would lead to his expulsion from the village, or being sold as a slave to the Aro (who are itinerant traders and slave dealers). He might even, with the concurrence of the other elders of the kindred, order him to be tied hand and foot and placed on a platform over a smoking fire for two days without food or drink. He might threaten to drive out of the family-group any young man who had shown himself to be lazy and taken no steps to obtain a wife. (But in a first offense, a recalcitrant son is brought to book by his own father or the head of the small family-group.) He [the *okpara*] might order a member of the family-group who owed a debt to a fellow-member, or to a member of another family-group, to pay the debt forthwith, under the penalty of having a taboo (a knotted palm-leaf) placed on his property. He might, in association with the other elders, inflict a severe fine on anyone committing adultery with the wife of a kinsman, and order the poisoning of one who had committed incest. He could, in former days, call on the father of twins or abnormal children to rid the kindred immediately of the "abominable thing." When gifts, fees, or sacrificial foods are divided he, as the holder of the senior *ǫfǫ*, takes the first share, and when meetings are held to settle disputes he announces the decision, holding the *ǫfǫ* in his right hand and quoting precedents for the decision.

The head of a kindred, or family-group, is not, however, an autocrat, unless he happens to be a man of outstanding personality. If he is weak and untrustworthy he has little influence, and his functions may, by common consent, be delegated to any suitable person. Even a young successful man may be accorded the position of leadership. One who has obtained a public office or title may overshadow the senior elder, and in some communities, if there is a priest of Ale in the kindred, he may, even if he is a comparatively young man, be accorded the position of principal authority. Furthermore, if the kindred is large, there is usually considerable jealousy between the various extended-families composing the kindred, and each extended-family endeavors, for its own honor, to settle quietly any case of delinquency on the part of one of its members, without bringing it to the notice of the head official of the kindred. The authority of the head of the kindred is also qualified by the fact that he cannot act solely on his own in-

itiative. In all important matters he is bound to consult and seek the support of the other elders and important persons of the kindred.

A well-known feature of the legal system is the collective responsibility of the family-group for the conduct of its members. The stock example of this is in cases of murder or manslaughter. Immediate retaliation was made by the kin of the murdered man on any member of the murderer's kin, and the property of the nearest relatives of the murderer was pillaged. In consequence of this rule the murderer was expected *by his own family* to commit suicide immediately, in order to save the whole family from attack and their property from spoliation. If the murderer failed to do this the whole of his kin had to seek refuge in flight.

When the anger of the murdered man's kin had subsided, the kin of the murderer could return, on condition that the murderer *or some other member of his family* committed suicide. Details will be given on this subject later, and it need only be remarked here that, in consequence of this rule of collective responsibility, the elders of a kindred constantly warned their young men to keep control over their feelings and avoid the use of lethal weapons. Further, as murder was considered an offense against Ale (the Earth-deity), the crime, if committed against a fellow-member of the same family, was not one which could be palliated or settled privately by the family itself. The whole community took action against the murderer, and his own brother might be the first to set fire to his house. Even if a man killed his brother accidentally, he had to fly and remain away for a period of one month. He was then permitted to return; but at the first festival of Ale he had to take a goat, fowl, new basket, cloth, and some yams to the shrine of Ale where he knelt down and said, "Ale, I bring these gifts to you. I did not kill my brother by design. I went out hunting like the rest, and killed him by an accident. Ale spare my life." The various articles brought were left at the shrine. The animals were not sacrificed. The goat became sacred and taboo, and was allowed to wander about unharmed. Indeed, it was given the right of way on the road. If it bore young ones they also became taboo, being known as "Ewu Ale." The goat was in fact a scapegoat, for it was stated that the "evil" which had moved the man to kill his fellow had passed into the goat, and that if anyone ate the flesh of that goat the inherent "evil" would cause his death. It is to be noticed that in a case of this kind (*i.e.*, of a man killing a member of his own extended-family or kindred) no blood-money was payable, on the ground that it would be heinous to derive profit from the death of a "brother."

The collective responsibility of the kinship group is shown also in numerous other ways. Thus (at Oduma), if a man had been summoned by the elders of the town to answer some charge, and refused to attend, the elders would send young men to bring him by force. If they could not find him they would capture any member of the accused's extended-family and keep him a prisoner until the accused appeared. This would induce the elders of the accused's extended-family to bring pressure on the parents of the accused to produce him or disclose his whereabouts. If the accused had run away to some distant town, the members of his extended-family would be called on to pay the penalty of the accused's offense. Similarly in cases of debt, if the creditor could not induce the debtor to repay the loan, he would go to the compound of any of the accused's relatives who happened to be absent on their farms, and capture goats or any other articles equivalent to or in excess of the amount of the debt. Later in the day he would send word to the owner of the property informing him of the reasons of his action. The owner in turn would bring pressure on the debtor to pay the sum he owed. If the creditor belonged to another village he might, if sufficiently adroit, appropriate property from anyone in the creditor's village, the elders of which would then force the debtor to pay. These regulations did not, of course, imply that there was any collective ownership of property or that a person was held morally responsible for the sins of his relatives. They were simply an obvious method of obtaining redress through those who were in a position to bring pressure. Nevertheless they served to maintain the kinship solidarity.

Just as the *umunna* is the basis of the social system, so the mode by which it is governed is the pattern of the mode of government of each larger group, whether it be an *onuma* (hamlet), *ṅkporo* (village), or *abodo* (village-area). It is government by the body of elders presided over by the senior elder. It was never government by a single individual,

though a single individual might exercise a position of leadership, either on account of some special office or exceptional influence or affluence.

In using the term "government" it is not to be supposed that public notice was taken of every case which was a breach of customary law. The governing body only concerned itself with cases which were (*a*) an offense against religion (or, as the Ibo would say, "abominable") and so would bring disaster on the community unless the steps prescribed by custom were taken, or (*b*) which were likely to break up the solidarity of the *umunna, onuma, ṅkporo,* or *obodo.* A man might steal from another and, if caught red-handed, be sold into slavery by the owner of the stolen property, without reference to the elders or any one else. Or a creditor might recover his debt by appropriating a goat or other property belonging to the debtor, or a member of his kinship or local group. Or again two parties to a dispute might refer their dispute not to the whole council of the group, but to certain arbitrators chosen by each side.

The term "government," moreover, was government only in a very qualified sense, for even in cases where the group solidarity was endangered the central council of elders might be powerless to intervene. The body of elders was a body of mediators and referees rather than of prosecutors and judges, and the community was a republic in the true sense of that term, *i.e.*, a corporation in which government was the concern of all.

Instances may now be given to illustrate the composition of the councils, and the methods of procedure. Firstly, as regards the personnel of the village or village-area courts or councils, though all the elders (heads of extended families) are members of the council and are nominally on an equal footing, there are particular personages or classes to whom special reference must be made. These are (*a*) the senior elder or holder of the senior *ofo*; (*b*) the announcers of decisions; (*c*) the holders of "staves of judgment," *i.e.*, a special class of judges or arbitrators found in certain communities; (*d*) rich or influential men who had attained a special position as arbitrators; (*e*) titled persons.

As regards the most senior elder, he generally acted as president of the council, to the extent that he opened the proceedings by a prayer to the gods and ancestors to be present at their deliberations, to enable them to arrive at a right decision, and punish any elder who attempted to pervert justice and any witness who gave false evidence. (The head of the senior family in the town is frequently known as the *Onyishi*, and in some communities, before he is given this formal title, he is made to swear that he will not adjudicate in secret, take sides in disputes, appropriate communal or other property by force, or apply public moneys to his own purposes.)

It may be noted, incidentally, that it was permissible for either party to a case to demand the withdrawal of any elder, on the ground that that elder was a hereditary enemy of his family. There was thus a system of challenging "jurors." Moreover, the general body of elders could by common consent call on any of their number who was known to be a bad character to withdraw from the proceedings.

The announcers of decisions were always prominent personages at councils or trials. They had usually to be men of good address and to have a sound knowledge of the customary procedure. They were commonly the holders of the senior *ọfọ*, but if the holder of the senior *ọfọ* was not a good speaker he had to delegate one of the family-group to act as his deputy. In some communities the duty of announcing decisions was not assigned to any particular person or office. Any good speaker would be called upon to perform this duty. But in other communities certain families had a special right of announcing decisions, and in some cases these families acted as principal arbiters in all disputes.

A man of outstanding wealth might in any group attain for himself a measure of chieftainship, if he was able and generous. With him rested the decision whether the group should go to war or not, for he could provide the powder and firearms. In this way he attained control over the younger age-grades, which readily placed themselves at his service for any purpose. He might even call on them to work on his farms. By rendering services to all who came to him for help he was constantly adding to the number of his free-born followers, and by demanding a major portion of captives taken in war (in return for providing powder and firearms) he was constantly adding to the number of his slaves. It is easy to understand, therefore, how a rich, generous man could become the principal judge and center of authority. His presence would be called for in every important case, and few would care to oppose his views.

Finally, we come to the groups of titled people who, as being the richest men in the community, took the most prominent part in its control. They included in their ranks the heads of the most important extended-families. They were in some communities the principal judges and principal executive officers, and enjoyed numerous privileges. Thus at Inyi those holding titles took the most important part in all judicial matters. Breaches of customary law were reported to the senior titleholder in the *ṅkporo* or quarter and he, together with other holders of the title, would go to the offender's house and capture or kill one of his goats, pending further investigation of the case. If the offense was small the loss of the goat might be considered a sufficient punishment, but if it was serious the holders of titles might order the man to be sold and divide the proceeds among themselves. If the culprit had taken refuge in the house of the priest of Ale, the holders of titles would capture and sell a boy or girl from his family. Fines were imposed on anyone who insulted a member of the order, and it is said that people were afraid even of offending a person whose brother was the holder of a title.

Among the Isu Ochi the holders of titles enjoyed numerous privileges. They inflicted heavy fines on anyone who assaulted one of their order, and if the offender was unable to pay the fine he was sold into slavery. Even to abuse the holder of a title was an offense, and it was an offense also for any non-titled person to enter the house of a titled person after dark. One who committed adultery with the wife of a titled man was sold into slavery (whereas in ordinary cases there was no official penalty unless the adultery had taken place in the husband's house, in which case the adulterer was fined). Creditors could distrain the property of debtors, but they could not do so if the debtor was the holder of a title. The holders of titles, besides taking a principal part in trials, acted as guardians of orphans and of their property, a rule which was found to be necessary, as the relatives of orphaned children had sometimes sold the children into slavery.

The holders of titles were distinguished by a spear or iron staff. Their influence has now in many areas completely disappeared, as, with the advent of the Government, they could no longer enjoy their former privileges.

In the Nsukka Division the control of the village was vested mainly in the titled personages known as Asogwa, who employed the minor titled officials known as Ndishi Iwu as their executive officers. In most villages the Ndishi Iwu used the cults of Qmabe or Qdo as the legal sanction, and, if any person broke a law or refused to obey an order of the council, the Iwu would proceed to his house with a masker of the cult and place a knotted palm-leaf in the roof, thereby interdicting the owner from touching anything until the taboo had been removed. In some localities the Ndishi Iwu were also the principal judges, but in others the principal judges were the holders of the Qzo title or that known as "Eze." In a few villages, the Eze or Ezes of the village had attained a position which almost amounted to chieftainship, but this was due to the influence of the Igala tribe. For among the Ibo the indigenous form of government is essentially of a democratic or conciliar character.

We may now give some examples of the legal procedure, and it is hardly necessary to remark that in order to understand Ibo legal procedure we must divest ourselves of many English legal conceptions, such as the rigid distinction between "civil" and "criminal" cases, or the idea that public notice had to be taken of every offense. Even in cases of "sin" no public action might be necessary, as the sinner might automatically punish himself in the manner prescribed by custom. Or, again, a criminal might be automatically punished by his own family or by the person against whom he had committed a crime. If a criminal was caught *flagrante delicto* in the presence of witnesses there was no necessity as a rule for any form of trial. Trials occurred in doubtful cases, and if, after the hearing of evidence, the matter still remained doubtful, it was decided by an oath or an ordeal. It must be remembered also that there was no hard and fast code. The community reacted in various ways according to the circumstances of the case. The elders who tried cases had to consider the social position of the accused, the attitude and strength of his

kindred, whether he was a useful member of society or not, and so on. Decisions were in fact judicious rather than judicial.

To commit murder was an offense against Ale, and it was the concern of the whole community to see that the steps prescribed by custom were carried out. If the murderer hanged himself forthwith (which he frequently did, either from remorse at having killed one of Ale's children, or in order to save his family from attack and the loss of their property, or because he was expected to do so) his brother was (at Owelle) required to offer sacrifice to Ale before burying the body of the murderer. He toook eight yams and one chicken to the priest of Ale who, standing before the symbol of the cult, spoke as follows, "Ale, this chicken and these yams have been given to you by the brother of the man who killed your child and then hanged himself. He beseeches you to accept this atonement and to refrain from pursuing the brothers and children of the murderer. He who killed a fellow-man has also killed himself. Let his crime therefore follow him to the next world." It will be observed from this rite that the family of the murderer was considered as sharing in the responsibility of the crime unless it took steps to dissociate itself from the murder. It had to provide a cow, goat, fowl, two yards of cloth, and a keg of powder for the funeral rites of the murdered man.

If the murderer did not immediately hang himself but took refuge in flight, his family had also to fly, for the kin of the murdered man (including maternal relatives) immediately made a raid on the compounds and property of the kin of the murderer. In this raid any members of the local group might join. The compounds of the murderer's family were burned to the ground, their yams were uprooted, and their palms cut down. All property found might be appropriated, but in some communities it was taboo for the patrilineal relatives of the murdered man to keep any of the raided property, on the ground that this would be "eating blood-money." But relatives in the female line might do so, as their Ale was not concerned with the death of men in other local groups.

The family of the murderer remained in exile for a period of at least one month, when they might be invited by the elders of their town to return, the consent of the kin of the murdered man having first been obtained. The murderer himself continued to remain in exile. In some communities (*e.g.*, at Oduma) the following rite was performed before the return of the exiled family. The senior *ada* or sister of each of the kindreds concerned went together to the compounds of the exiled family and swept them out thoroughly. They then took a cock and a hen, tied them together with a palm-leaf, and walked round the compounds, saying, "Ale, do not permit such a thing to occur again. Ale, be not angry with us." They then collected the sweepings of the compound and threw them and the two fowls into the "bush of evil." This rite of purification is known as *Eza fu ntu ochu, i.e.*, "The sweeping-out of the ashes of murder."

On the return of the exiled family a public meeting would be held to inquire into the matter and decide what atonement must be made by the murderer's kin. This meeting might be held in the compound of the priest of Ale, but the priest usually took no part in the discussions, from fear of making some mistake for which Ale would punish him. In some towns meetings connected with a murder were always held in an open space clear of all houses, lest the pollution of the murder should infect the houses. The proceedings were conducted principally by the elders or, in certain communities, by particular individuals who had special authority to deal with cases of homicide. These would consider all the circumstances of the case, and elicit whether the homicide was accidental or deliberate, and, if the latter, whether there were any extenuating circumstances. If it appeared that the homicide had been accidental, the manslayer might be allowed to return after twenty-eight days, and on his return would be required to offer sacrifice to Ale. But in some communities there was no difference in the penalty for accidental homicide and murder, owing to the belief that if a man killed another by what we should term an accident he must at some previous time have committed an act abominable to Ale. If there were extenuating circumstances he might be permitted to produce a substitute to be publicly killed. The substitute might be some notorious thief of whom the community wished to be rid, and the killing was carried out by a man hired from another town for the pur-

pose, as it was considered an offense against Ale to slay a fellow-townsman, even if that townsman had been guilty of murder. Sometime later the murderer was required to go through the form of dedicating a person to the service of Ale, as a substitute for the man he had killed. He went to another town and hired a man for this purpose. He took this hireling, together with a tortoise, an *aiagere* fowl, a piece of *ofo* wood, a pottery plate, and a pot, to the shrine of the priest of Ale. The hireling was stripped naked and the priest spoke as follows, "Ale, this man has been brought to you as a substitute for your son who was killed." The murderer added, "Please, Ale, let me go free and be not wrathful with me again." The hireling then knelt before the shrine. He did not apparently remain permanently as an *osu* or slave of Ale, but was allowed to return to his own town. (Persons permanently dedicated to the gods are known as *osu*. They are despised, and no free person will marry an *osu*. They are also feared, being regarded as dynamized by the god. If they committed theft, they were not prosecuted, lest the anger of the god should be incurred. Even at the present time some Court members are afraid of trying an *osu* on any charge.)

Whether there were extenuating circumstances or not, the murderer might in some communities be called on to hang himself if he re-appeared in the town. Or he might be required to produce some member of his family-group to hang himself in his stead. (It was not uncommon, *e.g.*, at Nengwe, for the brother of a murderer to hang himself as a substitute, on the ground that the murderer was a better man than himself.) But if a substitute hanged himself, the murderer (at Owelle) had to make atonement by the following rite. He summoned the priest of Ale to his house and presented him with a white chicken and a yam. The priest roasted the yam and, holding the chicken and yam in his hand, said, "Ale, I am giving this fowl to you to appease your wrath against this man. Ale, I am going to give this man a yam to eat, and I beseech you that you will refrain from taking his life when he partakes of anything which has been touched by a man of Owelle." The murderer was then given the yam to eat. The fowl was appropriated by the priest.

It may be noted in conclusion that no person who had been guilty of homicide and had been allowed to return home was permitted to take part in any festival of Ale. During such a festival he had either to absent himself from the town or else sit on a platform, as contact of his person with the ground was regarded as a pollution of the Earth-deity. No one would eat in the company of a murderer, and a murderer's wife abandoned him.

The procedure in cases of theft varied according to the nature of the article stolen, and according to whether the theft had been committed within or without the kinship group. But the procedure in one town might differ considerably from that in another.

If a man stole any article of property from a member of his own kinship group the owner of the property might merely warn the thief and take no further steps. Or he might report the theft to the elders, who would warn the thief and possibly order him to be tied up for several days without food. If the thief had committed similar thefts before, the elders might direct that he should be sold as a slave to the Aro.

In many localities, if a man stole an article from a member either of his own kinship or local group, he was merely subjected to ridicule and contempt. When people met him on the road they would say, *Uu!* "Thief!" (For some offenses a culprit might be sung through the town by one of the age-grades.) If he was the holder of a title he would no longer be accorded any share of dues received. Even if he repeated his offense he might not (in some groups) be sold, on the ground that in former times an epidemic had invaded the group as a consequence of selling a close kinsman.

But one caught red-handed stealing from a member of another local group or quarter was usually accorded different treatment—he was sold automatically by the owner of the stolen property. Under certain circumstances he was allowed to redeem himself. For if on some previous occasion a man of the thief's kindred had caught a man of the other kindred in the act of stealing his property, and had refrained from selling him, then it was incumbent on the victim's kindred in the present case to act with similar generosity.

Space does not permit of any detailed account of the legal procedure in offenses such as assault, adultery, the use of black magic, or other "abominable" acts. It may, however,

be noted that, while adultery within the kinship group was an "abomination" which necessitated public condemnation and a ritual purification, adultery outside the kinship group was a private injury with which the general public had usually no concern. But an adulterer was liable to be assaulted by the injured husband, and this might lead to a state of war between two groups. Or, if the adulterer refused to pay compensation to the husband, the members of the latter's group might violate women belonging to the adulterer's group, as opportunity occurred, until public peace became so endangered that the elders of the whole village-area found it necessary to intervene.

Twins, children born with teeth, children born with hand or foot first, cripples, and children who cut the upper before the lower teeth, were destroyed or handed over to Aro traders. A child who was unable to walk before he had reached the age of three was regarded as having committed an offense against Ale in his former life, and was destroyed or sold. A girl who donned a cloth like a male, or menstruated before she had taken to wearing a cloth, was also handed over to Aro traders. Her relatives and friends would wail on hearing the news, and four days after the girl's departure her mother would shave her head; for an evil thing had fallen on her head and had to be removed.

Disputes about land were, and still are, a common source of fighting, which may continue for a considerable time before the matter is finally threshed out in an assembly of elders. In olden days land disputes between individuals of the same group were commonly referred to one of the companies of warriors or head-getters, to whom the winner of the case paid a fee. This privilege of the warriors was considered an inducement to young men to acquit themselves bravely in battle.

The decisions of judges were not always tamely accepted. An unsuccessful litigant might dispute the decision and call on the judges to swear finally on their *ofọs* that their decision was in accordance with precedent; or he might leave the assembly shouting out that he would not abide by the decision. In such a case the elders would proceed to his house on the following day, and on arrival would keep tapping the ground with their staves. This would usually cause the man serious alarm, and he would ask them to desist, promising to carry out their behests. But as the conduct of such a one had been an insult to Ale and the ancestors, he would be called on to perform a rite known *Imfo jo Ale*, or "The appeasing of the Anger of Ale."

Meetings held to decide disputes frequently ended in an uproar or a fight, and the dispute might drag on for years. In other cases the evidence might be so inconclusive that the elders would direct the disputants to take their case to some distant oracle, such as the so-called "Long Juju" at Aro Chuku. In such cases the loser of the suit might be sold into slavery by the priests of the oracle, or if allowed to return home would have to pay heavy damages to the winner.

Laws were passed in an assembly of all the elders of the town, and were sometimes given formal validity by a sacrifice to Ale or some other deity. Thus, if it became apparent that market brawls were becoming frequent and likely to lead to murder and intra-kindred or intra-quarter fighting, the elders of the town might meet together and decide that, if anyone in future engaged in fighting in the market, he should be heavily fined. Having arrived at this decision they would buy a goat and take it to the priest of Ale, who, holding the goat by a rope, would say, "Ale, the elders of the town have brought this goat to you in order to inform you of their wishes touching the market. They say that it is not their desire that fights should occur in the market, lest this should lead to loss of life. Ale, it is not your desire that men should kill one another, as we are your children. They declare that if anyone breaks this rule he shall pay a fine of fourteen currency rods, and they ask you, Ale, to enforce this law by dealing with anyone who refuses to pay this fine. Ale, when the elders call upon you (to assist them in dealing with a law-breaker) do you answer their call (by bringing misfortune upon him)." He would then turn to the elders and say, "Is not this your wish?" They would all reply, "Ale, this is our wish." The priest would then kill the, goat, and as he put the knife to the goat's throat would say, "Take the life of this goat and spare our lives." The flesh of the goat would be cooked and divided, and morsels of the heart, liver, and kidneys would be deposited by the priest on the cultus-symbol.

The elders would then go home, and each would inform the members of his kindred of the passing of the law. If anyone subsequently broke the law he would be arrested by young men and handed over to the head of his kindred, who would be instructed to collect the fine and bring it to the market on the following market-day. On that day the elders would walk round the market beating their matchets and saying, "Fellow-townsmen, come and take what is yours." The head of the culprit's kindred would then hand the fourteen rods to the senior elder, who would say, "Fellow-townsmen, you have seen that the fine has been paid." They would reply, "We have. Let it be handed over to the keeper of fines." The rods would then be handed to a man delegated by the elders to receive fines and hold them until they were required for some general sacrifice. The culprit would be escorted by the elders and Ale priests to the shrine of Ale. He would hand a pot of palm-wine to the priest and then squat down before the cultus-symbol. The priest would pour a little of the wine into a buffalo-horn and pass the horn round the culprit's head, saying, "Ale, I and the elders of the town have brought this man before you to tell you that he has paid his fine for 'breaking' your market. He has brought this wine to appease your wrath. Pursue him not. A man's child may offend his father, but he is forgiven when he repents." He would then pour the libation, and the remainder of the wine would be drunk by all present, the culprit included.

The legal sanction was not always Ale. When a law was made the elders might call on the priest of any cult to bring some material object from the shrine. The priests and elders would then say, "We have made such and such a law. If anyone breaks this law may this spirit kill that person." The priest would then strike the ground with the object. If the law was broken the punishment might be left to the spirits. But the law-breaker would forestall punishment by going to the priest, who would perform sacrifice on the man's behalf, saying, "So-and-so admits that he has gone against you and he comes now to redeem himself."

In some cases rules would be made without any religious sanction. Thus the elders might announce in the market that wood was not to be cut in a certain area under the penalty of a fine of one goat. If a man was reported for breaking this rule, the elders would send young men to catch a goat from his kindred or local group. If the accused redeemed the goat the money obtained was divided out among the elders and the matter ended. But if he did not redeem it, the goat would be sold or killed, and if the accused lost his case he would be called on to pay two goats to the owner of the goat. If the accused won his case, his accuser had to pay the cost of the two goats. If the accused was a woman, her fine was payable by her husband or son. But in some towns her fine was payable by her parents through the person who had acted as middleman when her marriage had been arranged.

Other instances of legislation were (*a*) that no one should visit a neighboring town during an epidemic, and (*b*) that women should not visit the market of an unfriendly town. The elders might post young men on the roads to see that the rules were observed, and the young men were authorized to confiscate the property of anyone who attempted to break the rules. Rules might also be made forbidding the cutting of sticks (to be used for training yam tendrils) before a certain date.

In some cases an age-grade or group of age-grades might take the initiative in making rules. Thus, if it became apparent that stealing was on the increase, a group of age-grades might meet and decide that the penalties for stealing must be increased, and their decision would be announced to and accepted by the elders. Or an age-grade group might meet to fix the local price of palm-wine, or standardize the rate of the bride-price or rents chargeable for land.

This paper may be concluded by a few remarks on the changes in legal conceptions and practice which have occurred as a result of British Administration and direct contact with Western civilization.

When the British Government assumed the administration of the country, district Native Courts were established. This was a necessary step toward bringing the country under proper control and putting an end to practices which were considered inhuman or incompatible with modern civilization. The Native Courts were encouraged to administer native law as far as possible, but as most of the old legal sanctions now became illegal the native law administered in the Native Courts became a shadow of its former self. The elders, moreover, of the kindred, village, and village-area were deprived of their judicial functions and in consequence lost much of their authority. The Native Courts in fact acted as a disruptive agent on the social structure.

Recently, however, the Government, after close examination of the ancient system, has sought to restore the power of the elders by encouraging them to settle minor cases locally, and by giving formal recognition to the village-area councils. There is a general policy of decentralization, and the old district courts are being replaced, wherever possible, by "clan" courts. The personnel of the Native Courts has been enlarged so as to include as far as possible all the most important elders of each local group. A complete return, however, to the old system, by which each village-area, or even village, recognized no higher authority than itself, would be impracticable, and distasteful also to the people, who demand a higher form of central authority than formerly existed, having acquired a wider sense of solidarity. Nor is there any general desire for a complete return to the old forms of legal procedure, even were this permissible. For the younger generation has lost faith in many of the old legal sanctions, as a result of the rapid spread of Christianity. It is said with truth that the younger people no longer obey their elders as before, and the blame for this is often laid at the door of the Government. But the real reasons are religious and economic. Children who have become Christians are often compelled to disagree with their pagan parents, and to refuse to take part in practices which they have been taught to regard as heathen. Many of them, moreover, leave their homes for long periods in search of work, and live lives of freedom from the numerous restraints imposed in their own homes. Such tend to degenerate in character, and when they return home they find it difficult to resume their former life, more especially as they have acquired new wants which cannot be satisfied in their parent village.

But the extraordinary natural adaptability of the Ibo should enable them to surmount most of the difficulties of the present period of transition.

# Natchez Burial Customs

## Le Page du Pratz

This is the death of the Tattooed-serpent, my particular friend and the friend of all the French. He was great war chief of the Natchez Nation and brother of the great Sun, who allowed him an absolute authority over the entire nation. . . .

We entered his [the great Sun's] house, where he said aloud, *Ouitiguitlatagoup*, he is quite dead. Then he seated himself and bent over, resting his head on his hands. The instant he said that his brother was dead his wife, who was present, uttered loud cries. This was a signal of sadness for the entire nation, which was awaiting the outcome of this malady, which could not fail to be fatal to them as soon as the Tattooed-serpent should be dead. Then one heard groans and lamentations on all sides. The most doleful cries were made to resound under the neighboring trees. Almost immediately two consecutive discharges of guns were heard to warn all the villages, which replied a few moments afterwards.

I will spare the reader many scenes which would only sadden him, and I will report of the funeral honors which were rendered to the Tattooed-serpent only those which are extraordinary and of which Europeans have no knowledge.

A short time after these discharges the speaker (*porte-parole*) entered and began to weep. The great Sun raised his head and looked at his favorite wife, to whom he made a sign that we did not understand, until she had thrown a vessel of water on the fire, which was entirely extinguished by it. Then the speaker, or chancellor, of the great chief howled in salutation to his sovereign and went out. As soon as he was outside of the cabin he uttered a fearful cry, which was instantly repeated by all the people of the villages.

The fire extinguished in our presence and the redoubled cries of the entire nation made

*From John R. Swanton's translation of portions of* Histoire de la Louisiane, *3 vols., 1758, Paris, by Le Page du Pratz, in* Indian Tribes of the Lower Mississippi Valley and Adjacent Coast of the Gulf of Mexico. Bureau of American Ethnology Bulletin 43, *1911, pp. 144–149. By permission of the translator and the publisher.*

me fear, with reason, for the great Sun and even for ourselves, for who could guess the consequences of the despair in which we saw all plunged?

The great Sun being always bent over and his eyes closed, I approached a common Sun and asked him what the extinguished fire and the doleful cries signified. He replied that it was the signal to extinguish all the fires, and that it made all the Natchez tremble with reason, because the extinction of the fires was not done on account of the death of the Tattooed-serpent.

I understood by these words that the sovereign wished to die. . . .

He [the Tattooed-serpent] was on his bed of state, dressed in his finest clothing, his face painted with vermilion, moccasined as if to go on a journey, and wearing his crown of white feathers mingled with red. His arms had been tied to his bed. These consisted of a double-barreled gun, a pistol, a bow, a quiver full of arrows, and a war club. Around the bed were all the calumets of peace which he had received during his life, and near by had been planted a large pole, peeled and painted red, from which hung a chain of reddened cane splints, composed of 46 links or rings, to indicate the number of enemies he had killed. I do not at all pretend in reporting this fact to guarantee the number of the exploits of this man.

All his people were around him. Food was served to him at his accustomed hours, as if he had been living, and his retainer [or head servant—*loué*], seeing that he did not touch it, said to him, "You no longer wish, then, to take what we present you? Are these things no more to your taste? Why is it, then, that you rebuff us and our services do not please you any more? Ah! you do not speak as usual. Without doubt you are dead. Yes; it is done. You are going to the country of the spirits, and you are leaving us forever." Then he uttered the death cry, which was repeated by all those in the cabin. They replied in the village, and from voice to voice the same cry passed in an instant into the other villages of the nation, who all together made the air reverberate with their doleful cries.

The company in the cabin was composed of the favorite wife of the defunct, of a second wife, whom he kept in another village, to visit when his favorite wife was pregnant, his chan-

cellor, his doctor, his head servant (*loué*), his pipe bearer, and some old women, all of whom were going to be strangled at his burial.

To the number of the victims there joined herself a Noble woman, whom the friendship that she had for the Tattooed-serpent led to join him in the country of the spirits. The French called her La Glorieuse, because of her majestic bearing and her proud air and because she was intimate only with distinguished Frenchmen. I regretted her so much the more that, possessing a deep knowledge of simples, she had saved the lives of many of our sick, and I myself had drawn good lessons from her. These things filling us with sadness, the favorite wife, who perceived it, rose from her place, came to us with a smiling air, and spoke to us in these terms, "French chiefs and nobles, I see that you regret my husband's death very much. It is true that his death is very grievous, as well for the French as for our nation, because he carried both in his heart. His ears were always full of the words of the French chiefs. He has always traveled by the same road as the French, and he loved them more than himself. But what does it matter? He is in the country of the spirits, and in two days I will go to join him and will tell him that I have seen your hearts shake at the sight of his dead body. Do not grieve. We will be friends for a much longer time in the country of the spirits than in this, because one does not die there again. It is always fine weather, one is never hungry, because nothing is wanting to live better than in this country. Men do not make war there any more, because they make only one nation. I am going and leave my children without any father or mother. When you see them, Frenchmen, remember that you have loved the father and that you ought not to repulse the children of the one who has always been the true friend of the French." After this speech she went back to her place. . . .

[After the Frenchmen had prevailed upon the great Sun not to kill himself], the fire of the great Sun being relighted, the signal was given to relight all the others. . . .

A few moments afterwards the young Sun came to tell me that orders had been given (as he had promised, although feignedly) to have only those die who were in the cabin of the deceased, because they were his food; that besides there would be put to death a bad woman, if she had not already been killed, and an infant which had already been strangled by its father and mother, a forfeit which purchased their lives at the death of the great Sun, ennobled them, and raised them from the grade of Stinkards.

A few moments later the grand master of ceremonies appeared at the door of the dead man's house with the ornaments which were proper to his rank. . . . He uttered two words and the people in the cabin came out. These persons were the favorite wife and his other wife, his chancellor, his doctor, his head servant, his pipe bearer, and some old women. Each of these victims was accompanied by eight male relations, who were going to put him to death. One bore the war club raised as if to strike, and often he seemed to do so, another carried the mat on which to seat him, a third carried the cord for strangling him, another the skin, the fifth a dish in which were five or six balls of pounded tobacco to make him swallow in order to stupefy him. Another bore a little earthen bottle holding about a pint, in order to make him drink some mouthfuls of water in order to swallow the pellets more easily. Two others followed to aid in drawing the cord at each side.

A very small number of men suffices to strangle a person, but since this action withdraws them from the rank of Stinkards, puts them in the class of Honored men, and thus exempts them from dying with the Suns, many more would present themselves if the number were not fixed to eight persons only. All these persons whom I have just described walk in this order, two by two, after their relations. The victims have their hair daubed with red and in the hand the shell of a river mussel which is about 7 inches long by 3 or 4 broad. By that they are distinguished from their followers, who on those days have red feathers in their hair. The day of the death they have their hands reddened, as being prepared to give death.

Arrived in the open space the mats of the foremost are placed nearest the temple, the favorite to the right and the other wife to the left of the road, the others afterward according to their rank, 6 to 7 feet apart on the two sides of the road, the breadth of which between them is at least 30 feet. The persons who are going to die are made to sit down on their mats, then all together make the death cry behind them. The relatives dance the death dance and the victims on their mats dance in time also without leaving their places. After this dance the entire group returns to the cabin in the same order. This is a rehearsal of the tragedy which is going to be played the day of the funeral procession. It is done twice a day.

Everything was tranquil enough that day on the part of the great chief, who went to the temple after he had been shown the head of the bad woman. He ordered that her body be eaten by beasts without being buried, to carry the head to his brother, and then to throw it into the cypress swamp 2 leagues from his body.

The same day at sunrise, while we were engaged in restraining the great chief, a man named Ette-actal had been brought, escorted by 30 warriors. We all knew him because he had lived with M. de Bienville, commandant-general, with whom he had taken refuge. He had married a female Sun who had died, and according to the laws of his nation he ought to die with her. But this law not being to his taste, as soon as he had seen her in the agony [of death] he fled secretly toward the landing, took some provisions, descended night and day in a little dugout and went to place himself under the protection of Monsieur, the commandant of the capital, and offered himself to him as his hunter and one of his slaves. His service was accepted. The Natchez even promised his master that he had nothing to fear because, the ceremony being completed and he not having been found in that time, he was no longer a lawful prize. This native, thus reassured, went from time to time to see his relatives and friends, and nothing had ever been said to him. But this last time, the great Sun having learned from the French that M. de Bienville had been recalled to France, considered that the letters of reprieve of Ette-actal were abrogated by the absence of his protector. Thus he judged it suitable to make him pay his debt to the Tattooed-serpent in the capacity of a relation of his wife, and it was for this reason that they brought him.

When this man saw himself in the cabin of the great chief of war, in the number of victims who were going to be sacrificed to his manes, he was moved with the liveliest grief to see himself taken this time without hope of safety and began to weep very bitterly. The favorite wife having perceived this, said to him, "Are you not a warrior?" "Yes," said he, "I am one." "Nevertheless you weep," she replied, "your life is then dear to you? If it is so, then it is not good that you come with us. Go away with the women."

He replied, "Certainly life is dear to me. I have no children. It is well that I travel some time longer on the earth until the death of the great Sun and die with him." "Go away, I tell you," said she, "it is not good that you come with us and that your heart remain behind you on the earth. Once more, take yourself away from here, and let me see you no more."

Ette-actal had brought a little sack in which were the small utensils necessary for the ceremony, but without disturbing himself about them he left all, and, satisfied to have still time to himself before the death of the great Sun, he took to flight at the last word of the favorite and disappeared like a flash. But in the afternoon three old women were brought, two of whom were his relations, who, being extremely aged and wearied of life, offered themselves to pay his debt. Although these two women were so old that for many years they had totally lost the use of their limbs, their hair was no grayer than is commonly that of women of 50 in France. They appeared, besides, to bear themselves well.

The generosity of these two women purchased the life of the warrior, Ette-actal, and acquired for him the rank of Honored man. His condition having become much better and his life being thus assured, he became insolent, and profiting by the instructions which he had received from the French, he made use of it to deceive his countrymen.

The third old woman that they had brought had not been able to use her legs for at least fifteen years, without, however, experiencing any other difficulty in any part of the body. Her face was calm and her hair entirely white, a thing which I had never seen among the natives, and in spite of her great age, which surpassed a century, her skin was not too much wrinkled. All of these three old women were dispatched to the evening rehearsal, one to the door of the Tattooed-serpent and the two others to the square. . . .

The day of the funeral procession having arrived, we went to the house of the great Sun. The favorite wife, who knew that we were there, came with her company to bid us adieu. She had the Suns of both sexes and their children called, to whom she then addressed these words:

"It is very grievous that your father is dead. As for me, I am going with him to the country of the spirits, and he waits only for us in order to set out. It is also well since he is dead that I am no longer able to walk on the earth. For you who are young it is good that you walk a long time without design [*i.e.*, without duplicity] and with a straight heart. I leave you grain and my coffers, the keys [?] of which I here give you. Do not speak any evil of the French. Walk with them. Walk there as your father and I have walked, without design. Speak of them as he and I have spoken. Do nothing contrary to the friendship of the French. Never lie to them. They will give you food and the other things of which you have need, and if they give you nothing, return without murmuring. They were friends of your father, so love them all and never refuse to see them even when they will not receive you well.

"And you French chiefs," she added, turning toward us, "always be friends of the Natchez; trade with them, do not be too stingy with your goods, and do not repel what they bring you, but treat them with gentleness." Then having observed that one of our party was affected to tears by the spectacle, she said to him, "Do not weep. I know that my husband and I were great friends of the French, because we also loved you much, although I have never eaten with them, because I am a woman. But I am able to eat with them now, because I am going to the country of the spirits. Let them, then, bring us food to eat, so that I may eat with the French chiefs."

Immediately some dishes were brought, we seated ourselves, and we took the meal with her. She then rose, and followed by her company, she returned to the cabin of her husband with a firmness altogether surprising.

I have reported these speeches and the bearing of this favorite, who could be only of the common people, being the wife of a Sun, in order to show the skill with which she preserved the friendship of the French for her children, how much intelligence this nation has, and that it is not at all that which one ordinarily understands by the word savage, which the majority of people bestow on it very unsuitably.

I have said elsewhere that the temple, the house of the great chief, and that of the Tattooed-serpent were on the square; that that of the great Sun was built on a mound of earth carried to a height of about 8 feet. It was on this mound that we placed ourselves at the side of the dwelling of the great Sun, who had shut himself in in order to see nothing. His wife, who was also there, was able to hear us, but we had no fear that she would reveal what we might say against such a cruel custom. This law did not please her enough for her to find fault with those who spoke ill of it. As for the great Sun, he was on the other side and was not able to hear our remarks. From this place, without disturbing the ceremony, we were able to see everything, even into the interior of the temple, the door of which faced us.

At the appointed hour the master of ceremonies arrived, adorned with red feathers in a half crown on his head. He had his red baton, in the shape of a cross, at the end of which hung a cluster of black feathers. He had all the upper portion of his body reddened, with the exception of his arms, in order to let it be seen that he did not dip his hands in the blood. His belt, which girded him above his hips, was ornamented with feathers, of which one row was black and the following was red, and afterward alternately as far as the knees. His legs were of their natural color.

He entered the house of the great Sun in this dress to ask him, without doubt, for permission to start the funeral procession. We were not able to hear what reply was made to him, because this sovereign ordinarily spoke in a very low although serious tone. But we heard very distinctly the salutation which the master of ceremonies afterward made him, who went out instantly to proclaim the departure of the funeral procession. . . .

As soon as the master of ceremonies went to the door of the deceased he saluted him, without entering, with a great *hou*. Then he made the death cry, to which the people on the square replied in the same manner. The entire nation did the same thing and the echoes repeated it from afar. The body of the strangled infant was near the door by which the body of the dead man was to be brought out. Its father and its mother were behind it, leaning against the wall, their feet on some

Spanish moss, esteeming themselves unworthy to walk on the earth until the body of the deceased had passed over it. As soon as the body appeared they laid their infant down, then raised it when it was outside, in order to expose it at each circle which it [the body] made until it had reached the temple.

The Tattooed-serpent, having come out of his cabin in his state bed, as I have pictured it, was placed on a litter with two poles, which four men carried. Another pole was placed underneath toward the middle and crosswise, which two other men held, in order to sustain the body. These six men who carried it were guardians of the temple.

The grand master of ceremonies walked first, after him the oldest of the war chiefs, who bore the pole from which hung the cane links. He held this pole in one hand and in the other a war calumet, a mark of the dignity of the deceased. Then came the body, after which marched the procession of those who were going to die at his burial. Together they circled the house from which they had come out three times. At the third turn they took the road to the temple, and then the relatives of the victims placed themselves in the order which I have described for the rehearsal, but they walked very slowly, because they were going straight to the temple, while the body circled about as it advanced. . . . At each circuit made by the body the man of whom I have spoken threw his child in front of it in order that the body should pass over. He took it up again by one foot to do the same at the other circuits.

Finally the body reached the temple, and the victims put themselves in their places as determined in the rehearsals. The mats were stretched out. They seated themselves there. The death cry was uttered. The pellets of tobacco were given to them and a little water to drink after each one. After they had all been taken [each victim's] head was covered with a skin on which the cord was placed around the neck, two men held it in order that it should not be dragged away [to one side] by the stronger party, and the cord, which had a running knot, was held at each end by three men, who drew with all their strength from the two opposite sides. They are so skillful in this operation that it is impossible to describe it as promptly as it is done.

The body of the Tattooed-serpent was placed in a great trench to the right of the temple in the interior. His two wives were buried in the same trench. La Glorieuse was buried in front of the temple to the right and the chancellor on the left. The others were carried into the temples of their own villages in order to be interred there. After this ceremony the cabin of the deceased was burned, according to custom.

*selection  36*

# The Vision Quest and the Guardian Spirit

## George A. Pettitt

*From Primitive Education in North America,* University of California Publications in American Archaeology and Ethnology, *Vol. 43, No. 1, 1946, pp. 87–94. By permission of the author and the publisher.*

The wide distribution and relatively intensive development of the vision quest and the guardian-spirit concept in North America have led to the recognition of these traits as two important cultural characteristics of this area, and the vision pattern has been cited as the unifying religious fact among primitive tribes of the continent.

It is not my purpose to discuss these practices as discrete entities, for that has been done at some length by Ruth Benedict. Instead, I will indicate the relationship of these practices to educational procedures, and suggest, from an analysis of the functioning of the vision quest and the guardian-spirit concept in the process of intellectual and emotional development of the individual, that there is a fundamental kinship or social equivalence between these and other primitive practices involving the idea of supernaturally derived power. Incidentally, some light will be thrown on the essential nature of the psychic experiences supposedly involved in the vision.

In discussions of the vision quest and the guardian-spirit complex, it is usual to cite the Thompson Indians of the Plateau region of western Canada as the people who have accepted or developed the greatest number of traits which are typical of the complex wherever it is found on the continent. The Thompson Indians are said to present the type picture of vision questing and the acquisition of a guardian spirit. Therefore, the salient features of Thompson Indian practices are outlined below.

According to Teit, boys when old enough to dream of an arrow, a canoe, or a woman began an intensive search for a guardian spirit. This happened, usually, between the ages of twelve and sixteen. More will be said about the age of beginning the vision quest later, but it is important to recall that earlier reference has been made to the daily cold baths which many Indian boys were obliged to take, to food taboos, and to physical tests of one kind or another which enlivened the youngster's life from the time he was able to walk and run until he became a man. The beginning of the vision quest was perhaps a climax to these practices, rather than the introduction of a new discipline. The Thompson Indians are typical in this respect. They were given to annual, midwinter ceremonial whippings, also, in which the object was to frighten boys too young to be whipped, and encourage the stoicism of those old enough to volunteer for the ordeal. This, too, may be classed as a preliminary of the vision quest. But when a boy's dreams became propitious, regardless of chronological age, his vision quest began in earnest. As a ceremonial beginning he was required to run, with bow and arrows in his hands, until bathed in perspiration and on the point of exhaustion, when he was made to plunge in cold water. This was repeated four times a day for four days. The importance of the quest on which he was about to start was stressed by a coat of red paint on his face, a cedar bark or skin headband, ornaments of deer hoof tied to knees and ankles, and a skin apron symbolically decorated to indicate the life occupation for which he was most desirous of gaining supernatural power. The boy was, in other words, the center of public attention in this as in other aspects of primitive education. He was probably envied by his younger friends, and admired by the elders of the camp, and the pride engendered undoubtedly would help him to survive the not inconsiderable ordeals through which he had to pass. Although his first four days were consumed in running and bathing, the first four nights were given to

dancing, singing, and praying, with little or no sleep, around a fire on some nearby mountain peak. At dawn the boy solemnly drew his bow and discharged an arrow into the sky.

Having acted out the prologue, the boy then began to work in earnest. He went on lonely pilgrimages into the mountains, staying away from home and eating nothing for from four to eight days on end. It was a common practice to schedule these pilgrimages in winter, so that the boy would not be tempted by berries and roots. During these vigils the boy usually took nothing with him but a fire drill and a sleeping mat. He intensified the effect of his fasting by taking herbal concoctions with a purgative action, and by poking long twigs down his throat until he vomited. He also heated rocks, threw water over them, and sweated himself thoroughly, perhaps whipping his body with nettles at the same time. Then he would plunge into a mountain stream, following which he would gather the warm rocks from the sweat bath, start across country throwing the rocks as far as he could, running to pick them up, and throwing them again, to insure himself against disease, ill fortune, and laziness. To vary the monotony he might set up a small target at a considerable distance and shoot at it with an arrow. If he missed he would pick up the arrow, run about four miles, and then try his skill again. If he continually missed he might run all night. If he was unable to hit the target before dawn he knew that his greatest talents would not be exhibited as hunter. But if he shot some small animal and gave it to some old person to eat, that would improve his chances.

The boy continued this exhausting regime until he had a dream of some animal or bird which would be his protector through life, and received the inspiration for a spirit song with which to call his protector and secure power in all he might attempt. Often a father, if possessed of great power himself, would give his boy some amulet symbolic of his own guardian spirit, to dream over. It was believed that this was an effective way of encouraging the same or another guardian spirit to take pity on the boy. When the boy believed that he had an important dream, one that he did not quite understand, and which gave him a queer feeling, he would mention it to his father, and discuss the interpretation. If the conviction came to him that he had received a spirit-inspired dream or vision, he prepared a medicine bag of the skin of the spirit animal, and filled it with other objects which in the course of his quest had for some reason taken on significance. These were the tangible symbols of his power. If the spirit was that of a bird he gathered feathers from that bird and tied them to his hair. Then he polished his spirit song as suggested by his vigil or perhaps by remarks dropped by his father, and worked out a design symbolic of his power with which he decorated rocks in lonely parts of the mountains.

The more this and similar stories of Indian vision quests are studied the less satisfactory does it seem to classify the acquisition of a guardian spirit, as most writers do, in the category of religious education. There are too many other factors involved. As indicated earlier in this study, it is impossible to do justice to primitive pedagogy if educational practices are arbitrarily divided into religious and nonreligious. The Indians of North America had no specifically named, conceptual category equivalent to our generalization "religious." They undoubtedly could have differentiated between the natural and the supernatural if they wished, but they apparently saw no reason for so doing; and if a classificatory system which they did not use is applied to their practices, the result is to confuse the issue. To discuss primitive religious education seems to be as futile in reaching a complete understanding of primitive pedagogy as would be a treatise on the moving parts of an engine as distinct from the stationary parts in reaching an understanding of the mechanics of the device.

There is no doubt that religious concepts are involved in the vision quest and in the idea of a guardian spirit. But they were not used in the modern sense of escaping from things of the flesh. Rather, they were utilized in a practical attempt to give greater assurance of achieving comforts of the flesh. Morals and ethics were linked with religious practices and beliefs, but not so much through fear of the hereafter as through a desire to establish a reciprocal trade arrangement with the supernatural whereby success in the daily routine could be achieved. There was little implication of worshiping supernatural beings for what they had done in the past, or might do after death. Greater stress was laid on the immediate future, and gratitude entered the

picture strongly only if we define it as a lively anticipation of favors yet to come. Rasmussen relates an experience among the Eskimo which clearly illustrates this attitude. In September, 1907, he visited a group of Eskimo living in pristine paganism untouched by Christianity. In June, 1908, he visited the same group and discovered much to his surprise that, to the last man, they had been converted to a curious version of Christianity. Their former religious practices had dropped into the background. The reason for this sudden change, apparently, was a visit by a partly Christianized Eskimo hunter from a distant area. The garbled Christian prayers this man utilized as hunting charms seemed to be far more efficacious in attracting caribou; so the group dropped old practices and adopted the new. Later, when the prayers failed to work as well as expected, they advanced the theory that the white man's prayers, like his guns, wear out with use, and presumably they went back to their traditional beliefs.

As Radin states: "Can we, without further analysis, calmly assume that fear is the primordial emotion with which men began? The answer must be definitely in the affirmative, but not in the sense claimed by most ethnological theorists. They are fond of treating it as an instinct (fear of the dark, fear of the unknown, fear of the strange). But psychology aside, what does the documentary evidence we now possess for primitive cultures tell us? The answer is clear. Primitive man is afraid of one thing, of the uncertainties of the struggle for life." It may be added that the fear was not entirely of death, but rather of failing to live successfully.

It is not necessary to elaborate on the nature of primitive religion. The point to be made is merely that in the vision quest and the acquisition of a guardian spirit the objective was not to produce a disciple of a religious faith, but to produce an independent, self-confident, and self-reliant personality, buoyed up by an inner conviction of his ability to meet any and all situations. The painful ordeals through which the individual achieved a guardian spirit had a significance of their own, apart from increasing the susceptibility of the individual to a psychic experience. They strengthened his character, and supplied him with experience in withstanding physical suffering, which was probably just as important in giving him self-assurance as was the conviction that a supernatural being had extended a sheltering arm. That the individual's social and economic well-being was the objective is attested by evidence of many kinds. That a conviction of power was the goal is clear when we take into consideration all the other ways in which this goal was sought, through conferring power-freighted names, and through associating with and studying under men and women reputed to have power.

It is pertinent to note that among the previously cited Thompson Indians, where the vision quest was a dominant feature of a boy's training, and to a certain extent of a girl's as well, twin children were excused from the ordeal because they were believed to be born with more than ordinary spiritual power derived from "Grizzly Bear." Apparently their obvious advantage over their age mates in the ownership of a twin brother or sister, plus special ceremonies for them, and special rituals that they had to observe, were sufficient to give them the inner conviction of self-sufficiency and of supernatural affiliation without long vigils. The way in which this inner conviction worked can be illustrated by a statement from the life of John Tanner among the Ojibwa. He explains that his foster mother, as a young girl, had been blessed with a dream in which she saw an aged, white-haired woman walking with two canes. She had a conviction that this was herself and that it meant that come what would, she would live a long, long time. Tanner concludes: "In all her subsequent life, this excellent woman retained the confident assurance that she would live to extreme old age, and often, in times of the greatest distress from hunger, and of apparent danger from other causes, she cheered her family . . . and roused them to exertion by infusing some part of her confident reliance upon the protection of a superior and invisible Power."

Because the vision quest and the acquisition of a guardian spirit are commonly given their greatest overt expression as boys and girls approach maturity, this complex is often spoken of as a puberty-linked phenomenon. Actually, however, as has been intimated in the discussion of the Thompson Indians, the process of acquiring and maintaining power started in early childhood, and continued through maturity. The beginning of the quest has also been ascribed to individual initiative and imitation. The facts run contrary to this conclusion. The acquisition of power was not left to the individual's imitative faculties, at least as a general practice. It was urged upon him with an insistence inversely proportional to the amount of supernatural power he was believed to have inherited from famous forebears, or obtained as a gift from famous elders, or acquired from propinquity to powerful individuals, in connection with the name he bore, or ceremonies gone through, or personal property such as amulets, or articles of dress or use, or songs and prayers and rituals. In other words, the vision was just one of a number of ways, though the most important, perhaps, of obtaining an inner conviction of self-sufficiency, both as one personality among many in the social group, and as a seeker after long life and comfort in the theater of nature. Lowie finds that a Crow boy at the time of his vision quest did not need any prompting. We may suspect that this is so because the prompting had taken place earlier, for human beings are not born with the desire to go on a vision quest. Elsewhere Lowie stresses his point, that the Crow youth is conditioned to the vital importance of a vision from infancy up.

In the autobiography of Crashing Thunder, the Winnebago, it is pointed out that from earliest childhood, boys were encouraged to blacken their faces and to practice fasting in order some day to be able to obtain a vision. Among the Omaha, "small boys seven to eight years of age and upwards were sent out together in the early morning with faces covered with clay by their parents to one of a few selected spots. This happened every fine spring morning. . . . They were technically fasting as they went out before breakfast." Ohiyessa, the Sioux, states that his grandmother started him on the trail to the Great Mystery at the age of eight. Maximilian reports for the Hidatsa: "There have been instances of fathers subjecting their children, only six or seven years of age, to these tortures. We ourselves saw one suspended by the muscles of the back, after having been compelled to fast four days." For the Parry Island Ojibwa it is said: "The Ojibwa held that the Great Spirit, or his intermediaries, the *manides*, imparted [knowledge, power, or ability, the indispensables to success and happiness] in visions to each individual at the earliest possible age, that is to say, as soon as the soul and shadow were sufficiently awake to understand and appreciate them. Consequently, they carefully trained their children to make them receptive of these 'blessings.' They encouraged the children to dream, and to remember their dreams. Every morning, even now, Pegahmagabow lies beside his two boys, seven and nine years old, respectively, and asks them what dreams have come to them during the night."

When Pegahmagabow himself was about seven years old his parents made him swallow gunpowder to awaken his soul and shadow. Many boys are given charcoal and other substances for the same purpose, and are made to fast. These fasts become progressively longer until the moment has come when the child is psychologically ripe, either before, during, or after adolescence, and then solitary vigils are added to the fasting. Landes confirms these data for the Ojibwa of western Ontario, stating that boys of four to five years are already under siege by their relatives, and are being urged not to rest content with the protection of their name-power, but to fast in preparation for a vision. A boy's face is blackened so that all will know he is fasting and encourage him. If a little fellow fasts all day he is rewarded by choice bits of meat in the evening. From this time until puberty there is a constant harping on "dreaming for power." The parents arrange a schedule of fasting graduated to the child's age and strength and to their own fanaticism on the subject. He is greeted in the morning with the question, "Which will you eat, bread or charcoal?" If he chooses bread he is cuffed and asked again.

Farther east, among the Delaware, Harrington reports: "Parents were especially anxious, of course, that their sons should have supernatural aid, hence, when a boy reached the age of about twelve years, they would frequently pretend to abuse him, and would drive him, fasting, out into the forest to shift as best he might, in the hope that some *mani'te* would take pity on the suffering child and grant him some power or blessing that would be his dependence through life." Sometimes Delaware boys were taken out on vigils by their fathers, and were given daily doses of some drug to cause vomiting. By practice, they were occasionally able to go for twelve days on end eating only one bit of meat as large as the little finger each evening.

To the west, in the Plateau area, the Nez Percé boy "began his preparation for spiritual attainment almost in infancy. The child, either boy or girl, when less than ten years of age, was told by the father or the mother that it was time to have . . . spiritual power." The boys were sent on progressively longer vigils to mountains as far as twelve miles away from camp, to fast and to keep a fire blazing all night. Among the interior Salish, "children, especially boys, were sent at frequent intervals to solitary places, in order that one or another of these spirits might take pity on them. These journeys were begun early in life, among some tribes even at the age of five years." The first trip might be to the sweat house. Gradually the trips were lengthened, and to make sure that the child carried out instructions some task would be set, such as finding and bringing in an object previously left at the appointed place by the anxious relatives of the youngster.

The practice of arranging some task in order to check on the child's fulfillment of instructions, was quite common among the border tribes of the Northwest Coast area. For the Wishram, Spier and Sapir report: "A child began to train, that is, prepare for a spirit experience, when still quite young, six to twelve years old 'when he can talk plainly.' He was sent out at night . . . [to] finish an appointed task at the designated spot. This was always stereotyped; piling up rocks, pulling up young oak or fir trees, or making withes of the saplings. The task was accommodated to the child's strength."

Additional citations could be given to confirm the fact that children were carefully trained for the vision quest from an early age, but those already given are representative, and sufficient to indicate that such practices were at least quite general if not absolutely universal. The training given was not exclusively religious in nature, even though its eventual purpose was to stimulate what might be termed a "religious thrill"—a pervading sense of having witnessed or experienced some mystery. Incidentally, the children were hardened to fasting, to cold and exposure, to pain, and to loneliness at night in isolated spots frequented by prowling animals. The general effect, obviously, even aside from a successful vision, was to build the kind of character that the Indians admired.

Further evidence stresses the fact that the underlying idea of the quest for power and a guardian spirit was less the acquisition of religious tenets than the acquisition of an inner conviction of individual self-sufficiency, in which the supernatural played an important part because the ultimate authority for everything lay in that realm. Among the Dakota and Pawnee, for example, guardian spirits were obtained directly only by shamans. The lay individual merely had one assigned to him. The Crow, Arapaho, Hidatsa, Winnebago, Blackfoot, and other Indians might purchase power as a commodity, as well as find it for themselves. Among the Hidatsa, Crow, Arapaho, Pawnee, Arikara, Omaha, and the Central Algonkian, the power might be inherited and had only to be confirmed by an inner conviction of its potency in order to be used. This idea occurs also in the Northwest. We cannot be dogmatic on the subject of religious training among the North American Indians. All I desire to show is that the classifying of the vision quest and the acquisition of a guardian spirit as purely religious, in the modern conception of religion as a spiritual concern divorced from practical or intellectual activities, is a mistake. The object of the training and of the experience was success in life. Conversely, success in life was a substitute for intensive courting of the supernatural. The person who could get power, an inner conviction, without following the normal procedure, was not universally looked down upon, but was considered fortunate. The average layman worried about the spiritual only if he lacked an inner conviction of his own capability and luck.

Among the Ojibwa, according to Jenness: "Any Indian who through industry and good judgment is more successful than his neighbors rouses their suspicion that he possesses an unfair advantage; that his prosperity is due not to his natural talents and diligence, but to his acquisition of some powerful medicine which he carefully secretes from his fellowmen."

From the histories of Blackfoot ceremonial-bundle owners it is clear that the son of successful parents may procrastinate in his quest for power, whereas the young nobody is precociously assiduous. In the biographies of twenty-three Plains Indians it is clear that six never made a successful vision quest, but some of the six got along without it, apparently because they achieved a conviction of power in other ways. Wissler states there is often an implication that a man did not know he had dreamed power until he accomplished something worthwhile, then he decided that he must have done so. The same implication is found in the story of an Oto recorded by Whitman. Littlerump, a Crow, confessed to Lowie: "All who had visions were well-to-do. I was to be poor, that is why I had no visions." This confession is highly informative, for, among the Crow, a man could seek to have someone's power transferred to him if he could not get any of his own. The conclusion is that Littlerump was a man of little capability, and that this proved he had never been able to establish permanent contact with the supernaturals who doled out good fortune. He might have been very religious, and probably tried to be. The story of Hillside, another Crow, is also informative. He had been given very powerful medicine as a boy. But his first war parties were flagrant failures, and he lost his conviction of power in a wave of fear when he barely escaped from the last one with his life. While running away he decided he really did not have any medicine power. Then he fell to the ground exhausted, and had a dream, not of his own medicine but of his brother's. Thus he knew that he just had the wrong medicine, and when this vital mistake was rectified he immediately became successful.

In California, the same concept of power acquisition as a practical aid to success occurs. Kroeber says of the Yurok: "A wealthy man exhorts his sons to accost visitors in a quiet and friendly manner and invite them to their house; thus they will have friends. A poor man, on the other hand instructs his son not in policy but in means to acquire strength. He tells him where to bathe at night; then a being will draw him under the water and speak to him, and he will come away with powerful physique and courage." The important point in the Yurok curriculum for the training of the ideal, wealthy man was "concentration." Boys were told to concentrate on gaining wealth and to avoid thinking about anything else, especially women. Thus they became wealthy, and, naturally, along the way they must have acquired supernatural approval.

Similar statements to the effect that poor boys had to seek power, and that a successful man knew he had power, and that certain people obtained power at birth, or inherited it, or received it by gift, are frequent in the Northwest area. The clearest statement noted in any field report is that for the Wishram: "Since the measure of success was held to be directly dependent on the extent of power, and this was held to vary from one individual to another, we cannot but conclude that the actual causal sequence was the reverse: those who were successful credited themselves with unusual spirit power."

Additional insight into the educational significance of the vision quest and the acquisition of a guardian spirit is to be obtained from a study of the nature of the vision supposedly obtained by these primitive ascetics, on the one hand, and by an analysis of what takes place of a similar character in tribal groups lacking the vision—guardian-spirit complex, on the other.

*selection  37*

# The Hopi Snake Dance, Fact and Fancy

## Robert F. Heizer

*From* Ciba Symposia, *Vol. 5, 1944, pp. 1681–1684. By permission of the author and the publisher.*

The snake dance of the Hopi Indians of Arizona is perhaps the most widely known of all American Indian rituals. The horror and fascination of seeing the natives dance with live venomous snakes held in their mouth go far to explain the notoriety which this ceremony, of solemn and religious nature to the Indians, has attracted. The snake dance is held every two years and is performed conjointly by two fraternities named the Snakes and Antelopes. The whole ceremony, which is celebrated principally as a prayer for rain, lasts for 9 days, during which secret rites are performed, and teminates in the "public" dance where the live snakes are handled. The snake dance cannot be viewed as a form of ophiology. The snakes are not worshipped; they are looked upon as sacred messengers of the rain gods. During the first four days of the ceremony snake-gathering parties go out each day in one of the four cardinal directions. The captured snakes are kept in pottery jars in the *kiva*, a round subterranean ceremonial chamber. At noon of the ninth day the snakes are washed and dried. At sundown they are taken from the *kiva* to the central plaza of the pueblo and placed in the *kisi*, a small bower of cottonwood tree boughs.

The dancers, who are Snake priests, each elaborately painted and costumed, start with a swaying dance, then form into trios and dance toward the *kisi* where one of the three dancers receives a snake and grasps it in his mouth. He dances four times around the plaza when he drops the snake and returns to the *kisi* for another. When the snakes have all thus been carried on a circuit of the plaza and are held by the Antelope priests, a circle of ground corn meal is drawn on the ground, and all the snakes are thrown in a pile within the meal ring. (The number of snakes employed varies with the number of participants of the ceremony. Counts range from as few as 20 to over 150. The average is probably something under 100.) Now all the Snake priests rush to the pile of squirming snakes and each seizes as many of the snakes as he can hold in each hand. The priests then run off in the four cardinal directions with the snakes where they are liberated at some distance from the village.

Let us now consider how the Hopi Indians handle, without harm and in apparently careless fashion, these venomous snakes. The chief poisonous snake used in the ceremony seems to be the Prairie Rattlesnake (*Crotalus confluentus confluentus*) which seldom attains a length of over four feet, and is rated as carrying a small quantity (av. .055 gram dry) of highly toxic venom. The minimum lethal dose of this venom for a 350-gram pigeon has been determined to be .08 mg. The bite of a full-grown specimen with full venom glands would be quite serious, and there are many cases on record of deaths from the venom of the Prairie Rattlesnake. Non-venomous snakes are also used in the ceremony, the Arizona Gopher Snake (*Pituophis catenifer rutilus*) and the Great Basin Striped Racer (*Masticophis taeniatus taeniatus*) having been identified with certainty, though other species were also employed. There can be no doubt, however, that the Prairie Rattlesnake, a dangerously venomous species, is the preferred form for the snake-dance ceremony.

A very large number of theories, most of them unsupported by facts and contrary to recorded evidence of trained observers, have been advanced to explain how the Hopi freely handle venomous snakes. Some of these are: the audience is placed under mass-hypnosis (cf. the Indian rope trick where this explanation is often suggested); the priests who handle the snakes either take an internal protective medicine, are smeared with a disagreeable lotion which repels the snake, are covered with a paint which is invulnerable to the snake's fangs, are so constitutionally perfect from their outdoor life that the venom has no effect on them, possess an immunity built up by increasing dosages of venom, are fearless of snakes which then have no power to bite them, or actually are bitten with serious results and kept secret from outsiders. Conditions affecting the snakes also enter the list of theories. It is suggested that the snakes' venom glands and fangs have been removed, that their mouths are sewed shut, that they have had their venom glands milked, that they are tamed snakes used repeatedly for the ceremony, that they are doped, starved, hypnotized, blinded, paralyzed or tamed into submission, that they are held so that they cannot strike, or that the rattlesnakes are not venomous anyway.

There is no trustworthy evidence that mass hypnotism is employed, and the same may be said for the theories regarding natural or induced immunity of the Snake priests. Although the Hopi Indians, like most American Indian tribes who live in areas where venomous snakes are found, have a snake-bite antidote, it consists of an infusion of herbs taken by the mouth and can hardly have any effect on a virulent and rapid-acting venom in the blood stream. The Hopi snake venom antidote has been tested by Coleman and found to be completely ineffective. We may accept the statements of most observers to the effect that there is no evidence that the snakes are drugged, doped, starved, hypnotized, blinded, or tamed into submission. All recorders of the snake dance agreed that the snakes are sluggish and docile during the public ceremony in which they are carried in the priests' hands and mouths. Although this lethargic spirit is attributed by some to the effect of an opiate, there is general agreement in attributing the tractable nature of the rattlesnakes to their week's underground captivity in the *kiva*. It is well known that captivity of snakes, particularly in the presence or contact of human beings, induces a marked lessening of the rattlesnake's natural disposition to show fear or aggressive tendencies. Indeed, their chief thought in such surroundings seems to be escape. It has been noted that during the snake dance when a rattlesnake is dropped it shows only a momentary tendency to coil for defense, but then rapidly endeavors to use the occasion to fulfill its natural desire for escape. Of importance also is the attitude of the snake-handler. If he shows fear and hesitation the snake seems to sense it and accordingly reacts, as Klauber says, "in a hostile defense which is almost aggression," whereas if the handler acts with calmness, gentleness, and assurance the snake (particularly a captive specimen) reacts tractably and no aggressive symptoms are evidenced. The Hopi themselves appear to handle the captive snakes in this calm, fearless fashion which may go far to explain why there are not more reports of the priests and other snake-handlers being bitten.

No observer has ever seen evidence that the snakes' venom glands or fangs were interfered with in any manner. However, as the herpetologist Klauber points out, "If I were an Indian engaged in this dance I would not be satisfied to take a chance on the admitted and known docility of the rattlers. . . .

I would use the simplest, least apparent, and safest method of rendering the snakes almost innocuous, that is, by thoroughly emptying the poison glands. . . . To my mind the removal of the venom, either at the time of catching the snakes or later in the *kiva*, would be so easy and safe and so much more difficult to detect, that this is a more plausible explanation of how the Indians handle the snakes so fearlessly and with so few adverse effects." . . . In this connection it is of interest to observe that out of many reports of Snake priests being bitten during the public ceremony, there are ten instances which are definite and unequivocal. These priests were all bitten on the hands or face, and in no single instance were ill effects noted—the priest simply opened the snake's jaws and dislodged it and resumed dancing. Such impunity and carelessness in handling the snakes must have an explanation, particularly in view of the fact that at times the priests are bitten, and it seems probable that Klauber's hypothesis that the venom glands are milked, and that this feature is kept a careful secret by the Indians, is the likely one. Keeping this in mind as a likely possibility, and recalling the tractable nature of captive rattlesnakes, together with the capable and expert handling of the snakes by the Indians, the sensational and puzzling aspects of the Hopi snake dance seem to fall into the category of unusual but hardly mystifying human accomplishments.

selection 38

# The Logic of African Science and Witchcraft

## Max Gluckman

I have selected this book for the first appreciation in our journal, because it is one of the most notable contributions to the scientific understanding of African problems. Though the researches on which it is based were made in the Sudan, the general argument applies to all African tribes who believe in witchcraft, oracles or divination, and magic. The author describes clearly the functioning of witchcraft and magic in a book that is fascinating to the specialist, and is also written so simply and vividly that every layman who begins it will not be able to leave it till he has followed the argument to its close. For an understanding of the behavior of Africans, and, as will be seen, of ourselves where we do not act on scientifically valid grounds, it is a work which everyone should read. Since the book explains to us not only customs of the Sudan Azande, but also the basis of such wide fields of human behavior, I shall here set out the general lessons which it teaches, and then touch on the differences between the Azande and our own peoples. However, as Evans-Pritchard does not consider in detail aspects of Azande behavior other than what he calls the mystical, I begin by referring to these.

The title of this review poses the question: is there a fundamental difference between African and European logic, and if so, is it due to physical differences, or to psychological ones related to the different social conditions in which Africans and Europeans live? Without entering into the arguments for and against, I may say that the consensus of scientific opinion is that there is no proof of any great difference between the brains of

From The Logic of
African Science and
Witchcraft: An
Appreciation of
Evans-Pritchard's
"Witchcraft Oracles and
Magic among the Azande"
of the Sudan.
Rhodes-Livingston
Institute Journal,
June 1944, pp. 61–71.
By permission of the
author and publisher.

various races. If there are any differences, they are altogether insufficient to account for the great differences between cultures and modes of thought, and above all, they cannot account for the rapid spurts in cultural development which some countries achieved in very short time. That is, if we have to explain London and an African village, we cannot do so by bodily differences between Londoners and Africans: we must investigate their history and struggles, especially their contacts with other peoples, and other social factors. For if an African were brought up from birth by a Londoner, he would be a Londoner. We know that shipwrecked European children were distinguishable from their African foster-people only by their color.

Therefore, if the mind of the African differs from the European's, it is because he has grown up in a different society, where from birth his behavior and ideas are molded by those of his parents and fellows. If he inherits a "mind," he inherits it socially, and not physically.

Most Europeans are handicapped in judging Africans' intelligence, for they deal with them only as employees, working in unfamiliar ways. The sociologist is fortunate in having to act and converse with them in their own ideas and idiom, and most find that once one has grasped their idiom, they are intelligent and logical companions. They are also knowledgeable companions, for every African knows much about his own laws, politics, history, art, medicine, so that conversation with them often becomes general and philosophical.

First, the African has a wide technical knowledge which is accurate and scientific. For example, the Lozi people live in a large plain on the Zambezi which is flooded each year, and to make a living, they have to take into account soils, vegetation, the time of the flood's coming and its depth, rainfall and temperature, in order to decide where to make their gardens and when to plant them. Some gardens they build up above the waters, other places they drain. Government experts describe this Lozi agriculture as remarkable, and say that they can suggest no improvements in it unless they first experiment. The Lozi have twenty-two recorded methods of catching fish with nets, dams, traps, and weapons, and to use these they have to smelt and work iron, make string and rope from roots and bark, and know the movements of fish with the rise and fall of the flood.

They are also keen and penetrating lawyers. Their laws and procedure differ from ours, but within their framework they reason clearly, distinguishing the issues involved, and applying old laws precisely to new situations. Nevertheless, a European often cannot grasp the logic which underlies the course of argument and the decision in a case tried by African judges. This is because the background of African cases is different from our own. Very many African lawsuits are between relatives; this is largely so because Africans count their ties with very distant relatives, very much further than we do. When one relative sues another though he may come to court over a certain thing on which a case rests, what he wants investigated may not be that single dispute, but the whole behavior of this relative to him. Where our lawyers concern themselves only with the thing that the present quarrel is about, the African judges go into the rights and wrongs of the litigants' behavior to each other over a long period. Leakey says that when a Kikuyu pledges land against a loan of stock, if the pledgee works and improves the land he gets back only the stock he loaned; if he holds the land without working it, and it reverts to bush, he gets additional stock. The Kikuyu argue in the opposite way to us, but logically, that in improving the land the pledgee has got profit out of it, and this is his interest. He therefore is not entitled to compensation for his improvements or interest on the stock he lent to the pledgor.

In political debate the African is advanced and intelligent. Africans, like ourselves, are vexed in this war by rising prices, and I heard some Lozi indunas discuss the delicate problem of fixing the price of fish. Here are some of the economic arguments they raised. All distinguished clearly the rights of producers and consumers, saying that they themselves were both, since they fished and bought fish. One said that supplies of fish varied with the month and the state of the flood, and when fish were scarcer prices inevitably rose; he appreciated what we call the law of supply and demand. Another argued that if the fisherman needed money badly, he would accept little money, while the buyer, if staging a feast, would pay a lot. A third pointed out that with the prices of store-goods rising, the price of fish must rise; he saw the spiral of rising prices. On the other hand, another induna countered, fish are cheap and essential and a small rise would be accepted by the buyers; that is, the principle of marginal utility. Another, who came from a distant place near Livingstone, said that prices must vary with locality, for fish at Mongu were cheap because money was scarce, while at Sesheke fish were dear because money was plentiful. Thus he realized that money is a commodity, like other goods, affected by supply and demand. Some indunas pointed to the difficulty of enforcing a fixed price, with the people crowding into a "black market." Some said that the fisherman must not be allowed to profit at the general expense of the community; others were on his side, the fisherman had to make or buy his nets and work in cold waters from morning to night, and therefore he was entitled to a good price. Finally, the head of the Council said that they must check the rise in price, and as the government they must exert the power to check breaches of the law.

I have emphasized the African's intelligence, in technological and administrative matters, within his own culture. In these realms he reasons much as we do, though within much narrower ranges of facts, and of course without testing his theories by scientific experiment. This ability to reason clearly also appears where he works with beliefs and ideas that are different from ours, notably those about witchcraft and magic, a system of ideas which our civilization abandoned some 150 years ago. Many Europeans, particularly peasants, still hold them. That these beliefs subsisted till so recently in educated Europe and America, shows that they are not innate in Africans, but are part of their culture, as they were of ours. Anyone who follows Evans-Pritchard's exposition of the intellectual aspect of Zande magic and witchcraft will be fascinated by their logical skill. At the beginning of his book, Evans-Pritchard stresses that he is excluding their technological knowledge, examples of which, for the Lozi, I have given above.

The fundamental point is that the African is born into a society which believes in witchcraft and therefore the very texture of his thinking, from childhood on, is woven of magical and mystical ideas. More important still, since magic and witchcraft are lived, far more than they are reasoned about, his daily actions are conditioned by these beliefs, till at every turn he is confronted by the threat of witchcraft and meets it with divination and magic. The weight of tradition, the actions and behavior of his elders, the support which chiefs give to the system, all impress on the African the truth of the system, and since he cannot measure it against any other system, he is continually caught in the web of its making. Evans-Pritchard stresses too, that the African does not go about his business in constant terror of witchcraft nor does he approach it with an awesome fear of the supernatural; when he finds it is working against him he is angry against the witch for playing a dirty trick on him.

These points emerge from a brief analysis of the essential characteristics of the system of witchcraft-divination-magic beliefs and behavior. The Azande, like many other Central African tribes, believe witchcraft to be a physical condition of the intestines (as found in a corpse, it is probably a passing state of digestion), which enables the soul of the witch to go out at night and harm his fellows. There is also sorcery (which is more commonly believed in in Southern Africa) which is the use of magical substances for anti-social purposes. A man may have witchcraft in his body, and yet not use it; his witchcraft may be "cool." Africans are not interested in witchcraft as such, but in the particular witch who is bewitching them at a certain moment. They do not get the idea that they are being bewitched and are therefore going to suffer some misfortune, such as to fall ill and die. What happens is that they suffer misfortune, and after it has occurred blame it on a witch; and if it is a misfortune past and done with, they find out who the witch is and get him to withdraw his evil influence or tackle it with magic. Therefore Evans-Pritchard says he knows of no Zande who would die in terror of witchcraft, and this is confirmed by other trained observers.

The problem which the African answers with his belief in witchcraft is this, "Why misfortune to me?" He knows that there are diseases which make people ill; he knows that hippos upset dugouts and drown people. But he asks himself, "Why should I be ill and not other people?" The man whose son has drowned when a hippo upset his dugout, in effect says, "My son frequently traveled by dugout on the river where are are always hippo, why on this one occasion should the hippo have attacked and drowned him?" This he answers, "Because we were bewitched." He knows full well that his son was crossing the river to visit his mother's family, and that the hippo, irritable because it had a calf, was migrating upstream when it met the dugout. We say that it was providence or ill-luck which brought the hippo and the son together so that the son died, as we do when a man crossing the road from one shop to another is run over by a car; when the African says it is witchcraft that caused these deaths, he is explaining a coincidence which science leaves unexplained, except as the intersection of two series of events. The African is fully aware that his son drowned because his lungs filled with water; but he argues that it was a witch, or a sorcerer by his medicines, who brought together the paths of dugout and an angry mother-hippo to kill the son. The Azande explain it by a hunting simile. The first man who hits a buck shares the meat with the man who puts the second spear in it. "Hence if a man is killed by an elephant Azande say that the elephant is the first spear (existing in its own right) and witchcraft is the second spear and that together they killed the man. If a man spears another in war the slayer is the first spear and witchcraft is the second spear and together they killed him."

Witchcraft thus explains why, but not how, misfortunes happen to you. A sociologist in the Union gives an illuminating illustration. The child of a well-educated African teacher died of typhus, and the teacher said that the child was killed by a witch. The sociologist remonstrated that typhus was caused by an infected louse. The teacher replied, "I know that it was a louse from a person ill with typhus which gave my child typhus, and that he died of typhus, but why did the louse go to my child and not to the other children with whom he was playing?" Scientists may explain why some unhappy people attract lice more than others do, but largely it is chance that puts one child, and not another, in the path of an infected louse; we say providence, bad luck, chance; the African says, witchcraft.

Africans thus immediately they suffer misfortune think that a witch has been working against them. Every kind of accident or of ill may be ascribed to witchcraft. But this does not mean that the African does not recognize lack of skill and moral lapses. For an unskilled potter to say that his pots broke in firing because he was bewitched, would not convince his fellows if he had left pebbles in the clay; but the skilled potter who had followed all the rules of his craft would be supported in saying this. It would not be a sound defense for a criminal to plead that he did wrong because he was bewitched to do so, for it is not believed that witchcraft makes a man lie, steal, betray his chief, or commit adultery.

This is how witchcraft works as a theory of causes. The African goes further. Witchcraft does not harm people haphazardly, for the witch wants to hurt people he hates, has quarreled with, of whom he is envious. So that when a man falls ill, or his crops fail (for on good soil crops should not fail), he says that someone who envied him his many children, the favor of his chief, or his good employment by Europeans and his fine clothes, therefore hated him and has used medicines or evil power to do him ill. Witchcraft is thus a moral theory for witches are bad people, hating, grudging, envious, spiteful. A witch does not just attack his fellows, he attacks those whom he has reason to hate. There is a clear distinction between the man who has witchcraft in him but is a good man and does not use it against his fellows, the man who wants to do others harm but has not the power of witchcraft or cannot get the evil medicines of sorcery, and the witch himself— the man who has the power to bewitch and uses that power. Since people are only interested in whether their fellows are witches when they suffer misfortunes, they seek among their enemies for those who may have this power. They think of someone with whom they have quarreled, and suspect him of the evil deed. We find thus that witchcraft as a theory of causes of misfortunes is related to personal relations between the sufferer and his fellows, and to a theory of moral judgments as to what is good and bad.

When a man suffers a misfortune which he cannot remedy, such as the breaking of his pots in firing, he may just accept it, as witchcraft, just as we would say, "Bad luck." But when witchcraft is making him ill and may cause him to die, when it is blighting his crop, or when by divination he finds that it is threatening him in the future, he does not sit down hopelessly under it. He has to scotch its evil working. This he does by using medicines against it, which will stop the witchcraft and possibly kill the witch, or by calling in a diviner to find out who is the witch so that he can be put out of business, or persuaded to remove his witchcraft. The diviner does not seek for the witch haphazardly. Most methods of divination allow one of two possible answers, yes or no, to a stated question. For example, the Azande give a "poison" (of course they do not know it is a poison) with strychnine properties to fowls which die or do not die to say "yes" or "no" to a question of the form, "Is A the witch who is harming me?" Thus a man, seeking for the witch among the people he thinks wish him ill, must eventually get the answer "yes" to one of them. This particular oracle is out of human control; others, including witch doctors, are less trusted by the Azande as being subject to human manipulation. But even the Zande witch doctor, though he works on his knowledge of local gossip, does not often deliberately cheat. He may seek, or be asked by his client to seek, for the witch among say four names. These are the names of enemies of the client, and though the witch doctor may choose from these, or others whom he knows wish his client ill, by unconscious selection, there is a moment when by bodily sensation he knows that the medicines, which give him his divining power, say, "It is A who is the witch, not B." Or the diviner will indicate someone generally without specifying a name—*e.g.*, "one of your wives," "an old woman"—and the client will fix on some definite person, among his neighbors, who is thus described and whom therefore he thinks has reason to wish him ill. Charges of witchcraft thus reflect personal relations and quarrels. Often a man accuses not someone who hates him, or who is envious of him, but someone whom he hates or envies. The African knows this, and may stress it when he is not involved in the case or when he is the accused, but he forgets it when he is making the accusation. In Zululand a man accused his brother of having bewitched him because he was jealous of him. An old diviner, aware of psychological projection, told me,

"Of course, it is obvious that it is the complainant who hates his brother, though he thinks it is his brother who hates him." But that diviner believed firmly in his own power to detect witchcraft. . . .

The theory of witchcraft is thus seen to be reasonable and logical, even if it is not true. Since it explains the intersection of two chains of events by the enmity of people with evil power, it works in fields our modern science leaves unexplained. Thus the African cannot see that the system is untrue and moreover he has to reason with the system as we do with our scientific beliefs. Wherever the system might conflict with reality its beliefs are vague, and deal with transcendent non-observable facts: the witch works at night with his soul, the soul of the poison oracle (which is not personified, but has consciousness) finds out the witchcraft. The theory is a complete whole, in which every part buttresses every other part. Illness proves that a witch is at work, he is discovered by divination, he is persuaded to withdraw his witchcraft. Even though he may feel himself that he is not the real witch, he will at least show that he intends no harm to the sick man. Or he is attacked with magic. It is difficult for the African to find a flaw in the system. Skepticism exists, and is not socially repressed, and Evans-Pritchard writes that the "absence of formal and coercive doctrine permit Azande to state that many, even most, witch doctors, are frauds. No opposition being offered to such statements they leave the main belief in the prophetic and therapeutic powers of witch doctors unimpaired. Indeed, skepticism is included in the pattern of belief in witch doctors. Faith and skepticism are alike traditional. Skepticism explains failures of witch doctors, and being directed toward particular witch doctors even tends to support faith in others." Even the witch doctor who works by sleight of hand believes that there are doctors who have the magic to make this unnecessary. "In this web of belief every strand depends upon every other strand, and a Zande cannot get out of its meshes because this is the only world he knows. The web is not an external structure in which he is enclosed. It is the texture of his thought and he cannot think that his thought is wrong. Nevertheless, his beliefs are not absolutely set but are variable and fluctuating to allow for different situations and to permit empirical observation and even doubts." Within this web, the African may reason as logically as we do within the web of scientific thought. If your house, which you have protected with lightning-conductors, is nevertheless struck by lightning you say that the workman was bad, the wires poor, or there was a break in the wiring. If the African has had his village protected with medicines against storms and it is struck by lightning, he says the magician was bad, his medicine poor, or a taboo was broken. This method of reasoning, within a system, is remarkably illustrated in a book which the Nazis published. It consisted of a collection of anti-Hitler cartoons from the newspapers of the whole world, and contained many by Low. The cartoons did not show the German people what the decent world thought of Hitler, but proved to them that if other governments allowed the god Hitler to be thus attacked, these other countries must be vile and hostile to Germany, as Hitler maintained. So the African's mind, in his system, works as the European's mind does.

I have given other examples in my article on *The Difficulties, Limitations and Achievements of Social Anthropology* [in this same issue of the Rhodes-Livingstone Institute Journal] to show how Evans-Pritchard's analysis of witchcraft illuminates the working of human thought in other spheres. For instance, he makes this comparison. The Azande as we have seen exclude witchcraft as a cause of moral lapses. "As in our own society a scientific theory of causation, if not excluded, is deemed irrelevant in questions of moral and legal responsibility, so in Zande society the doctrine of witchcraft, if not excluded, is deemed irrelevant in the same situations. We accept scientific explanations of the causes of diseases, and even of the causes of insanity, but we deny them in crime and sin because here they militate against law and morals which are axiomatic. The Zande accepts a mystical explanation of the causes of misfortune, sickness, and death, but he does not allow this explanation if it conflicts with social exigencies expressed in law and morals."

I make one final point here, in answer to the oft-made statement that witchcraft charges are based on cheating. Evans-Pritchard emphasizes that the patient, who wishes to abolish the witchcraft harming him, above all

people does not wish to cheat, for what good is it to him if he detects the wrong person as witch? But he does accuse his personal enemies.

When the African, with these beliefs, comes to deal with Europeans, there are many ways in which they affect his behavior so that it seems incomprehensible to us. For example, he queries, "It is true that the White doctors are very good in treating disease, but while they cure the disease they don't treat the witchcraft which caused the disease, and that will continue to do harm." Evans-Pritchard shows that the Zande's oracles are "his guide and councillor," whom he consults about every enterprise. Evans-Pritchard himself lived thus, and found it as good a way as any other of ordering his affairs. But because of it, Europeans often cannot understand Azande behavior: why a Zande will suddenly move from his home to shelter in the bush (because of witchcraft), why a homestead will suddenly be moved (because of witchcraft attacking them in that spot), and so on. Frequently his guests suddenly departed without bidding him farewell, and he was angry till he realized that the oracles had told them that witchcraft was threatening them. "I found that when a Zande acted toward me in a manner that we would call rude and untrustworthy his actions were often to be accounted for by obedience to oracles. Usually I have found Azande courteous and reliable according to English standards, but sometimes their behavior is unintelligible till their mystical notions are taken into account. Often Azande are tortuous in their dealing with one another, but they do not consider a man blameworthy for being secretive or acting contrary to his declared intentions. On the contrary they praise his prudence for taking account of witchcraft at every step. . . . With the European it is different. We only know that a Zande has said he will do something and has done nothing, or has done something different, and we naturally blame the man for lying and being untrustworthy, for the European does not appreciate that Azande have to take into account mystical forces of which he knows nothing." Evans-Pritchard gave a feast to which a prince promised to come; he sent to tell that he would not come. Suddenly he arrived. He arranged to stay the night; in the night he disappeared. He had been told that witchcraft threatened him, and it was a great compliment to the sociologist that he attended the feast; his wayward actions were to deceive the witches. I myself had a favored informant in my employ who kept replying to my summonses, that he would come; but stayed away until I moved my home. He had been threatened with witchcraft at the one spot, not the other. For notions of place and time in witchcraft thought vary from ours; witchcraft may threaten a man now from the future, so the future is in the present, and has to be avoided by not adopting a line of action which was contemplated, as going on a journey; or a man will decide to build his homestead on a certain spot, by eliminating other spots where witchcraft will threaten him, though he has not yet built on them.

There is a second way in which witchcraft behavior may affect Africans when we deal with them. Under these beliefs, people who produced good crops while their neighbors' harvests were meager; who had large healthy families while all around was illness; whose herds and fishing prospered exceedingly; these fortunate people were sometimes believed to make good by magic and witchcraft at the expense of their fellows. We have seen in a quotation above that they believed themselves open to attack from witches. The Zande "knows that if he becomes rich the poor will hate him, that if he rises in social position his inferiors will be jealous of his authority, that if he is handsome the less favored will envy his looks, that if he is talented as a hunter, a singer, a fighter, or a rhetorician, he will earn the malice of those less gifted, and that if he enjoys the regard of his prince and of his neighbors he will be detested for his prestige and popularity." These are the motives that lead to witchcraft. Such beliefs were only possible in a society with nowhere to sell surplus goods, no profit motives, without storable goods, with no luxuries so that there was no heavy pressure on any member to produce more than he required for his own needs. Africans have come from a society with these beliefs into our economic system where they are expected to work long and hard, trying to outdo their fellows, and perhaps the beliefs deter them in this struggle and affect their efficiency. I know Africans who blame their misfortunes on witches envious of their higher wages, or their fine would-be

European-style houses. It is possible that fear of witchcraft prevents Africans developing what skill and capacity they have, in their work for Europeans, though this fear would be unimportant in comparison with other factors preventing their development, such as disease and social barriers.

I have given part of the argument of Evans-Pritchard's book to set out the main framework of magic-witchcraft thought. I hope I have shown how skillfully the argument is set out. In my short review I am unable to do more than indicate its unlimited riches of delight, which make reading and rereading it an unfailing fascination. Everyone who is interested in human problems in this region should own the book. But I must warn the layman that in applying its conclusions to our own tribes, he must do so with care. The central argument applies absolutely, but there are certain important differences. Among the Azande, witchcraft was not a crime but a delict, for which compensation was paid only on a death. In many Southern African tribes witchcraft is a crime, and the state punished witches by killing them. Also in Southern Africa sorcery (the deliberate use of evil magic) was believed to be at work, rather than witchcraft (causing ill by inherent evil power plus malice). This produces important changes in the whole system, which can be traced. . . .

In quoting Evans-Pritchard to show how beliefs in witchcraft affect Africans' behavior and thought, I have emphasized that often their minds work in the same logical patterns as ours do, though the material with which they think is different, so that it is clear that if they were given the same education and cultural background as we have, they would think with the same materials and in the same way as we do. But it is not only beliefs in witchcraft that differentiate the African's ideas from ours. His whole way of life is different from ours, he is considered to be inferior, and he is certainly on the whole abjectly poor. A Bechuana chief, lecturing to a University audience, said that the coming of Western civilization to his people had put a square bed into a round hut. Where the African behaves differently from us, we must remember that he comes from a round hut, usually without a square bed, into our homes with their comparative wealth of furniture, that he comes from a simple axe and hoe to our complicated machinery. In his hut, close to the ground, of the earth earthy, full of flies and without taps or washbasins, with only a basket of meal and some dried fish in it, he cannot have the same standards of efficiency and cleanliness as we have. Even if he, for example, grasps the connection of disease with dirt and insects, he cannot avoid them. Therefore, when he works for Europeans, and when he is away from his work, he is living by two different sets of standards, not with a different mind. These are weighty explanations of his vagaries, not only his pre-knowledge of mystical forces in the future; changes in his way of life, as well as the operation of economic forces in our highly productive system, are tending to break down his system of thought. Further, Wilson has indicated that the personal animosities, which are the basis of witchcraft charges, can lie only in a small-scale primitive society where social relationships are highly personal, and not in the modern world system where men's lives are affected by large-scale impersonal organizations. Therefore, new forces will break down the closed mystical system of Africa. . . .

*selection   39*

# One Hundred Per Cent American

## Ralph Linton

*From* The American Mercury, *Vol. 40, 1937, pp. 427–429. By permission of the author and the publisher.*

There can be no question about the average American's Americanism or his desire to preserve this precious heritage at all costs. Nevertheless, some insidious foreign ideas have already wormed their way into his civilization without his realizing what was going on. Thus dawn finds the unsuspecting patriot garbed in pajamas, a garment of East Indian origin; and lying in a bed built on a pattern which originated in either Persia or Asia Minor. He is muffled to the ears in un-American materials: cotton, first domesticated in India; linen, domesticated in the Near East; wool from an animal native to Asia Minor; or silk whose uses were first discovered by the Chinese. All these substances have been transformed into cloth by methods invented in Southwestern Asia. If the weather is cold enough he may even be sleeping under an eiderdown quilt invented in Scandinavia.

On awakening he glances at the clock, a medieval European invention, uses one potent Latin word in abbreviated form, rises in haste, and goes to the bathroom. Here, if he stops to think about it, he must feel himself in the presence of a great American institution; he will have heard stories of both the quality and frequency of foreign plumbing and will know that in no other country does the average man perform his ablutions in the midst of such splendor. But the insidious foreign influence pursues him even here. Glass was invented by the ancient Egyptians, the use of glazed tiles for floors and walls in the Near East, porcelain in China, and the art of enameling on metal by Mediterranean artisans of the Bronze Age. Even his bathtub and toilet are but slightly modified copies of Roman originals. The only purely American contribution to the ensemble is the steam radiator, against which our patriot very briefly and unintentionally places his posterior.

In this bathroom the American washes with soap invented by the ancient Gauls. Next he cleans his teeth, a subversive European practice which did not invade America until the latter part of the eighteenth century. He then shaves, a masochistic rite first developed by the heathen priests of ancient Egypt and Sumer. The process is made less of a penance by the fact that his razor is of steel, an iron-carbon alloy discovered in either India or Turkestan. Lastly, he dries himself on a Turkish towel.

Returning to the bedroom, the unconscious victim of un-American practices removes his clothes from a chair, invented in the Near East, and proceeds to dress. He puts on close-fitting tailored garments whose form derives from the skin clothing of the ancient nomads of the Asiatic steppes and fastens them with buttons whose prototypes appeared in Europe at the close of the Stone Age. This costume is appropriate enough for outdoor exercise in a cold climate, but is quite unsuited to American summers, steam-heated houses, and Pullmans. Nevertheless, foreign ideas and habits hold the unfortunate man in thrall even when common sense tells him that the authentically American costume of gee string and moccasins would be far more comfortable. He puts on his feet stiff coverings made from hide prepared by a process invented in ancient Egypt and cut to a pattern which can be traced back to ancient Greece, and makes sure that they are properly polished, also a Greek idea. Lastly, he ties about his neck a strip of bright-colored cloth which is a vestigial survival of the shoulder shawls worn by seventeenth-century Croats. He gives himself a final appraisal in the mirror, an old Mediterranean invention, and goes downstairs to breakfast.

Here a whole new series of foreign things confronts him. His food and drink are placed before him in pottery vessels, the popular name of which—china—is sufficient evidence of their origin. His fork is a medieval Italian invention and his spoon a copy of a Roman original. He will usually begin the meal with coffee, an Abyssinian plant first discovered by the Arabs. The American is quite likely to need it to dispel the morning-after effects of overindulgence in fermented drinks, invented in the Near East; or distilled ones, invented by the alchemists of medieval Europe. Whereas the Arabs took their coffee straight, he will probably sweeten it with sugar, discovered in India; and dilute it with cream, both the domestication of cattle and the technique of milking having originated in Asia Minor.

If our patriot is old-fashioned enough to adhere to the so-called American breakfast, his coffee will be accompanied by an orange, domesticated in the Mediterranean region, a cantaloupe domesticated in Persia, or grapes domesticated in Asia Minor. He will follow this with a bowl of cereal made from grain domesticated in the Near East and prepared by methods also invented there. From this he will go on to waffles, a Scandinavian invention, with plenty of butter, originally a Near-Eastern cosmetic. As a side dish he may have the egg of a bird domesticated in Southeastern Asia or strips of the flesh of an animal domesticated in the same region, which have been salted and smoked by a process invented in Northern Europe.

Breakfast over, he places upon his head a molded piece of felt, invented by the nomads of Eastern Asia, and, if it looks like rain, puts on outer shoes of rubber, discovered by the ancient Mexicans, and takes an umbrella, invented in India. He then sprints for his train —the train, not the sprinting, being an English invention. At the state he pauses for a moment to buy a newspaper, paying for it with coins invented in ancient Lydia. Once on board he settles back to inhale the fumes of a cigarette invented in Mexico, or a cigar invented in Brazil. Meanwhile, he reads the news of the day, imprinted in characters invented by the ancient Semites by a process invented in Germany upon a material invented in China. As he scans the latest editorial pointing out the dire results to our institutions of accepting foreign ideas, he will not fail to thank a Hebrew God in an Indo-European language that he is a one hundred per cent (decimal system invented by the Greeks) American (from Americus Vespucci, Italian geographer).

*selection 40*

# Body Ritual among the Nacirema

## Horace Miner

*From* American Anthropologist, *Vol. 58, No. 3, 1956, pp. 503–507. By permission of the author and the publisher.*

The anthropologist has become so familiar with the diversity of ways in which different peoples behave in similar situations that he is not apt to be surprised by even the most exotic customs. In fact, if all of the logically possible combinations of behavior have not been found somewhere in the world, he is apt to suspect that they must be present in some yet undescribed tribe. This point has, in fact, been expressed with respect to clan organization by Murdock. In this light, the magical beliefs and practices of the Nacirema present such unusual aspects that it seems desirable to describe them as an example of the extremes to which human behavior can go.

Professor Linton first brought the ritual of the Nacirema to the attention of anthropologists twenty years ago, but the culture of this people is still very poorly understood. They are a North American group living in the territory between the Canadian Cree, the Yaqui and Tarahumare of Mexico, and the Carib and Arawak of the Antilles. Little is known of their origin, although tradition states that they came from the east. . . .

Nacirema culture is characterized by a

highly developed market economy which has evolved in a rich natural habitat. While much of the people's time is devoted to economic pursuits, a large part of the fruits of these labors and a considerable portion of the day are spent in ritual activity. The focus of this activity is the human body, the appearance and health of which loom as a dominant concern in the ethos of the people. While such a concern is certainly not unusual, its ceremonial aspects and associated philosophy are unique.

The fundamental belief underlying the whole system appears to be that the human body is ugly and that its natural tendency is to debility and disease. Incarcerated in such a body, man's only hope is to avert these characteristics through the use of the powerful influences of ritual and ceremony. Every household has one or more shrines devoted to this purpose. The more powerful individuals in the society have several shrines in their houses and, in fact, the opulence of a house is often referred to in terms of the number of such ritual centers it possesses. Most houses are of wattle and daub construction, but the shrine rooms of the more wealthy are walled with stone. Poorer families imitate the rich by applying pottery plaques to their shrine walls.

While each family has at least one such shrine, the rituals associated with it are not family ceremonies but are private and secret. The rites are normally only discussed with children, and then only during the period when they are being initiated into these mysteries. I was able, however, to establish sufficient rapport with the natives to examine these shrines and to have the rituals described to me.

The focal point of the shrine is a box or chest which is built into the wall. In this chest are kept the many charms and magical potions without which no native believes he could live. These preparations are secured from a variety of specialized practitioners. The most powerful of these are the medicine men, whose assistance must be rewarded with substantial gifts. However, the medicine men do not provide the curative potions for their clients, but decide what the ingredients should be and then write them down in an ancient and secret language. This writing is understood only by the medicine men and by the herbalists who, for another gift, provide the required charm.

The charm is not disposed of after it has served its purpose, but is placed in the charmbox of the household shrine. As these magical materials are specific for certain ills, and the real or imagined maladies of the people are many, the charm-box is usually full to overflowing. The magical packets are so numerous that people forget what their purposes were and fear to use them again. While the natives are very vague on this point, we can only assume that the idea in retaining all the old magical materials is that their presence in the charm-box, before which the body rituals are conducted, will in some way protect the worshipper.

Beneath the charm-box is a small font. Each day every member of the family, in succession, enters the shrine room, bows his head before the charm-box, mingles different sorts of holy water in the font, and proceeds with a brief rite of ablution. The holy waters are secured from the Water Temple of the community, where the priests conduct elaborate ceremonies to make the liquid ritually pure.

In the hierarchy of magical practitioners, and below the medicine men in prestige, are specialists whose designation is best translated "holy-mouth-men." The Nacirema have an almost pathological horror of and fascination with the mouth, the condition of which is believed to have a supernatural influence on all social relationships. Were it not for the rituals of the mouth, they believe that their teeth would fall out, their gums bleed, their jaws shrink, their friends desert them, and their lovers reject them. They also believe that a strong relationship exists between oral and moral characteristics. For example, there is a ritual ablution of the mouth for children which is supposed to improve their moral fiber.

The daily body ritual performed by everyone includes a mouth-rite. Despite the fact that these people are so punctilious about care of the mouth, this rite involves a practice which strikes the uninitiated stranger as revolting. It was reported to me that the ritual consists of inserting a small bundle of hog hairs into the mouth, along with certain magical powders, and then moving the bundle in a highly formalized series of gestures.

In addition to the private mouth-rite, the people seek out a holy-mouth-man once or twice a year. These practitioners have an impressive set of paraphernalia, consisting of a variety of augers, awls, probes, and prods. The use of these objects in the exorcism of the evils of the mouth involves almost unbelievable ritual torture of the client. The holy-mouth-man opens the client's mouth and, using the above mentioned tools, enlarges any holes which decay may have created in the teeth. Magical materials are put into these holes. If there are no naturally occurring holes in the teeth, large sections of one or more teeth are gouged out so that the supernatural substance can be applied. In the client's view, the purpose of these ministrations is to arrest decay and to draw friends. The extremely sacred and traditional character of the rite is evident in the fact that the natives return to the holy-mouth-men year after year, despite the fact that their teeth continue to decay.

It is to be hoped that, when a thorough study of the Nacirema is made, there will be careful inquiry into the personality structure of these people. One has but to watch the gleam in the eye of a holy-mouth-man, as he jabs an awl into an exposed nerve, to suspect that a certain amount of sadism is involved. If this can be established, a very interesting pattern emerges, for most of the population shows definite masochistic tendencies. It was to these that Professor Linton referred in discussing a distinctive part of the daily body ritual which is performed only by men. This part of the rite involves scraping and lacerating the surface of the face with a sharp instrument. Special women's rites are performed only four times during each lunar month, but what they lack in frequency is made up in barbarity. As part of this ceremony, women bake their heads in small ovens for about an hour. The theoretically interesting point is that what seems to be a preponderantly masochistic people have developed sadistic specialists.

The medicine men have an imposing temple, or *latipso*, in every community of any size. The more elaborate ceremonies required to treat very sick patients can only be performed at this temple. These ceremonies involve not only the thaumaturge but a permanent group of vestal maidens who move sedately about the temple chambers in distinctive costume and headdress.

The *latipso* ceremonies are so harsh that it is phenomenal that a fair proportion of the really sick natives who enter the temple ever recover. Small children whose indoctrination is still incomplete have been known to resist attempts to take them to the temple because "that is where you go to die." Despite this fact, sick adults are not only willing but eager to undergo the protracted ritual purification, if they can afford to do so. No matter how ill the supplicant or how grave the emergency, the guardians of many temples will not admit a client if he cannot give a rich gift to the custodian. Even after one has gained admission and survived the ceremonies, the guardians will not permit the neophyte to leave until he makes still another gift.

The supplicant entering the temple is first stripped of all his or her clothes. In everyday life the Nacirema avoids exposure of his body and its natural functions. Bathing and excretory acts are performed only in the secrecy of the household shrine, where they are ritualized as part of the body-rites. Psychological shock results from the fact that body secrecy is suddenly lost upon entry into the *latipso*. A man, whose own wife has never seen him in an excretory act, suddenly finds himself naked and assisted by a vestal maiden while he performs his natural functions into a sacred vessel. This sort of ceremonial treatment is necessitated by the fact that the excreta are used by a diviner to ascertain the course and nature of the client's sickness. Female clients, on the other hand, find their naked bodies are subjected to the scrutiny, manipulation and prodding of the medicine men.

Few supplicants in the temple are well enough to do anything but lie on their hard beds. The daily ceremonies, like the rites of the holy-mouth-men, involve discomfort and torture. With ritual precision, the vestals awaken their miserable charges each dawn and roll them about on their beds of pain while performing ablutions, in the formal movements of which the maidens are highly trained. At other times they insert magic wands in the supplicant's mouth or force him to eat substances which are supposed to be healing. From time to time the medicine men come to their clients and jab magically treated needles into their flesh. The fact that these temple ceremonies may not cure, and may even kill the neophyte, in no way decreases the people's faith in the medicine men.

There remains one other kind of practitioner, known as a "listener." This witch-doctor has the power to exorcise the devils that lodge in the heads of people who have been bewitched. The Nacirema believe that parents bewitch their own children. Mothers are particularly suspected of putting a curse on children while teaching them the secret body rituals. The counter-magic of the witch-doctor is unusual in its lack of ritual. The patient simply tells the "listener" all his troubles and fears, beginning with the earliest difficulties he can remember. The memory displayed by the Nacirema in these exorcism sessions is truly remarkable. It is not uncommon for the patient to bemoan the rejection he felt upon being weaned as a babe, and a few individuals even see their troubles going back to the traumatic effects of their own birth.

In conclusion, mention must be made of certain practices which have their base in native esthetics but which depend upon the pervasive aversion to the natural body and its functions. There are ritual fasts to make fat people thin and ceremonial feasts to make thin people fat. Still other rites are used to make women's breasts larger if they are small, and smaller if they are large. General dissatisfaction with breast shape is symbolized in the fact that the ideal form is virtually outside the range of human variation. A few women afflicted with almost inhuman hyper-mammary development are so idolized that they make a handsome living by simply going from village to village and permitting the natives to stare at them for a fee.

Reference has already been made to the fact that excretory functions are ritualized, routinized, and relegated to secrecy. Natural reproductive functions are similarly distorted. Intercourse is taboo as a topic and scheduled as an act. Efforts are made to avoid pregnancy by the use of magical materials or by limiting intercourse to certain phases of the moon. Conception is actually very infrequent. When pregnant, women dress so as to hide their condition. Parturition takes place in secret, without friends or relatives to assist, and the majority of women do not nurse their infants.

Our review of the ritual life of the Nacirema has certainly shown them to be a magic-ridden people. It is hard to understand how they have managed to exist so long under the burdens which they have imposed upon themselves. But even such exotic customs as these take on real meaning when they are viewed with the insight provided by Malinowski when he wrote:

"Looking from far and above, from our high places of safety in the developed civilization, it is easy to see all the crudity and irrelevance of magic. But without its power and guidance early man could not have mastered his practical difficulties as he has done, nor could man have advanced to the higher stages of civilization."

*part 7*

*Language*

# Being and Value in a Primitive Culture

## Dorothy Lee

*From* The Journal of
Philosophy, *Vol. 46,
No. 13, 1949, pp. 401–415.
By permission of the
author and the publisher.*

Anthropologists have realized in recent years
that people of other cultures than our own
not only act differently, but that they have
a different basis for their behavior. They act
upon different premises; they perceive reality
differently, and codify it differently. In this
codification, language is largely instrumental.
It incorporates the premises of the culture,
and codifies reality in such a way that it
presents it as absolute to the members of
each culture. Other aspects of behavior also
express, if not as clearly, the specific phrasing of reality which each culture makes for
itself. Therefore, through an intensive analysis
of language, ceremonial and everyday behavior, myths and magical formulas, it is
possible to arrive at the philosophic basis of
a culture, and to see to some extent how
reality appears to its members.

I present in the following pages such an
analysis: a study of being and value in the
culture of the Trobriand Islanders of the Archipelago stretching between New Guinea and
the Solomon Islands. This society has been
described at length by Bronislaw Malinowski,
whose works have furnished the data for this
study.

The Trobrianders are concerned with being,
and being alone. Change and becoming are
foreign to their thinking. An object or event
is grasped and evaluated in terms of itself
alone, that is, irrespective of other beings.
The Trobriander can describe being for the
benefit of the ethnographer; otherwise, he
usually refers to it by a word, one word only.
All being, to be significant, must be Trobriand being, and therefore experienced at the
appropriate time as a matter of course by the
members of each Trobriand community; to

describe it would be redundant. Being is never defined, in our sense of the word. Definition presents an object in terms of *what it is like* and *what it is unlike*, that is, in terms of its distinguishing characteristics. The Trobriander is interested only in *what it is*. And each event or being is grasped timelessly; in our terms, it contains its past, present, and future, but these distinctions are nonexistent for the Trobriander. There is, however, one sense in which being is not self-contained. To be, it must be part of an ordained pattern; this aspect will be elaborated below.

Being is discrete and self-contained; it has no attributes outside of itself. Its qualities are identical with it and without them it is not itself. It has no predicate; it is itself. To say a word representing an object or act is to imply the existence of this, and all the qualities it incorporates. If I were to go with a Trobriander to a garden where the *taytu*, a species of yam, had just been harvested, I would come back and tell you, "There are good *taytu* there; just the right degree of ripeness, large and perfectly shaped; not a blight to be seen, not one rotten spot; nicely rounded at the tips, with no spiky points; all first-run harvesting, no second gleamings." The Trobriander would come back and say, "*Taytu*"; and he would have said all that I did and more. Even the phrase "There are *taytu*" would represent a tautology, since existence is implied in being, is, in fact an ingredient of being to the Trobriander. And all the attributes, even if he could find words for them at hand in his own language, would have been tautological, since the concept of *taytu* contains them all. In fact, if one of these were absent, the object would not have been a *taytu*. Such a tuber, if it is not at the proper harvesting ripeness, is not a *taytu*. If it is unripe, it is a *bwanawa*; if overripe, spent, it is not a spent *taytu* but something else, a *yowana*. If it is blighted it is a *nukunokuna*. If it has a rotten patch, it is a *taboula*; if misshapen, it is an *usasu*; if perfect in shape but small, it is a *yagogu*. If the tuber, whatever its shape or condition, is a post-harvest gleaning, it is an *ulumadala*. When the spent tuber, the *yowana*, sends its shoots underground, as we would put it, it is not a *yowana* with shoots, but a *silisata*. When new tubers have formed on these shoots, it is not a *silisata* but a

*gadena*. An object cannot change an attribute and retain its identity. Some range of growth or modification within being is probably allowed, otherwise speech would be impossible; but I doubt whether they are conscious of it. As soon as such change, if we may introduce one of our concepts here, is officially recognized, the object ceases to be itself.

As being is identical with the object, there is no word for *to be*; as being is changeless, there is no word meaning *to become*. Becoming involves temporality, but Trobriand being has no reference to time. With us, change in time is a value, and place in a developmental sequence is necessary for evaluation. We cannot respond with approval or disapproval, unless we know that a thing is getting bigger or better or surer. If I am told that Robert Smith is an instructor at $3000, I cannot respond to this adequately, unless I know that he is just out of graduate school, or that he used to be a professor at the age of forty, but now, at sixty, he has been demoted to this position. Our language is full of terms such as the one I have just used—demotion—giving us tools for the evaluation of being in terms of place in a climactic historical sequence. By dint of constant viligance, we can refrain from using these terms; but we have no choice when it comes to placing events in time. Our language codifies reality in such a way as to predispose us to view events in terms of temporality. Even if I decide to use such expressions as "it be" or "it flow," I have achieved nothing, since you who hear me automatically make these acceptable to yourself by translating them into "it is" and "it flows," merely putting me down as uneducated. Whenever I make an assertion, I have to give it temporal limits, in reference to past, present, or future, or at any rate I have to imply temporality. Trobriand verbs are timeless, making no temporal distinctions. A Trobriander can, if he chooses, refer to an act as completed, but that, it seems to me, is an aspect of the act, not a temporal reference. History and mythical reality are not "the past" to the Trobriander. They are forever present, participating in all current being, giving meaning to all his activities and all existence. A Trobriander will speak of the garden which his mother's brother planted, or the one which the mythical Tudava planted, in exactly the same terms with which he will refer to the garden which he himself is planting now; and it will give him satisfaction to do so.

Being is apprehended as a whole, not in terms of attributes. This is something very difficult for members of our culture to achieve; we rarely value sheer being in itself, except perhaps when we are "blindly" in love. Even mothers are often incapable of valuing their children in this way, demanding instead attributes and achievements before they will respond with love. I watched a college student once in a predicament created by this inability to react to being itself. Faced with a vivid, gurgling infant in the presence of its mother, she felt it necessary to react but had no basis for doing so. She tried hard to discover attributes to guide her, asking, "Does she talk?" "Does she creep?" hoping for something on which to base approval; and, finally, having received a negative answer to all her questions, she remained dumb and immobilized. The Trobriander does not say, "how bright" or "how big"; his equivalent in this situation would have been "how baby."

Being is evaluated discretely, in terms of itself alone, not in comparison with others. This, again, is foreign to our thinking, except perhaps in the sphere of art. To return to Robert Smith, if you tell me that he is an instructor at $3000 a year, I can respond to this with approbation, commiseration, etc., only if I know what the rank and pay of other men instructors are apt to be. To evaluate, I have to compare this being with other beings of its kind. To be good, being has to be as good as, if not better than. For the Trobriander, being is good only as itself.

Now our own language makes it easy, though not imperative, to compare beings at every turn. It provides us with a large number of comparatives, through morphology and vocabulary. Our speech is studded with terms such as better, bigger, inferior, average, compared to, normal, equal, in relation to, etc., showing that we constantly are passing judgment according to a comparative standard. The Trobriander has no such means, unless we accept his rarely used words "it-sames" and "it-differents" as comparative. The magic formulas given by Malinowski are full of similes, as only in this way can they be made comprehensible to his readers. But in Tro-

briand, these are all metaphors. Where Malinowski's translation reads, for example, "thy shoots are as quick as the eyes of the black ant," the Trobriand text reads, "no thine eye, thine eye black-ant." When Malinowski says, "I am your senior," the Trobriand text reads, "old man I."

We can see this emphasis on *being* alone when we analyze the Trobriand sentence. Here we find that the words are presented discretely, without elements to show the relation of one word to the other. A verb contains its subject, a noun contains its "predicate" as well as its other attributes. The few words which Malinowski translated as adjectives are either nouns—a big-one, or verbs—it-goods. The language does not even express an object-to-object relationship, as our does, for example, when it relates grammatical subject to the object which is acted upon. In English, we express this relationship through word order; when we say, for example, "Mary ate the pie," or, "John kicked Mary," we clearly distinguished the actor from the one acted upon, by order of precedence, and we can not avoid making the distinction. The Trobriander, on the other hand, merely expresses act and participants; *i-wo-ye tau* "it-beat-man" means either that the man is beating someone or that someone is beating the man. Such a phrase usually refers either to a known situation, which needs no elucidation, or is told within a context which makes its meaning clear. If, however, the Trobriander for some reason feels that he must specify, he can do so; but he does not do so as a matter of course, as we do, since his language does not predispose or constrain him to do so.

To be, an object must be true to itself, not in terms of its relationship with other beings. To be good, it must be the same always. Sameness is a value to the Trobrianders. Trobriand being never came into existence; it has always been, exactly as now, above ground in "historic" times, below ground in mythical times. At some time the ancestress of each group emerged from a specific hole, bringing with her all the customs, skills, and beliefs of that group, their patterns of behavior, the details of their magic, their pedigreed yams. This "past" is immanent in all Trobriand being. Instead of description in terms of attributes, the Trobriander gives an account of historical or mythical past, presenting essence. In all his undertakings, this "past" is present, giving to them validity and value. Wherever he goes, his surroundings have meaning for him; every waterhole, rock, or cleft is imbued with mythical significance. Myth and history, as intrinsic to being, enhance value. For example, the Trobrianders have certain important valuables which constitute the gifts in the *kula*, an endless circular series of ceremonial gift-givings which occupies, with the preparation involved, perhaps half the life of Trobriand men. These objects have value, but no "utility"; they are "ornaments" which can not be used to adorn the "owner"; and they can be possessed only a few months by each recipient. Giving-in-itself, that is, nonpurposive giving, is good; through participation in this gift-giving pattern the *kula* valuables are good. Each valuable is named and its personal history known. In this lies much of its value; giver and recipient, and the village of the "owner," get satisfaction out of the recounting of the specific *kula* acts of which the article was a part, going from named giver to named recipient. Chronology and historical sequence are irrelevant; the history is important not as development but as the ingredient of being.

The Trobriander has no word for history. When he wants to distinguish between different kinds of occasions, he will say, for example, "Molubabeba in-child-his," that is, "in the childhood of Molubabeba," not a previous phase of *this* time, but a different kind of time. For him, history is an unordered repository of anecdote; he is not interested in chronological sequence. For example, Malinowski recorded an account of a famine which was given with complete disregard to chronology; an effect which is achieved only deliberately by our sophisticated writers. If we rearrange the clusters of statements so that they represent for us a historical sequence, we have to give them in the following order; one, four, three, two, five.

For us, chronological sequence is of vital importance, largely because we are interested not so much in the event itself, but rather in its place within a *related* series of events; we look for its antecedents and its consequences. We are concerned with the causal or telic relationship between events or acts. To the Trobriander, events do not fall of themselves into a pattern of causal relationships, as they do for us. I am not here concerned with the question of whether causality is given, or is read into existence. Whichever may be the case, we in our culture automatically see and seek relationships, not essence, and express relationship mainly in terms of cause or purpose. The maddeningly persistent question of our young children is "why," because this is the question implicit in most of our ordinary statements and other behavior, to be answered either in causal or telic terms, since cause and purpose are equally dynamic for us, and are identified in our use of "why." (This does not mean that Trobriand parents are relieved from such questions; they are probably constantly asked "what." According to Margaret Mead this is what the Manus children are continually asking adults.) Esthetically, as well as practically, cause and purpose are both important to us; cause gives us a satisfying explanation and purpose ennobles or gives meaning to the act. We teach the importance of purposive action to infants, directly and indirectly by act and speech. We teach it in the schoolroom, in sports, in politics, in moral precept. The unreflective scientist takes causation for granted, the orthodox historian studies history to discover the causes for events. To the Trobriander, on the other hand, being or event remains discrete, sufficient unto itself, true and of value as itself, judged and motivated and understood in terms of itself alone. In the face of this apprehension of being, concepts such as causation and purpose appear irrelevant; I have introduced them here only because they are so basic to our thinking that we accept them as given in experience, and their presence is assumed by us in all cultures, as a matter of course. (This absence of causal concepts, as well as of a comparative standard, seemed at first so striking to me that I wrote a paper describing Trobriand thought in terms of what it was not, as noncausal and noncomparative. It now seems to me that I was viewing the Trobrianders then through the eyes of my own culture, relationally, seeing them according to what they were unlike, and so stressing the absence of concepts which have no relevance to their thought. . . . The paper in question is A Primitive System of Values. *Philosophy of Science*, Vol. 7, No. 3, 1940, pp. 355–378.) In the language of the Trobrianders, there are no terms such as because, so as to, cause, reason, effect, purpose, to this end, so that, why. This does not mean that the Trobrianders are incapable of explaining a sequence in terms of cause and effect, but rather that this relationship is of no significance. In the texts given by Malinowski *for* (*pela*) occurs occasionally, in such a context that it is possible to translate it as *because*, as Malinowski does, and it sounds natural that one should do so; and, once or twice, "what-thing-for" is used in such a position that we can take it to mean "for what purpose." It is significant that *pela* is verbal, meaning *to jump*, not a connecting link but a leap to another. I shall not go here into discussion of the meaning of the doubtful *pela*; I do not think it is an expression of causality, but even if it is, it occurs extremely rarely and does not contradict the conclusion that, for the Trobriander, events do not automatically fall into the mold of causality or telelogy. Malinowski's frequent "why" evoked from the Trobrianders either confused and self-contradictory answers, or the usual "It was ordained of old,"—not an explanation but a description of value, tautological but necessary for the ignorant ethnographer.

We ask here, how is influence or motivation or effect phrased among the Trobrianders? How is magical action understood, for example? The answer is, it is understood in exactly these terms, as action, not cause. The magician does not *cause* certain things to be; he *does* them. As the gardener with his material implements burns the brush, breaks the clods, etc., so the garden magician with his various formulas "awakens the sprout," "drives up the shoots overground," "throws the headgear of the *taytu*," "makes several branches," "pushes the *taytu* tubers into the soil," according to Trobriand account. This is not influence, nor the force of magic; rather it is "to magic." Malinowski, in presenting accounts of magic, uses purposive phraseology, since in this way only can his readers understand magic. But where he gives in translation, "The *okwala* rite is made so that *taytu* might really grow, so that it might ripen," the Trobriand has actually said: "*okwala*, it-grow truly, it-ripen"; just a number of events. It so happens, in the example, that the sequence in the account corresponds to the actual order of fact; but quite often there is

not even such correspondence. And in the acts themselves there is often not even the sequence into which we could at least read causality. For example, when the Trobriander wants to fell a tree he first exorcizes the *tokway*, the tree-dwelling spirit, reciting a spell which gets the *tokway* down. After that he gives the *tokway* some food. If the food was offered first, on the ground, or at least promised, we could see this as a causal inducement. Actually, the *tokway* has no alternative and no freedom of choice at all; he is brought down by the spell. The offering of the food itself is merely part of the established procedure, and is not causally related to the exorcism.

It follows that the Trobriander performs acts because of the activity itself, not for its effects; that he values objects because they are good, not good for; in fact, objects and activities that are good for, are of no value to him. Take, for example, his yams and his yam gardening. To Malinowski, who spent many months with them, dependent upon them socially as well as materially, gardening meant yam gardening, and food meant yams. It was only after he had occupied himself with his Trobriander material for about fifteen years and written several books on the subject, that he realized that taro was an ancient and substantial item of food, much easier to grow than yams, less demanding of care and good soil, perhaps almost as important as yams from the point of view of sheer material nourishment. But taro is only good for; it is only good for food, or, less than that, for stopping hunger; and it is grown for such use. Therefore it was of no value or importance to the Trobriander, and escaped Malinowski's notice. Yams, on the other hand, incorporate the social good. They are good in themselves, and participate daily in good situations, as free, nonutile gifts.

A man gardens yams with the expenditure of much care and effort, with physical and magical skills, putting in long, hot hours of work. He gardens as many plots as he is capable of—not as many as his neighbors, or as many as he "needs." About half of these he sets aside as the *urigubu* plots. These he harvests with pride, exhibiting beautiful heaps of *taytu*. Then he sends this harvest, by festively arrayed youths and maidens, not to his yam house, but to the hamlet of his sister's husband. In this man's garden the *taytu* are heaped again, and it is this man now who exhibits them with pride as the gift. Finally, his yam house is put in order, and magic is performed in it. Ideally, the magic makes the *taytu* rot uneaten in the yam house; it fills the owners with nausea at the thought of eating the *taytu*; it gives them, instead, an urge to go to the bush and eat what grows there. This keeps the *taytu* free of purpose; ideally, they are not food. *Taytu* are constantly being given and received as gifts, in a system of free giving without what we call ulterior motives; not for altruism, not in barter or exchange for. Most of the gift *taytu* are usually eaten eventually, but only incidentally. In the *urigubu* gardens of the man who grew them, have remained all the tubers which are not *taytu*; the ones which are misshapen, or unduly small or blighted in some way. These go to the gardener's not-good yam house. They are merely to be eaten, and we do not hear of them again. The *taytu*, however, have a very important place in the everyday, as well as the ceremonial, life of the people. *Taytu* are not, like the taro, good for. *Taytu* have value, not use; value lies in being, not in relationship.

The pariahs among the Trobrianders are the people who barter. There is one such unfortunate district of highly skilled manufacturers who have no adequate soil for the growing of *taytu*. They barter manufactured articles, spending their time in this not-good occupation, but more than that, they are lacking in the growing of *taytu* and in pure gift-giving, that is, in good. They are greatly despised by the agricultural villages. The coastal villages also cannot grow many yams, and acquire more through what seems to us an exchange of fish for yams. However, this has been patterned along gift-giving lines, and escapes the purposiveness of barter. A man of a specific interior village will have a life-long gift-partner in a fishing village. Whenever he wants to, he arrives at the fishing village with some baskets of yams, and leaves them as a gift at a specific spot. This precipitates a pattern of events which ends in his returning home with a gift of fish. He cannot go to *any* village with his *taytu*, or to *any* man within this village; the gift to anyone else would have no meaning, neither would it induce anyone else to go fishing. His *taytu* were not pay or inducement, but the opening step

in a specific patterned procedure involving a specific individual.

Here another aspect of Trobriand being is involved. I have spoken of being as discrete, and apprehended as itself alone. I must now qualify this statement. Being has no independent existence. It is itself only as part of an established pattern. To members of our culture, being is defined by its attributes, relationships, and functions; temporally in terms of becoming, spatially in terms of its relationships. For the Trobrianders, being is defined by a fixed place in an established pattern. It is perhaps too much to ask my readers to believe that one element in a pattern can be and is perceived only in terms of its specific position within the pattern itself, and without reference to any other element; that in fact a pattern is conceived as something other than a system of relationships. Nevertheless, I believe such to be the case among the Trobrianders. Being is not seen in terms of its relationships to a plurality of elements in the pattern, but rather as a fixed point in a single, changeless whole. Only in this place can being be itself; only as it fills its place is it desired or valued. Being is good and true in terms of pattern. Gift-giving, for example, is good only within a patterned Trobriand situation. It is neither virtuous nor altruistic; both these terms involve meaningless relational concepts. In Trobriand gift-giving, the need of the recipient, or the effect upon him, is not involved. I doubt whether the Trobrianders could be persuaded to send yams to the starving Bikinians; and even if they did send yams, their act would not have value. The harvest gift to the sister's husband is not an act of altruism. The giver is concerned only with fulfilling his role, his place in a specific Trobriand pattern. If he gave taro to his sister's husband, the gift would not have been good; if he gave the yams to his own brother, his act would not have been good. What is good in this situation is the *urigubu*. To be good, this gift must be *urigubu*; to be true, that is, to be *urigubu*, it must be, (*a*) a gift of *taytu*; (*b*) from man to sister's husband; (*c*) at harvest time. Both the good and the true are defined by place in pattern. *Taytu* figure as gifts upon different occasions, between different individuals. In each case the gift is named and valued differently. When *taytu* are given to a friend at the launching of a canoe, they follow a different procedure, and are *kabigodoya;* when they are a harvest gift to a specialist, they are a *karibudaboda. Taytu,* then, are *urigubu, kabigodoya, karibudaboda,* according to their place in different patterns; and each gift derives different being, and different value in accordance to the pattern in which it has place. I should explain here that in each case the *taytu* remain *taytu* though they participate in different situations; it is the gift which is different according to its place in a different pattern.

This conception of being and value gave the early pearl traders much trouble. They found out soon that money or the things they offered were no inducement to work. They noticed, however, that the Trobrianders set great store by certain large blades made of stone. At first, they had these imitated carelessly, but found that the natives did not want them; then they had them made of slate in Europe, but these also were rejected by the Trobrianders. Finally they had the native stone quarried and sent to Parisian craftsmen; but these beautiful blades also were rejected. These things, of course, could not be valued, since they were not truly Trobriand, had not been made "as ordained of old"; but more than that, they could not be an inducement, and could have no meaning, since they were external to the pattern. When the Trobrianders were finally persuaded to dive for pay, it was only the natives of those villages which had always dived for oysters who were persuaded; those of the other coastal villages, where diving had not been ordained of old, would not dive. And the natives of the appropriate villages did so grudgingly. To the disgust of the pearl traders, they would leave their diving and go off fishing for the day, as soon as a number of baskets of yams made their appearance on the beach, even though the traders offered them twenty times as many yams. The natives would work for extraneous inducement as long as there was no good undertaking to indulge in; but when their gift-partners arrived with yams, they initiated a patterned situation which had meaning for the natives.

You will say, "But is not this an inducement or cause?" I think it is not. By themselves, the few baskets of yams on the beach are just a few baskets of yams. Offered by the trader they would have had no meaning. Brought from a different Trobriand village, they would have effected nothing; and when they come

from the appropriate village, it is only the partners of the specific givers who go off fishing as a matter of course. Given from anyone to anyone, the *taytu* are of no value. I think the yams are not an inducement to action. The giving of them, however, starts a pattern; once the gift has taken place, the pattern becomes evident and the recipient is presented with a role which holds value for him; to get satisfaction from it, to be a good Trobriander, he must fill it. By us, the two acts, the receiving of the yams and the procuring of the fish, are seen in relationship; and this relationship is seen as dynamic; one act influences the other, or causes the other. To the Trobriander, what is dynamic is the validity and value derived from the pattern. The coastal villager goes fishing because (this is my own word) he gets satisfaction from fulfilling his role in the pattern.

The appearance of the baskets of yams is not a cause, but it does precipitate a pattern. The Trobrianders have their own equivalent for cause, in terms of their concept of pattern. For this they use the term *u'ula,* a word very commonly used, for what we would call a variety of meanings. It stands for the trunk of a tree below the branches, for the base of a pole, or the bottom of a structure; it means the organizer of an expedition or the initiator of any undertaking; it refers to the first part of a magical formula. The *u'ula* is sometimes contemporaneous with the rest of the object or pattern, sometimes not. To the Trobriander, I think, it indicates place, not temporality. Realized or not, the pattern is always there; the pole has a bottom, the spell a beginning; and this pattern is known as a whole, not as a temporal process. Once made evident through the *u'ula,* the total must be realized. To this extent, and in our terms only, can we understand *u'ula* to be the equivalent of *cause;* the *u'ula* is dynamic but only in reference to the pattern, not toward the next event. The *u'ula* precipitates the next event but only incidentally, because it precipitates the patterned procedure, through its place in the pattern; it so happens that the next event is a part of this pattern.

This is how we can understand the "actual" and mythical behavior of the Trobrianders. For example, when an *uvalaku,* a *kula* expedition of a special kind, has been organized to sail to distant tribes where the Trobrianders will receive as gifts certain necklaces from specific partners, the chief gives a *kayguya'u*, a great ceremonial distribution of food. This is an act very serious in its implications, and performed after much consultation and deliberation; because, once this *kayguya'u* is given, the expedition must be carried out to its end, however unfavorable the winds, or the conditions within the village. Once the pattern has been initiated, has been given evidence, the whole must be realized, or, to put it differently, the whole is inevitably there; I am floundering here because my language cannot reproduce the Trobriand identity of the concepts underlying *has been, must be,* and *is.* Knowing the pattern, the Trobriander knows how to act to the end of the pattern. Conversely, the *kayguya'u* is an *u'ula*, has meaning, and can even be said to be itself, only by virtue of its place in the *uvalaku* pattern. Outside of it, it is just another food-distribution, initiating nothing, unless it is something else as part of another pattern.

For us, not only purpose, but previous action, is used as a basis or guide for determining what to do next. For the Trobriander, who does not see acts in relation, pattern is the guide; though actually it does not "lead" him to a decision, since his act is predetermined by the pattern. There is a sequence in one of the myths which exemplifies this. Toweyre kills his brother who has been acting in an un-Trobriand fashion, working for individual ends. This act of Toweyre is not part of a Trobriand pattern; however, this does not mean that he now has to come to an independent decision on how to act on the basis of murdering his brother. A brother's death itself initiates a pattern. As the next of kin (in Trobriand society, a man's children and his father are not his kin), Toweyre goes back to the village and instructs his dead brother's children to prepare the body for the funeral, and he himself arranges for the appropriate food distribution, the *sagali*.

Within the pattern the Trobriander feels safe and acts with assurance. Away from home, he likes to reproduce known previous order, even physically. When a food distribution, a *sagali*, is given to which many different hamlets from a distance are invited, the geographic location of these hamlets is reproduced on the beach. (I am afraid it is impossible for me to show conclusively that this is not an interest in relative position.) Again, in one of the myths is given a description of a shipwreck, a dreadful event since it plunges the sailors into witch-infested waters. The crew of the large canoe drift ashore clinging to the outrigger, onto which they have jumped from their places in the canoe. As they reach shore, they are in great danger from the flying witches; in the face of it, they walk in exactly the order in which they have drifted ashore; when they sit waiting for night to come and hide them from the witches, they maintain this order; in this order they finally march to their village where they are medicated magically to free them from danger. Now they are safe again, and the order need not be maintained. Again, it is impossible for us not to see here the order of lineal relationship; but I do not think that it appears as relational to the Trobrianders.

For members of our culture, value lies ideally in change, in moving away from the established pattern; and safety is ensured through scientific prediction, not exact experience. We hopefully expect next year to be better, brighter, different; if, as we hope, it brings change, we can safely meet it with the use of logic and science. Our advertisers thrive on this value of the different, the not-experienced; our industries have long depended on our love for new models. The Trobriander, on the contrary, expects and wants next year to be the same as this year and as the year before his culture emerged from underground. Advertising is nonsense for the Trobriander, because the new is not good and the old is known and valued, so to talk about it persuasively is nonsense. In repetition of the experienced, in sameness, he finds, not boredom, but satisfaction as well as safety. Members of our culture go into uncharted seas fearlessly, depending on compass and the science of navigation; they explore new lands eagerly. The Trobrianders go into *known* waters; they recount the *kula* myths, and then go from known landmark to known landmark, myth-imbued and full of history; they do not even set their course by the stars or the sun. They repeat old journeyings, their own or those of mythical or historical *kula* figures.

Something must be said here about individual and pattern; how does an individual Trobriander enter a pattern? There are various ways in which he does so and we in our culture would distinguish them according to the principle of whether he enters automatically, or whether he does so by act of will. By virtue of being born, an individual enters certain patterns of behavior in terms of certain people, those, for example, who are his relatives by blood or affinity. Here he has no choice; the pattern happens to him through the accident of his birth. Again, when his sister marries, or his wife dies, or his *kula* partner arrives, this precipitates a pattern of activities involving his participation, where he has no choice, unless, of course, he is ready to be un-Trobriand. There are certain patterns, however, where he does have freedom of choice; here, whether the pattern is to be precipitated or not, devolves on an act of will of his own. This is the only point where he does have freedom; once he initiates the pattern, he must follow an established procedure. However, I think the concept of freedom of choice is incommensurate with Trobriand value or behavior, and, in fact, a false measure. For us, to act as we want to act necessarily involves freedom of choice, but for the Trobriander the concept is meaningless. I think the Trobriander has no more and no less freedom when he initiates than when he continues an ordained pattern. In each case, he acts as he wants to, because the act, and the pattern which validates it, holds satisfaction for him; he acts in this way because he is Trobriand, and the pattern is Trobriand. To be Trobriand is to be good. "Act of will" and "freedom of choice" are irrelevant as principles of classification or evaluation.

Then comes the question of whether all beings are part of a pattern, and its corollary: is all being good? Is any being good apart from pattern? I do not think that all being is good; rather, that the good, or value, is found in being, but not in all being. There is much giving going on daily, but it is not good giving; it may be merely desultory giving from husband to wife or a man to his brother— gift situations which are not part of any gift pattern. Much of the unpatterned everyday behavior is not good; eating is not good, nor is love-magic, or love-making. On the other hand, some being is good apart from the pattern in which it participates. Such are the *vaygu'a* with which the pearl traders failed so miserably; such also is the *taytu*. In each case, the history of these is a pattern in itself. The *taytu*, for example, is planted and grown according to an ordained pattern. Each part of the procedure is inaugurated by a garden magician, and no member of the gardening group can act independently, can choose to leave his scrub not burned or have it burned at a different time, or set fire to it himself rather than wait for the magician to do the initial firing. At one time the resident magistrate ignorantly set fire to the scrub himself and thus initiated a year of drought. On the other hand, taro is not good; but none of the activities concerned with it are patterned. The gardener in this case proceeds as he likes, and incorporates whatever magic he chooses into the process. Ultimately, then, it is pattern that bestows value; but good being may incorporate its own pattern. Whether this is a difference between good being (*taytu* or *kula* givings) and not-good being (taro and gifts to one's brother) or whether it is rather a difference between being and mere existence, I am not qualified to say.

Is the Trobriander truly blind to relationship? Does he never respond to external motivation? The gardening of the Trobriander certainly can be seen as work toward the end of growing yams. Obviously—to us—when a man gives the harvest gift, this act brings giver and receiver into relation; how can the Trobriander fail to see this relation? We would say that it is impossible to have pattern without having elements in relation to one another. These objections are inherent to our own codification of reality. We make them because it is impossible for members of our culture to apprehend being without relationships. We can see motivation only as coming from outside, in relationship, and would therefore say that where we have acts there must be motivation, and where there is motivation relationships must be recognized. Again, we are accustomed to equate change with the dynamic, sameness with the static; and to put these pairs in opposition. So it is hard for us to see that sameness itself can be dynamic, as it is for the Trobriander, who does not need "motivation" for his acts, since their very sameness holds value, so that they "motivate" themselves.

These objections raise a further, and a more basic, question: is the Trobriander blind to relationships, or are there no relationships? Do we who base our behavior on relationships read these relationships into reality, or are they given? Which codification is true to reality? I would say that the two are not mutually exclusive. They represent different facets of reality and different meaningful phrasings for each culture. The fact that each culture has chosen to base itself on only one aspect does not mean that the other is false. Our peculiar codification makes us blind to other aspects of reality, or makes these meaningless when presented. But one codification does not exhaust reality; neither, if it were false, would a society, I believe, be able to survive with it at its base. The Trobrianders, according to our view of life, should be bored automatons. Actually they act as they want to act, poised and sure, in activities which hold meaning and satisfaction. Whether they are given or read into reality by us, temporality, causation, teleology, and relationship in general have neither meaning nor relevance for Trobriand behavior; but Trobriand behavior is nevertheless good because it is concerned with being; and being, in its appropriate pattern, incorporates value and truth.

*selection 42*

# The Aztec Writing System

## Charles E. Dibble

The Aztecs were highly skilled in the art of writing. As in many cultures, literacy was not the province of all but rather of a select few. An Aztec native trained and skilled in the art of recording the thoughts and events of the Aztecs was known as a *Tlacuilo.*

The art was often transmitted from father to son, the wisdom and skill of these select families being highly respected and appraised by the rulers. The reading of the codices was taught in the colleges where the priests initiated the novice in the ways of interpreting and deciphering the religious writings.

The materials utilized to provide a writing surface varied—the most common materials being deerskin, fiber paper and woven cotton cloth. A thin layer of chalk was often spread on the material to assure a smoother and whiter writing surface. The colors most commonly employed were shades of white, black, blue, red, green, yellow, and brown. The colors were essentially plant and mineral pig-

*This hitherto unpublished paper is used by permission of the author. Illustrations are by David E. Reiser.*

ments, luster and brilliance being supplied with oils, resins, and gums. Sometimes the figures were painted on both sides of a large sheet. Sometimes the codex formed a roll; more often the codex was in the form of a strip about twelve inches wide and several feet long, which strip was folded as a scenic post card.

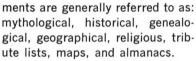

The order and manner of reading varied from codex to codex. Some were read from bottom to top, others from right to left or left to right and still others from top to bottom. Once the manner of reading is established it follows through consistently on the succeeding pages.

The content of codices was as varied as the topics they desired to record. The docu-

ments are generally referred to as: mythological, historical, genealogical, geographical, religious, tribute lists, maps, and almanacs.

Various stages in the development of writing were utilized side side in the Aztec documents. Many of the hieroglyphic recordings were pictographic, *i.e.*, the picture tells the story. Thus a temple in flames tells us of the destruction of a sanctuary by fire. Other portions of the same codices reveal recordings which are ideographic, *i.e.*, the important thing is the idea, abstract or concrete, which the picture calls forth rather than the picture itself. Two persons from d i f f e r e n t tribes in battle dress and poised for conflict express the idea of two tribes at war rather than two persons.

Cholula (Chololan) was an aboriginal religious center near present-day Puebla, Mexico. The name neams "Place of the Flight," because the city was on the road transversed by the mythological Quetzalcoatl in his flight to the East. *Choloa* is the Aztec verb for flee, run or jump. But, the deer is an animal which flees, runs and jumps. Thus the Aztec writers indicated the city of Cholula ideographically by painting the two front feet of

the deer. Also, much of the Aztec writing was syllabic or alphabetic, *i.e.*, the picture told no story; called forth no idea, but indicated a syllable or a single sound. The Aztec flag (*pantli*) could be used, not to recall a flag but the syllable  "pan." The word for teeth was  *tlantli*; so teeth could be pictured to indicate the syllable "tlan." Water (*atl*) was frequently utilized by the *Tlacuilo* when he desired to express the sound "a."

Thus the town "Apan" was indicated by combining water (*atl*) and flag (*pantli*).

"Atlan" was expressed by representing water (*atl*) and teeth (*tlantli*).

The Aztec numbering system was vigesimal. In our decimal system $10 \times 1 = 10$; $10 \times 10 = 100$; $10 \times 100 = 1,000$; $10 \times 1000 = 10,000$; etc. In the vigesimal system progression is by 20s: $20 \times 1 = 20$; $20 \times 20 = 400$; $20 \times 400 = 8,000$; $20 \times 8000 = 160,0000$, etc.

The Aztecs expressed numbers up to nineteen with dots. 1 was one dot ⊙ ; 3 was three dots ; 6 was six dots ; 19 was nineteen dots . Twenty was expressed with a flag.

Forty was expressed with two flags $(2 \times 20 = 40)$

Three hundred and eighty was indicated with nineteen flags $(19 \times 20 = 380)$.

The sign for 400 resembled a pine tree.

Eight hundred would be indicated with two pine trees (2 × 400 = 800).

The next unit, 8,000, was shown by a pouch for holding copal.

By combining these signs any number could be recorded; 8,859 would require one copal pouch (8,000),

two pine trees (2 × 400 = 800),

two flags (2 × 20 = 40),

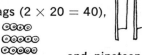

and nineteen dots.

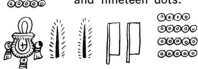

Important in Aztec hieroglyphic interpretation is their calendar system, because, without an accurate chronology, the historic material is rendered confused and almost valueless. They named their years after four objects, which also served as names of days. The first year was Rabbit (*Tochtli*);

the second year was Cane (*Acatl*);

the third year was Flint Knife (*Tecpatl*);

and the fourth year was House (*Calli*). The four always occurred in this order, and the sequence was never broken. However, to further differentiate the years, numerical coefficients from 1 to 13 were attached to the four "year bearers." Once the sequence of 1 to 13 was attached to the sequence of four the combination was never interrupted. By mathematical calculation it is apparent that the

same year sign will have the same numerical coefficient in $4 \times 13 = 52$ years.

This period of 52 years occasioned by the reoccurrence of the same year sign with the same numerical coefficient constituted the Aztec cycle. The completion of each cycle was the cause for festivity, celebration and the creation of a new sacred fire.

In the writing and interpreting of codices, certain conventionalized representations occurred with such frequency that a listing of them facilitates immeasurably the process of decipherment:

Women are recognized by posture,

hair dress,

and a garment known as *huipil*.

Man is distinguished by posture,

hair dress,

and the breech cloth (*maxtli*).

Old age was shown by wrinkles on the face.

A baby in a cradle-basket expresses birth.

Marriage is expressed by the husband facing the wife and the children of the couple appear below them. People were named after animals, birds, plants, and natural phenomena.

The name glyph was attached
to the nape of the neck.

Often, when the individual's name was of
secondary importance and his tribal affinity
was of paramount concern, the tribal hieroglyph was attached to the neck.

A mummy bundle seated on a mat-covered
throne means the death of a ruler.

A living person seated
on the same mat-covered throne tells us who
has been the successor.

Warfare is expressed by a shield and flag
(symbols of war),

or by means of two warriors in combat,

or by one warrior hold-
ing a prisoner by the hair of the head. Migration, or movement of a person, is told by
footprints, the direction of the footprints indicating the direction of travel.

A series of hieroglyphs can, of course, be combined to frame a full sentence.
For example,

A servant is pictured speaking with his emperor, Maxtla. The hieroglyphs in their order are: deer's feet (the deer being an animal which flees, his feet are used to express the verb "to flee"—*choloa*—see hieroglyph for *choloa* on page 271; Tlacateotzin (person); Texcoco (city); Nezahualcoyot! (person); canoe. The series is to be deciphered as: "Tlacateotzin fled, or is fleeing, with Nezahualcoyotl to or toward Texcoco in a canoe."

A second combination gives a more complex thought.

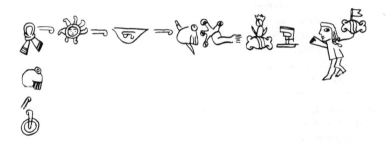

The historian, Ixtilxochitl, explains its meaning:

"The tyrant has ordered the taking of Chimalpopoca's life and the life of Tlacateotzin of Tlatelolco, that there should be neither king nor ruler of the Mexican and Aculhua nations, and that all should be subject to the domination of the court of the Tepaneca Monarch."

Deciphering the hieroglyphs of the series in their order, we conclude definitely that they give the content of the quotation. In order they are: skull (take the life of—an ideographic expression of death); Maxtla (name hieroglyph of the tyrant); Tlacateotzin (name hieroglyph of person); Tlatelolco (name hieroglyph of the city); skull with arrow (there should be neither king nor ruler); Aculhua (name hieroglyph of tribe or nation); house (be under the domain of the court of the monarch); and the last hieroglyph represents a Tepaneca warrior, indicating rule and domination.

# By Their Speech Shall Ye Know Them

## Clyde Kluckhohn and Dorothea Leighton

Any language is more than an instrument for the conveying of ideas, more even than an instrument for working upon the feelings of others and for self-expression. Every language is also a means of categorizing experience. What people think and feel, and how they report what they think and feel, is determined, to be sure, by their individual physiological state, by their personal history, and by what actually happens in the outside world. But it is also determined by a factor which is often overlooked; namely, the pattern of linguistic habits which people have acquired as members of a particular society. The events of the "real" world are never felt or reported as a machine would do it. There is a selection process and an interpretation in the very act of response. Some features of the external situation are highlighted; others are ignored or not fully discriminated.

Every people has its own characteristic classes in which individuals pigeonhole their experiences. These classes are established primarily by the language through the types of objects, processes, or qualities which receive special emphasis in the vocabulary and equally, though more subtly, through the types of differentiation or activity which are distinguished in grammatical forms. The language says, as it were, "Notice this," "Always consider this separate from that," "Such and such things belong together." Since persons are trained from infancy to respond in these ways they take such discriminations for granted, as part of the inescapable stuff of life. But when we see two people with different social traditions respond in different ways to what appear to the outsider to be identical stimulus-situations, we realize that

From the Tongue of the People. In The Navaho, Harvard University Press, 1948, pp. 197–208. Copyright 1946 by the President and Fellows of Harvard College. By permission of the author, the publisher, and the copyright holders.

experience is much less a "given," an absolute, than we thought. Every language has an effect upon what the people who use it see, what they feel, how they think, what they can talk about.

As pointed out in the section on grammar, [not given here] the language of The People delights in sharply defined categories. It likes, so to speak, to file things away in neat little packages. It favors always the concrete and particular, with little scope for abstractions. It directs attention to some features of every situation, such as the minute distinctions as to direction and type of activity. It ignores others to which English gives a place. Navaho focuses interest upon doing—upon verbs as opposed to nouns or adjectives.

Striking examples of the categories which mark the Navaho language are the variations in many of its verb stems according to the types of their subjects or objects. As has been illustrated above, the verb stem used often depends upon whether its subject (or object) is in the long-object class (such as a pencil, a stick, or a pipe), the granular-mass class (such as sugar and salt), the things-bundled-up class (such as hay and bundles of clothing), the animate-object class, and many others.

It must not be thought that such classification is a conscious process every time a Navaho opens his mouth to speak. It would, of course, paralyze speech if one had to think, when about to say a verb, "Now I must remember to specify whether the object is definite or indefinite; whether it is something round, long, fluid, or something else." Fortunately this is no more necessary in Navaho than in English. The Navaho child simply learns that if he is talking about dropping baseballs or eggs or stones he uses a word different from the word he would use if he spoke of dropping a knife or a pencil or a stick, just as the English-speaking child learns to use different words (herd, flock, crowd) in mentioning a group of cows, sheep, or people.

The important point is that striking divergences in manner of thinking are crystalized in and perpetuated by the forms of Navaho grammar. Take the example of a commonplace physical event: rain. Whites can and do report their perception of this event in a variety of ways: "It has started to rain," "It is raining," "It has stopped raining." The People can, of course, convey these same ideas—but they cannot convey them without finer specifications. To give only a few instances of the sorts of discrimination the Navaho must make before he reports his experience: he uses one verb form if he himself is aware of the actual inception of the rain storm, another if he has reason to believe that rain has been falling for some time in his locality before the occurrence struck his attention. One form must be employed if rain is general round about within the range of vision; another if, though it is raining round about, the storm is plainly on the move. Similarly, the Navaho must invariably distinguish between the ceasing of rainfall (generally) and the stopping of rain in a particular vicinity because the rain clouds have been driven off by wind. The People take the consistent noticing and reporting of such differences (which are usually irrelevant from the white point of view) as much for granted as the rising of the sun.

Navaho is an excessively literal language, little given to abstractions and to the fluidity of meaning that is so characteristic of English. The inner classification gives a concreteness, a specificity, to all expression. Most things can be expressed in Navaho with great exactness by manipulating the wide choice of stems in accord with the multitudinous alternatives offered by fusing prefixes and other separable elements in an almost unlimited number of ways. Indeed Navaho is almost overneat, overprecise. There is very little "give" in the language. It rather reminds one of a Bach fugue, in which everything is ordered in scrupulous symmetry.

The general nature of the difference between Navaho thought and English thought—both as manifested in the language and also as forced by the very nature of the linguistic forms into such patterns—is that Navaho thought is prevailingly so much more specific, so much more concrete. The ideas expressed by the English verb "to go" provide a nice example. To Germans the English language seems a little sloppy because the same word is used regardless of whether the one who goes walks or is transported by a train or other agency, whereas in German these two types of motion are always sharply distinguished in the two verbs *gehen* and *fahren*. But Navaho does much more along this line. For example, when one is talking about travel by horse, the speed of the animal may be expressed by the verb form chosen. The following all mean "I went by horseback."

*łį́į́ shił níyá,* (at a walk or at unspecified speed).

*łį́į́ shił yíldloozh,* (at a trot).

*łį́į́ shił neeltą́ą́ʼ,* (at a gallop).

*łį́į́ shił yílghod,* (at a run).

When a Navaho says that he went somewhere he never fails to specify whether it was afoot, astride, by wagon, auto, train, or airplane. This is done partly by using different verb stems which indicate whether the traveler moved under his own steam or was transported, partly by naming the actual means. Thus, "he went to town" would become:

*kintahgóó ʼííyá,* He went to town afoot or in a nonspecific way.

*kintahgóó bił ʼiʼííbą́ą́z,* He went to town by wagon.

*kintahgóó bił ʼoʼootʼaʼ,* He went to town by airplane.

*kintahgóó bił ʼiʼííʼééł,* He went to town by boat.

*kintahgóó bił ʼoʼooldloozh,* He went to town by horseback at a trot.

*kintahgóó bił ʼoʼooldghod,* He went to town by horseback at a run (or perhaps by car or train).

*kintahgóó bił ʼiʼnooltą́ą́ʼ,* He went to town by horseback at a gallop.

Moreover, the Navaho language insists upon another type of splitting up of the generic idea of "going" to which German is as indifferent as English. The Navaho always differentiates between starting to go, going along, arriving at, returning from a point, etc., etc. For instance, he makes a choice between:

*kintahgi níyá,* He arrived at town.

*kintahgóó ʼííyá,* He went to town and is still there.

*kintahgóó naayá,* He went to town but is now back where he started.

Let us take a few more examples. The Navaho interpreter, even though his behavior or side comments may make it perfectly apparent that he feels there is a difference, will translate both *háájish ʼííyá* and *háágósh ʼííyá* as

"where did he go." If you say to him, "The Navaho sounds different in the two cases and there must be some difference in English meaning," the interpreter is likely to reply, "Yes, there is a difference all right, but you just can't express it in English." Now this is not literally true. Almost anything which can be said in Navaho can be said in English and vice versa, though a translation which gets everything in may take the form of a long paraphrase which sounds strained and artificial in the second language. In the case of the examples given above, the nearest equivalents are probably: "in what direction did he leave" and "for what destination did he leave."

In English one might ask, "Where did he go" and the usual answer would be something like, "He went to Gallup." But in Navaho one would have to select one of eight or ten possible forms which, if rendered exactly into English, would come out something like this: "He started off for Gallup," "He left to go as far as Gallup," "He left by way of Gallup," "He left, being bound for Gallup (for a brief visit)," "He left, being bound for Gallup (for an extended stay)," etc.

The People are likewise particular about other differentiations, similar to some of those discussed earlier in this chapter:

*kin góneʼ yah ʼiikai,* We went into the house (in a group).

*kin góneʼ yah ʼahiikai,* We went into the (one after another).

or:

*chizh kin góne yahʼíínil,* I carried the wood into the house (in one trip).

*chizh kin góne yah ʼakénil,* I carried the wood into the house (in several trips).

It is not, of course, that these distinctions *cannot* be made in English but that they *are not* made consistently. They seem of importance to English-speakers only under special circumstances, whereas constant precision is a regular feature of Navaho thought and expression about movement.

The nature of their language forces The People to notice and to report many other distinctions in physical events which the nature of the English language allows speakers to neglect in most cases, even though their senses are just as able as those of the Navaho to register the smaller details of what goes on in the external world. For example, suppose a Navaho range rider and a white supervisor see that the wire fence surrounding a demonstration area is broken. The supervisor will probably write in his notebook only: "The fence is broken." But if the range rider reports the occurrence to his friends he must say either *béésh 'alc'ast'i* or *béésh 'alc'aat'i*; the first would specify that the damage has been caused by some person, the second that the agency was nonhuman. Further, he must choose between one of these statements and an alternative pair—the verb form selected depending on whether the fence was of one or several strands of wire.

Two languages may classify items of experience differently. The class corresponding to one word and one thought in Language A may be regarded by Language B as two or more classes corresponding to two or more words and thoughts. For instance, where in English one word "rough" (more pedantically, "rough-surfaced") may equally well be used to describe a road, a rock, and the business surface of a file, Navaho finds a need for three different words which may not be used interchangeably (see Figure 1). While the general tendency is for Navaho to make finer and more concrete distinctions, this is not invariably the case. The same stem is used for "rip," "light beam," and "echo," ideas which seem diverse to white people. One word is

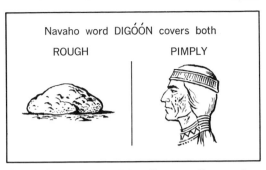

**Figure 2** Here, English will generally use two different words rather than the same one for both conditions.

used to designate a medicine bundle with all its contents, the skin quiver in which the contents are wrapped, the contents as a whole, and some of the distinct items of the contents. Sometimes the point is not that the images of Navahos are less fluid and more delimited but rather just that the external world is dissected along different lines. For example, *digóón* may be used to describe both a pimply face and a nodule-covered rock. In English a complexion might be termed "rough" or "coarse" but a rock would never, except facetiously, be described as "pimply." Navaho differentiates two types of "rough rock"—the kind which is rough in the manner in which a file is rough, and the kind which is nodule-encrusted. In these cases (see Figure 2) the difference between the Navaho and the English ways of seeing the world cannot be disposed of merely by saying that Navaho is more precise. The variation rests in the features which the two languages see as essential. Cases can even be given where Navaho is notably less precise: Navaho gets along with a single word

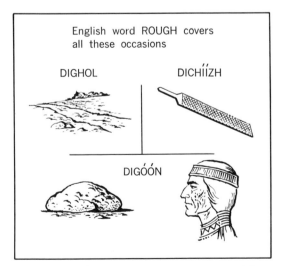

**Figure 1** In this case, Navaho distinguishes more kinds of roughness than does English.

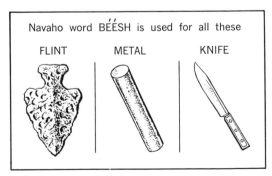

**Figure 3** These are all one sort in the Navaho view—mostly because metals and knives came to them at the same time to take the place of flint.

for flint, metal, knife, and certain other objects of metal (see Figure 3). This, to be sure, is due to the historical accident that, after European contact, metal in general and knives in particular largely took the place of flint. But in the last analysis most linguistic differentiations, like other sorts of cultural selectivity, rest upon the historical experience of the people.

How the Navaho and English languages dissect nature differently perhaps comes out most clearly when we contrast verbal statements. Take a simple event such as a person dropping something. The different "isolates of meaning" (thoughts) used in reporting this identical experience will be quite different in Navaho and in English (see Figure 4). The only two elements which are the same are "I" and "sh," both of which specify who does the dropping. A single image "drop" in Eng-

**Figure 4** "I drop it."

ENGLISH specifies
1. Subject: *I*
2. Type of action: *drop*
3. Time of action: while speaking or just before

NAVAHO specifies
1. Subject: *sh*
2. Direction of action: downward—*Naa*
3. Definite or indefinite object: (verb form)
4. Type of object: (verb stem) here a bulky, roundish, hard object—*Naa*
5. Amount of control of subject over process:

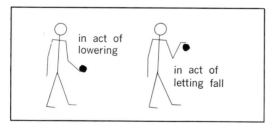

6. From area of the hand: *-lak'ee*

| *Naash'aah lak'ee* | *Naashne' lak'ee* |
|---|---|
| (I am in the act of lowering the definite, bulky, roundish, hard object from my hand.) | (I am in the act of letting the definite, bulky, roundish, hard object fall from my hand.) |

lish requires two complementary images (*naa* and *'aah*) in Navaho. English stops with what from the Navaho point of view is a very vague statement—"I drop it." The Navaho must specify four particulars which the English leaves either unsettled or to inference from context:
1. The form must make clear whether "it" is definite or just "something."
2. The verb stem used will vary depending upon whether the object is round, or long, or fluid, or animate, etc., etc.
3. Whether the act is in progress, or just about to start, or just about to stop or habitually carried on or repeatedly carried on must be rigorously specified. In English, "I drop it" can mean once or can mean that it is customarily done (e.g., in describing the process of getting water from my well by a bucket). All the other possibilities are also left by English to the imagination.
4. The extent to which the agent controls the fall must be indicated: *naash'aah* means "I am in the act of lowering the round object" but *naashne'* means "I am in the act of letting the round object fall."

To make the analysis absolutely complete, it must be pointed out that there is one respect in which the English is here a bit more exact. "I drop it" implies definitely (with the exception of the use of the "his-

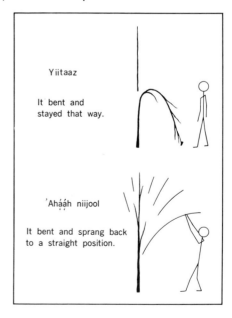

**Figure 5** "It bent."

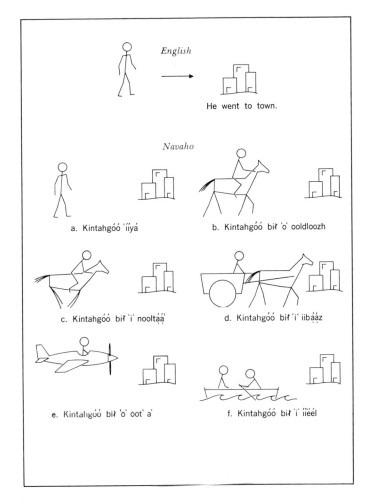

**Figure 6** "He went to town."

The verb here implies *means of locomotion* because, for example, b. and c. would be used mostly for a horse, d. for something that rolls, e. for something that flies. In b. and c., *speed of locomotion* is also indicated.

torical present") that the action occurs as the speaker talks or just an instant before, while the two Navaho verbs given above could, in certain circumstances, refer either to past or to future time. In other words, Navaho is more interested in the type of action (momentaneous, progressing, continuing, customary, etc.) than in establishing sequences in time as related to the moving present of the speaker.

Many other sorts of difference could be described, some of which are illustrated [on pages 282–284]. A full technical treatment would require a whole book to itself. The widest implications have been beautifully phrased by

one of the great linguists of recent times, Edward Sapir:

Language is not merely a more or less systematic inventory of the various items of experience which seem relevant to the individual, as is so often naively assumed, but is also a self-contained, creative symbolic organization, which not only refers to experience largely acquired without its help but actually defines experience for us by reason of its formal completeness and because of our unconscious projection of its implicit expectations into the field of experience. In this respect language is very much like a mathematical system which, also, records experience

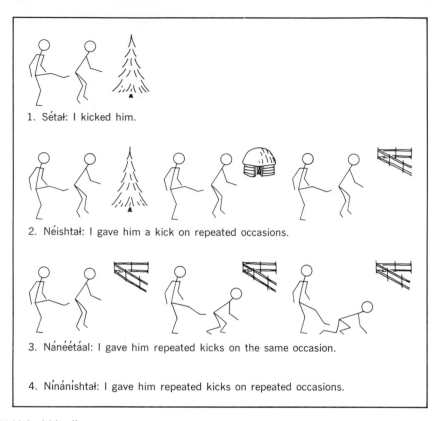

1. Sétał: I kicked him.

2. Néishtał: I gave him a kick on repeated occasions.

3. Náńéétáal: I gave him repeated kicks on the same occasion.

4. Nínánishtał: I gave him repeated kicks on repeated occasions.

**Figure 7** "I kicked him."

in the truest sense of the word, only in its crudest beginnings, but, as time goes on, becomes elaborated into a self-contained conceptual system which previsages all possible experience in accordance with certain accepted formal limitations. . . . [Meanings are] not so much discovered in experience as imposed upon it, because of the tyrannical hold that linguistic form has upon our orientation in the world. Inasmuch as languages differ very widely in their systematization of fundamental concepts, they tend to be only loosely equivalent to each other as symbolic devices and are, as a matter of fact, incommensurable in the sense in which two systems of points in a plane are, on the whole, incommensurable to each other, if they are plotted out with reference to differing systems of coordinates . . .

In many ways the Navaho classifications come closer to a freshly objective view of the nature of events than do those of such languages as English or Latin. . . .

*part 8*

# *Society and Culture*

# The Symbol: The Origin and Basis of Human Behavior

## Leslie A. White

### I

*From* Etc.: A Review of General Semantics, *Vol. 1, 1944, pp. 229–237. By permission of the author and the publisher.*

In July, 1939, a celebration was held at Leland Stanford University to commemorate the hundredth anniversary of the discovery that the cell is the basic unit of all living tissue. Today we are beginning to realize and to appreciate the fact that the symbol is the basic unit of all human behavior and civilization.

All human behavior originates in the use of symbols. It was the symbol which transformed our anthropoid ancestors into men and made them human. All civilizations have been generated, and are perpetuated, only by the use of symbols. It is the symbol which transforms an infant of *Homo sapiens* into a human being; deaf mutes who grow up without the use of symbols are not human beings. All human behavior consists of, or is dependent upon, the use of symbols. Human behavior is symbolic behavior; symbolic behavior is human behavior. The symbol is the universe of humanity.

### II

The great Darwin declared that "there is no fundamental difference between man and the higher mammals in their mental faculties," that the difference between them consists "solely in his [man's] almost infinitely larger power of associating together the most diversified sounds and ideas." Thus the difference between the mind of man and that of other mammals is merely one of degree, and it is not "fundamental."

Essentially the same views are held by many present day students of human behavior. Professor Ralph Linton, an anthropologist, writes: "The differences between men and animals in all these [behavior] respects are enormous, but they seem to be differences in quantity rather than in quality." "Human and animal behavior can be shown to have so much in common," Professor Linton observes, "that the gap [between them] ceases to be of great importance." Dr. Alexander Goldenweiser, likewise an anthropologist, believes that "in point of sheer psychology, mind as such, man is after all no more than a talented animal" and "the difference between the mentality here displayed [by a horse and a chimpanzee] and that of man is merely one of degree."

That there are numerous and impressive similarities between the behavior of man and that of apes is fairly obvious; it is quite possible that even chimpanzees in zoos have noted and appreciated them. Fairly apparent, too, are man's behavioral similarities to many other kinds of animals. Almost as obvious, but not easy to define, is a difference in behavior which distinguishes man from all other living creatures. I say "obvious" because it is quite apparent to the common man that the nonhuman animals with which he is familiar do not and cannot enter, and participate in, the world in which he, as a human being, lives. It is impossible for a dog, horse, bird, or even an ape, ever to have *any* understanding of the meaning of the sign of the cross to a Christian, or of the fact that black (white among the Chinese) is the color of mourning. But when the scholar attempts to *define* the mental difference between animal and man he sometimes encounters difficulties which he cannot surmount and, therefore, ends up by saying that the difference is merely one of degree: man has a bigger mind, "larger power of association," wider range of activities, etc.

There is a *fundamental* difference between the mind of man and the mind of nonman. This difference is one of kind, not one of degree. And the gap between the two types is of the greatest importance—at least to the science of comparative behavior. Man uses symbols; no other creature does. A creature either uses symbols or he does not; there are no intermediate stages.

## III

A symbol is a thing the value or meaning of which is bestowed upon it by those who use

it. I say "thing" because a symbol may have any kind of physical form; it may have the form of a material object, a color, a sound, an odor, a motion of an object, a taste.

The meaning, or value, of a symbol is in no instance derived from or determined by properties intrinsic in its physical form: the color appropriate to mourning may be yellow, green, or any other color; purple need not be the color of royalty; among the Manchu rulers of China it was yellow. The meaning of the word "see" is not intrinsic in its phonetic (or pictorial) properties. "Biting one's thumb at" someone [used by Shakespeare in *Romeo and Juliet*,] might mean anything. The meanings of symbols are derived from and determined by the organisms who use them; meaning is bestowed by human organisms upon physical forms which thereupon become symbols.

All symbols must have a physical form otherwise they could not enter our experience. But the meaning of a symbol cannot be perceived by the senses. One cannot tell by looking at an $x$ in an algebraic equation what it stands for; one cannot ascertain with the ears alone the symbolic value of the phonetic compound $si$; one cannot tell merely by weighing a pig how much gold he will exchange for; one cannot tell from the wave length of a color whether it stands for courage or cowardice, "stop" or "go"; nor can one discover the spirit in a fetish by any amount of physical or chemical examination. The meaning of a symbol can be communicated only by symbolic means, usually by articulate speech.

But a thing which in one context is a symbol is, in another context, not a symbol but a sign. Thus, a word is a symbol only when one is concerned with the distinction between its meaning and its physical form. This distinction *must* be made when one bestows value upon a sound-combination or when a previously bestowed value is discovered for the first time; it *may* be made at other times for certain purposes. But after value has been bestowed upon, or discovered in, a word, its meaning becomes identified, in use, with its physical form. The word then functions as a sign rather than a symbol. (A *sign* is a physical form whose function is to indicate some other thing—object, quality, or event. The meaning of a sign may be intrinsic, inseparable from its physical form and nature, as in the case of the height of a column of mercury as an indication of temperature; or it may be merely identified with its physical form, as in the case of a hurricane signal displayed by a weather bureau. But in either case, the meaning of the sign is perceived by the senses.) . . . This fact that a thing may be both symbol (in one context) and non-symbol (in another context) has led to some confusion and misunderstanding.

Thus Darwin says, "That which distinguishes man from the lower animals is not the understanding of articulate sounds, for as everyone knows, dogs understand many words and sentences."

It is perfectly true, of course, that dogs, apes, horses, birds, and perhaps creatures even lower in the evolutionary scale, can be taught to respond in a specific way to a vocal command. But it does not follow that no difference exists between the meaning of "words and sentences" to a man and to a dog. Words are both signs and symbols to man; they are merely signs to a dog. Let us analyze the situation of vocal stimulus and response.

A dog can be taught to roll over at the command "Roll over!" A man can be taught to stop at the command "Halt!" The fact that a dog can be taught to roll over in Chinese, or that he can be taught to "go fetch" at the command "roll over" (and, of course, the same is true for a man) shows that there is no necessary and invariable relationship between a particular sound combination and a specific reaction to it. The dog or the man can be taught to respond in a certain manner, to *any* arbitrarily selected combination of sounds, for example, a group of nonsense syllables, coined for the occasion. On the other hand, any one of a great number and variety of responses may become evocable by a given stimulus. Thus, so far as the *origin* of the relationship between vocal stimulus and response is concerned, the nature of the relationship, *i.e.*, the meaning of the stimulus, is not determined by properties intrinsic in the stimulus.

But, once the relationship has been established between vocal stimulus and response, the meaning of the stimulus becomes *identified with the sounds*; it is then *as if* the meaning were intrinsic in the sounds themselves. Thus, "halt" does not have the same meaning as "hilt" or "malt." A dog may be conditioned to respond in a certain way to a sound of a

given wave length. Sufficiently alter the pitch of the sound and the response will cease to be forthcoming. The meaning of the stimulus has become identified with its physical form; its value is perceived with the senses.

Thus we see that in establishing a relationship between a stimulus and a response the properties intrinsic in the stimulus do not determine the nature of the response. But, *after the relationship has been established* the meaning of the stimulus is *as if* it were *inherent* in its physical form. It does not make any difference what phonetic combination we select to evoke the response of terminating self-locomotion. We may teach a dog, horse, or man to stop at any vocal command we care to choose or devise. But once the relationship has been established between sound and response, the meaning of the stimulus becomes identified with its physical form and is, therefore, perceivable with the senses.

So far we have discovered no difference between the dog and the man; they appear to be exactly alike. And so they are as far as we have gone. But we have not told the whole story yet. No difference between dog and man is discoverable so far as learning to respond appropriately to a vocal stimulus is concerned. But we must not let an impressive similarity conceal an important difference. A porpoise is not yet a fish.

The man differs from the dog—and all the other creatures—in that *he can and does play an active role in determining what value the vocal stimulus is to have, and the dog cannot*. As John Locke aptly put it, "All sounds [*i.e.*, in language] . . . have their signification from the arbitrary imposition of men." The dog does not and cannot play an active part in determining the value of the vocal stimulus. Whether he is to roll over or go fetch at a given stimulus, or whether the stimulus for roll over be one combination of sounds or another is a matter in which the dog has nothing whatever to "say." He plays a purely passive role and can do nothing else. He learns the meaning of a vocal command just as his salivary glands may learn to respond to the sound of a bell. But man plays an active role and thus becomes a creator: Let *x* equal three pounds of coal and it does equal three pounds of coal; let removal of the hat in a house of worship indicate respect and it becomes so. This creative faculty, that of freely, actively, and arbitrarily bestowing value upon things, is one of the most commonplace as well as *the* most important characteristic of man. Children employ it freely in their play: "Let's pretend that this rock is a wolf."

The difference between the behavior of man and other animals, then, is that the lower animals may receive new values, may acquire new meanings, but they cannot create and bestow them. Only man can do this. To use a crude analogy, lower animals are like a person who has only the receiving apparatus for wireless messages; he can receive messages but he cannot send them. Man can do both. And this difference is one of kind, not of degree; a creature can either "arbitrarily impose signification," to use Locke's phrase, can either create and bestow values, or he cannot. There are no intermediate stages. (Professor Linton, speaks of "the faintest foreshadowings of language . . . at the animal level," but precisely what these "faintest foreshadowings" are he does not say.) This difference may appear slight, but, as a carpenter once told William James in discussing differences between men, "it's very important." All *human* existence depends upon it and it alone.

The confusion regarding the nature of words and their significance to men and the lower animals is not hard to understand. It arises, first of all, from a failure to distinguish between the two quite different contexts in which words function. The statements, "The meaning of a word cannot be perceived with the senses," and "The meaning of a word can be perceived with the senses," though contradictory, are nevertheless equally true. (What we have to say here would, of course, apply equally well to gestures—*e.g.*, the "sign of the cross," a salute—a color, a material object, etc.) In the *symbol* context the meaning cannot be perceived with the senses; in the *sign* context it can. This is confusing enough. But the situation has been made worse by using the words "symbol" and "sign" to label, not the *different contexts*, but *one and the same thing:* the word. Thus a word is a symbol *and* a sign, two different things. It is like saying that a vase is a *doli* and a *kana*— two different things—because it may function in two contexts, esthetic and commercial. (Like a word, the value of a vase may be perceived by the senses or be imperceptible to them depending upon the context in which

it is regarded. In an esthetic context its value is perceived with the senses. In the commercial context this is impossible; we must be *told* its value—in terms of price.)

That which is a *symbol* in the context of origination becomes a *sign* in use thereafter. Things may be either signs or symbols to man; they can be only signs to other creatures.

## IV

Very little indeed is known of the organic basis of the symbolic faculty; we know next to nothing of the neurology of symbolizing. And very few scientists—anatomists, neurologists, physical anthropologists—appear to be interested in the problem. Some, in fact, seem to be unaware of the existence of such a problem. The duty and task of giving an account of the organic basis of symbolizing does not fall within the province of the sociologist or the cultural anthropologist. On the contrary, he should scrupulously exclude it as irrelevant to his problems and interests; to introduce it would bring only confusion. It is enough for the sociologist or cultural anthropologist to take the ability to use symbols, possessed by man alone, as given. The use to which he puts this fact is in no way affected by his, or even the anatomist's, inability to describe the symbolic process in neurological terms. However it is well for the social scientist to be acquainted with the little that neurologists and anatomists do know about the structural basis of "symboling." We, therefore, review briefly the chief relevant facts here.

The anatomist has not been able to discover why men can use symbols and apes cannot. So far as is known the only difference between the brain of man and the brain of an ape is a quantitative one: ". . . man has no new kinds of brain cells or brain cell connections." Nor does man, as distinguished from other animals, possess a specialized "symbol-mechanism." The so-called speech areas of the brain should not be identified with symbolizing. These areas are associated with the muscles of the tongue, larynx, etc. But symbolizing is not dependent upon these organs. One may symbolize with the fingers, the feet, or with any part of the body that can be moved at will. (The misconception that speech is dependent upon the so-called [but miscalled] organs of speech, and, furthermore, that man alone has organs suitable for speech, is not uncommon even today. Thus Professor L. L. Bernard lists "The fourth great organic asset of man is his vocal apparatus, also characteristic of him alone."

The great apes have the mechanism necessary for the production of articulate sounds: "It seemingly is well established that the motor mechanism of voice in this ape [chimpanzee] is adequate not only to the production of a considerable variety of sounds, but also to definite articulations similar to those of man." Also: "All of the anthropoid apes are vocally and muscularly equipped so that they could have an articular language if they possessed the requisite intelligence."

Furthermore, the mere production of articulate sounds would not be symbolizing any more than the mere "understanding of words and sentences" is. John Locke made this clear two and a half centuries ago: "Man, therefore had by nature his organs so fashioned, as to be *fit to frame articulate sounds, which we call words.* But this was not enough to produce language; for parrots, and several other birds, will be taught to make articulate sounds distinct enough, which yet, by no means, are capable of language. Besides articulate sounds, therefore, it was further necessary, that he should be *able to use these sounds as signs of internal conceptions;* and to make them stand as marks for the ideas within his own mind, whereby they might be made known to others. . . ."

And J. F. Blumenbach, a century later, declared, . . . "That speech is the work of reason alone, appears from this, that other animals, although they have nearly the same organs of voice as man, are entirely destitute of it" [quoted, Yerkes and Yerkes, 1929, p. 23]).

To be sure, the symbolic faculty was brought into existence by the natural processes of organic evolution. And we may reasonably believe that the focal point, if not the locus, of this faculty is in the brain, especially the forebrain. Man's brain is much larger than that of an ape, both absolutely and relatively. (Man's brain is about two and one-half times as large as that of a gorilla. "The human brain is about 1/50 of the entire body weight, while that of a gorilla varies from 1/150 to 1/200 part of that weight.")

And the forebrain especially is large in man as compared with ape. Now in many situations we know that quantitative changes give rise to qualitative differences. Water is transformed into steam by additional quantities of heat. Additional power and speed lift the taxiing airplane from the ground and transform terrestrial locomotion into flight. The difference between wood alcohol and grain alcohol is a qualitative expression of a quantitative difference in the proportions of carbon and hydrogen. Thus a marked growth in size of the brain in man may have brought forth a *new kind* of function.

## V

All culture (civilization) depends upon the symbol. It was the exercise of the symbolic faculty that brought culture into existence and it is the use of symbols that makes the perpetuation of culture possible. Without the symbol there would be no culture, and man would be merely an animal, not a human being.

Articulate speech is the most important form of symbolic expression. Remove speech from culture and what would remain? Let us see.

Without articulate speech we would have no *human* social organization. Families we might have, but this form of organization is not peculiar to man; it is not *per se, human.* But we would have no prohibitions of incest, no rules prescribing exogamy and endogamy, polygamy or monogamy. How could marriage with a cross cousin be prescribed, marriage with a parallel cousin proscribed, without articulate speech? How could rules which prohibit plural mates possessed simultaneously but permit them if possessed one at a time, exist without speech?

Without speech we would have no political, economic, ecclesiastic, or military organization; no codes of etiquette or ethics; no laws; no science, theology, or literature; no games or music, except on an ape level. Rituals and ceremonial paraphernalia would be meaningless without articulate speech. Indeed, without articulate speech we would be all but toolless; we would have only the occasional and insignificant use of the tool such as we find today among the higher apes, for it was articulate speech that transformed the nonprogressive tool-using of the ape into the progressive, cumulative tool-using of man, the human being.

In short, without symbolic communication in some form, we would have no culture. "In the Word was the beginning" of culture—and its perpetuation also. ("On the whole, however, it would seem that language and culture rest, in a way which is not fully understood, on the same set of faculties. . . ." It is hoped that this essay will make this matter more "fully understood.")

To be sure, with all this culture man is still an animal and strives for the same ends that all other living creatures strive for: the preservation of the individual and the perpetuation of the race. In concrete terms these ends are food, shelter from the elements, defense from enemies, health, and offspring. The fact that man strives for these ends just as all other animals do has, no doubt, led many to declare that there is "no fundamental difference between the behavior of man and of other creatures." But man does differ, not in *ends* but in *means*. Man's means are cultural means: culture is simply the human animal's way of living. And, since these means, culture, are dependent upon a faculty possessed by man alone, the ability to use symbols, the difference between the behavior of man and of all other creatures is not merely great, but basic and fundamental.

## VI

The behavior of man is of two distinct kinds: symbolic and nonsymbolic. Man yawns, stretches, coughs, scratches himself, cries out in pain, shrinks with fear, "bristles" with anger, and so on. Nonsymbolic behavior of this sort is not peculiar to man; he shares it not only with other primates but with many other animal species as well. But man communicates with his fellows with articulate speech, uses amulets, confesses sins, makes laws, observes codes of etiquette, explains his dreams, classifies his relatives in designated categories, and so on. This kind of behavior is unique; only man is capable of it; it is peculiar to man because it consists of, or is dependent upon, the use of symbols. The nonsymbolic behavior of man is the behavior of man the animal; the symbolic behavior is that of man the human being.

It is the symbol which has transformed man from a mere animal to a human animal. (It is for this reason that observations and experiments with apes, rats, etc., can tell us nothing about human behavior. They can tell us how ape-like or rat-like man is, but they throw no light upon human behavior because the behavior of apes, rats, etc., is nonsymbolic.

The title of the late George A. Dorsey's best seller, *Why We Behave Like Human Beings*, was misleading for the same reason. This interesting book told us much about vertebrate, mammalian, primate, and even man-animal behavior, but virtually nothing about symbolic, *i.e.*, human behavior. But we are glad to add, in justice to Dorsey, that his chapter on the function of speech in culture in *Man's Own Show: Civilization*, is probably the best discussion of this subject that we know of in anthropological literature.)

As it was the symbol that made mankind human, so it is with each member of the race. A baby is not a human being so far as his behavior is concerned. Until the infant acquires speech there is nothing to distinguish his behavior qualitatively from that of a young ape.

The baby becomes a human being when and as he learns to use symbols. Only by means of speech can the baby enter and take part in the human affairs of mankind. The questions we asked previously may be repeated now. How is the growing child to know of such things as families, etiquette, morals, law, science, philosophy, religion, commerce, and so on, without speech? The rare cases of children who grew up without symbols because of deafness and blindness, such as those of Laura Bridgman, Helen Keller and Marie Heurtin, are instructive. Until they "got the idea" of symbolic communication they were not human beings, but animals; they did not participate in behavior which is peculiar to human beings. They were *in* human society as dogs are, but they were not *of* human society. And, although the present writer is exceedingly skeptical of the reports of the so-called "wolf-children," "feral men," etc., we may note that they are described, almost without exception, as without speech, "beastly," and "inhuman." (In their fascinating account of their experiment with a baby chimpanzee, kept for nine months in their home and treated as their infant son was treated, Professor and Mrs. Kellogg speak of the "humanization" of the little ape: "She may thus be said to have become 'more humanized' than the human subject. . . ."

This is misleading. What the experiment showed so strikingly was *how like an ape a child of Homo sapiens* is *before he learns to talk.* The boy even employed the ape's "food bark"! The experiment also demonstrated the ape's utter inability to learn to talk, which means an inability to become humanized at all.)

## VII

SUMMARY  The natural processes of organic evolution brought into existence in man, and man alone, a new and distinctive ability: the ability to use symbols. The most important form of symbolic expression is articulate speech. Artic-

ulate speech means communication of ideas; communication means preservation—tradition—and preservation means accumulation and progress. The emergence of the organic faculty of symbol-using has resulted in the genesis of a new order of phenomena: a superorganic, or cultural, order. All civilizations are born of, and are perpetuated by, the use of symbols. A culture, or civilization, is but a particular kind of form (symbolic) which the biologic, life-perpetuating activities of a particular animal, man, assume.

Human behavior is symbolic behavior; if it is not symbolic, it is not human. The infant of the genus *homo* becomes a human being only as he is introduced into and participates in that supraorganic order of phenomena which is culture. And the key to this world and the means of participation in it is the symbol.

*selection  45*

# The Superorganic

*A. L. Kroeber*

*From* The Nature of Culture. *University of Chicago Press, 1952, pp. 22–51. Copyright 1952, University of Chicago. By permission of the publisher and copyright holder.*

*Originally published in the "American Anthropologist," this essay was reprinted with stylistic revisions ten years later by the Sociological Press of Hanover, New Hampshire. For many years now, the article has excited little stir among anthropologists, presumably because its contentions have largely passed into their common body of assumptions. It has however continued to attract some interest among sociologists, historians, and social scientists generally, for which reason it is included here without abbreviation.*

*In the vista of a third of a century, the essay appears like an antireductionist proclamation of independence from the dominance of the biological explanation of sociocultural phenomena. Yet, as I look back, I cannot recall, in the two decades preceding 1917, any instances of oppression or threatened annexation by biologists. What was hanging over the study of culture, as I sense it now, was rather*

*a diffused public opinion, a body of unaware as-*
*sumptions, that left precarious the autonomous rec-*
*ognition of society, and still more that of culture.*
*It was the intelligent man on the street and those*
*who wrote for him, social philosophers like Herbert*
*Spencer, Lester Ward, Gustave Le Bon—it was*
*against their influence that I was protesting. The*
*biologists, in fact, were generally ignoring society*
*and culture. The few who did not ignore it, like*
*Galton and Pearson, presented analyzed evidence*
*that was handleable and might therefore be con-*
*strued also in a contrary sense. Indeed, Galton has*
*always evoked my complete respect and has been*
*one of the largest intellectual influences on me.*
*What the essay really protests is the blind and bland*
*shuttling back and forth between an equivocal*
*"race" and an equivocal "civilization"—a shuttling*
*that is referred to at the end of one of the middle*
*paragraphs. That confusion was certainly still prev-*
*alent at the time.*

*Two reservations are necessary in mid-twentieth*
*century. First, society and culture can no longer be*
*simply bracketed as "the social," as was customary*
*then, in contrast to "the organic." In most contexts*
*they are separable, and it is preferable to distin-*
*guish them. When the meaning is clearly inclusive,*
*that fact can now be made clear by the use of*
*"sociocultural," as is Sorokin's consistent practice.*
*It was Bernhard Stern who pointed out in "Social*
*Forces" in 1929 that my "social" in this essay was*
*ambiguous. Ants and termites possess societies but*
*no culture. Only man has both, necessarily always*
*associated, though conceptually differentiable. Hazi-*
*ness today about the distinction is an intellectual*
*fault only a little less gross than confusion of the*
*organic and the superorganic. That my "super-*
*organic" of 1917 referred essentially to culture is*
*clear not only from all the concrete evidence cited*
*but from the constant use of "civilization," "cul-*
*tur," "history," and their adjectival forms. Of the*
*final twenty paragraphs, only three do not contain*
*one or more occurrences of these interchangeably*
*used terms. I should feel happier if I had been*
*farsighted enough in 1917 consistently to say "cul-*
*tural" or "sociocultural" wherever I did instead*
*say "social" in a mistaken attempt to conform to*
*prevalent usage—to pour new wine into the old*
*bottle. Still I did not, I think, anywhere in the*
*essay discuss or name "society," which fact shows*
*that when I said "the social" I used it either in a*
*wider sense to include culture or in a limiting*
*sense to denote culture outright.*

*Second, I retract, as unwarranted reification, the*
*references in the fourteenth, tenth, and sixth para-*
*graphs from the last and in the final paragraph to*
*organic and superorganic "substances," entities, or*
*fabrics. While it certainly is often needful to view*
*different kinds of phenomena as of different orders*
*and to deal wtih them on separate levels of appre-*
*hension, there is no need for metaphysically constru-*
*ing levels of conception or orders of attribute into*
*substantial entities or different kinds of substance.*

*The notion expressed in the seventy-third para-*
*graph that civilization or culture "is not mental*
*action but a body or stream of products of mental*
*exercise" may be contested—apart from its some-*
*what old-fashioned wording—but is still being ar-*
*gued today. We seem not yet to have attained a*
*concise, unambiguous, inclusive, and exclusive defi-*
*nition of culture.*

*I am conscious of a degree of rhetorical ponder-*
*ousness in the phrasing of the essay. I trust this*
*will be forgiven—as it has been in the past—as a*
*by-product of the fervor of realizations that at the*
*time seemed both new and important. The 1927*
*wording has been retained unaltered except for one*
*change of a preposition.*

A way of thought characteristic of our western civilization has been the formulation of
complementary antitheses, a balancing of exclusive opposites. One of these pairs of ideas
with which our world has been laboring for
some two thousand years is expressed in the
words *body* and *soul*. Another couplet that has
served its useful purpose, but which science
is now often endeavoring to rid itself of, at
least in certain aspects, is the distinction of
the *physical* from the *mental*. A third discrimination is that of the *vital* from the *social*, or
in other phraseology, of the *organic* from the
*cultural*. The implicit recognition of the difference between organic qualities and processes and social qualities and processes is of
long standing. The formal distinction is however recent. In fact the full import of the
significance of the antithesis may be said to
be only dawning upon the world. For every
occasion on which some human mind sharply
separates organic and social forces, there are
dozens of other times when the distinction
between them is not thought of, or an actual
confusion of the two ideas takes place.

One reason for this current confusion of
the organic and the social is the predominance, in the present phase of the history
of thought, of the idea of evolution. This idea,
one of the earliest, simplest, and also vaguest
ever attained by the human mind, has received its strongest ground and fortification
in the domain of the organic; in other words,
through biological science. At the same time,
there is an evolution, or growth, or gradual
development, apparent also in other realms

than that of plant and animal life. We have theories of stellar or cosmic evolution; and there is obvious, even to the least learned, a growth or evolution of civilization. In the nature of things there is little danger of the carrying over of the Darwinian or post-Darwinian principles of the evolution of life into the realm of burning suns and lifeless nebulae. Human civilization or progress, on the other hand, which exists only in and through living members of the species, is outwardly so similar to the evolution of plants and animals, that it has been inevitable that there should have been sweeping applications of the principles of organic development to the facts of cultural growth. This of course is reasoning by analogy, or arguing that because two things resemble each other in one point they will also be similar in others. In the absence of knowledge, such assumptions are justifiable as assumptions. Too often, however, their effect is to predetermine mental attitude, with the result that when the evidence begins to accumulate which could prove or disprove the assumption based on analogy, this evidence is no longer viewed impartially and judiciously, but is merely distributed and disposed of in such a way as not to interfere with the established conviction into which the original tentative guess has long since turned.

This is what has happened in the field of organic and social evolution. This distinction between them, which is so obvious that to former ages it seemed too commonplace to remark upon, except incidentally and indirectly, has been largely obscured in the last fifty years through the hold which thoughts connected with the idea of organic evolution have had on minds of the time. It even seems fair to say that this confusion has been greater and more general among those to whom study and scholarship are a daily pursuit than to the remainder of the world.

And yet many aspects of the difference between the organic and that in human life which is not organic, are so plain that a child can grasp them, and that all human beings, including the veriest savages, constantly employ the distinction. Everyone is aware that we are born with certain powers and that we acquire others. There is no need of argument to prove that we derive some things in our lives and make-up from nature through heredity, and that other things come to us through agencies with which heredity has nothing to do. No one has yet been found to assert that any human being is born with an inherent knowledge of the multiplication table; nor, on the other hand, to doubt that the children of a negro are born negroes through the operation of hereditary forces. Some qualities in every individual are however clearly debatable ground; and when the development of civilization as a whole and the evolution of life as a whole are compared, the distinction of the processes involved has too often been allowed to lapse.

Some millions of years ago, it is currently taught, natural selection, or some other evolutionary agency, first caused birds to appear in the world. They sprang from reptiles. Conditions were such that the struggle for existence on the earth was hard; while in the air there were safety and room. Gradually, either by a series of almost imperceptible gradations through a long line of successive generations, or by more marked and sudden leaps in a shorter period, the group of birds was evolved from its reptilian ancestors. In this development, feathers were acquired and scales lost; the grasping faculty of the front legs was converted into an ability to sustain the body in the air. The advantages of resistance enjoyed by a cold-blooded organization were given up for the equivalent or greater compensation of the superior activity that goes with warm-bloodedness. The net result of this chapter of evolutionary history was that a new power, that of aerial locomotion, was added to the sum total of faculties possessed by the highest group of animals, the vertebrates. The vertebrate animals as a whole, however, were not affected. The majority of them are without the power of flight as their ancestors were millions of years ago. The birds, in turn, had lost certain faculties which they once possessed, and presumably would still possess were it not for the acquisition of their wings.

In the last few years human beings have also attained the power of aerial locomotion. But the process by which this power was attained, and its effects on the species, are as different from those which characterized the acquisition of flight by the first birds as it is possible for them to be. Our means of flying are outside of our bodies. A bird is born with a pair of wings, but we have invented the aeroplane. The bird renounced a potential pair of hands to get his wings; we, because our new faculty is not part of our congenital make-up, keep all the organs and capacities of our forefathers but add to them the new ability. The process of the development of civilization is clearly one of accumulation: the old is retained, in spite of the incoming of the new. In organic evolution, the introduction of new features is generally possible only through the loss or modification of existing organs or faculties.

In short, the growth of new species of animals takes place through, and in fact consists of, changes in their organic constitution. As regards the growth of civilization, on the other hand, the one example cited is sufficient to show that change and progress can take place through an invention without any such constitutional alteration of the human species.

There is another way of looking at this difference. It is clear that as a new species originates, it is derived wholly from the individual or individuals that first showed the particular traits distinguishing the new species. When we say that it is derived from these individuals we mean, literally, that it is descended. In other words, the species is composed only of such individuals as contain the "blood"—the germ-plasm—of particular ancestors. Heredity is thus the indispensable means of transmission. When however an invention is made, the entire human race is capable of profiting thereby. People who have not the slightest blood kinship to the first designers of aeroplanes can fly and are flying today. Many a father has used, enjoyed, and profited by the invention of his son. In the evolution of animals, the descendant can build upon the inheritance transmitted to him from his ancestors, and may rise to higher powers and more perfect development; but the ancestor is, in the very nature of things, precluded from thus profiting from his descendant. In short, organic evolution is essentially and inevitably connected with hereditary processes; the social evolution which characterizes the progress of civilization, on the other hand, is not, or not necessarily, tied up with hereditary agencies.

The whale is not only a warm-blooded mammal, but is recognized as the remote descendant of carnivorous land animals. In some few million years, as such genealogies are usually reckoned, this animal lost his legs for running, his claws for holding and tearing, his original hair and external ears that would be useless or worse in water, and acquired fins and fluke, a cylindrical body, a layer of fat, and the power of holding his breath. There was much that the species gave up; more, on the whole, perhaps than it gained. Certainly some of its parts have degenerated. But there was one new power that it did achieve: that of roaming the ocean indefinitely.

The parallel and also contrast is in the human acquisition of the identical faculty. We do not, in gradual alteration from father to son, change our arms into flippers and grow a tail. We do not enter the water at all to navigate it. We build a boat. And what this means is that we preserve our bodies and our natal faculties intact, unaltered from those of our fathers and remotest ancestors. Our means of marine travel is outside of our natural endowment. We make it and use it: the original whale had to turn himself into a boat. It took him countless generations to attain to his present condition. All individuals that failed to conform to type left no offspring; or none that went into the blood of the whales of today.

Again, we may compare human and animal beings when groups of them reach a new and arctic environment, or when the climate of the tract where the race is established slowly becomes colder and colder. The non-human mammal species comes to have heavy hair. The polar bear is shaggy; his Sumatran relative sleek. The arctic hare is enveloped in soft fur; the jack-rabbit in comparison is shabbily thin and moth-eaten. Good furs come from the far north, and they lose in richness, in quality, and in value, in proportion as they are stripped from animals of the same species that inhabit milder regions. And this difference is racial, not individual. The jack-rabbit would quickly perish with the end of summer in Greenland; the caged polar bear suffers from temperate warmth within the massive coat which nature has fastened on him.

Now there are people who look for the same sort of inborn peculiarities in the Arctic Eskimo and Samoyed; and find them, because they look for them. That the Eskimo is furry, no one can assert: in fact, we are hairier than he. But it is asserted that he is fat-protected —like the blubber-covered seal that he lives on; and that he devours quantities of meat and oil because he needs them. The true amount of his fat, compared with that of other human beings, remains to be ascertained. He probably has more than the European; but probably no more than the normal full-blood Samoan and Hawaiian from under the tropics. And as to his diet, if this is seal and seal and seal all winter long, it is not from any congenital craving of his stomach, but because he does not know how to get himself anything else. The Alaskan miner, and the arctic and antarctic explorer, do not guzzle blubber. Wheat-flour, eggs, coffee, sugar, potatoes, canned vegetables—whatever the exigencies of their vocation and the cost of transportation permit—make up their fare. The Eskimo is only too anxious to join them; and both he and they can thrive on the one diet as on the other.

In fact, what the human inhabitant of intemperate latitudes does, is not to develop a peculiar digestive system, any more than he grows hair. He changes his environment, and thereby is able to retain his original body unaltered. He builds a closed house, which keeps out the wind and retains the heat of his body. He makes a fire or lights a lamp. He skins a seal or a caribou of the furry hide with which natural selection or other processes of organic evolution have endowed these beasts; he has his wife make him a shirt and trousers, boots and gloves, or two sets of them; he puts them on; and in a few years, or days, he is provided with the protection which it took the polar bear and the arctic hare, the sable and the ptarmigan, untold periods to acquire. What is more, his baby, and his baby's baby, and his hundredth descendant are born as naked, and unarmed physically, as he and his hundredth ancestor were born.

That this difference in method of resisting a difficult environment, as followed respectively by the polar bear species and the human Eskimo race, is absolute, need not be asserted. That the difference is deep, is unquestionable. That it is as important as it is often neglected, it is the object of this essay to establish.

It has long been the custom to say that the difference is that between body and mind; that animals have their physiques adapted to their circumstances, but that man's superior intelligence enables him to rise superior to such lowly needs. But this is not the most significant point of the difference. It is true that without the much greater mental faculties of man, he could not achieve the attainments the lack of which keeps the brute chained to the limitations of his anatomy. But the greater human intelligence in itself does not cause the differences that exist. This psychic superiority is only the indispensable condition of what is peculiarly human; civilization. Directly, it is the civilization in which every Eskimo, every Alaskan miner or arctic discoverer is reared, and not any greater inborn faculty, that leads him to build houses, ignite fire, and wear clothing. The distinction between animal and man which counts is not that of the physical and mental, which is one of relative degree, but that of the organic and social which is one of kind. The beast has mentality, and we have bodies; but in civilization man has something that no animal has.

That this distinction is actually something more than that of the physical and mental, appears from an example that may be chosen from the non-bodily: speech.

On the surface, human and animal speech, in spite of the enormously greater richness and complexity of the former, are much alike. Both express emotions, possibly ideas, in sounds formed by bodily organs and understood by the hearing individual. But the difference between the so-called language of brutes and that of men is infinitely great; as a homely illustration will set forth.

A newly-born pup is brought up in a litter of kittens by a fostering cat. Familiar anecdotes and newspaper paragraphs to the contrary, the youngster will bark and growl, not purr or miaow. He will not even try to do the latter. The first time his toe is stepped on, he will whine, not squeal, just as surely as when thoroughly angered he will bite as his never-beheld mother did, and not even attempt to claw as he has seen his foster-mother do. For half his life seclusion may keep him from sight or sound or scent of another dog. But then let a bark or a snarl reach him through the restraining wall, and he will be all attention—more than at any voice ever uttered by his cat associates. Let the bark be repeated, and interest will give way to excitement, and he will answer in kind, as certainly as, put with a bitch, the sexual impulses of his species will manifest themselves. It cannot be doubted that dog speech is ineradicably part of dog nature, as fully contained in it without training or culture, as wholly part of the dog organism, as are teeth or feet or stomach or motions or instincts. No degree of contact with cats, or deprivation of association with his own kind, can make a dog acquire cat speech, or lose his own, any more than it can cause him to switch his tail instead of wagging it, to rub his sides against his master instead of leaping against him, or to grow whiskers and carry his drooping ears erect.

Let us take a French baby, born in France of French parents, themselves descended for numerous generations from French-speaking ancestors. Let us, at once after birth, entrust the infant to a mute nurse, with instructions to let no one handle or see her charge, while she travels by the directest route to the interior heart of China. There she delivers the child to a Chinese couple, who legally adopt it, and rear it as their son. Now suppose three or ten or thirty years passed. Is it needful to discuss what the growing or grown Frenchman will speak? Not a word of French; pure Chinese, without a trace of accent and with Chinese fluency; and nothing else.

It is true that there is a common delusion, frequent even among educated people, that some hidden influence of his French-talking ancestors will survive in the adopted Chinaman: that it is only necessary to send him to France with a batch of real Chinamen, and he will acquire his mother's tongue with appreciably greater facility, fluency, correctness, and naturalness than his Mongolian companions. That a belief is common, however, is as likely to stamp it a common superstition as a common truth. And a reasonable biologist, in other words, an expert qualified to speak of heredity, will pronounce this answer to this problem in heredity, superstition. He might merely choose a politer phrase.

Now there is something deep-going here. No amount of association with Chinese would turn our young Frenchman's eyes from blue to black, or slant them, or flatten his nose, or coarsen or stiffen his wavy, oval-sectioned hair; and yet his speech is totally that of his associates, in no measure that of his blood kin. His eyes and his nose and his hair are his from heredity; his language is non-hereditary—as much so as the length to which he

allows his hair to grow, or the hole which, in conformity to fashion, he may or may not bore in his ears. It is not so much that speech is mental and facial proportions are physical; the distinction that has meaning and use is that human language is non-hereditary and social, eye-color and nose-shape hereditary and organic. By the same criterion, dog speech, and all that is vaguely called the language of animals, is in a class with men's noses, the proportions of their bones, the color of their skin, and the slope of their eyes, and not in a class with any human idiom. It is inherited, and therefore organic. By a human standard, it is not really language at all, except by the sort of metaphor that speaks of the language of the flowers.

It is true that now and then a French child would be found that under the conditions of the experiment assumed, would learn Chinese more slowly, less idiomatically, and with less power of expression, than the average Chinaman. But there would also be French babies, and as many, that would acquire the Chinese language more quickly, more fluently, with richer power of revealing their emotions and defining their ideas, than the normal Chinese. These are individual differences, which it would be absurd to deny, but which do not affect the average, and are not to the point. One Englishman speaks better English, and more of it, than another, and he may also through precocity, learn it much sooner; but one talks English no more and no less truly than the other.

There is one form of animal expression in which the influence of association has sometimes been alleged to be greater than that of heredity. This is the song of birds. There is a good deal of conflicting opinion, and apparently of evidence, on this point. Many birds have a strong inherent impulse to imitate sounds. It is also a fact that the singing of one individual stimulates the other—as with dogs, wolves, cats, frogs, and most noisy animals. That in certain species of birds capable of a complex song the full development will not often be reached in individuals raised out of hearing of their kind, may probably be admitted. But it seems to be clear that every species has a song or call distinctively its own; that this minimum is attainable without association by every normal member of the singing sex, as soon as conditions of age, food, and warmth are proper, and the requisite stimulus of noise, or silence, or sex development, is present. That there has been serious conflict of opinion as to the nature of bird song, will ultimately be found to be chiefly due to the pronouncement of opinions on the matter by those who read their own mental states and activities into animals— a common fallacy that every biological student is now carefully trained against at the outset of his career. In any event, whether one bird does or does not in some degree "learn" from another, there is no fragment of evidence that bird song is a tradition, that like human speech or human music it accumulates and develops from age to age, that it is inevitably altered from generation to generation by fashion or custom, and that it is impossible for it ever to remain the same: in other words, that it is a social thing or due to a process even remotely akin to those affecting the constituents of human civilization.

It is also true that there is in human life a series of utterances that are of the type of animal cries. A man in pain moans without purpose of communication. The sound is literally pressed from him. A person in supreme fright may shriek. We know that his cry is unintended, what the physiologist calls a reflex action. The true shriek is as liable to escape the victim pinned before the approaching engineerless train, as him who is pursued by thinking and planning enemies. The woodsman crushed by a rock forty miles from the nearest human being, will moan like the run-over city dweller surrounded by a crowd waiting for the speeding ambulance. Such cries are of a class with those of animals. In fact, really to understand the "speech" of brutes, we must think ourselves into a condition in which our utterances would be totally restricted to such instinctive cries —"inarticulate" is their general though often inaccurate designation. In an exact sense, they are not language at all.

This is precisely the point. We undoubtedly have certain activities of utterance, certain faculties and habits of sound production, that are truly parallel with those of animals; and we also have something more that is quite different and without parallel among the animals. To deny that something purely animal underlies human speech, is fatuous; but it would be equally narrow to believe that be-cause our speech springs from an animal foundation, and originated in this foundation, it therefore is nothing but animal mentality and utterances greatly magnified. A house may be built on rock; without this base it might be impossible for it to have been erected; but no one will maintain that therefore the house is nothing but improved and glorified stone.

As a matter of fact, the purely animal element in human speech is small. Apart from laughter and crying, it finds rare utterance. Our interjections are denied by philologists as true speech, or at best but half admitted. It is a fact that they differ from full words in not being voiced, generally, to convey a meaning—nor to conceal one. But even these particles are shaped and dictated by fashion, by custom, by the type of civilization to which we belong, in short by social and not by organic elements. When I drive the hammer on my thumb instead of on the head of the nail, an involuntary "damn" may escape me as readily if I am alone in the house, as if companions stand on each side. Perhaps more readily. So far, the exclamation does not serve the purpose of speech and is not speech. But the Spaniard will say "carramba" and not "damn"; and the Frenchman, the German, the Chinaman, will avail himself of still different expression. The American says "outch" when hurt. Other nationalities do not understand this syllable. Each people has its own sound: some even two—one used by men and the other by women. A Chinaman will understand a laugh, a moan, a crying child, as well as we understand it, and as well as a dog understands the snarl of another dog. But he must learn "outch," or it is meaningless. No dog, on the other hand, ever has given utterance to a new snarl, unintelligible to other dogs, as a result of having been brought up in different associations. Even this lowest element of human speech, then, this involuntary half-speech of exclamations, is therefore shaped by social influences.

Herodotus tells of an Egyptian king, who, wishing to ascertain the parent tongue of humanity, had some infants brought up in isolation from their own kind, with only goats as companions and for sustenance. When the children, grown older, were revisited, they cried the word "bekos," or, subtracting the ending which the normalizing and sensitive

Greek could not endure omitting from anything that passed his lips, more probably "bek." The king then sent to all countries to learn in what land this vocable meant something. He ascertained that in the Phrygian idiom it signified bread, and, assuming that the children were crying for food, concluded that they spoke Phrygian in voicing their "natural" human speech, and that this tongue must therefore be the original one of mankind. The king's belief in an inherent and congenital language of man, which only the blind accidents of time had distorted into a multitude of idioms, may seem simple; but naïve as it is, inquiry would reveal crowds of civilized people still adhering to it.

This however is not our moral to the tale. That lies in the fact that the one and only word attributed to the children, "bek," was, if the story has any authenticity whatsoever, only a reflection or imitation—as the commentators of Herodotus long since conjectured —of the bleating of the goats that were the children's only associates and instructors. In short, if it is allowable to deduce any inference from so apocryphal an anecdote, what it proves is that there is no natural and therefore no organic human language.

Thousands of years later another sovereign, the Mogul emperor Akbar, repeated the experiment with the intent of ascertaining the "natural" religion of mankind. His band of children were shut up in a house. When, the necessary time having elapsed, the doors were opened in the presence of the expectant and enlightened ruler, his disappointment was great: the children trooped out as dumb as deaf-mutes. Faith dies hard, however; and we may suspect that it would take a third trial, under modern chosen and controlled conditions, to satisfy some natural scientists that speech, for the human individual and for the human race, is wholly an acquired and not a hereditary thing, entirely outward and not at all inward—a social product and not an organic growth.

Human and animal speech, then, though one roots in the other, are in the nature of a different order. They resemble each other only as the flight of a bird and of an aeronaut are alike. That the analogy between them has frequently deceived, proves only the guilelessness of the human mind. The operative processes are wholly unlike; and this, to him

who is desirous of understanding, is far more important than the similarity of effect. The savage and the peasant who cure by cleaning the knife and leaving the wound unattended, have observed certain indisputable facts. They know that cleanness aids, dirt on the whole impedes recovery. They know the knife as the cause, the wound as the effect; and they grasp, too, the correct principle that treatment of the cause is in general more likely to be effective than treatment of the symptom. They fail only in not inquiring into the process that may be involved. Knowing nothing of the nature of sepsis, of bacteria, of the agencies of putrefaction and retardation of healing, they fall back on agencies more familiar to themselves, and use, as best they may, the process of magic intertwined with that of medicine. They carefully scrape the knife; they oil it; they keep it bright. The facts from which they work are correct; their logic is sound enough; they merely do not distinguish between two irreconcilable processes—that of magic and that of physiological chemistry—and apply one in place of another. The student of today who reads the civilizationally moulded mind of men into the mentality of a dog or ape, or who tries to explain civilization—that is, history—by organic factors, commits an error which is less antiquated and more in fashion, but of the same kind and nature.

It is only in small measure a question of high and low as between man and animal. Many purely instinctive activities of the beasts lead to far more complex and difficult achievements than some of the analogous customs of this or that human nation. The beaver is a better architect than many a savage tribe. He fells larger trees, he drags them farther, he builds a closer house; he constructs it both below and above water; and he does what many nations never attempt to do: he makes himself a suitable topography for a habitat by erecting a dam. But the essential point is not that after all a man can do more than a beaver, or a beaver as much as a man; it is that what a beaver accomplishes he does by one means, and a man by another. The rudest savage, who builds but a shack of a wind-pierced hut, can be taught, innumerable times has been taught, to saw and nail together boards, to mortar stone on stone, to sink foundations, to rear an iron frame. All human history concerns itself primarily with just such changes. What were the ancestors of ourselves, of us steel-building Europeans and Americans, but hut-dwelling savages of a few thousand years ago—a period so short that it may barely suffice for the formation of an occasional new species of organism? And on the other side, who would be so rash as to affirm that ten thousand generations of example and instruction would convert the beaver from what he is into a carpenter or a bricklayer—or, allowing for his physical deficiency in the lack of hands, into a planning engineer?

The divergence between social and organic forces is perhaps not fully grasped until the mentality of the so-called social insects, the bees and ants, is thoroughly realized. Social the ant is, in the sense that she associates; but she is so far from being social in the sense of possessing civilization, of being influenced by non-organic forces, that she would better be known as the antisocial animal. The marvelous powers of the ant cannot be underestimated. There is no one to whom the full exploitation of their understanding will be of more service than to the historian. But he will not use this understanding by applying his knowledge of ant mentality to man. He will use it to fortify and render precise by intelligent contrast, his conception of the agencies that mould human civilization. Ant society is as little a true society, in the human sense, as a caricature is a portrait.

Take a few ant eggs of the proper sexes—unhatched eggs, freshly laid. Blot out every individual and every other egg of the species. Give the pair a little attention as regards warmth, moisture, protection, and food. The whole of ant "society," every one of the abilities, powers, accomplishments, and activities of the species, each "thought" that it has ever had, will be reproduced, and reproduced without diminution, in one generation. But place on a desert island or in a circumvallation two or three hundred human infants of the best stock from the highest class of the most civilized nation; furnish them the necessary incubation and nourishment; leave them in total isolation from their kind; and what shall we have? The civilization from which they were torn? One tenth of it? No, not any fraction; nor a fraction of the civilizational attainments of the rudest savage tribe. Only a pair or a troop of mutes, without arts, knowledge, fire, with-

out order or religion. Civilization would be wiped out within these confines—not disintegrated, not cut to the quick, but obliterated in one sweep. Heredity saves for the ant all that she has, from generation to generation. But heredity does not maintain, and has not maintained, because it cannot maintain, one particle of the civilization which is the specifically human thing.

The mental activity of the animals is partly instinctive, partly based on individual experience; the content, at least, of our own minds comes to us through tradition, in the widest sense of the word. Instinct is what is "pricked in"; an unalterable pattern inherent in the goods; indelible and inextinguishable, because the design is nothing but the warp and the woof, coming ready-made from the loom of heredity.

But tradition, what is "given through," handed along, from one to another, is only a message. It must of course be carried; but the messenger after all is extrinsic to the news. So, a letter must be written; but as its significance is in the meaning of the words, as the value of a note is not in the fiber of the paper but in the characters inscribed on its surface, so tradition is something superadded to the organisms that bear it, imposed upon them, external to them. And as the same shred can bear any one of thousands of inscriptions, of the most diverse force and value, and can even be tolerably razed and reinscribed, so it is with the human organism and the countless contents that civilization can pour into it. The essential difference between animal and man, in this illustration, is not that the latter has finer grain or the chaster quality of material; it is that his structure and nature and texture are such that he is inscribable, and that the animal is not. Chemically and physically, there is little difference between a lump of pulp and a sheet of paper. Chemically and physically, it is of slight consequence to trouble about such minute difference. But chemically and physically there is still less difference between the treasury note stamped with "one" and that stamped with "thousand"; and yet less between the check with an honored signature and that written with the same pen, the same ink, the same strokes even, by a forger. The difference that counts between the valid and the counterfeit check, is not the broader or the narrow line, the continuous curve of a letter in place of the broken one, but the purely social one that one signer has a valid account in the bank and the other has not; which fact is surely extrinsic to the paper and even to the ink upon it.

Exactly parallel to this is the relation of the instinctive and traditional, the organic and the social. The animal, so far as social influences are concerned, is as unsuitable as a dish of porridge is for writing material; or when like the beach sand, it is inscribable, by domestication, it can retain no permanent impression, as a species. Hence it has no society, and therefore no history. Man, however, comprises two aspects: he is an organic substance, that can be viewed as a substance, and he is also a tablet that is written upon. One aspect is as valid and as justifiable as another; but it is a cardinal mistake to confuse the two views.

The mason builds in granite and roofs with slate. The child learning its letters knows nothing of the qualities of its slate, but puzzles whether to write $c$ or $k$. The mineralogist gives no precedence to one of the stones over the other; each has a constitution, a structure, properties, and uses. The educator ignores the granite; but, though he uses the slate, he does not therefore rate it higher, or deny the serviceability of the other material; he takes his substance as he finds it. His problem is whether the child should begin with words or letters; at what age, for what hours, in what sequence, and under what conditions, its education toward literacy should commence. To decide these issues upon crystallogical evidence because his pupils write upon a variety of stone would be as futile as if the geologist were to employ his knowledge of rocks for inferences as to the soundest principles of pedagogy.

So, if the student of human achievement were to try to withdraw from the observation of the natural historian and the mechanical philosopher the human beings upon whom is inscribed the civilization which he himself investigates, he would be ridiculous. And when on the other hand, the biologist proposes to rewrite history, in whole or in part, through the medium of heredity, he reveals himself in little more favorable light, though he would have the sanction of some precedent. There have been many attempts to make

precise the distinction between instinct and civilization, between the organic and the social, between animal and man. Man as the clothing animal, the fire-using animal, the tool-using or tool-making animal, the speaking animal, are all summations that contain some approximation. But for the conception of the discrimination that is at once most complete and most compact, we must go back, as for the first precise expression of so many of the ideas with which we operate, to the unique mind that impelled Aristotle. "Man is a political animal." The word political has changed in import. We use instead the Latin term social. This, both philosopher and philologist tell us, is what the great Greek would have said were he speaking in English today. Man is a social animal, then; a social organism. He has organic constitution; but he has also civilization. To ignore one element is as shortsighted as to overlook the other; to convert one into the other, if each has its reality, is negation. With this basic formulation more than two thousand years old, and known to all the generations, there is something puny, as well as obstinately destructive, in the endeavor to abrogate the distinction, or to hinder its completest fruition. The attempt today to treat the social as organic, to understand civilization as hereditary, is as essentially narrow as the alleged mediaeval inclination to withdraw man from the realm of nature and from the ken of the scientist because he was believed to possess an immaterial soul.

But unfortunately the denials, and for every denial a dozen confusions, still persist. They pervade the popular mind; and thence they rise, again and again, into the thoughts of avowed and recognized science. It seems, even, that in a hundred years we have retrograded. A century and two centuries ago, with a generous impulse, the leaders of thought devoted their energies, and the leaders of men their lives, to the cause that all men are equal. With all that this idea involves, and with its correctness, we need not here concern ourselves; but it certainly implied the proposition of equality of racial capacity. Possibly our ancestors were able to maintain this liberal stand because its full practical imports did not yet face them. But, whatever the reason, we have certainly gone back, in America and in Europe and in their colonies, in our application of the assumption; and we have receded too in our theoretic analysis of the evidence. Hereditary racial differences of ability pass as approved doctrine, in many quarters. There are men of eminent learning who would be surprised to know that serious doubts were held in the matter.

And yet, it must be maintained that little really satisfactory evidence has been produced to support the assumption that the differences which one nation shows from another—let alone the superiority of one people to another—are racially inherent, that is organically founded. It does not matter how distinguished the minds are that have held such differences to be hereditary—they have in the main only taken their conviction for granted. The sociologist or anthropologist can, and occsionally does, turn the case inside out with equal justification; and he then sees every event, every inequality, the whole course of human history, confirming his thesis that the distinctions between one group of men and another, past and present, are due to social influences and not to organic causes. Real proof, to be sure, is as wanting on one side as on the other. Experiment, under conditions that would yield satisfying evidence, would be difficult, costly, and perhaps contrary to law. A repetition of Akbar's interesting trial, or some modification of it, intelligently directed and followed out, would yield results of the greatest value; but it would scarcely yet be tolerated by a civilized government.

There have been some attempts to investigate so-called racial distinctions with the apparatus of experimental psychology. The results incline superficially toward confirmation of organic differences. But too much stress may not as yet be laid on this conclusion, because what such investigations have above all revealed is that social agencies are so tremendously influential on every one of us that it is difficult to find any test which, if distinctive racial faculties were inborn, would fairly reveal the degree to which they are inborn.

It is also well to remember that the problem of whether the human races are or are not in themselves identical, has innumerable practical bearings, which relate to conditions of life and to views that have emotional relations, so that an impartially abstract predisposition is rather rarely to be encountered. It is practically futile, for instance, even to touch upon the question with most Americans from the Southern states, or those tinged by Southern influences, no matter what their education or standing in the world. The actual social cleavage which is fundamental to all life in the South, and which is conceived of mainly as a race question, is so overshadowing and inevitable, that it compels, for the individual almost as firmly as for his group, a certain line of action, an unalterable and conscious course of conduct; and it could not well be otherwise than that opinions which flagrantly clash with one's habitual activities and with their associated ideals, should arouse hostility. It is then but natural if the Southerner frequently receives the profession of racial equality, when it can be made to carry the conviction of sincerity to him, as an affront; and that he often meets even the most abstract, impersonal, and judicial consideration of the issues involved, with resentment, or, where this is checked by courtesy, with internal dissatisfaction.

The attitude of the Englishman in India, of the continental European in his colonies, is perhaps less extremely manifested; but all accounts indicate that it is no less settled.

On the other hand, the avowed and thoroughgoing Socialist or Internationalist must take the opposite stand, however unsympathetic it may be to him personally, or renounce the aspirations that he holds dear. His inclination therefore, if generally less clearly defined, is no less predetermined and persistent.

Impartiality is thus not to be expected in this great case, except in some measure on the part of really detached and therefore uninfluential students; so that the maximum of assertion and rancor, and minimum of evidence, which prevail, are to be accepted as regrettable indeed, but as unavoidable and scarcely to be censured.

The problem, being in the present state of our knowledge unprovable, is really also not arguable. What is possible, however, is to realize that a complete and consistent explanation can be given, for so-called racial differences, on a basis of purely civilizational and non-organic causes; and to attain also to the recognition that the mere fact of the world in general assuming that such differences between one people and another are inborn and ineradicable except by breeding, is no evidence in favor of the assumption being true.

The final argument, that one can actually *see* such national peculiarities born into each generation, and that it is unnecessary to verify the assumption because its truth is obvious to every one, has the least weight of all. It is of a kind with the contention that might be made that this planet is after all the fixed central point of the cosmic system because everyone can see for himself that the sun and stars move and that our earth stands still. The champions of the Copernican doctrine had this in their favor: they dealt with phenomena to which exactitude was readily applicable, about which verifiable or disprovable predictions could be made, which an explanation either fitted or did not fit. In the domain of human history this is not possible, or has not yet been found possible; so that an equal neatness of demonstration, a definitiveness of proof, a close tallying of theory with the facts to the exclusion of all rival theories, is not to be hoped for at present. But there is almost as fundamental a shifting of mental and emotional point of view, as absolute a turning upside down of attitude involved when the current thought of today is asked to view civilization as a nonorganic affair, as when the Copernican doctrine challenged the prior conviction of the world.

Most ethnologists, at any rate, are convinced that the overwhelming mass of historical and miscalled racial facts that are now attributed to obscure organic causes, or at most are in dispute, will ultimately be viewed by everyone as social and as best intelligible in their social relations. That there may be a residuum in which hereditary influences have been operative, it would be dogmatic to deny; but even this residuum of organic agencies will perhaps be found to be operative in quite other manners than those which are customarily adduced at present.

The opinion may further be uncompromisingly maintained, that for the historian—him who wishes to understand any sort of social phenomena it is an unavoidable necessity, today, to disregard the organic as such and to deal only with the social. For the larger number who are not professional students of civilization, insistence upon these articles would be an unreasonable demand, under our present inability to substantiate them by proof. On the other hand, the social as something distinct from the organic is an old enough

concept, and is a plain enough phenomenon about us in daily life, to warrant the claim that it cannot be outright dispensed with. It is perhaps too much to expect any one wedded, deliberately or unknowingly, to organic explanations, to discard these wholly in the face of such incomplete evidence as is available to the contrary of these explanations. But it does seem justifiable to stand unhesitatingly on the proposition that civilization and heredity are two things that operate in separate ways; that therefore any outright substitution of one for the other in the explanation of human group phenomena is crass; and that the refusal to recognize at least the possibility of an explanation of human achievement totally different from the prevailing tendency toward a biological explanation, is an act of illiberality. When once such recognition, of the rationality of this attitude of mind which is diametrically opposed to the current one, shall have become general, far more progress will have been made on the road towards a useful agreement as to the truth, than by any present attempts to win converts by argument.

One of the minds endowed with as eminent power of perception and formulation as any of the last generation, Gustave Le Bon, whose name ranks high even if his regardless fearlessness has gained him but little of an avowed following, has carried the interpretation of the social as organic to its consistent consequence. His *Psychology of Peoples* is an attempt to explain civilization on the basis of race. Le Bon is really an historian of unusually keen sensitiveness and perspicacity. But his professed attempt to resolve the civilizational materials with which he deals, directly into organic factors, leads him on the one hand to renounce his skilful interpretations of history until only intermittent flashes remain; and on the other hand, to rest his professed solutions ultimately on such mystic essences as the "soul of a race." As a scientific concept or tool, a race soul is as intangible and useless as a phrase of mediaeval philosophy, and on a par with Le Bon's ready declaration that the individual is to the race as the cell is to the body. If instead of soul of the race, the distinguished Frenchman had said spirit of civilization, or tendency or character of culture, his pronouncements would have commanded less appeal, because seeming vaguer; but he would not have had to rest his thought upon a supernatural idea antagonistic to the body of science to which he was trying to attach his work; and if nonmechanistic, his efforts at explanation would at least have earned the respect of historians.

As a matter of fact, Le Bon clearly operates with social phenomena, however insistently he gives them organic names and proclaims that he has resolved them organically. That "not the 18 Brumaire but the soul of his race established Napoleon," is biologically, and under any aspect of the science that deals with mechanical causality, a meaningless statement; but it becomes excellent history as soon as for "race" we substitute "civilization," and of course take "soul" in a metaphorical sense.

When he says that "cross breeding destroys an ancient civilization" he affirms only what many a biologist would be ready to maintain. When he adds: "because it destroys the soul of the people that possess it," he gives a reason that must inspire a scientist with a shudder. But if we change "cross breeding," that is, the mixture of sharply differentiated organic types, into "sudden contact or conflict of ideals," that is, mixture of sharply differentiated social types, the profound effect of such an event is indisputable.

Again, Le Bon asserts that the effect of environment is great on new races, on races forming through cross breeding of peoples of contrary heredities; and that in ancient races solidly established by heredity the effect of environment is nearly nil. It is obvious that in an old and firm civilization the actively changing effect of geographical environment must be small because the civilization has long since had ample opportunity to utilize the environment for its needs; but that on the other hand when the civilization is new—whether because of its transportation, because of its proceeding fusion from several elements, or from mere internal development—the renewing of relationship between itself and the surrounding physical geography must go on at a rapid rate. Here again good history is turned into bad science by a confusion that seems almost deliberately perverse.

A people is guided far more by its dead than by its living, Le Bon says. He is trying to establish the importance of heredity on national careers. What, though unrecognized by himself, lies at the bottom of his thought, is

the truth that every civilization rests in the past, that however much its ancient elements are no longer living as such, they nevertheless form its trunk and body, around which the live sap-wood of the day is only a shell and a surface. That imposed education, a formal and conscious thing, can not give the substance of a new or another civilization to a people, is a verity that Le Bon has seized with vigor. But when he deduces this maxim as an inference from the unbridgeable abyss that externally exists between races, he rests an obvious fact, which no person of discrimination has yet disputed, upon a mystical assertion.

It might nearly have been foreseen, after the above citations, that Le Bon would lay the "character" of his "races" to "accumulation by heredity." It has already been shown that if there is anything that heredity does not do, it is to accumulate. If, on the other hand, there is any one method by which civilization may be defined as operating, it is precisely that of accumulation. We add the power of flight, the understanding of the mechanism of the aeroplane, to our previous accomplishments and knowledges. The bird does not; he has given up his legs and toes for wings. It may be true that the bird is on the whole a higher organism than his reptilian ancestor, that he has traveled farther on the road of development. But his advance has been achieved by a transmutation of qualities, a conversion of organs and faculties, not by an increasing summation of them.

The whole theory of heredity by acquirement rests upon the confusion of these two so diverse processes, that of heredity and that of civilization. It has been nourished, perhaps, by unsatisfied needs of biological science, but it has never obtained the slightest unchallengeable verification from biology, and has in fact long been assailed, by a sound and vigorous instinct, as well as in consequence of the failure of observation and experiment, from within that science. It is a doctrine that is the constant blazon of the dilettante who knows something of both history and life, but has no care to understand the workings of either. Le Bon's studies being an attempt to explain one by the other, his utilization, sooner or later, of the doctrine of heredity by acquisition or accumulation, could almost have been predicted.

From a different and less aggressive temperament springs the wail that Lester Ward has voiced for a wide and aspiringly earnest element. Heredity by acquirement must take place, he argues, or there would be no hope of permanent progress for humanity. To believe that what we have gained will not be at least in part implanted in our children, removes the incentive to effort. All the labor bestowed upon the youth of the world would be in vain. Mental qualities are not subject to natural selection; hence they must be accumulated in man by acquirement and fixed by heredity. This view may be heard again and again from people who have arrived at the attitude through their own reflections, who have probably never read Ward directly or indirectly, and whose world seems to crash when its foundation of heredity is shaken. It is, if not a deep view, a common one; and for that reason Ward's formulation is, however worthless intrinsically, representative and significant. It reveals the tenacity, the insistence, with which many conscientious intellects of the day will not and can not see the social except through the glass of the organic. That this habit of mind can itself be depressing, that it forever prelimits development and eternally chains the future to the poverties and paucities of the present, does not dawn upon its devotees; is in fact probably the fixity which gives it its emotional hold.

It would seem probable that the greatest of the champions of acquired heredity, Herbert Spencer, was led to his stand by a similar motive. The precise method by which organic evolution takes place is after all essentially a biological problem, and not a philosophical one. Spencer, however, like Comte, was a sociologist as much as a philosopher. That he should have contested so stubbornly what in itself is a technical question of biology, is hardly intelligible except on the supposition that he felt the question to bear vitally on his principles; and that, in spite of his happy coinage of the term which has been prefixed as title to the present essay, he did not adequately conceive of human society as holding a specific content that is non-organic.

When R. R. Marett, in opening his *Anthropology*—one of the most stimulating books produced in this field—defines the science as "the whole history of man as fired and pervaded by the idea of evolution," and adds that "anthropology is the child of Darwin—Dar-

winism makes it possible," he is unfortunately depicting the recent condition of this science with some truth; but as a program or an ideal his delineation must be challenged. Anthropology may be biology; it may be history; it may be an attempt to ascertain the relations of the two; but as history, the study of the social, shot through with the idea of organic evolution, it would be a jumble of diverse methods, and therefore no science in any sense of the term.

Of all the comminglings of the cultural with the vital, that which has crystallized under the name of the eugenics movement is the most widely known and of directest appeal. As a constructive program for national progress, eugenics is a confusion of the purposes to breed better men and to give men better ideals; an organic device to attain the social; a biological short cut to a moral end. It contains the inherent impossibility of all short cuts. It is more refined but no less vain than the short cut which the savage follows, when, to avoid the trouble and danger of killing his foe in the body, he pierces, in safety and amid objurgations uttered in the convenience of his own home, a miniature image addressed by the name of the enemy. Eugenics, so far as it is more than an endeavor at social hygiene in a new field, is a fallacy; a mirage like the philosopher's stone, the elixir of life, the ring of Solomon, or the material efficacy of prayer. There is little to argue about it. If social phenomena are only or mainly organic, eugenics is right, and there is nothing more to be said. If the social is something more than the organic, eugenics is an error of unclear thought.

Galton, the founder of the eugenics propaganda, was one of the most truly imaginative intellects produced by his country. Pearson, its distinguished living protagonist with scientific weapons, possesses one of the keenest minds of the generation. Hundreds of men of ability and eminence have professed themselves converts. It is plain that a simple fallacy must have presented itself in an envelope of enticing complications to be acceptable to them. Such men have not confounded important things that are intrinsically distinct, without a good reason. The explanation that Galton, Pearson, and the majority of the most creative of their followers were professional biologists, and therefore inclined to see the world through the lenses of the organic, is insufficient. Mere interest in one factor does not lead thinking minds practically to deny the existence of other factors. What then is the reason of the confusion into which they have precipitated themselves?

The cause seems to be a failure to distinguish between the social and the mental. All civilization in a sense exists only in the mind. Gunpowder, textile arts, machinery, laws, telephones are not themselves transmitted from man to man or from generation to generation, at least not permanently. It is the perception, the knowledge and understanding of them, their *ideas* in the Platonic sense, that are passed along. Everything social can have existence only through mentality. Of course, civilization is not mental action itself; it is carried by men, without being in them. But its relation to mind, its absolute rooting in human faculty, is obvious.

What, then, has occurred is that biology, which correlates and often identifies the "physical" and the mental, has gone one natural but as yet unjustified step further, and assumed the social as mental; whence the explanation of civilization in physiological and mechanical terms was an unavoidable consequence.

Now, the correlation by modern science of the physical and mental is certainly correct. That is, it is justifiable as a method which can be consistently employed toward a coherent explanation of phenomena, and which leads to intellectually satisfactory and practically useful results. The correlation of the two sets of phenomena is made, or admitted, by all psychologists; it clearly holds for all faculties and instincts; and it has some definite physiological and chemical corroboration, though of a more crude and less completely established kind than is sometimes imagined. At any rate, this correlation is an unchallenged axiom of those who concern themselves with science: all mental equipment and all mental activity have an organic basis. And that is sufficient for present purposes.

This inseparability of physical and mental must be true also in the field of heredity. It is well known that where instincts are definite or specialized, as in insects, they are inherited as absolutely as are organs or structure. It is a matter of common experience that our own mental traits vary as much and as frequently tally with those of ancestors, as physical fea-

tures. There is no logical reason, and nothing in the observation of daily life, that operates against the belief that an irascible temper is as heritable as the red hair with which it is traditionally associated, and that certain forms of musical aptitude may be as wholly congenital as blue eyes.

Of course there is much false inference in these matters, as regards man, through the interpretation of accomplishment as evidence of the degree of faculty. The discrimination of the two is not always easy; it frequently requires painstakingly acquired knowledge of facts, as well as careful judgment; and popular reasoning is likely to be scant of both. A powerful congenital faculty may establish the father successfully in a pursuit. This in turn may give an environmental influence, or a deliberate training, that will elevate the mediocre son, so far as his attainments are concerned, far above what his unaided natural faculties would have secured for him, and above many another individual of greater inherent capacities. The earning of a million is normally an indication of ability; but it normally requires intenser ability to earn a million after starting with nothing than to begin with a million received as a gift and increase it to three. That a musician is more frequently the son of a musician than not, at least when relative numbers are taken into account, is in itself no evidence at all that musical talent is heritable, for we know of purely social influences, such as Hindu caste, which attain similar results with far greater regularity than any one can assert heredity plus social influences to bring about among ourselves.

But it would be as unreasonable to exaggerate this caution into an outright denial of mental heredity, as to disregard it entirely.

There is then nothing in an off-hand survey of the situation to lead to a disbelief, and a large body of common experience to confirm the conviction, that characters of mind are subject to heredity much like traits of the body.

In addition, there is some proof, which, although not extensive, is hard to resist. Galton, in a fairly large series of records, has found the amount of regression—a quantitative index of the potency of heredity—to be the same for artistic faculty as for bodily stature. In another work he has investigated the blood relatives of eminent men, with the finding that eminence occurs among them with a frequency and in a degree exactly like the influence of heredity in respect to physical characters. Pearson has ascertained that the correlation—the degree of resemblance, quantitatively expressed, of phenomena available in numbers—between brothers is substantially the same for conscientiousness as for the shape of the head, for intellectual ability as for hair color, and so forth for other mental or moral and physical qualities. There is of course the possibility that in the data that underlie these results, as well as Galton's, there has been some confounding of temper with bad manners, of native intelligence with training of the intellect, of congenital artistic faculty with cultivated taste. But the attention of those who have made the records seems to have been pretty definitely directed to innate individual traits. Further, all the coefficients or figures for the inheritance of these psychic characteristics agree as closely as could be expected wtih the corresponding ones relating to bodily features. The case may therefore be fairly regarded as substantially proved, at least until new evidence is available.

In spite of a wide acceptance of these demonstrations, especially by those predisposed to sympathize with biological progress, they have also met with some opposition, and with more ignoring than their bearing on a question of general interest warranted. In part this negative attitude may be due to a persistence of religious beliefs, in the main already superseded but not yet defunct, that center around the old concept of the soul, and which see in every linkage of mind and body an effacement of the cherished distinction of body and soul. But this belated conservatism will not account for all the failure of the Galton-Pearson demonstrations to meet universal acceptance or arouse wide enthusiasms.

The remainder of the opposition has been caused by Galton, Pearson, and their adherents themselves, who have not confined themselves to their well-supported conclusions, but have pressed on to further inferences that rest only on assertion. That heredity operates in the domain of mind as well as that of the body, is one thing; that therefore heredity is the mainspring of civilization, is an entirely different proposition, without necessary connection and without established connection with the former conclusion. To maintain both doctrines, the second as a necessary corollary of the first, has been the habit of the biological school; and the consequence has been that those whose intellectual inclinations were otherwise, or who followed another method of research, have avowedly or tacitly rejected both propositions.

The reason why mental heredity has so little if anything to do with civilization, is that civilization is not mental action but a body or stream of products of mental exercise. Mental activity, as biologists have dealt with it, being organic, any demonstration concerning it consequently proves nothing whatever as to social events. Mentality relates to the individual. The social or cultural, on the other hand, is in its essence non-individual. Civilization, as such, begins only where the individual ends; and whoever does not in some measure perceive this fact, even though only as a brute and rootless one, can find no meaning in civilization, and history for him must be only a wearying jumble, or an opportunity for the exercise of art.

All biology necessarily has this direct reference to the individual. A social mind is as meaningless a nonentity as a social body. There can be only one kind of organicness: the organic on another plane would no longer be organic. The Darwinian doctrine relates, it is true, to the race; but the race, except as an abstraction, is only a collection of individuals; and the bases of this doctrine, heredity, variation, and competition, deal with the relation of individual to individual, from individual, and against individual. The whole key of the success of the Mendelian methods of studying heredity lies in isolating traits and isolating individuals.

But a thousand individuals do not make a society. They are the potential basis of a society; but they do not themselves cause it; and they are also the basis of a thousand other potential societies.

The findings of biology as to heredity, mental and physical alike, may then, in fact must be, accepted without reservation. But that therefore civilization can be understood by psychological analysis, or explained by observations or experiments in heredity, or, to revert to a concrete example, that the destiny of nations can be predicted from an analysis of the organic constitution of their members, assumes that society is merely a collection of individuals; that civilization is only an aggregate of psychic activities and not also an entity beyond them; in short, that the social can be wholly resolved into the mental as it is thought this resolves into the physical.

It is accordingly in this point of the tempting leap from the individually mental to the culturally social which presupposes but does not contain mentality, that the source of the distracting transferences of the organic into the social is to be sought. A more exact examination of the relation of the two is therefore desirable.

In a brilliant essay written, under Pearsonian influence, on heredity in towns, Thorndike arrives anew, and by a convincing use of statistical evidence, at the conclusion that so far as the individual is concerned heredity is everything and environment nothing; that the success of our path in life is essentially determined at birth; that the problem of whether each one of us shall outstrip his fellows or lag behind them, is settled when the parental germ cells unite, and already long closed when the child emerges from the womb, all our careers run under the light of the sun being nothing but an unwinding, longer or shorter according to accident beyond our control, of the thread rolled on the spool before the beginning of our existence.

This finding is not only thoroughly elucidated by the author, but has the support of our common experience in life. No one can deny some measure of truth to the proverbial sow's ear that cannot be made into a silk purse. Every one numbers among his acquaintance individuals of energy, of address and skill, of what seems an uncanny prescience, or of a strength of character, that leave no doubts in our judgment that whatever their lot of birth, they would have risen above their fellows and have been marked men and women. And on the other hand, we also admit regretfully the maladroit and sluggish, the incompetent and commonplace, who, born in any station, would have been of the mediocrities or unfortunates of their time and class. That Napoleon, set in another land and era, would not have conquered a continent, is sufficiently certain. The contrary affirmation may with fairness, it seems, be said to evince an absence of understanding of history. But the belief that under the circumstances this eternal beacon flame might have remained a household lamp, that his forces would never have been called forth, that a slight change of the accidents of epoch, place, or surroundings

might have left him a prosperous and contented peasant, a shopkeeper or a bureaucrat, a routine captain retired on a pension—to maintain this argues a lack or a perverted suppression of knowledge of human nature. It is important to realize that congenital differences may have but limited effect on the course of civilization. But it is equally important to realize that we may and must concede the existence of such differences and their inextinguishability.

According to a saying that is almost proverbial, and true to the degree that such commonplaces can be true, the modern schoolboy knows more than Aristotle; but this fact, if a thousand times so, does not in the least endow him with a fraction of the intellect of the great Greek. Socially—because knowledge must be a social circumstance—it is knowledge, and not the greater development of one individual or another, that counts; just as, to measure the true force of the greatness of the person, the psychologist or genetist disregards the state of general enlightenment, the varying degree of civilizational development, to make his comparisons. A hundred Aristotles among our cave-dwelling ancestors would have been Aristotles in their birthright no less; but they would have contributed far less to the advance of the science than a dozen plodding mediocrities in the twentieth century. A super-Archimedes in the ice age would have invented neither firearms nor the telegraph. Bach born in the Congo instead of Saxony could have composed not even a fragment of choral or sonata, though we can be equally confident that he would have outshone his compatriots in some manner of music. Whether or not a Bach ever had birth in Africa, is another question—one to which a negative answer cannot be given merely because no Bach has ever appeared there, a question that in fairness we must admit to be unanswered but in regard to which the student of civilization, until some demonstration has been made, can make but one reply and pursue only one course: to assume, not as an end but as a condition of method, that there have been such individuals; that genius and ability occur with substantially regular frequency, and that all races or large enough groups of men average substantially alike and the same in qualities.

These are extreme cases, whose clearness is little likely to arouse opposition. Normally, the differences between individuals are less imposing, the types of society more similar, and the two elements involved are separable only by the exercise of some discrimination. It is then that the confusions begin. But if the factor of society and that of natal personality are distinct in the glaring examples, they are at least distinguishable in the more subtly shaded and intricate ones; provided only we wish to keep them apart.

If this is true, it follows that all so-called inventors of appliances or discoverers of thoughts of note were unusually able men, endowed from before birth with superior faculties, which the psychologist can hope to analyze and define, the physiologist to correlate with functions of organs, and the genetic biologist to investigate in their hereditary origins until he attains not only system and law but verifiable power of prediction. And, on the other hand, the content of the invention or discovery springs in no way from the make-up of the great man, or that of his ancestors, but is a product purely of the civilization into which he with millions of others is born as a meaningless and regularly recurring event. Whether he in his person becomes inventor, explorer, imitator, or user, is an affair of forces that the sciences of mechanistic causality are concerned with. Whether his invention is that of the cannon or the bow, his achievement a musical scale or a system of harmony, his formulation that of the soul or that of the categorical imperative, is not explainable by the medium of mechanistic science—at least, not by methods now at the command of biological science—but finds its meaning only in such operations with the material of civilization as history and the social sciences are occupied with.

Darwin, whose name has been cited so frequently in the preceding pages, provides a beautiful exemplification of these principles. To deny this great man genius, mental eminence, inherent superiority to the mass of the human herd, would be fatuous. In Galton's famous classification, he would probably attain, by general opinion, at least to grade G, perhaps to the still higher—the highest—grade X. That is, he was an individual born with capacities such as but fourteen, or more likely one, or still fewer, persons in every million possess. In short, he would have towered intellectually above his fellows in any society.

On the other side, no one can sanely believe that the distinction of Darwin's greatest accomplishment, the formulation of the doctrine of evolution by natural selection, would now stand to his credit had he been born fifty years sooner or later. If later, he would have been infallibly anticipated by Wallace, for one thing; by others, if an early death had cut off Wallace. That his restless mind would have evolved something noteworthy is as likely as it is away from the point: the distinction of the particular discovery which he did make, would not have been his. Put on earth by contrary supposition, a half-century earlier, his central idea would not have come to him as it failed to come to his brilliant predecessor, the evolutionist Lamarck. Or, it would have risen in his own mind, as it did in all its essentials in that of Aristotle, only to be discarded as logically possible indeed, but as unworthy of actual consideration. Or, finally, the thought might indeed have germinated and grown in him, but been ignored and forgotten by the world, a mere unfruitful accident, until European civilization was prepared, a few decades later, and hungry as well as prepared, to use it—when its rediscovery and not its barren formal discovery would have been the event of historical significance. That this last possibility is no idle conjecture is evidenced by its actual taking place in the case of one of the greatest of Darwin's contemporaries, his then unknown brother in arms, Gregor Mendel.

It is inconceivable that the independent occurrence of the idea of selection as the motive force of organic evolution, synchronously in the minds of Darwin and Wallace, should have been an affair of pure chance. The immediate acceptance of the idea by the world, proves nothing as to the intrinsic truth of the concept; but it does establish the readiness of the world, that is of the civilization of the time, for the doctrine. And if civilization was prepared and hungry for the doctrine, the enunciation seems to have been destined to come almost precisely when it did come. Darwin carried with himself the germ of the idea of natural selection for twenty long years before he dared put forward the hypothesis which previously he had felt would be received with hostility, and which he must have thought insufficiently armed. It was only the briefer expression of the same insight by Wallace that led Darwin to publicity. Can it be imagined, if Wallace had met death at sea among the Malay islands, and Darwin, unspurred by his competitor colleague's activity, had carried his theory in hesitant privacy a few years longer and then suddenly succumbed to mortal illness, that we of the civilized world of today should have lived all our intellectual lives without a definite mechanism for evolution and therefore without any active employment of the evolutionary idea—that our biologists would be still standing where Linnaeus, Cuvier, or at most Lamarck stood? If so, the great currents of history would be absolutely conditioned by the lodgment or dislodgment of a bacillus in a particular human frame on a certain day; which conviction would certify to as much understanding as we should credit to him, who, finding in the high Andes the ultimate source of the tiny streamlet farthest removed in tortuous miles from the Atlantic ocean, should set his foot in the bubbling spring and believe that so long as he held it there the Amazon ceased to drain a continent and to pour its tide into the sea.

No. Wallace's crowding on Darwin's heels so that his too was a share, though a minor one, of the glory of the discovery, evidences that behind him trod still others, unnamed and perhaps forever themselves unconscious; and that had the leader or his second fallen by one of the innumerable accidents to which individuals are subject, the followers, one or several or many, would have pressed forward, would have been pressed forward, it would be better to say, and done their work—immediately, as history reckons time.

The failure of Mendel's revolutionizing experiments in exact heredity to achieve the least recognition during their author's life, and for years after, has already been alluded to as an instance of the inexorable fate in store for the discoverer who anticipates his time. He is fortunate indeed if he is permitted to live out his lot in obscurity; and to escape the crucifixion which seemed a meet punishment for the first circumnavigator of Africa who saw the sun on his north. It has been said that Mendel's essay, in which are contained most of the vital principles of the branch of science that now bears his name, was published in a remote and little known source, and therefore failed for a generation to come to the notice of biologists. The last assertion may be challenged as unproved and inherently improbable. It is far more likely that biologist after biologist saw the essay, that some even read it, but that, one and all, it remained meaningless to them—not because they were unusually stupid men, but because they lacked the transcendent superiority of the occasional individual to see issues that lie ahead of those with which the world of their day is wrestling. Slowly, however, time rolled on and a change of content of thought was preparing. Darwin himself had been concerned with the origin and nature of variations. When the first shock of overpowering novelty of his central discovery had begun to be assimilated by scientific conscience, this variation question trended to the front. The investigations of De Vries and Bateson, though their recognized outcome seemed only a destructive analysis of one of the pillars of Darwinism, were accumulating knowledge as to the actual operation of heredity. And then suddenly in 1900, with dramatic eclat, three students, independently and "within a few weeks of each other," discovered the discovery of Mendel, confirmed its conclusions with experience of their own, and a new science was launched on a career of splendid fulfillment.

There may be those who see in these pulsing events only a meaningless play of capricious fortuitousness; but there will be others to whom they reveal a glimpse of a great and inspiring inevitability which rises as far above the accidents of personality as the march of the heavens transcends the wavering contacts of random footprints on clouds of earth. Wipe out the perception of De Vries, Correns, and Tschermak, and it is yet clear that before another year had rolled around, the principles of Mendelian heredity would have been proclaimed to an according world, and by six rather than three discerning minds. That Mendel lived in the nineteenth century instead of the twentieth, and published in 1865, is a fact that proved of the greatest and perhaps regrettable influence on his personal fortunes. As a matter of history, his life and discovery are of no more moment, except as a foreshadowing anticipation, than the billions of woes and gratifications, of peaceful citizen lives or bloody deaths, that have been the fate of men. Mendelian heredity does not date from 1865. It was discovered in 1900 because it could have been discovered only then, and because it infallibly must have been discovered then— given the state of European civilization.

The history of inventions is a chain of parallel instances. An examination of patent office records, in any other than a commercial or anecdotic spirit, would alone reveal the inexorability that prevails in the advance of civilization. The right to the monopoly of the manufacture of the telephone was long in litigation; the ultimate decision rested on an interval of hours between the recording of concurrent descriptions by Alexander Bell and Elisha Gray. Though it is part of our vulgar thinking to dismiss such conflicts as evidences of unscrupulous cupidity and legal inadequacy or as melodramatic coincidence, it behooves the historian to see beyond such childlike plays of the intellect.

The discovery of oxygen is credited to both Priestley and Scheele; its liquefaction to Cailletet as well as to Pictet whose results were attained in the same month of 1877 and announced in one session. Kant as well as La Place can lay claim to the promulgation of the nebular hypothesis. Neptune was predicted by Adams and by Leverrier; the computation of the one, and the publication of that of the other, had precedence by a few months.

For the invention of the steamboat, glory is claimed by their countrymen or partisans for Fulton, Jouffroy, Rumsey, Stevens, Symmington, and others; of the telegraph, for Steinheil and Morse; in photography Talbot was the rival of Daguerre and Niepce. The doubly flanged rail devised by Stevens was reinvented by Vignolet. Aluminum was first practically reduced by the processes of Hall, Heroult, and Cowles. Leibnitz in 1684 as well as Newton in 1687 formulated calculus. Anaesthetics, both ether and nitrous oxide, were discovered in 1845 and 1846, by no less than four men of one nationality. So independent were their achievements, so similar even in details and so closely contemporaneous, that polemics, lawsuits, and political agitation ensued for many years, and there was not one of the four but whose career was embittered, if not ruined, by the animosities arising from the indistinguishability of the priority. Even the south pole, never before trodden by the foot of human beings, was at last reached twice in one summer.

A volume could be written, with but few years' toil, filled with endlessly repeating but ever new accumulation of such instances. When we cease to look upon invention or discovery as some mysterious inherent faculty of individual minds which are randomly dropped in space and time by fate; when we center our attention on the plainer relation of one such advancing step to the others; when, in short, interest shifts from individually biographic elements—which can be only dramatically artistic, didactically moralizing, or psychologically interpretable—and attaches whole heartedly to the social or civilizational, evidence on this point will be infinite in quantity, and the presence of majestic forces or sequences pervading civilization will be irresistibly evident.

Knowing the civilization of an age and a land, we can then substantially affirm that its distinctive discoveries, in this or that field of activity, were not directly contingent upon the personality of the actual inventors that graced the period, but would have been made without them; and that, conversely, had the great illuminating minds of other centuries and climates been born in the civilization referred to, instead of their own, its first achievements would probably have fallen to their lot. Ericsson or Galvani eight thousand years ago might have polished or bored the first stone; and in turn the hand and mind whose operation set in inception the neolithic age of human culture, would, if held in its infancy in unchanging catalepsy from that time until today, now be devising wireless telephones and nitrogen extractors.

Some reservations must be admitted to this principle. It is far from established, rather the contrary, that extraordinary ability, however equal in intensity, is identical in direction. It is highly unlikely that Beethoven put in Newton's cradle would have worked out calculus, or the latter have given the symphony its final form. We can and evidently must admit congenital faculties that are fairly specialized. Everything shows that the elementary mental faculties such as memory, interest, and abstraction, are by nature uneven in individuals of equivalent ability but distinctive bent; and this in spite of cultivation. The educator who proclaimed his ability to convert a native memory for absolute numbers or for mathematical formulas into an equally strong retention of single tones or of complex melodies, would be distrusted. But it does not essentially matter if the originating faculty is one or several in mind. If Eli Whitney could not have formulated the difference between the subjective and the objective and Kant in his place would have failed to devise a practical cotton gin, Watt or Fulton or Morse or Stephenson could in the place of the former, have accomplished his achievement, and Aristotle or Aquinas the task of the latter. It is possibly not even quite accurate to maintain that the individualities of the unknown inventor or inventors of the bow and arrow and those of firearms could have been interchanged, for the first production of the bow necessarily involved mechanical and even manual faculty, while the discovery of gunpowder and of its applicability to weapons may have required the different ability to perceive certain peculiar qualities of a more highly dynamic or chemical nature.

In short, it is a debatable point, though one of the greatest psychological interest, how far human faculty is divisible and subdivisible into distinct kinds. But the matter is not vital in the present connection, for there will hardly be any one rash enough to maintain that there exist as many distinguishable faculties as there are separate human beings; which in fact would be to assert that abilities do not differ in intensity or degree but only in direction or kind; in short, that while no two men were alike, all were equal in potential capacity. If this view is not correct, then it matters little whether the kinds of ability are several or many, because in any case they will be very few compared with the endless number of human organisms; because there will accordingly be so many individuals possessing each faculty, that every age must contain persons with low and mediocre and high measure of intensity of each; and the extraordinary men of one sort in one period will therefore still be substitutable for those of another time in the manner indicated.

If, therefore, anyone's interpretation of mentality is disturbed by some of the particular equivalences that have been suggested, he can easily find others that seem more just, without dissenting from the underlying principle that the march of history, or as it is current custom to name it, the progress of civilization, is independent of the birth of particular personalities; since these apparently averaging substantially alike, both as regards genius and normality, at all times and places, furnish the same substratum for the social.

Here, then, we have an interpretation which allows to the individual, and through him to heredity, all that the science of the organic can legitimately claim on the strength of its actual accomplishments; and which also yields the fullest scope to the social in its own distinctive field. The accomplishment of the individual measured against other individuals depends, if not wholly then mainly, on his organic constitution as compounded by his heredity. The accomplishments of a group, relative to other groups, are little or not influenced by heredity because sufficiently large groups average much alike in organic makeup.

This identity of average is incontestable for some instances of the same nations in closely successive ages—as Athens in 550 and 450, or Germany in 1800 and 1900—during which brief periods their hereditary composition could not have altered to a small fraction of the degree in which cultural achievement varied; it is certainly probable even for people of the same blood separated by long intervals of time and wide divergences of civilization; and it is, while neither proved nor disproved, likely to be nearly true, as suggested before, for the most distant races.

The difference between the accomplishments of one group of men and those of another group is therefore of another order from the difference between the faculties of one person and another. It is through this distinction that one of the essential qualities of the nature of the social is to be found.

The physiological and the mental are bonded as aspects of the same thing, one resolvable into the other; the social is, directly considered, not resolvable into the mental. That it exists only after mentality of a certain kind is in action, has led to confusion of the two, and even their identification. The error of this identification, is a fault that tends to pervade modern thinking about civilization, and which must be overcome by self-discipline before our understanding of this order of phenomena that fill and color our lives can become either clear or serviceable.

If the relation of the individual to culture here outlined is a true one, a conflicting view sometimes held and already alluded to, is unentertainable. This view is the opinion that all personalities are, while not identical, potentially equal in capacity, their varying degrees of accomplishment being due solely to different measures of accord with the social environment with which they are in touch. This view has perhaps been rarely formulated as a generic principle; but it seems to underlie, though usually vaguely and by implication only, many tendencies toward social and educational reform, and is therefore likely to find formal enunciation at some time.

This assumption, which would certainly be of extensive practical application if it could be verified, seems to rest ultimately on a dim but profound perception of the influence of civilization. More completely though this influence of civilization is upon national fortunes than upon individual careers, it nevertheless must influence these latter also. Mohammedanism—a social phenomenon—in stifling the imitative possibilities of the pictorial and plastic arts, has obviously affected the civilization of many peoples; but it must also have altered the careers of many persons born in three continents during a thousand years. Special talents which these men and women possessed for delineative representation may have been suppressed without equal compensation in other directions, in those whose endowment was unique. Of such individuals it is true that the social forces to which they were subject depressed each of them from successful attainment to more mediocre. And without question the same environment elevated many an individual to high rank above his fellows whose special abilities, in some other age and country, would have been repressed to his private disadvantage. The personality born with those qualities that lead to highly successful leadership of religious brigands, for instance, is undoubtedly assured of a more prosperous and contented career in Morocco than in Holland of today.

Even within one nationally limited sphere of civilization, similar results are necessarily bound to occur. The natural logician or administrator born into a caste of fisherman or street sweepers is not likely to achieve the satisfaction in life, and certainly not the success, that would have been his lot had his parents been Brahmins or Kshatriyas; and what is true formally of India holds substantially for Europe.

But, that a social environment may somewhat affect the fortunes and career of the individual as measured against other individuals, does not prove that the individual is wholly the product of circumstances outside of himself, any more than the opposite is true that a civilization is only the sum total of the products of a group of organically shaped minds. The concrete effect of each individual upon civilization is determined by civilization itself. Civilization appears even in some cases and in some measure to influence the effect of the individual's native activities upon himself. But to proceed from these realizations to the inference that all the degree and quality of accomplishment by the individual is the result of his moulding by the society that encompasses him, is assumption, extreme at that, and at variance with observation.

Therefore it is possible to hold the historical or civilizational interpretation of social phenomena without proceeding to occupy the position that the human beings that are the given channels through which civilization courses, are only and wholly the products of its stream. Because culture rests on the specific human faculty, it does not follow that this faculty, the thing in man that is supraanimal, is of social determination. The line between the social and the organic may not be randomly or hastily drawn. The threshold between the endowment that renders the flow and continuance of civilization possible and that which prohibits even its inception, is the demarcation—doubtful enough once, in all probability, but gaping for a longer period than our knowledge covers—between man and animal. The separation between the social itself, however, the entity that we call civilization, and the non-social, the pre-social or organic, is the diversity of quality or order which exists between animal and man conjointly on the one hand, and the products of the interactions of human beings on the other. In the pervious pages the mental has already been subtracted from the social and added to the physically organic which is subject to the influence of heredity. In the same way it is necessary to eliminate the factor of individual capacity from the consideration of civilization. But this elimination means its transfer to the group of organically conceivable phenomena, not its denial. In fact nothing is further from the path of a just prosecution of the understanding of history than such a negation of differences of degree of the faculties of individual men.

In short, social science, if we may take that

word as equivalent to history, does not deny individuality any more than it denies the individual. It does refuse to deal with either individuality or individual as such. And it bases this refusal solely on denial of the validity of either factor for the achievement of its proper aims.

It is true that historical events can also be viewed mechanically, and expressed ultimately in terms of physics and chemistry. Genius may prove definable in unit characters or the constitution of chromosomes, and its particular achievements in osmotic or electric reactions of nerve cells. The day may come when what took place in the tissue of Darwin's brain when he first thought the concept of natural selection, can be profitably studied, or even approximately ascertained, by the physiologist and chemist. Such an achievement, destructive as it may seem to those to whom revelation appeals, would be not only defensible but of enormous interest, and possibly of utility. Only, it would not be history; nor a step toward history or social science.

To know the precise reactions in Darwin's nervous system at the moment when the thought of natural selection flashed upon him in 1838, would involve a genuine triumph of science. But it would mean nothing historically, since history is concerned with the relation of doctrines such as that of natural selection to other concepts and social phenomena, and not with the relation of Darwin himself to social phenomena or other phenomena. This is not the current view of history; but, on the other hand, the current view rests on the endlessly recurring but obviously illogical assumption that because without individuals civilization could not exist, civilization therefore is only a sum total of the psychic operations of a mass of individuals.

As, then, there are two lines of intellectual endeavor in history and in science, each with its separate aim and set of methods; and as it is only the confounding of the two that results in sterility; so also two wholly disparate evolutions must be recognized: that of the substance which we call organic and that of the phenomena called social. Social evolution is without antecedents in the beginnings of organic evolution. It commences late in the development of life—long after vertebrates, after mammals, after the primates even, are established. Its exact point of origin we do not know, and perhaps shall never know;

but we can limit the range within which it falls. This origin occurred in a series of organic forms more advanced, in general mental faculty, than the gorilla, and much less developed than the first known race that is unanimously accepted as having been human, the man of Neandertal and Le Moustier. In point of time, these first carriers of the rudiments of civilization must antedate the Neandertal race by far, but must be posterior to other extinct human ancestors of the approximate intellectual level of the modern gorilla and chimpanzee.

The beginning of social evolution, of the civilization which is the subject of history, thus coincides with that of mystery of the popular mind: the missing link. But the term "link" is misleading. It implies a continuous chain. But with the unknown bearers of the primeval and gradually manifesting beginnings of civilization, there took place a profound alteration rather than an improved passing of the existing. A new factor has arisen which was to work out its own independent consequences, slowly and of little apparent import at first, but gathering weight, and dignity, and influence; a factor that had passed beyond natural selection, that was no longer wholly dependent on any agency of organic evolution, and that, however rocked and swayed by the oscillations of the heredity that underlay it, nevertheless floated unimmersibly upon it.

The dawn of the social thus is not a link in a chain, not a step in a path, but a leap to another plane. It may be likened to the first occurrence of life in the hitherto lifeless universe, the hour when that one of infinite chemical combinations took place which put the organic into existence, and made it that from this moment on there should be two worlds in place of one. Atomic qualities and movements were not interfered with when that seemingly slight event took place; the majesty of the mechanical laws of the cosmos was not diminished; but something new was inextinguishably added to the history of this planet.

One might compare the inception of civilization to the end of the process of slowly heating water. The expansion of the liquid goes on a long time. Its alteration can be observed by the thermometer as well as in bulk, in its solvent power as well as in its internal agitation. But it remains water. Finally, however, the boiling point is attained. Steam is produced: the rate of enlargement of volume

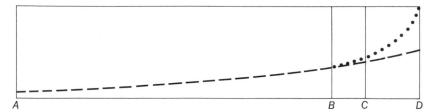

is increased a thousand fold; and in place of a glistening, percolating fluid, a volatile gas diffuses invisibly. Neither the laws of physics nor those of chemistry are violated; nature is not set aside; but yet a saltation has taken place: the slow transitions that accumulated from zero to one hundred have been transcended in an instant, and a condition of substance with new properties and new possibilities of effect is in existence.

Such, in some manner, must have been the result of the appearance of this new thing, civilization. We need not consider that it abolished the course of development of life. It certainly has not in any measure done away with its own substratum of the organic. And there is no reason to believe that it was born full fledged. All these incidents and manners of the inception of the social are after all of little consequence to an understanding of its specific nature, and of the relation of that nature to the character of the organic substance that preceded in absolute time and still supports it. The point is, there was an addition of something new in kind, an initiation of that which was to run a course of its own.

We may sketch the relation which exists between the evolutions of the organic and of the social (see figure above). A line progressing with the flow of time, rises slowly, but gatheringly. At a certain point, another line begins to diverge from it, insensibly at first, but ascending ever farther above it on its own course; until, at the moment where the curtain of the present cuts off our view, each is advancing, but far from the other, and uninfluenced by it.

In this illustration, the continuous line denotes the level inorganic; the broken line, the evolution of the organic; the line of dots, the development of civilization. Height above the base is degree of advancement, whether that be complexity, heterogeneity, degree of coördination, or anything else. A is the beginning of time on this earth as revealed to our understandings. B marks the point of the true missing link, of the first human precursor, the first animal that carried and accumulated tradition. C would denote the state reached by what we are accustomed to call primitive man, that Neandertal *Homo* who was our forefather in culture if not in blood; and D, the present moment.

It is inevitable that if there is foundation for the contentions that have been set forth, an arguing from one of these lines to the other must be futile. To assert, because the upper line has risen rapidly just before it is cut off, that the one below it must also have ascended proportionally more in this period than in any before, is obviously uncompelling. That our institutions, our knowledge, the exercising of our minds, have advanced dizzyingly in twenty thousand years is no reason that our bodies and brains, our mental equipment and its physiological basis, have advanced in any corresponding measure as is sometimes argued by scientists and generally taken for granted by men at large. If anything, it might be an evidence that the lower, organic line has fallen off in its rate of ascent. The bodies and minds in this line have continued to carry civilization; but this civilization has met the struggle of the world in such a way that much of the stress has been directed away from these bodies and minds. We do not argue that the progress of organic evolution is *prima facie* indication that inorganic matter is more complex, more advanced in its combinations, or in any sense "higher," than it was fifty million years ago; much less that organic evolution has taken place through an inorganic evolution as cause. And no more can we infer from social development to a progress of the hereditary forms of life.

In fact, not only is the correlation of the lines of organic and social development as unjustified theoretically as it would be to argue from the compressibility or weight of water to that of steam; but all evidence directs us as to the conviction that in recent periods civilization has raced at a speed so far outstripping the pace of hereditary evolution, that the latter has, if not actually standing still, afforded all the seeming, relatively, of making no progress. There are a hundred elements of civilization where there was one in the time when the Neandertal skull enclosed a living brain; and not only the content of civilization but the complexity of its organization has increased a hundredfold. But the body and the associated mind of that early man have not attained a point a hundred times, nor even twice, as fine, as efficient, as delicate, or as strong, as they were then; it is doubtful if they have improved by a fifth. There are, it is true, those who make the contrary assertion. Yet it seems the fair-minded must avow that such assertions rest not on objective interpretation of the facts, but on a wish to find a correlation, a desire to make the thread of evolution a single, unbranching one, to see the social only as organic.

Here, then, we have to come to our conclusion; and here we rest. The mind and the body are but facets of the same organic material or activity; the social substance—or unsubstantial fabric, if one prefers the phrase —the thing that we call civilization, transcends them for all its being rooted in life. The processes of civilizational activity are almost unknown to us. The factors that govern their workings are unresolved. The forces and principles of mechanistic science can indeed analyze our civilization; but in so doing they destroy its essence, and leave us without understanding of the very thing which we seek. The historian as yet can do little but picture. He traces and he connects what seems far removed; he balances; he integrates; but he does not really explain, nor does he transmute phenomena into something else. His method is not mechanistic; but neither can the physicist or physiologist deal with historical material and leave it civilization nor convert it into concepts of life and leave nothing else to be done. What we all are able to do is to realize this gap, to be impressed by it with humility, and to go our paths on its respective sides without self-deluding boasts that the chasm has been bridged.

*selection 46*

# Diffusionism and Darwinism

## Erik K. Reed

*From Brief Communications.* American Anthropologist, *Vol. 63, No. 2, Part 1, 1961, pp. 375–377. By permission of the author and the publisher.*

Among the important points which seem to me to have been missed, overlooked, or distorted in recent—and not so recent— discussions of evolutionism in archeology-anthropology (e.g., papers by various authors in the Anthropological Society of Washington symposium volume, *Evolution and Anthropology: a Centennial Appraisal*, Washington, D. C., 1959;

publications by Julian Steward and by Leslie White) is this: The concept of unilinear and uniform progress through certain stages, and consequent expectations and attempts to find the same identical stages in different parts of the world, with the concomitant notion of psychic unity of mankind applied to specific details and utilized to explain close correspondences in culture—all this may be *called* evolutionism, as it has been, but it certainly is not, or was not, Darwinism. Neither the fact of biological evolution nor the theory which best explains it, that of variation and selection, requires or in any way suggests unilinear world-wide progression through uniform stages.

Actually, the extreme diffusionists probably are closer to corresponding with biological evolution. The rise of a new species, and hence also the appearance of a new genus or larger taxon, occurs initially within a subdivision or population of a previously existing species, and takes place gradually by increase and spread of variations, with or without disappearance of the previous form as such. The essence of transformation by variation and selection, in fact, is precisely that no species, or other grouping of living individuals, plant or animal, is ever abruptly and completely changed to a different and new form. Surely no biologist would ever have said that all cultural sequences—that is, all men—must pass or have passed through similar levels of development quite separately, independent but parallel. That would be like claiming that all fishes are going to become amphibians eventually, or that all Eocene horses changed simultaneously from having four toes on their front feet to three toes when they learned of the imminent arrival of Oligocene times.

The diffusionist view of cultural change is almost identical with normal biological evolution: a variation arises within an existing form (and uniquely, appearing only once; at a definite, if generally unknown, time and place) and, if it is a favorable variation (acceptance by other people would here represent or constitute survival value), it spreads.

Attacks on "unilinear evolutionism" have been largely unnecessary or misdirected, consequently. And few of the founders of evolutionism in anthropology ever said, either, that all men have to pass through all stages in the proper order. Tylor, for example, simply pointed out that advanced civilizations are "results of gradual development from an earlier, simpler, and ruder state of life. No stage of civilization comes into existence spontaneously, but grows or is developed out of the stage before it"—which is manifestly self-evident to the point of truism. And similarly, Morgan asserted that "savagery preceded barbarism . . . as barbarism is known to have preceded civilization." In these and other statements by these men and others, at least those few of Tylor's caliber, I see neither teleology and orthogenesis nor insistence on widespread uniformity. Boas was, I judge, attacking only minor and incidental misconceptions of evolution in advising that "we renounce the vain endeavor to construct a uniform systematic history of the evolution of culture."

In a paper entitled "Conflict and Congruence in Anthropological Theory," the situation is cogently summarized by Linton C. Freeman:

In E. B. Tylor's work we find evolution in its purest form; it includes not only the search for diachronic relationships, but the use of evaluative criteria as well. Tylor lived and wrote in a period and place where the dominant theme of the culture was progress . . . if we reinterpret Tylor's stress upon evolutionary stages, we find that he has suggested a characteristic relationship among his variables. He has proposed, for example, that a change in settlement pattern will be accompanied by a change in occupational specialization. . . . In short, Tylor has proposed a specific interrelationship among a set of societal variables.

Mr. Freeman then points out that the structural-functionalists are simply making the same statement but from a purely synchronic point of view.

There has been, admittedly, such misuses and misconceptions as Boas was rightly criticizing. The idea that a nomadic pastoral stage was required in the central basis or general and theoretical sequence and should be interpolated between hunters-gatherers and sedentary agriculturalists was based on logic, not evidence, and had to be discarded; but at least it was, after all, logical and simply happened to be wrong. The idea that all of the same cultural periods, all of the same stone-working stages and other successive technological developments, should be expected and found in the same order, in every area, likewise is not theoretically unreasonable, but obviously had to be qualified considerably. And it can be a diffusionist concept rather than automatically and necessarily leading inevitably to the idea of psychic unity and parallel independent development; but using it with diffusion—variation and radiation—in mind, the absence of certain stages, and of many important specific traits, in various areas is much more readily acceptable.

The concept or phrase "multilinear evolution" is a perfectly acceptable one for a sort of quick descriptive summary reference to what has gone on; but I am not sure that it adds very much—evolution *is* multilinear. The histories of, say, Galápagos finches on separate islands are different; those of, say, Old World primates and South American monkeys differ far more widely. The histories of separate cultures in various parts of the world are, naturally, different. But the tremendous complexity of the history of human culture and the enormous number of its variations do not obviate, though they quite evidently obscure, the simple basic fact, recognized from Tylor and before to Leslie White, that the

more complex forms follow and are based on and essentially derived from simpler ones, in culture as among living things.

The theory of succession in social organization from promiscuity through matrilineal organization followed by patriarchy and polygyny to bilateral monogamy is not acceptable; but the statement that social stratification and specialization occur with advanced complex technology presumably would be. Urban civilizations not only came later in time than unspecialized villages, they develop out of them. Sedentary agricultural societies followed and grew out of less sedentary groups dependent entirely on wild foods. This does not mean that all food-collectors must in time become agriculturalists, or that they must necessarily have polished stone or pottery before they can become sedentary and agricultural, or bronze before iron, or else, that they must inevitably acquire or develop bronze and pottery shortly after they have become farmers grouped in villages.

But neither does this flexibility mean that there are no regularities, no continuous line or trends in human history, no cultural evolution, and no sense to it all.

*selection* 47

# Limited Possibilities in Culture

## Alexander Goldenweiser

*From* History, Psychology, and Culture. *Alfred A. Knopf, Inc., 1933, pp. 45–49. By permission of the publisher.*

### The Limitation of Possibilities and Convergence

A limitation of possibilities checks variety. In relation to historical series of linked objects or features, this means that wherever a wider range of variability in origins and developments coexists with a limitation of end results, there will be reduction in variability, decrease in dissimilarity, and increase in similarity or convergence. Most patent illustrations of this principle can be found in the domain of material culture or technology. Take an oar. Arms can be used as oars. Also all kinds of materials, stone, bone, bark, even metal. Oars can be long or short, light or heavy, circular in cross-section or flat, wide or narrow, of even width or otherwise. Now, in accordance with local conditions, or chance, most of these materials and shapes have been used for oars at one time or another and are still being so used, in a pinch. But if you want a *good* oar—and this is what you do want, at length—the end result is limited by the conditions of use. The oar must not be so short as not to reach the water or only barely so, or too long; it must not be so heavy as to be unwieldy, or so light as to preclude the resistance desirable in measured rhythmic movement; it should not be brittle or so pliable as to render it unfit as a lever in a dense medium. The manner in which an oar is used precludes uniformity of shape throughout its length. The blade, in order to offer proper resistance to the water and thus enhance propulsion, must be flat, also somewhat curved longitudinally and laterally, like a shallow spoon open at the end, with the concavity on the side opposite to the direction of the movement of the boat. The butt end, on the other hand, must be adjusted to manipulation; it must not be flat but circular in cross-section, not too bulky nor too slight. The middle section of the oar is a connecting link between the blade and the butt; its length is determined by the desirable length of the oar; it must be strong enough to withstand the stresses; and so on. It is desirable, finally, that the oar be of material that can float, so that it could be readily recovered from the water. The limitation imposed by conditions of use is here so drastic that every oar is emphatically—an oar, implying numerous points of similarity between all oars. Now, no one but a wholly myopic diffusionist would believe that the oar has been invented but once in the history of culture. It would be equally absurd to assume that the precise stages, initial and subsequent, in the development of oars in different localities were identical or even markedly similar. But sooner or later, in one way or another, they all had to come about, to result

in the *good* oar, a tool with certain relatively fixed features determined by conditions of effective use. Thus the histories of the oar in different places represent a set of convergent processes.

Similar settings encounter us on all sides. There may be all sorts of pots, but any pot, in addition to being a particular kind of pot or this specific individual pot, is, first of all, a pot; that is, a receptacle fit to hold things, to put things or pour liquids into; it is a receptacle similar to a bottle or a vase, but also different from both. As such, it has and must have certain features that are diagnostic —for a pot. The art of fashioning a fit, handy pot will be learned. This process of learning, taking generations, differs in different places, but ultimately there emerges—a pot, a good pot fit for use. Such a pot is, in many essential particulars, like any other pot. There is here, once more, convergence.

And so it is with practically any object, tool or weapon. In many technologically indifferent features the range of variability is unlimited; but the requirements of effective use impose limitations, more or less stringent, on the variability of other features—there is a narrowing of the range if the object is to function as intended. Now, these diagnostic features, earmarks of fitness, can but seldom be intuited in advance of experience; rather are they discovered in the course of operation, in the painful school of trial and error, where an object, tool, weapon, which is not what it should be, exacts a penalty from the operator. All such processes are strictly historical and, as such, subject to the incidents of time, place, ability, traditional pattern, chance; but if persisted in long enough, these processes will converge in certain features to culminate in the desired goal—a thing fit for its uses.

What is so patent in technology applies equally to other aspects of culture, where, however, the operation of the principle is less readily discernible.

Decorative art, from certain angles, appears as an extension of the technological field. Designs on basketry, for example, are characterized by angularity owing to certain peculiarities of basketry technique. The limitation here lies in the latter. As a result, patterns of whatever provenience, when drawn into the basketry field, acquire the characteristic traits of angular designs, being thus reduced, in a measure, to a common denominator. There is convergence.

If geometrical designs in different regions are examined from the standpoint of rectilinearity and curvilinearity, what we find is not a haphazard utilization of both, but the predominance or even absolute sway of either one or the other, or, in certain instances, a combination of both with certain fixed limitations. The limitation here is not technological but psychological. Rectilinearity and curvilinearity are not indifferent elements in design. On the contrary, they strike the eye and command attention. What we observe, then, is that as soon as one or the other type of design gains the ascendancy—and this may happen for all sorts of reasons—it will push on to complete dominance, ultimately excluding the other type altogether. Or, again, the two tendencies will come to a compromise, as it were, the result being a mixed type. Before a geometrical art reaches relative stability, it will have to assume one of these three forms. To these forms then all geometrical arts, of whatever origin or history, will converge.

The same holds in the philosophical level, with reference, for example, to materialism and spiritualism. Entities, if not material, must be spiritual or, at least, not wholly material. In the subconscious philosophy of the primitives, both categories were accepted, no attempt being made to reduce one to the other. In the deliberate rationalistic philosophies of later ages such attempts at reduction to monism were made again and again; either spirit or mind (which, if conceived as an entity, is no more nor less than spirit) was reduced to matter, or vice versa; or, as in Spinoza or Spencer, the two were regarded as different aspects of something third. Neither the origins nor the histories of these intellectual approaches were the same, but the end results were identical or strictly comparable, of necessity so, owing to the limitation of possibilities. Once more, there was convergence.

In *dependent convergence* the limitation of possibilities is introduced by the prevailing patterns. Any thing or custom coming in from outside, for example, will have to assimilate itself to such a pattern or be rejected. A business organization, a club, a spiritualistic doctrine, may be borrowed from "abroad" where different patterns prevail. Each one of these cultural features will have to converge to the pattern prevalent in the new home, or acclimatization will be impossible, or difficult. The cultural intercourse between Europe and India, for example, abounds in convergences of this last type, working, in this case, in both directions. In two countries, finally, belonging to a wider culture area, such as France and Germany, many cultural patterns are of necessity the same. The pattern, as we saw, here provides the limitation. Suppose then a foreign custom or idea-complex strikes France and also Germany. In each it will converge to the local pattern. But, the two patterns being similar, the resulting convergences—in France and Germany—will also be similar. Thus a new item of similarity will be added to the cultures of the two countries.

Limitation, then, invites convergence. Whenever convergence is pitted against diffusion, while historic evidence is lacking, it thus becomes necessary to examine each instance for a possible limiting factor. Should such a one be present, convergence becomes probable, and the burden of proof then falls on the diffusionist.

# Some Aspects of Culture Change in the Northern Philippines

## Fred Eggan

The peoples of the northern Philippines, including both the pagans of the Mountain Province and the Christianized natives of the coastal regions, offer an excellent opportunity to study certain problems of culture contact and change under relatively controlled conditions. There has been considerable interest in the field of culture change in recent years, and enough pioneer studies have been carried out to enable various students of acculturation to clarify the relevant concepts, outline the processes of culture change, and suggest future lines of research.

In regard to the general *results* of culture contact, however, these studies have little to offer so far. The only constant phenomenon in situations of acculturation, according to Linton, "is the establishment in the two cultures involved, of mutual modifications and adaptations which will enable the two groups to live together." One reason for this situation seems to be that the field of acculturation is a relatively new one and the studies have been exploratory rather than intensive, in the main. For students who are interested in making generalizations about the results of culture contact under specified conditions, however, an intensive study of instances of acculturation should be very rewarding.

Herskovits and others have pointed out the greater historical control which can be exerted over the data in studies of acculturation; by a careful selection of instances of acculturation it should be possible to extend this control in another dimension. By studying a series of tribes with similar cultures but subject to

*From* American Anthropologist, *Vol. 43, No. 1, 1941, pp. 11–18. By permission of the author and the publisher.*

varying degrees or kinds of contact, or conversely, by studying the reactions of different cultures to similar contacts, it should be possible, by comparison, to isolate some of the factors responsible for certain changes and to generalize as to the results of various classes of culture contact.

Redfield has been engaged for several years on an intensive comparative study of culture change in Yucatan and Guatemala, with the assistance of several associates. Here he has been interested in defining the changes undergone by various groups under influences emanating from the city, and he has tried to state these changes in general terms so that they might be tested in other regions. In Yucatan, for example, he found a uniform series of changes from a primitive or "folk" type of culture to modern urban civilization, as he went from isolated Maya villages in the bush, through less isolated villages, to the capital at Merida.

In 1934-1935 the writer spent a year among the Tinguian in the northern Philippines initiating a study of culture change which might furnish information to test or modify the generalizations made on the basis of the studies in Middle America and elsewhere. The Tinguian offer an unusual opportunity for the study of cultural change since they have been subjected to varying degrees of contact. The earlier influences from the Hindu empires in Sumatra and Java, and the Chinese, and possibly Japanese, influences can be dealt with only in general terms, but the Spanish period is better documented. The Tinguian were thoroughly studied by Dr. and Mrs. Cole in 1907-1908 at the end of a long period of Spanish contact; almost a century earlier we have Gironiere's account of his journey through a portion of the Tinguian country, an account which gives a base for evaluating changes during the Spanish regime. During the period since 1900 there has been rather intensive and direct contact with American civilization, consequent upon our occupation of the Philippines, so that certain changes have taken place rather rapidly. Further, various communities among the Tinguian and their neighbors have been affected differentially, being subjected to varying degrees, or different kinds, of acculturation; these could be studied simultaneously and the results compared with the historical sequences.

A preliminary analysis of the data collected indicated that culture change among the Tinguian was a highly complex affair. Comparisons of accounts at different time levels, or for villages subject to differential contacts, gave sequences which could be correlated with outside influences, whether native or European. But further investigation suggested that many of these changes were a part of larger changes which involved a whole series of tribes in Northern Luzon; hence culture change among the Tinguian could not be satisfactorily studied without projecting it against the larger outline of culture change in the region as a whole.

There are, in Northern Luzon, a series of tribes with similar basic cultures—Ilocano, Tinguian, Apayao, Bontoc, Ifugao, and Igorot, among others. These people are organized in villages and their economic activities center around the cultivation of rice. Each participates in a common set of institutions to a certain extent, but there is considerable variation from one group to another. When this variation is examined more closely, it is found not to be haphazard, nor is it organized concentrically. As one goes from the interior down to the coast, from Ifugao through Bontoc, Tinguian, and Ilocano, a regular series of changes takes place in social, political, economic, and religious institutions, a series of changes which has a definite direction.

An awareness of this "cultural drift" (to paraphrase the late E. Sapir) is essential to a proper understanding of changes in Tinguian culture. Changes, which on the surface seemed to be the results of Spanish or American contacts, turned out on closer inspection to be native cultural changes. Resistance to change, on the one hand, or rapid acceptance, on the other, seemed explicable in many cases in terms of this "drift."

As we go from the interior to the coast— from the Ifugao to the Ilocano—the social and political organization becomes more and more complex. Among the Ifugao the villages are small and usually scattered along the valleys. There is no village political organization, kinship is practically the sole social bond, and social control outside the kin group is embodied in a large number of specific rules and regulations. Bontoc villages are large, but village organization is not centralized; rather the villages are divided into a series of wards

(*atos*), each with its own council and a considerable degree of independence of action.
The *atos* tend to patrilocal residence but there
is no conscious patrilineal organization. Tinguian villages are often larger, with clusters
of barrios about a central nucleus, and with
a central authority, the village headman or
*lakay*. Ilocano villages are also large, and
often two or more were combined under a
single political authority, according to the
early Spanish accounts.

Correlated with this shift in village organization are variations in the kinship system and
in social control. The Ifugao have a pure
"Hawaiian" kinship system organized on a
strict generation pattern and extending bi-
laterally to a wide but definite range. All
cousins, for example, are siblings, and definite obligations extend as far as third cousins
(descendants of the great-great-grandparents)
and a little beyond. The Bontoc kinship system
is not so well known but there is a partial
differentiation of relatives in the direction of
the European system and the effective range
seems less than among the Ifugao. The Tinguian carry this differentiation further but still
class all cousins together. While the system is
widely extended, the effective range of obligations is even further reduced. The Ilocano
system approximates the European system
and the effective range of kin obligations is
still further reduced, not extending much beyond first cousins.

As kinship gradually differentiates and its
effective range narrows, social units based
upon territorial ties, the *ato*, barrio, and village,
become more important, though kin ties still
operate as an integrating mechanism binding
them together. Social responsibilities correl-
atively shift from kinship groups to *ato*
groups, barrio groups, and village groups; and
social control from family heads to *ato* councils, to the *lakay* or headman of the village.
Customary law among the Ifugao is highly
developed with a multitude of specified offenses and associated fines. Each family is
responsible for the enforcement of the customary law, with the assistance of a temporary "go-between" who gives advice and
mediates but has no legal standing. Fines
when collected go to the family, though when
a "go-between" is called in he gets a fee
also. Among the Bontoc customary law seems

fairly well developed, but the *ato* councils
mediate the cases and apparently take a portion of the fine for themselves. The *lakay*
decides cases among the Tinguian, assisted
by an informal council of old men. For most
offenses there is a single fine—thirty pesos—
but in practice the *lakay* varies the amount in
accordance with the circumstances of the case
and the financial standing of the parties concerned. Ilocano practice today is based upon
modern Filipino political and legal organization; what the older practices were is not
known in detail but they probably approxi-
mated to those of the Tinguian. Thus, with the
development of central political authority, customary law decreases in complexity and development until it practically vanishes.

Economic organization everywhere centers
around land—particularly rice land. The terracing of rice lands reaches its highest development among the Ifugao and decreases
as one goes towards the coast, but that is
partly a result of topography and water supply, though the time factor and population
pressure may be important also. Wealth—
measured in rice lands—is the key to social
status. In all groups there are relatively fixed
social classes based largely upon the ownership and control of land. Class lines seem to
be more sharply drawn as one goes from
the interior to the coast; in early times the
Ilocano had a class of "slaves," in addition
to rich, middle, and poor classes. The
amount of wealth per capita increases sharply
as one goes toward the coast; there are relatively few rich men among the Ifugao and
Bontoc, many among the Tinguian, and still
more among the Ilocano.

Marriage customs seem here to be correlated with these differences in wealth.
Among the Ifugao and Bontoc marriage for
the great majority is a matter of free choice—
a result of trial matings in special sleeping
dormitories—followed by a series of regular
marriage rituals. The Ifugao do not allow
marriage within the range of the effective kinship unit—which includes third cousins on
both sides—without special ceremonies; the
Bontoc enforce an informal *ato* exogamy. The
rich families in both groups, however, do not
allow their children to marry in the ordinary
way, but arrange their marriages for them.
The reason given is that it is necessary to

conserve their property in rice lands. Since there are relatively few rich men, it is probable that these arranged marriages are often with closer relatives than in the case of the trial matings.

Among the Tinguian, who are relatively much wealthier, all marriages are arranged by the parental groups. Such arranged marriages are always with a distant relative, preferably a third or fourth cousin. Second cousins are considered too close except in the lowland villages near the coast where such marriages are common. The reasons given are to keep the families united and to keep rice fields and other wealth in the kinship group. The Ilocano likewise arrange a considerable number of marriages, at least, and here several marriages of first cousins were recorded, the reasons given being the same.

Separation or divorce is relatively easy and frequent among the Ifugao and Bontoc, but is difficult and expensive among the Tinguian. At present, the Ilocano, being Catholic, find divorce almost impossible; the earlier situation is difficult to ascertain.

In religious beliefs and rituals, also, there are definite changes from the interior to the coast. The Ifugao have an elaborate hierarchy of deities who are invoked by male priests and controlled by verbal rituals and offerings. Souls of the dead are important but serve largely as intermediaries between the people and the more important deities. Among the Bontoc, the souls of the dead seem relatively more important, though less is known of Bontoc religion. Most Ifugao men act as priests at one time or another, though some specialize more completely; among the Bontoc the priesthood seems more highly restricted and specialized. In both groups Lumauig is the important culture hero; in neither is there evidence of a single supreme deity.

For the Tinguian non-human spirits take precedence over the souls of the dead, who are relatively unimportant. Female mediums, of little importance in the interior, here occupy the center of the stage in the curing rituals and the prestige ceremonies, although men usually conduct the communal ceremonies. Kabunian, the culture hero, is similar to Lumauig; there is in addition a central deity called Kadaklan. The Ilocano likewise believe in a host of spirits as well as the Christian god, Apo Dios; formerly they believed in Kabunian also. The souls of the dead are no longer important factors in religious life.

This "cultural drift"—this regular series of changes in cultural institutions as one goes from the interior to the coast, or vice versa—is in part a phenomenon of acculturation, of course. The direction of these changes seems to be from the interior to the coast in many cases, but certain of the variations may have been part of the cultural heritage brought from earlier homes; we cannot assume that the interior peoples present the early forms of institutions in all cases.

The factors responsible for certain of these variations are both external and internal. Long continued contacts with Asiatic and European peoples have brought about both direct and indirect changes; these have affected the coastal peoples more profoundly but have also penetrated into the interior. But certain of the changes seem based upon internal socio-economic factors which vary from one region to another and which operate relatively independently. Thus the shift in village organization seems more closely related to topography and water distribution than to acculturation phenomena. Likewise, the variations in social organization which we have noted seem to represent a series of correlated phenomena which has an internal consistency and which is related to factors such as population density, relative wealth per capita, and the like, rather than to external contacts.

The variations in the kinship systems and the shift from a kinship to a kinship-territorial organization, and the corresponding changes in political organization and social control, seem at first glance to be primarily the results of contact with western European cultures. But, with the exception of the Ilocano, who have long been subject to direct Spanish contacts, I am not convinced that this is entirely the case. There is little of the disorganization of native society which such contacts often engender, and when the institutions are studied comparatively it is difficult (with the possible exception of religion) to find direct evidence of outside influence. On the other hand these variations in cultural institutions seem highly interrelated and it may be possible to state these relations in the form of correlations and to explain them, in part at least, as the result of internal factors. These correlations may then be tested and modified by comparison with the results of similar studies elsewhere.

Returning to the problem of acculturation among the Tinguian, we pointed out earlier that some aspects of culture change, at least, could not be satisfactorily understood without seeing them against this larger background of change in the whole region. The Spanish, for example, have usually received credit for stopping the "vicious circle" of head-hunting in the Tinguian region, thus enabling trade and other contacts to develop over a wider area. A closer examination of the situation among the Tinguian and their neighbors, however, suggests that the Tinguian had themselves developed an effective mechanism for stopping head-hunting. They had long since made peace between neighboring villages and maintained it through intermarriage; being at a disadvantage in conflicts with villages over the mountains to the east they had developed "peace pacts" with them, based on the same principles as the marriage agreements between two families, and called by the same term. These were rigidly enforced by the headmen and made trade and travel possible over a wide area. The relative ease with which head-hunting was stopped in the Tinguian region, compared with the difficulties encountered in the Ifugao and Bontoc areas, seems as much a result of the shift in type of social integration as of the efforts of the Spanish authorities.

On the other hand, the Spanish worked in vain to Christianize the Tinguian, while the Americans have struggled to break down the class system through the introduction of free public education and universal suffrage. The class lines seem to be stronger as we approach the coast. The Spanish had great success with the coastal peoples because they set themselves on top of the class structure but continued to maintain it. The American authorities, correspondingly, have had greater success among the interior peoples in their efforts to break down the class system; the coastal peoples have resisted these efforts at every turn.

The Spanish Christianized the Ilocano rather rapidly in the sixteenth and seventeenth centuries, whereas the Tinguian at first glance show little in their religious practices that looks Christian; in actual practice, however, the two groups are not very different. The Tinguian supreme deity, Kadaklan, may represent a borrowing from the Ilocano version of the Spanish deity, Apo Dios, but this is an indirect rather than a direct influence. The Tinguian have not developed any nativistic religious movements so far, probably because their socio-economic life has not been seriously disturbed; some of the movements among the Ilocano, however, partake of the character of such nativistic movements.

The marriage and divorce practices among the Tinguian, which appear to correspond much better to European standards of morality than do those of the interior, are in all probability not the results of Spanish influences but rather the results of the particular situations in regard to land and wealth which we have noted. The Ilocano, who carry some of these practices still further, often violate Catholic regulation by the marriage of first cousins, a tendency which is intelligible in terms of the wider changes we have noted.

These brief comments suggest that the study of cultural change in a single group may be more profitable when that change is seen against the background of larger changes which may be going on in the region. In the case of the northern Philippines, these larger changes form a regular series with a definite direction; this series of correlated changes offers interesting problems in itself. Further, an adequate understanding of this larger picture will enable a better interpretation of the changes in any one of the component cultural groups. Here is an instance where historical and comparative studies may cooperate to create a better understanding of the processes and results of culture change.

# The Social Consequence of a Change in Subsistence Economy

## Ralph Linton

*From the Tanala of Madagascar. In Abram Kardiner (ed.),* The Individual and His Society, *Columbia University Press, 1939, pp. 282–290. By permission of the author and the publisher.*

The culture . . . described is that of the Tanala of the dry rice cultivation. Wet rice cultivation, which introduced so many elements in social change that the whole culture was eventually altered, was borrowed from their Betsileo neighbors to the east. It was at first an adjunct to dry rice carried on by individual families. Before the new method was introduced on a large scale, there were already rice swamps of permanent tenure, which never reverted to the village for re-assignment. But land favorable for this use was very limited, because of natural factors. Thus there gradually emerged a group of landowners, and with the process came a breakdown in the joint family organization. The cohesiveness of this older unit was maintained by economic interdependence and the need for cooperation. But an irrigated rice field could be tended by a single family, and its head need not recognize any claim to share it with anyone who had not contributed to its produce.

This group of permanent rice sites formed the nucleus of a permanent village, because the land could not be exhausted as was the land exploited by the dry method. As land suitable for wet rice near the village was presently all taken up, the landless households had to move farther and farther away into the jungle. So far away would they be that they could not return the same day. These distant fields also became household rather than joint family affairs.

The moving of the older unit from one land site to another had kept the joint family intact. But now single landless households were forced to move, while there were in the same unit landowners who had a capital investment and no incentive to move. The migrant groups were thus cross-sections of the original lineages. Each original village had a group of descendant villages, each one surrounded by irrigated fields and private ownership.

The mobile villages had been self-contained and endogamous. The settled villages were much less so. The joint family retained its religious importance, based on the worship of a common ancestor, even after its component households had been scattered. Family members would be called together on ceremonial occasions, and thus the old village isolation broke down. Intermarriages became common. In this way, the transformation from independent villages to a tribal organization took place.

The process brought further changes in the patterns of native warfare. The old village had to be defended; but not at so great a cost nor with the necessity for permanent upkeep. When the village became permanent the defenses had to be of a powerful kind, involving big investments and permanent upkeep.

Slaves, who were of no economic significance in the old system, now acquired economic importance. This gave rise to new techniques of ransom. Thus the tribal organization grew in solidity, and with the change the old tribal democracy disappeared. The next step was a king at the head who exercised control over the settled elements but not over the mobile ones. The kingdom came to an end before any adequate machinery of government could be established. This king built himself an individual tomb, thus breaking an ancient custom.

The changes were therefore, a king at the head, settled subjects, rudimentary social classes based on economic differences, and lineages of nothing but ceremonial importance. Most of these changes had already taken place among the Betsileo. The cooperative system made individual wealth impossible. Nor was the change devoid of serious stresses on the individual; a new class of interests, new life goals, and new conflicts came into being.

One of the Tanala clans, the Zafimaniry, was one of the first to take up the new wet rice cultivation. They continued it for a time, but finally abandoned it, and returned to the dry rice method. They offered as the reason for returning to the old method the fact that they had been attacked by an enemy, which scattered the men of the various households. The tribe tabooed the raising of wet rice, and still continues to refuse to take up wet rice despite depletion of the jungle.

Although we are not in possession of all the facts, and a great many unknown factors may have operated, we are justified in looking into the culture of the Betsileo for a contrast with the ultimate changes coincident with wet rice culture. The traditions of the Betsileo have it that there was a time when all people were equal and all land was held in common. Moreover, the cultural similarity to the Tanala leaves no doubt that in the main we are dealing with two cultures springing from a cognate source. Or to be more accurate, the changes we find in Betsileo culture were engrafted on a culture similar in all respects to the one we found in Tanala.

Whatever adventitious changes took place, basically we can regard Betsileo as the Tanala culture, after all the changes consequent upon wet rice had become consolidated, organized, and institutionalized. We are therefore observing an important experiment in the dynamics of social change.

In Betsileo society the gens is still the foundation of social life, descent being traced through the male line from a single ancestor. But the organization of the village as in Tanala culture is gone; it apparently disappeared accordng to the steps outlined above.

The local clan groups were administered by heads appointed by the king, one head for each gens. Members of several gentes live in the same village. Instead of free access to gens lands, as in Tanala culture, we have here a rigid system of ground rent levied on the land in the form of a proportion of rice produce.

Instead of the previous democracy as among the Tanala there is a rigid caste system with a king at the head, nobles, commoners, and slaves. The powers of the king are absolute over the life and property of everyone. The commoners are the bulk of the population, the nobles, to all intents, feudal lords whose chief control is over land by royal assignment; the slaves are war captives or their descendants.

The powers of the king far exceeded those of a lineage head in Tanala society and in some ways were greater than those of the ancestral ghosts. He could take the life, property, or wife of anyone; he could elevate and degrade the status of anyone at will, and no redress was possible. In accordance with these powers, a great many secondary mores, which accentuate the enhanced prestige of the king, are present. There are taboos about his person and concerning his children; there are special clothes forbidden to anyone else; special words must be used to designate the condition or anatomy of the king. A king was not sick, he was "cold." He did not have eyes, he had "clearness." The souls of dead kings were called Zanahary-so-and-so. Succession was decided from among the king's sons, but not necessarily the oldest. Notwithstanding his great powers and prestige, he might work like a commoner in the rice fields. Though his powers were absolute and he could not be dethroned, he could be counseled to mend his ways.

Though the king owned all the land, he allotted it for use on a basis which was a charter of ownership, revocable at his will. The king dispensed this land in quantities proportional to the importance of, and the potential return from, the individual concerned. He would give the biggest allotments in return for the greatest support. The large landowner, a noble, could now rent any portion of this land to tenant farmers, who would pay rent in the form of a proportion of produce. Land thus owned could be sold or bequeathed as long as it did not become subject to another king. In short, here was a feudal system of a kind.

The staple crop was rice by the wet method; but other crops were cultivated as well— manioc, maize, millet, beans, and sweet potatoes. The chief adjunct to wet rice cultivation was the possibility of transporting water by irrigation, a factor which added to the permanency of the whole organization and took something of the premium away from the swamps and valleys. Irrigation methods made it possible to use the terraced hillsides for agriculture. But control of irrigation, and even perhaps its installation, made a strong central power essential.

The significance of cattle was the same as in Tanala culture; they had little economic but high prestige value. Cows were used chiefly for sacrifice and hence an instrument of power with the gods. The chief source of meat food was chickens, as with the Tanala.

Parallel to the powers of the king were the powers of the father in the individual household; in Betsileo he exercised an unchecked absolutism. All property belonged to the father during the latter's lifetime except his wives' clothes and the gifts he might make to his wives or children. The profits from exploitation of the land went to him. The inheritance laws resembled those of the Tanala except that land could now be inherited.

In the life cycle of the individual we begin to note important changes. The approaching birth of a child is not announced, for fear of sorcery. The afterbirth is buried and various superstitions are connected with it. As in Tanala culture, some days are propitious for birth, others are not. A child born on a certain day (the equivalent of Sunday) must be thrown on the village rubbish heap for a while, or washed in a jug of dirty dishwater. This is supposed to avert evil destiny. The belief is that a child born on one of these unlucky days will destroy its family. Children born in the month of *Alakaosy* are killed either by drowning, or by having cattle walk over them. Should they survive these exposures, they are kept, with the due precaution of changing their destiny through an *ombiasy*. Adoption is frequent; so also is the changing of names.

The basic disciplines are like those of the Tanala. But here in Betsileo society strong emphasis falls on the training in various shades of deference to elders and rank. Manners elevate the status of one individual as against another: the father is served separately, etc.

Incest taboos are the same as those of the Tanala, and observance is with the same general laxity. Premarital chastity is expected of women and punishment is sterility—as with the Tanala. The endogamy of marriage is now within caste lines, though elevation in status of a slave can take place. There is considerably more homosexuality than in Tanala.

The levirate is practiced in Tanala culture but not in Betsileo. A man who married his brother's widow would be strongly suspected of having killed his brother with sorcery or poison. Polygamy is the rule, as in Tanala.

The disciplinarian in Betsileo society is the father. He has the sole right to punish his children, a right which is, however, rarely exercised. Children may desert their parents in Betsileo, something which is almost inconceivable in Tanala. In one family eight children deserted their parents, whereupon the father changed his name to mean, "I have wiped away excrement for nothing."

The religion of Betsileo is much like that of Tanala, but significant changes can be noted. The rigid belief in fate is changed somewhat to mean that god arranges everything in advance. Sorcery (*mpamosavy*) is now the cause of illness, but the sorcerer is only an executive of god. We find new concepts in Betsileo culture which are unknown in Tanala. For example, god is angry if anyone oppresses the poor. There is a strong belief now in retaliation for aggression against anyone. A man is rich because his Zanahary is good.

The immediate supernatural executives are ghosts and spirits of various kinds. There are for example the *vazimba*, who once lived in the land of the Betsileo and were driven out. Their souls did not go to heaven but remained in the tombs and are, therefore, hostile. *Mpamosavy* bury bait in the tombs of the *vazimba* to kill the person from whom the bait was taken. They also believe in several other varieties of evil spirits in the form of birds or animals. The Betsileo make a clear distinction between life and soul. Life ceases with death, the soul continues. The soul may leave the body by breaking a taboo, through excessive chagrin or fright. The souls of the dead observe the same caste distinctions as obtained in life. The souls of the disowned are evil, and can seduce good souls to do mischief to their own families. A good funeral for a relative insures his good will after death. The soul of a king is transformed into a snake.

Possession by spirits is much more common than in Tanala. In the latter we noted occasional *tromba* (possession by a ghost), and very rarely *mpamosavy*. In Betsileo one is possessed by evil spirits. The incidence is very common and the manifestations much more severe. These spirit illnesses are due to either human or nonhuman spirits. In one type of possession (*aretondolo*) the victim sees these spirits which are invisible to everyone else. They persecute the victim in a large number of ways. They pursue him and he flees across the country; he may be dragged along and made to perform all varieties of stunts. But the remarkable thing is that the victim never shows marks of injury. These seizures come suddenly, and after the first attack, the victim is liable to others. His seizure ends in a spell of unconsciousness from which he awakes normal. Another form of possession is called *salomanga*, which is possession by a once human spirit.

The chief method of worship is by means of sacrifice and thanks. The Betsileo make sacrifices for favors desired or received; they sacrifice for plenty and for scarcity. There is, however, a novelty in the form of taking a vow, which in essence is a promise to make a sacrifice, usually a cow or fowl, pending the outcome of certain events in the individual's favor. The rituals are filled with all kinds of repetitious ceremonials; the same thing must be done a certain number of times to be effectual.

The *ombiasy* has the same functions as in Tanala. He cures the sick, performs *sikidy*, designates good and bad days for undertakings, and makes charms. The *ombiasies* are as in Tanala, *nkazo* and *ndolo*, the latter being chiefly women.

There are in addition to the legitimate *ombiasies* the malevolent sorcerers, *mpamosavy*. These are very scarce in Tanala, but very numerous—or at least suspected to be so—in Betsileo. The practice is secret, and hereditary. The *mpamosavy* is an agent of Zanahary and is possessed by the god. These sorcerers do evil deeds at night, and run out of their homes naked except for a turban. Everyone is suspected of being *mpamosavy*. They work chiefly by planting charms in places where they can do harm. The techniques by which the *mpamosavy* work are similar to those in Tanala. One such charm is a small wooden coffin containing medicines and a small dead animal. When this is destroyed the charm is broken. Nail parings, hair cuttings, leftover food, clothing, earth from a footprint, can be used to injure its owner; urine, feces, and spittle are not so used. In Tanala we noted that these could not be used for malevolent magic as "bait." As a result in Betsileo all nail parings, hair cuttings, etc., are kept in one common heap. The charms used by *mpamosavy*, powerful in themselves, are strengthened and reinforced by evil ghosts. Anyone apprehended in the practice of *mpamosavy*, is ostracized or driven into exile.

There is perhaps one additional concept in Betsileo culture not found in Tanala; the breaking of a taboo can be atoned for by an act of purification.

Much more general apprehension exists in Betsileo than Tanala, as shown by the increase in belief in omens, dreams, and superstitions. The difference is quantitative. Some of the superstitions are rather telling. When a person dies at the moment of a good harvest, he has been killed by his wealth. The superstitions all indicate some fear of retaliatory misfortune. The type of reasoning is largely by analogy. Thus, if anyone strikes a snake but does not kill it, the offender will suffer as the snake suffers; if it is sick he will be sick, if it dies, he will die.

There is also considerable increase in crime, stealing in particular, but also murder. For this latter crime there is indemnity and retaliation by vendetta. The Tanala do not engage in boxing; the Betsileo do. Suicide is very uncommon; but I have heard of a case of suicide in which the man vowed to use his soul to persecute the man who drove him to it. Blood brotherhood exists as in Tanala.

One additional custom should be noted, as of contrast to Tanala. There the village tomb contains all the dead. In Betsileo, burial was in individual family tombs, the women being laid on one side, the men on the other. The king's body was mummified, with special rituals insuring the liberation from the body of a small embryo which later turns into a snake. Tombs became one of the favorite ways of displaying wealth and ostentation. Technological development of weaving and pottery in Betsileo was very much more highly developed than in Tanala. However, the Betsileo made contact with several neighboring peoples where these arts were highly developed, whereas the Tanala did not.

In conclusion we can say that Tanala and Betsileo cultures were identical in the main. The differences are traceable to the change in productive methods from dry to wet rice cultivation. This is proved by several circumstances: The traditions in Betsileo indicate an old culture very like Tanala; the institutions of both indicate a common source, and many of them are still identical; the changes in Tanala were gradual, and were well on the way to becoming identical with Betsileo when the French took over; and finally some of the Tanala tribes took over the wet rice method and abandoned it because of the serious incompatibilities it created in the social structure. The spread of wet rice cultivation cannot be attributed solely to diffusion; wet rice culture was endemic in Tanala and coincident with dry rice. Its spread was favored largely by the exhaustion of the dry method. Hence in examining the changes secondary to this main innovation, we need not depend exclusively on diffusion for an explanation.

# Gossip and Scandal

## Max Gluckman

It has taken the development of anthropological interest in the growth and break-up of small groups to put gossip and scandal into their proper perspective, as among the the most important societal and cultural phenomena we are called upon to analyse. Perceptive, anthropologists dealt with these phenomena from the early days of field observation. Paul Radin, in his *Primitive Man as a Philosopher*, described the way in which

*From* Current Anthropology, *Vol. 4, No. 3, 1963, pp. 307–315. Copyright 1963, Wenner-Gren Foundation for Anthropological Research. By permission of the author, the publisher, and the copyright holder.*

primitive people are indeed among the most persistent and inveterate of gossips. Contestants for the same honours, possessors of the sacred rites of the tribe, the authorized narrators of legends, all leave you in little doubt as to the character and proficiency of their colleagues. "Ignoramus," "braggart," and not infrequently "liar" are liberally bandied about. . . .

Before I examine a study which demonstrated this fully, I glance in general terms at our problems. Their importance is indicated by the fact that every single day, and for a large part of each day, most of us are engaged in gossiping. I imagine that if we were were to keep a record of how we use our waking-time, gossiping would come only after "work"—for some of us—in the score. Nevertheless, popular comments about gossip tend to treat it as something chance and haphazard and often as something to be disapproved of. It is against the canons of the Church. Yet it is possible to show that among relatively small groups, gossip, in all its very many varieties, is a culturally determined process, which has its own customary rules, trespass beyond which is heavily sanctioned. I propose to illustrate the social affiliations of this process and to suggest that gossip, and even scandal, have important positive virtues. Clearly they maintain the unity, morals and values of social groups. Beyond this, they enable these groups to control the competing cliques and aspiring individuals of which all groups are composed. And finally, they make possible the selection of leaders without embarrassment. . . .

The more exclusive the group, the greater will be the amount of gossip in it. There are three forms of social group which test this hypothesis. The one is the professional group, like lawyers or anthropologists, whose gossip is built into technical discussion so tghtly that the outsider cannot always detect the slight personal knockdown which is concealed in a technical recital, or the technical sneer which is contained in a personal gibe. This is, therefore, the most irritiating kind of group to crash into, because one has no clue to the undercurrents, no apparatus for taking soundings. And this is why old practitioners of a subject can so easily put a comparative newcomer into his place, can make him feel a neophyte. They have only to hint in a technical argument at some personal fact about the person who advanced the theory discussed, to make the eager young student feel how callow he is. Again, the more highly organized the profession, the more effective is the role of gossip here.

I have glanced already at the second type of highly exclusive group—that feels it has high social status from which it wishes to exclude parvenus. But we must notice that these groups tend to become hereditary; and once they are, it means that each group comprises not only the present members of the group, but also the past dead members. And here lies great scope for gossip as a social weapon. To be able to gossip properly, a member has to know not only about the present membership, but also about their forbears. For members can hit at one another through their ancestors, and if you cannot use this attack because you are ignorant, then you are in a weak position. Gossip here is a two-edged weapon; for it also means that you have no ancestors in the group to be attacked through—in short that you have no ancestors. And each time that someone in your presence refers to a scandal about another's ancestor, or even his own ancestor, he is gently rubbing in the fact that you have no ancestors and do not belong properly to the group, and are a parvenu.

The third type of exclusive group is that which has exclusiveness trust upon it—either by being in a minority, by isolaton of locality, or by other distinguishing criterion which the members cannot overcome. I shall illustrate the function of gossip and scandal in this type of group in detail, since here (as far as I know) these important phenomena were most fully subjected to an illuminating anthropological investigation. . . .

The Makah Indians were a small group of Red Indians resident in the Puget Sound area at the tip of Cape Flattery, opposite Vancouver Island. It was estimated that in 1780 they numbered some 2,000 people. A century later, smallpox and other vicissitudes had reduced them in number to under 700 and in 1942, when Dr. Colson studied them, there were 400-odd on the tribal roll. The Makah belonged to the Northwest Coast group of American Indians, famous in anthropological literature for their performance of the *potlatch*. A *potlatch* was a ceremonial feast to which one group or individual invited social rivals in order to demonstrate family prerogatives. The host aggressively asserted his and his family's ownership of particular property in resources, titles, songs and ceremonial privileges while feasting and make presents to the visitors. The visitors then had to give a return feast on a bigger scale or lose face.

Before the Makah came under American protection and care by treaty they lived in five villages, divided into longhouses in which dwelt extended families. The people were divided into chiefs, commoners, and slaves.

The American Indian Service set out a century ago to turn the Makah into American citizens—agriculturalists in an environment suitable only for fishing, hunting and collecting; Sunday School addicts, aware of the value of money and averse to destroying their own property, living in houses by small families, wearing clothes, eating off tables and the like. Children were taken by compulsion from their parents and sent to boarding school to cut them off from their parents and Indian tradition. All things Indian were prohibited by the local agent of the Indian Service. This process of indoctrination was kept up until 1932, when the policy of the Indian Service changed, and it began to encourage the development of Indian cultural individuality within the general American pattern.

Colson tried, in her study, to assess how

far ths process of Americanization had succeeded. She found that the Makah in practice had made a satisfactory adjustment to the modern American world. From the beginning, they had paid their way economically, unlike the Plains Indians, who had been put on Government rations after the destruction of the buffalo. The Makah were protected in a part of their ancient territory by their treaty with the United States Government; and from their Reservation they had been able to earn a living first at sealing, and then at fishing for halibut, and also by working for the lumber company exploiting the forests on the Reservation. . . .

Colson saw that the Makah were able to adapt themselves to the new conditions and that this was possible because they were able to earn a good living from the sea and from work on their Reservation as well as outside it. Yet they still cling together as a group, partly because they have economic interests in being Indians. As wards of the United States Government, they cannot be taxed by State or local authorities, either directly or through purchase sales tax, entertainment tax, petrol tax, etc. They are not subject, while on the Reservation, to certain processes of law, such as garnishee orders on their wages or attachment of goods acquired by hire purchase and taken on the Reservation. They are entitled to free dental and medical treatment, and their children to free lunches at school as Whites are not. There are many advantages in being an Indian and also in being a Makah. This entitles a man to free rights in the Makah Reservation and ultimately to a share in the proceeds when the Reservation or parts of it are sold as provided in the Treaty. Therefore the Makah collectively and theoretically strive to keep their numbers low in total, in order that shares shall be greater, though in practice individuals will try to insure that the descendants of their own relatives are on the tribal roll, whatever their parentage, while they try to keep the descendants of others off.

I have summarized a beautifully presented argument and analysis to give a background to Colson's perception of the virtues of gossip and scandal among the Makah. Here we have a very small group (400 people) set against the mighty mass of the American population. They are hostile in many ways to the Whites with whom they associate. They feel that the Whites have robbed them of a culture and a way of life that was theirs, that the Whites have despoiled them and their Indian brothers of land, and so forth. One would expect that they would array themselves in unity in order to maintain their independence and their identity as Makah. Far from it. They are torn by internal dissension and struggles for status and they constantly use the tongue of scandal to keep one another in proper place.

Colson, knowing that the Makah had previously been divided into chiefs, commoners, and slaves, sought to establish the nature of this ranking in the past. She found great certainty about the rules as expressed by various people. But, unfortunately, some rules contradicted others, and the application of each was always uncertain. Someone would tell her that chieftainship was determined absolutely by birth, both on father's and mother's sides; and add, of course, that he was thus descended. Others would corroborate these rules, but would point out that the first informant was descended from a Nootka slave woman, and therefore was low class. Then others would say that birth was of some account, but it was more important that a man, to be high-class, should achieve something himself, by being a doctor or whale-hunter, or the like, and of course his father was a great whale-hunter or doctor or the like. Yet others would then run down these pretensions. Again, under the *potlatch* system, a man had had to give feasts to show his greatness; so today a man ought to be generous if he is to be esteemed. But now that anyone can earn money, if a man gives feasts his rivals can say that he is a *nouveau riche* trying to cover his low-class and that the real high-class people do not need to do this since their status is well known. Others will then accuse them of meanness, inappropriate to high-class, until they become prodigal, when they are *nouveau riche*. Finally, you can always down another by alleging that his family is addicted to sorcery (poisoning). And to use sorcery means that one is of low class —for the man or woman who is secure in social position does not need to use sorcery to secure his ends. Everyone is likely to accuse others of being sorcerers and to be accused in turn. . . .

So it went from person to person until I found that everyone in the village accused others of being low-class and not entitled to speak for the Makah or to hold up their heads in front of the really good people.

The result is that in Neah Bay today a class system theoretically exists, but it is impossible for the observer to place any single person in his proper class because there are no generally accepted standards as to what constitutes a valid claim to class status. Nor is there any generally accepted placing of individuals in various classes recognized by all Makah themselves. Yet, they are conscious of class and it enters into their thinking with references to other Makah to an extent that is incomprehensible to a newcomer. Each individual claims high-class status for himself and his immediate ancestors; each usually derides the claims of other Makah unless they happen to be close relatives—and even a close relative is not safe since his claims to status can always be derided on the ground that through some line not shared with you he descends from low-class people, or it may be claimed that he has not achieved enough to justify his equal position with your own. . . .

In this analysis Colson clearly establishes the important point that specific and restricted gossip within a group marks it off from other groups, both like and unlike. The gossip and scandal which are so biting in Makah life unite them into a group outside of general American society. And, as she points out, since this gossip and scandal involve the criticism and assessment of people against the traditional values of Makah society, they maintain the tribe as Indians against Whites, and as Makah against other Indians. These Makah values and traditions largely persist in the gossip and in no other way. To be a Makah, you must be able to join in the gossip, and to be fully a Makah you must be able to scandalize skillfully. This entails that you know the individual family histories of your fellows; for the knowledgeable can hit at you through your ancestry, and you must be able to retort in kind. You have also have got to have some knowledge of the old ways of the Makah tribe. . . .

Hence, I suggest, Makah gossip does not show merely that general interest in the doings, and the virtues and vices, of others, which characterizes any group. The gossip passes beyond this stage and becomes vicious scandal, aimed at demonstrating that the other parties are not worthy to be Makah. The different groups and individuals in the tribe fight an unceasing battle to demonstrate their own true Makahship, as against the failure of others to attain Makahship. But this involves

them in a continual process of remaining Makah, which (as Colson says) gives high importance to the scandalizing itself, as a mechanism for maintaining the Makah as a group encysted in the American nation, whose other members are excluded from this war of scandal. And the practice of this scandel is developed to a high art, culturally defined. Scandalizing is one of the principal means by which the group's separateness is expressed, even though it is also the principal manner in which internal struggles are fought. This combination of functions of scandal makes the hostility itself a mode through which the tribe remains united. . . .

Gossip and even scandal unite a group within a larger society, or against another group, in several ways. Firstly, all groups try to thrust their roots into the past; scandal by creating a past history for the members in relation to one another, into which newcomers have to be inducted if they are to be full members, achieves this; Secondly, no groups are completely undifferentiated. All of them consist in the first place, of individuals, and, secondly, most consist of smaller groupings of individuals, cliques. These individuals and cliques may be competitively aligned against each other. They struggle for status and prestige. These struggles have to be kept within bounds, while the general values of the group are asserted, if the group is to survive. The values of the group are clearly asserted in gossip and scandal, since a man or woman is always run down for failing to live up to these values. But the struggles to fulfil those values by individuals and cliques are also restrained because the methods of achieving them are defined by gossip and scandal: and these themselves punish any excess. For they control disputation by allowing each individual or clique to fight fellow members of the larger group with an acceptable, socially instituted customary weapon, which blows back on excessively explosive users. For the battle of scandal has its own rules, and woe to him who breaks these rules. By the act of carrying his scandalizing too far, he himself oversteps the values of the group and his scandal will turn against him, will prove that he or his small clique is unworthy of the larger group. And the scandal will in fact redound to the credit of the person attacked, since he will have been unfairly assailed. Colson tells the story of two Makah women who were on bad terms. On one occasion one woman in the streets hurled strings of insults at the other, who kept walking along, singing, "The bear went over the mountain." "Both women knew that one was behaving like a 'low-class' person, the other like a 'high-class' person, and the advantage lay with the one who ignored the insults." Thus the gross scandalmonger overreaches himself and is hoist with his own slander. (Similarly, gamesmanship is the art of winning games without actually cheating.) In this way, the internal struggles within the group are fought with concealed malice, by subtle innuendo, and by pointed ambiguities. Yet all of these have their own moral norms, which must not be overstepped. The main moral norm is that you must scandalize about an opponent behind his back, if your allegations are at all open, to his face, you must be delicate and never give him ground to state that you have insulted him. For insults of this kind, if open, make impossible the pretence of group amity. Similarily, misplaced behind-the-back gossip may force the group either to expel the person slandered or to turn on the gossiper. More than this, the process of scandal enables a group to evaluate people for their work, their qualities of leadership, and their moral character, without ever confronting them to their faces with failures in any sphere. Thus animosities between individuals and cliques are built into the larger social order through the cultural techniques of gossip and scandal. . . .

The important things about gossip and scandal are that generally these are enjoyed by people about others with whom they are in a close social relationship. Hence when we try to understand why it is that people in all places and at all times have been so interested in gossip and scandal about each other, we have also to look at those whom they exclude from joining in the gossiping or scandalizing. That is, the right to gossip about certain people is a privilege which is only extended to a person when he or she is accepted as a member of a group or set. It is a hallmark of membership. Hence rights to gossip serve to mark off a particular group from other groups. There is no easier way of putting a stranger in his place than by beginning to gossip: this shows him conclusively that he does not belong. On the other hand, if a man does not join in the gossip and scandal, he shows that he does not accept that he is a party to the relationship; hence we see that gossiping is a duty of membership of the group. That is why it is good manners to gossip and scandalize about your dearest friends with those who belong, even though it be their dearest friends—but it is bad manners—which is a moral judgment and hence a sanction—to tell unpleasant stories about your friends to strangers. For when you gossip about your friends to other mutual friends you are demonstrating that you all belong to one set which has the duty to be interested in one another's vices as well as virtues. When you gossip about your friends to strangers you are either showing the strangers that they do not belong, or you are admitting them to a privilege and to membership of a group without consulting the other people involved. So that if you want to run down a friend to a stranger you should first ask that friend's permission. You do not need his permission to run him down to mutual friends—provided that they are in the same set of relationships with yourself. I think it would be bad manners to run two people down to one another, even though they are mutually acquainted, if you are not associated with them in the same way. . . . For scandal is only virtuous if its aim be to demonstrate some kind of social unity. Scandal when directed by members of a group against another group is unifying in another, and an obvious, way—it asserts the superiority of the scandalizing group.

I am sure that if you reflect on your own experience you will realise how sound Colson's analysis is. Its significance emerges most clearly if we consider the way in which a new member of a group is inducted into the group. He may learn the rules of technique which keep the group in being, and he may be on excellent terms with the other members of the group, but he does not belong to the group until it is impossible for him to be rude to one of its members unintentionally. That is, he must know so much about each of the members' histories and likings and dislikes, that he will never say something which is hurtful to anyone unless he wants to hurt him (or her). Correspondingly, the badge of membership is that a person can quite allusively, and apparently naively, cut another member to the quick by a seemingly innocent statement. And of course, it is important that the person offended knows that the allusion is intended but not be able to pin it down, and that the injurer should know that the offended knows, and that the offended should know that the injurer knows that the offended knows—and so on *ad infinitum*.

Therefore a most important part of gaining membership of any group is to learn its scandals: what you can say with apparent innocence and what you may say by indirect rude allusion. Anthropology is a very tightly knit profession: it is one of the few professions which still has an initation ceremony. You must have studied some exotic community. We maintain our tight bonds of friendship by a vast store of scandal and gossip as well as by legends. A most important part of my duty in training research workers is to teach them the scandals. I believe I am not alone among senior anthropologists in finding it more interesting to teach students about anthropologists than about anthropology. It is worth noting here that the Greek Lexicon defines "anthropologist" not as "anthropos plus logos," a "student of man," but only as "a scandalmonger;" and in the *Nicomachean Ethics*, Aristotle—who anticipated us all—says of the great-souled man: "He is no scandalmonger (*anthropologos*): he will not talk either about himself or another person." . . .

I note finally that I have discussed gossip only within small groups. Gossip about royalty, by the lower classes about the upper, and the upper by the lower, has to be related to other areas of social relations. I think we can say that men and women do wish to talk about personal matters, for reasons on which I am not clear, and in the great conurbations the discussion of, for example, stars of film and sport, produces a basis on which people transitorily associated can find something personal to talk about. Frankenberg reports that when he was studying the Welsh village, the first time he went to buy a loaf of bread he was back in five minutes. His landlady said scornfully: "Back already? It takes me an hour to buy a loaf of bread." When Frankenberg had been in the village for some time, as soon as he went into a shop, the tea-kettle was put on the fire: after all, as *anthropologos*, he was

the scandalmonger par excellence. And I myself have found through my interest in soccer and cricket, that I have steadily expanded my commercial transactions with shopkeepers into warm friendships, even into a kind of blood brotherhood, in which our ritual alliance moves jerkily from elation to despair with the fate of our city's teams, and our county eleven at cricket. To buy a packet of tobacco may take me twenty minutes. But this field of gossip and scandal still awaits study of the kind deployed by Colson upon the Makah. Meanwhile, for small groups alone, my conclusion is that we might formulate a law to say, the more exclusive a social group is, the more will its members indulge in gossip and scandal about one another. And the more persistently will they repeat the same gossip again and again and again without getting bored. . . .

Outsiders frequently complain that anthropologists are able to find that anything social has a useful function and they may therefore conclude that anthropologists approve of everything. Thus it has been argued that the criminal classes are as important as the police for the maintenance of law in a society; they provide people who commit crimes but who can easily be caught by the police and publicly tried. Their trials demonstrate to the society at large, and particularly to its growing youngsters, not only that crime is wrong—which is true, but also that crime does not pay—which is not true. Amateur criminals, less easily caught, are not so useful. But this does not mean we approve of crime. We argue only that the commission of a crime, provided that the criminal is caught, tried, and punished, serves useful ends in maintaining the law, and therefore society. My argument about gossip and scandal is similar, if I suggest that gossip and scandal are socially virtuous and valuable, this does not mean that I always approve of them. Indeed, in practice I find that when I am gossiping about my friends as well as my enemies I am deeply conscious of performing a social duty; but that when I hear they gossip viciously about me, I am rightfully filled with righteous indignation.

# Cultural Transmission and Cultural Change

## Edward M. Bruner

Students of acculturation agree that in every contact situation some aspects of the native culture change more than others, but they do not agree on why this is so, nor on how to characterize that which has changed and that which has not in categories that have cross-cultural validity. Nor do they understand why a change in one area of culture sometimes precipitates radical change or disorganization throughout the entire culture pattern while other times a very modest or even negligible readjustment occurs. . . .

*From* Southwestern Journal of Anthropology, *Vol. 12, No. 2, 1956. pp. 191–197. By permission of the author and the publisher.*

### Differential Change

A rather striking pattern of differential change emerges from a comparison of the contemporary culture, as I observed it in 1951, 1952-53, among the unacculturated segment of the Mandan-Hidatsa population, with the aboriginal culture, described in the published ethnologies of Wilson, Lowie, Bowers, and others, which refer to the time period of approximately 1850-1860. This division into contemporary and aboriginal periods is convenient and provides a time span of about one century.

Within the social organization the Crow type kinship system is still largely intact but the entire age-grade society system, which was such a colorful feature of aboriginal life, has completely disappeared. The extended family has given way to the nuclear family, residence is no longer matrilocal, and the clans have diminished in importance.

Far-reaching economic changes have occurred, but there has not been change in the basic roles of male and female. The aboriginal Mandan-Hidatsa had a dual economy adjusted to the fertile river bottom lands. The women attended to household tasks, and engaged in maize, bean, and squash horticulture in small garden plots, while the men fought hostile nomads and hunted bison, antelope, deer, and small game. Fishing, gathering, and a wide network of trading relationships were important supplements to the economy. In the contemporary period major changes were precipitated by the dependency relationship to the government and by necessary adjustments to the American economy. Nevertheless, sexual role conceptions have persisted. Women see themselves as housekeepers, mothers, and gardners, while Indian men derive most satisfaction from the roles of soldier, cowboy, athlete, and hunter. A relatively large non-cash income is derived from the woman's labor in small garden plots and in the gathering of wild fruits and berries, and from the man's ability as a hunter of deer and pheasant. Unacculturated Indian men have never taken to large-scale farming for the market nor have any but a few become economically successful cattlemen.

The aboriginal Mandan-Hidatsa had a very complex and highly developed ceremonial system, which no longer exists. Sacred public ceremonies are not performed in contemporary society, and everyone has been converted to the Congregational or Catholic Church. Christianity may not be deeply felt nor fully understood by the Indian people, but it has replaced the native religion. However, particular aspects of the religious system have persisted. Shamans continue to cure the sick with the aid of their medicine bundles, and there is a widely accepted belief in ghosts who are thought to be returning spirits of the dead.

The value system, as I have inferred it from my observations among the Mandan-Hidatsa and from the published ethnologies, shows a remarkable persistence. A good man was, and is, one who respects the old people, is brave and demonstrates fortitude, conforms to the obligations of the kinship system, is devoted to village coöperation and unity, is generous, gives away property in public, gets along well with others, and avoids overt expressions of aggression in interpersonal relationships.

Thus kinship, values, and traditional role conceptions have persisted virtually intact, despite vast change in the larger units of social organization, in the economy, and in most of the religious-ceremonial system. With the pos-sible exception of values, there has been change and persistence within each aspect of culture.

### Previous Hypotheses

Our problem becomes: What general propositions enable us to understand these results? The literature on acculturation contains a number of hypotheses which have been offered as explanations why some aspects of culture change more than others. A few will be mentioned here; all go beyond such notions as that of culture lag or survivals, which only identify the phenomenon but which do not explain it.

One is the principle of integration. Kroeber feels this principle is most crucial and suggests that a practice will persist if it has become integrated into ". . . an organized system of ideas and sentiments . . . [if] it is interwoven with other items of culture into a larger pattern." This principle does not appear to apply to my data. The age-grade society system, for example, did not persist, yet it formed a large organized pattern. It was the most highly developed graded society system on the Plains and was, in aboriginal times, interwoven with the warfare and hunting complex, the kinship system, and the social, educational, and religious structures.

A second principle is that of function. If a complex is functional, i.e., if its consequences are adaptive or adjustive for a given system, supposedly it will not change. There is a methodological difficulty in relating functionalism to culture change, a kind of circularity: one is tempted to identify that which is functional by the fact of its persistence. Nevertheless, I submit that the aboriginal ceremonial complex was functional, that its functions outweighed its dysfunctions, yet it did not persist. Nor do I see in contemporary Mandan-Hidatsa society any alternate forms which have replaced the vital functions performed by aboriginal ceremonialism.

Other principles to explain differential culture change have appeared in the literature such as: the principle of utility, that a people will retain the old or accept the new depending upon which has greater usefulness; the principle of concreteness, the more concrete a complex the less its resistance to change; the principle of consensus, the more a pattern requires common consent within a culture the greater its tendency to persist. I am not suggesting, of course, that the principles mentioned here have not had validity and explanatory value in other acculturation situations, nor even that they have no relevance in this case. I do say that other general propositions do not explain as much of the Mandan-Hidatsa data as an alternate hypothesis which I should now like to suggest.

## The Early Learning Hypothesis

That which was traditionally learned and internalized in infancy and early childhood tends to be most resistant to change in contact situations. This suggests that we view a culture from the perspective of cultural transmission, the process by which the content of culture is learned by and communicated to members of the society. It says that if we knew the point in the life career of an individual at which every aspect of culture was transmitted, we would find that what changes most readily was learned late in life and what was most resistant to change was learned early.

A re-examination of the Mandan-Hidatsa data from the perspective of cultural transmission and the early learning hypothesis reveals the following: that which persists, i.e., kinship, role conceptions and values, was learned early, and the primary agents of cultural transmission were members of ego's lineage. The age-grade society system and the religious complex, which no longer exist, were learned late, from agents of transmission who were not members of ego's lineage and who were all respect-relatives.

A widely extended kinship system was the basis of aboriginal Mandan-Hidatsa social structure; every interpersonal relationship was determined by kinship. Thus it was absolutely essential that the growing child learn kin terms and behavior early in life, so that he could relate properly to others. The kinship system was learned by a young boy mainly from his mother, older brother, maternal grandfather, and mother's brother who was classified as an older brother; and by a young girl mainly from her mother, older sister, and maternal grandmother. These are all members of the same lineage. The father took little part in routine economic and social training.

The Crow type kinship system is still learned early in contemporary Mandan-Hidatsa society. We studied kinship among children between the ages of six to ten, and found that unacculturated children knew how to behave toward their relatives in terms of the Crow pattern, although no child had any conception of the kinship system as a system. Some children did not know the correct behavior toward relatives with whom they interacted infrequently, as in the case of those who lived in another village, but no child behaved incorrectly toward a close relative with whom he had frequent contact.

Religious knowledge was learned late in life in aboriginal Mandan-Hidatsa society and is in sharp contrast with, for example, the practice among Catholics, where children begin religious training at a relatively early age. With few exceptions a man under the age of thirty did not, and was not, expected to know the traditions, origin myths, or religious rituals of the tribe. In Mandan-Hidatsa thought a man younger than thirty was not mature: he was thought to be reckless and irresponsible. Religious knowledge and lore were slowly revealed to a man after the age of thirty, and this process of religious learning continued throughout his entire life career.

The agents of religious transmission were primarily members of the father's lineage and clan, all of whom were respect-relatives. Religious knowledge was not freely given: it had to be purchased from selected ceremonial fathers. A man spent a considerable portion of his productive time in the acquisition of goods which he gave to ceremonial fathers in return for religious knowledge. An old man who had purchased many ceremonies had attained the cultural objective: he was successful and was respected by all. He subsisted in part on gifts and on the goods he received from the sale of religious knowledge to younger men.

Some evidence has been given that kinship persists and was learned early, and that religion did not persist and was learned late. Additional evidence to support the hypothesis could be offered from other segments of the culture. It is in the context of kinship and at the same point in the life career that role conceptions and the value system are internalized. The age-grade society system was not even entered by an individual until the age of seven to eight, and serious society activity did not begin for a boy until the age of fifteen to seventeen, with the first fasting experience. The graded structure of the societies was such that only an older person, who had passed through the entire system, had full knowledge and understanding of this aspect of aboriginal culture. Parts of religion that do persist, such as fear of ghosts, were learned early in that returning spirits of the dead were and are used in Mandan-Hidatsa society to frighten and discipline young children, and are comparable in function to our bogeyman and the Hopi Soyoko Kachinas.

That religion is learned after the age of thirty in Mandan-Hidatsa society should not be regarded as unique in cultural transmission. All cultures vary not only according to their culture patterns, but also according to the age-grading of the educational process, the age at which each aspect of culture is internalized. The variation in this important dimension of culture is well-known in traditional anthropology, and is amply documented in the life cycle sections of many ethnological reports. For example, in Trukese society such key activities as weaving, canoe building, complex religious techniques, and genealogical knowledge are not acquired until about the age of forty. It is frequently stated that in primitive society the social world of the child coincides with adult reality but the reverse may prove to be the case—that there will always be a discrepancy between childhood and adult learning. This may be universal, since the situation of the child is universally, by the biological nature of the case, different from the adult, and because this situational difference is intensied, universally, by cultural definition.

## Discussion

A final question concerns the applicability of the early learning hypothesis to cases of culture contact other than the Mandan-Hidatsa. If it is applicable it will have relevance to those applied programs in many parts of the world where the question is asked: What are the hard and soft parts of culture; what is most and what is least resistant to change?

As a working assumption, I submit that the early learning hypothesis is universal, as it identifies one variable that may aid in the understanding of differential culture change everywhere, although its explanatory value and importance will vary considerably in different situations. Any principle must always be considered in conjunction with alternate hypotheses as no one principle will ever be sufficient to explain the totality of differential change in any given case. Even within the framework suggested here, resistance to change may be a function of other factors in addition to relative age of learning, such as the degree of affect and ego involvement in the learning situation. The early learning hypothesis will work out differently in different cases as the acculturation process itself is selective. Cases vary according to the availability of alternatives, the extent and direction of pressures for change, and the general circumstances in which the people find themselves. *The early learning hypothesis simply orders the cultural content in terms of potential resistance to change; the actual sequence of change is dependent upon a multiplicity of factors in the contact situation.* Change in any segment of culture, whether learned early or late, will not occur unless there is. a reason for it to change.

Partial support for the universality of the early learning hypothesis is provided by two frequently stated anthropological findings as to which aspects of culture tend to persist longest in contact situations. One group of students has found that core culture, implicit values, cultural orientations, and personality are most resistant to change. Another group of students interested in social structure suggests that family and kinship institutions tend to persist.

These findings are not unrelated. Values and personality on the one hand and family and kinship on the other may well be aspects of life that are generally learned in infancy and early childhood and thus tend to be most resistant to change. Indeed, personality and kinship are usually separated by us as being in different categories, but from the point of view of the individual who internalizes them, both come across early in the socialization process and in the same bundle. Psychoanalysts tell us that the first self-other differentiation is basically, in our lingo, a kinship one, when the child differentiates self from mother and later mother from other objects. This is how a kinship system is built into and internalized by an individual and how it, in turn, provides the context for the further development of personality.

But these are speculations and very general. The early learning hypothesis itself is, I trust, quite clear and specific. That which is learned and internalized in infancy and early childhood is most resistant to change in contact situations. The hypothesis directs our attention to the age in the individual life career at which each aspect of culture is transmitted as well as to the full context of the learning situation and the position of the agents of socialization in the larger social system. Its relevance to instances of culture contact other than the Mandan-Hidatsa will, I hope, become a problem for future research.

*selection 52*

# Steel Axes for Stone Age Australians

## Lauriston Sharp

### The Problem

Like other Australian aboriginals, the Yir Yoront group at the mouth of the Coleman River on the west coast of tropical Cape York Peninsula originally had no knowledge of metals. Technologically their culture was of the old stone age or paleolithic type; they supported themselves by hunting and fishing, obtaining vegetable foods and needed materials from the bush by simple gathering techniques. Their only domesticated animal was the dog, and they had no domesticated plants of any kind. Unlike some other aboriginal groups, however, the Yir Yoront did have polished stone axes hafted in short handles, and these implements were most important in their economy.

Toward the end of the nineteenth century metal tools and other European artifacts began to filter into the Yir Yoront territory. The flow increased with the gradual expansion of the white frontier outward from southern and eastern Queensland. Of all the items of western technology thus made available, none was more acceptable, none more highly valued by aboriginals of all conditions than the hatchet or short-handled steel axe. . . .

*From Edward H. Spicer (ed.),* Human Problems in Technological Change. *Russell Sage Foundation, 1952, pp. 69–90. Copyright 1952, Russell Sage Foundation. By permission of the author, and the publisher and copyright holder.*

What changes in the life of the Yir Yoront still living under aboriginal conditions in the Australian bush could be expected as a result of their increasing possession and use of the steel axe? . . .

In 1915 an Anglican mission station was established near the mouth of the Mitchell River in the territory of a tribe neighboring the Yir Yoront on the south and about three days' march from the heart of the Yir Yoront country. Some of the Yir Yoront refused to have anything to do with the mission or to go near it, others visited it on occasion, while a few eventually settled more or less permanently in one of the three "villages" at the mission.

Thus the majority of the Yir Yoront continued to live their old self-supporting life in the bush, protected until 1942 by the government reserve and the intervening mission from the cruder realities of the encroaching new order which had come up from the south. To the east was poor country, uninhabited. To the north were other bush tribes extending on along the coast to the distant Archer River Presbyterian mission with which the Yir Yoront had no contact. Westward was the expanse of the shallow Gulf of Carpentaria, on which the natives saw only a mission lugger making its infrequent dry-season trips to the Mitchell River. In this protected environment for over a generation the Yir Yoront were able to recuperate from former shocks received at the hands of civilized society. During the 1930's their raiding and fighting, their trading and stealing of women, their evisceration and two- or three-year care of their dead, their totemic ceremonies continued apparently uninhibited by western influence. In 1931 they killed a European who wandered into their territory from the east, but the investigating police never approached the group whose members were responsible for the act. In 1934 the anthropologist observed a case of extratribal revenge cannibalism. The visitor among the bush Yir Yoront at this time found himself in the presence of times past, in an essentially paleolithic society which had been changed, to the casual eye, chiefly by the addition of oddments of European implements and goods put to a variety of uses.

As a direct result of the work of the Mitchell River mission, all Yir Yoront received a great many more western artifacts of all kinds than they ever had obtained before. As part of their plan for raising native living standards, the missionaries made it possible for aboriginals at the mission to earn some western goods, many of which were then given or traded out to natives still living under bush conditions; or they handed out gratis both to mission and to bush aboriginals certain useful articles which were in demand. They prevented guns, liquor, and damaging narcotics, as well as decimating diseases, from reaching the tribes of this area, while encouraging the introduction of goods they considered "improving." As has been noted, no item of western technology that was available, with the possible exception of trade tobacco, was in greater demand among all groups of aboriginals than the short-handed steel axe. A good supply of this type of axe was therefore always kept in stock at the mission for sale; and at Christmas parties or other mission festivals steel axes were given away to mission or visiting aboriginals indiscriminately and in considerable numbers. In addition, some steel axes, as well as other European goods, were still traded in to the Yir Yoront by natives in contact with cattle stations established south of the missions. Indeed, such axes had probably come to the Yir Yoront along established lines of aboriginal trade long before any regular contact with whites had occurred.

### Relevant Factors

If we concentrate our attention on Yir Yoront behavior centering about the original stone axe, rather than on the axe—the thing—we should get some conception of the role this implement played in aboriginal culture. This conception, in turn, should permit us to forsee with considerable accuracy some of the results of the displacement of stone axes by steel axes acquired directly or indirectly from Europeans by the Yir Yoront.

The production of a stone axe required a number of simple skills. With the idea of the axe in its various details well in mind, the adult men—and only the adult men— could set about producing it, a task not considered appropriate for women or children. First of all, a man had to know the location and properties of several natural resources found in his immediate environment: pliable wood, which could be doubled or bent over the axe head and bound tightly to form a handle; bark, which could be rolled into cord for the binding; and gum, with which the stone head could be firmly fixed in the haft. These materials had to be correctly gathered, stored, prepared, cut to size, and applied or manipulated. They were plentifully supplied by nature, and could be taken by a man from anyone's property without special permission. Postponing consideration of the stone head of the axe, we see that a simple knowledge of nature and of the technological skills involved, together with the possession of fire (for heating the gum) and a few simple cutting tools, which might be nothing more than the sharp shells of plentiful bivalves, all of which were available to everyone, were sufficient to enable any normal man to make a stone axe.

The use of the stone axe as a piece of capital equipment for the production of other goods indicates its very great importance in the subsistence economy of the aboriginal. Anyone—man, woman, or child—could use the axe; indeed, it was used more by women, for theirs was the onerous, daily task of obtaining sufficient wood to keep the campfire of each family burning all day for cooking or other purposes and all night against mosquitoes and cold (in July, winter temperature might drop below forty degrees). In a normal lifetime any woman would use the axe to cut or knock down literally tons of firewood. Men and women, and sometimes children, needed the axe to make other tools, or weapons, or a variety of material equipment required by the aboriginal in his daily life. The stone axe was essential in making the wet-season domed huts, which keep out some rain and some insects; or platforms, which provide dry storage; or shelters, which give shade when days are bright and hot. In hunting and fishing and in gathering vegetable or animal food the axe was also a necessary tool; and in this tropical culture without preservatives or other means of storage, the native spends more time obtaining food than in any other occupation except sleeping.

In only two instances was the use of the stone axe strictly limited to adult men: Wild honey, the most prized food known to the Yir Yoront, was gathered only by men who usually used the axe to get it; and only men could make the secret paraphernalia for ceremonies, an activity often requiring use of the axe. From this brief listing of some of the

activities in which the axe was used, it is easy to understand why there was at least one stone axe in every camp, in every hunting or fighting party, in every group out on a "walkabout" in the bush.

While the stone axe helped relate men and women and often children to nature in technological behavior, in the transformation of natural into cultural equipment, it also was prominent in that aspect of behavior which may be called conduct, primarily directed toward persons. Yir Yoront men were dependent upon interpersonal relations for their stone axe heads, since the flat, geologically recent alluvial country over which they range, provides no stone from which axe heads can be made. The stone they used comes from known quarries four hundred miles to the south. It reached the Yir Yoront through long lines of male trading partners, some of these chains terminating with the Yir Yoront men, while others extended on farther north to other groups, having utilized Yir Yoront men as links. Almost every older adult man had one or more regular trading partners, some to the north and some to the south. His partner or partners in the south he provided with surplus spears, and particularly fighting spears tipped with the barbed spines of sting ray which snap into vicious fragments when they penetrate human flesh. For a dozen spears, some of which he may have obtained from a partner to the north, he would receive from a southern partner one stone axe head. . . . Thus trading relations, which may extend the individual's personal relationships out beyond the boundaries of his own group, are associated with two of the most important items in a man's equipment, spears and axes, whether the latter are of stone or steel. Finally, most of the exchanges between partners take place during the dry season at times when the great aboriginal fiestas occur, which center about initiation rites or other totemic ceremonials that attract hundreds and are the occasion for much exciting activity besides trading.

Returning to the Yir Yoront, we find that not only was it adult men alone who obtained axe heads and produced finished axes, but it was adult males who retained the axes, keeping them with other parts of their equipment in camp, or carrying them at the back slipped through a human hair belt when traveling. Thus, every woman or child who wanted to use an axe—and this might be frequently during the day—must get one from some man, use it promptly, and return it to the man in good condition. While a man might speak of "my axe," a woman or child could not; for them it was always "your axe," addressing a male, or "his axe."

This necessary and constant borrowing of axes from older men by woman and children was done according to regular patterns of kinship behavior. A woman on good terms with her husband would expect to use his axe unless he were using it; a husband on good terms with his wives would let any one of them use his axe without question. If a woman was unmarried or her husband was absent, she would go first to her older brother or to her father for an axe. Only in extraordinary circumstances would she seek a stone axe from a mother's brother or certain other male kin with whom she had to be most circumspect. A girl, a boy, or a young man would look to a father or an older brother to provide an axe for her or his use, but would never approach a mother's brother, who would be at the same time a potential father-in-law, with such a request. Older men, too, would follow similar rules if they had to borrow an axe.

It will be noted that these social relationships in which the stone axe had a place are all pair relationships and that the use of the axe helped define and maintain the character of the relationships and the roles of the two individual participants. Every active relationship among the Yir Yoront involved a definite and accepted status of superordination or subordination. A person could have no dealings with any other on exactly equal terms. Women and children were dependent on, or subordinate to, older males in every action in which the axe entered. Among the men, the younger was dependent on the older or on certain kinds of kin. The nearest approach to equality was between brothers, although the older was always superordinate to the younger. Since the exchange of goods in a trading relationship involved a mutual reciprocity, trading partners were usually a kind of brother to each other or stood in a brotherly type of relationship, although one was always classified as older than the other and would have some advantage in case of dispute. It can be

seen that repeated and widespread conduct centering on the axe helped to generalize and standardize throughout the society these sex, age, and kinship roles, both in their normal benevolent and in exceptional malevolent aspects, and helped to build up expectancies regarding the conduct of others defined as having a particular status. . . .

The stone axe was an important symbol of masculinity among the Yir Yoront (just as pants or pipes are among ourselves). By a complicated set of ideas which we would label "ownership" the axe was defined as "belonging" to males. Everyone in the society (except untrained infants) accepted these ideas. Similarly spears, spear throwers, and fire-making sticks were associated with males, were owned only by them, and were symbols of masculinity. But the masculine values represented by the stone axe were constantly being impressed on all members of society by the fact that non-males had to use the axe and had to go to males for it, whereas they never borrowed other masculine artifacts. Thus, the axe stood for an important theme that ran all through Yir Yoront culture: the superiority and rightful dominance of the male, and the greater value of his concerns and of all things associated with him. We should call this androcentrism rather than patriarchy, or paternal rule. It is the recognition by all that the values of the man (*andros*) take precedence over feminine values, an idea backed by very strong sentiments among the Yir Yoront. Since the axe had to be borrowed also by the younger from the older, it also represented the prestige of age, another important theme running all through Yir Yoront behavior. . . .

## Analysis

The introduction of the steel axe indiscriminately and in large numbers into the Yir Yoront technology was only one of many changes occurring at the same time. It is therefore impossible to factor out all the results of this single innovation alone. Nevertheless, a number of specific effects of the change from stone axes to steel axes may be noted; and the steel axe may be used as an epitome of the European goods and implements received by the aboriginals in increasing quantity and of their general influence on the native culture. The use of the steel axe to illustrate such influences would seem to be justified, for it was one of the first European artifacts to be adopted for regular use by the Yir Yoront; and the axe, whether of stone or steel, was clearly one of the most important items of cultural equipment they possessed.

The shift from stone to steel axes provided no major technological difficulties. While the aboriginals themselves could not manufacture steel axe heads, a steady supply from outside continued; and broken wooden axe handles could easily be replaced from bush timbers with aboriginal tools. Among the Yir Yoront the new axe never acquired all the uses it had on mission or cattle stations (carpentry work, pounding tent pegs, use as a hammer, and so on); and, indeed, it was used for little more than the stone axe had been, so that it had no practical effect in improving the native standard of living. It did some jobs better, and could be used longer without breakage; and these factors were sufficient to make it of value to the native. But the assumption of the white man (based in part on a realization that a shift from steel to stone axe in his case would be a definite regression) that his axe was much more efficient, that its use would save time, and that it therefore repre-sented technical "progress" toward goals which he had set for the native was hardly borne out in aboriginal practice. Any leisure time the Yir Yoront might gain by using steel axes or other western tools was invested, not in "improving the conditions of life," and certainly not in developing aesthetic activities, but in sleep, an art they had thoroughly mastered.

Having acquired an axe head through regu-lar trading partners of whom he knew what to expect, a man wanting a stone axe was then dependent solely upon a known and an ade-quate nature and upon his own skills or easily acquired techniques. A man wanting a steel axe, however, was in no such self-reliant posi-tion. While he might acquire one through trade, he now had the new alternative of dispensing with technological behavior in rela-tion with a predictable nature and conduct in relation with a predictable trading partner and of turning instead to conduct alone in relation wth a highly erratic missionary. If he attended one of the mission festivals when steel axes were handed out as gifts, he might

receive one simply by chance or if he had happened somehow to impress upon the mis-sion staff that he was one of the "better" bush aboriginals (their definition of "better" being quite different from that of his bush fellows). Or he might—but again almost by pure chance—be given some brief job in connec-tion with the mission which would enable him to earn a steel axe. In either case, for older men a preference for the steel axe helped create a situation of dependence in place of a situation of self-reliance and a behavior shift from situations n technology or conduct which were well structured or defined to situations in conduct alone which were ill defined. It was particularly the older ones among the men, whose earlier experience or knowledge of the white man's harshness in any event made them suspicious, who would avoid hav-ing any relations with the mission at all, and who thus excluded themselves from acquiring steel axes directly from that source.

The steel axe was the root of psychological stress among the Yir Yoront even more sig-nicantly in other aspects of social relations. This was the result of new factors which the missionary considered all to the good: the simple numerical increase in axes per capita as a result of mission distribution; and dis-tribution from the mission directly to younger men, women, and even children. By winning the favor of the mission staff, a woman might be given a steel axe. This was clearly intended to be hers. The situation was quite different from that involved in borrowing an axe from a male relative, with the result that a woman called such an axe "my" steel axe, a pos-sessive form she never used for a stone axe. (Lexically, the steel axe was differentiated from the stone by an adjectival suffix signify-ing "metal," the element "axe" remaining identical.) Furthermore, young men or even boys might also obtain steel axes directly from the mission. A result was that older men no longer had a complete monopoly of all the axes in the bush community. Indeed, an old man might have only a stone axe, while his wives and sons had steel axes which they considered their own and which he might even desire to borrow. All this led to a revolu-tionary confusion of sex, age, and kinship roles, with a major gain in independence and loss of subordination on the part of those able now to acquire steel axes when they had been unable to possess stone axes before.

The trading partner relationship was also affected by the new situation. A Yir Yoront might have a trading partner in a tribe to the south whom he defined as a younger brother, and on whom as an older brother he would therefore have an edge. But if the partner were in contact with the mission or had other easier access to steel axes, his subordination to his bush colleague was obviously decreased. Indeed, under the new dispensation he might prefer to give his axe to a bush "sweetheart" in return for favors or otherwise dispose of it outside regular trade channels, since many steel axes were so distributed between natives in new ways. Among other things, this took some of the excitement away from the fiesta-like tribal gatherings centering around initiations during the dry season. These had traditionally been the climactic annual occasions for exchanges between trading partners, when a man might seek to acquire a whole year's supply of stone axe heads. Now he might find himself prostituting his wife to almost total strangers in return for steel axes or other white men's goods. With trading partnerships weakened, there was less reason to attend the fiestas, and less fun for those who did. A decline in one of the important social activities which had symbolized these great gatherings created a lessening of interest in the other social aspects of these events.

Not only did an increase in steel axes and their distribution to women change the character of the relations between individual and an individual, the paired relationships that have been noted, but a new type of relationship, hitherto practically unknown among the Yir Yoront, was created in their axe-acquiring conduct with whites. In the aboriginal society there were almost no occasions outside the immediate family when one individual would initiate action to several other people at once. For in any average group, while a person in accordance with the kinship system might be superordinate to several people to whom he could suggest or command action, at the same time he was also subordinate to several others, in relation with whom such behavior would be tabu. There was thus no over-all chieftainship or authoritarian leadership of

any kind. Such complicated operations as grass-burning, animal drives, or totemic ceremonies could be carried out smoothly because each person knew his roles both in technology and conduct.

On both mission and cattle stations, however, the whites imposed upon the aboriginals their conception of leadership roles, with one person in a controlling relationship with a subordinate group. Aboriginals called together to receive gifts, including axes, at a mission Christmas party found themselves facing one or two whites who sought to control their behavior for the occasion, who disregarded the age, sex, and kinship variables among them of which they were so conscious, and who considered them all at one subordinate level. Or the white might impose similar patterns on a working party. (But if he placed an aboriginal in charge of a mixed group of post hole diggers, for example, half of the group, those subordinate to the "boss," would work while the other half, who were superordinate to him, would sleep.) The steel axe, together, of course, with other European goods, came to symbolize for the aboriginal this new and uncomfortable form of social organization, the leader-group relationship.

The most disturbing effects of the steel axe, operating in conjunction with other elements also being introduced from the white man's subcultures, developed in the realm of traditional ideas, sentiments, and values. These were undermined at a rapidly mounting rate, without new conceptions being defined to replace them. The result was a mental and moral void which foreshadowed the collapse and destruction of all Yir Yoront culture, if not, indeed, the extinction of the biological group itself.

From what has been said it should be clear how changes in overt behavior, in technology and conduct, weakened the values inherent in a reliance on nature, in androcentrism or the prestige of masculinity, in age prestige, and in the various kinship relations. A scene was set in which a wife or young son, his initiation perhaps not even yet completed, need no longer bow to the husband or father, who was left confused and insecure as he asked to borrow a steel axe from them. For the woman and boy the steel axe helped establish a new degree of freedom which was accepted readily as an escape from the unconscious stress of the old patterns, but which left them also confused and insecure. Ownership became less well defined, so that stealing and trespass were introduced into technology and conduct. Some of the excitement surrounding the great ceremonies evaporated, so that the only fiestas the people had became less festive, less interesting. Indeed, life itself became less interesting, although this did not lead the Yir Yoront to invent suicide, a concept foreign to them. . . .

*selection 53*

# The Backwash of the Frontier: The Impact of the Indian on American Culture

## A. Irving Hallowell

Although Frederick Jackson Turner and his disciples have made little point of the influence of the American Indian upon our civilization, it is the Indian's continuing presence throughout our whole colonial and national history that has given many aspects of our culture a special coloring. In this respect, our national experience differs from that of any western European nation, though our culture is continuous with that of Europe. . . .

Discernible Indian influences of this sort that have formed what I have called "the backwash of the frontier," fertile silt carried on the currents and eddies left by the turmoil on the borderlands. Many other factors besides frontier conditions were involved in the further development of these influences—factors too complex to analyze here. And the problem is complicated by the extreme diversity of America's reactions to the Indian and his cultures; by the manner in which Indian influences have been mediated, the varying forms they have assumed at different periods of our national existence, and their

*From* Annual Report of the Board of Regents of the Smithsonian Institution, *1958, publication 4354. U.S. Printing Office, 1959, pp. 447–472, as reprinted from Walker D. Wyman and Clifton B. Kroeber (eds.),* The Frontier in Perspective. *The University of Wisconsin Press, 1957, pp. 229–257. Copyright, 1957 by The Regents of the University of Wisconsin. By permission of the author, the publishers, and the copyright holder.*

depth. Most often they have been manifested at the vernacular level of American culture, one expression of our cultural provincialism, which is perhaps the reason so little systematic attention has been paid to them. *Our contacts with the Indians have affected our speech, our economic life, our clothing, our sports and recreations, certain indigenous religious cults, many of our curative practices, folk and concert music, the novel, poetry, drama, and even some of our basic psychological attitudes, and one of the social sciences, anthropology* [Italics added].

To the outside world there is a closer association of the Indian with the image of America than perhaps we are aware of. For example, Cooper's "The Last of the Mohicans" is not only read by every American schoolchild, but it has been said to be the best-known American novel in the world. So too, "Hiawatha," Longfellow's poetic image of the Indian, is widely read and translated in other countries. Ivan Bunin, the Russian poet and novelist, "is probably as well recognized for his translation of 'Hiawatha' as for any of his original works."

Americans have created a whole succession of images of the Indian, some literary and interpretative, some growing out of direct contact of particular types of white men with him and changing with historical circumstances. Although the Pope declared as far back as 1512 that the natives of America were descended from Adam and Eve, in colonial New England Cotton Mather thought that "probably the *Devil* decoy'd . . . [them] . . . hither, in hopes that the gospel of the Lord Jesus Christ would never come here to destroy or disturb his absolute empire over them." As God's elected agents and under his "wonder-working Providence," the colonists must convert these "tawney serpents" or annihilate them. However, the Indian was never simply The Enemy. On the earliest frontiers, the colonists were befriended by the natives. Who has not heard of Squanto? White men from the beginning profited in many practical ways from the Indians' knowledge of their own country and through intimate contacts learned about their customs, manner of thought, and character, and were influenced by them.

During the 18th century, when in England and on the Continent a literary image of the noble savage, partly derived from ideas about the Indian, was being created, the colonists greatly deepened their firsthand knowledge of the American natives. Trading activities brought tribal groups over a wider range into contact with the colonists. The Indians were not always fought against; on occasion they were comrades-in-arms, and aboriginal methods of fighting influenced the colonists. The speeches made by Indians in treaty negotiations aroused so much interest in native oratory that a novel literary form, with no prototype in Europe, emerged. Verbatim reports of these conferences were widely circulated and read in printed form. It has even been said that information about the organization and operation of the League of the Iroquois, which Franklin picked up at various Indian councils, suggested to him the pattern for a United States of America. In any case it was Franklin whose appreciation of the attitude of the Indians toward their own culture led him to express the anthropological principle of the relativity of culture norms when, in 1784, he wrote: "Savages we call them, because their manners differ from ours, which we think the Perfection of Civility: they think the same of theirs."

As the eastern frontier receded westward and for most Americans the contemporary Indians could be viewed at a comfortable distance, it was their decline that became a romantic literary theme. As expressed in poetry, drama, and the novel, it was an early backwash of the frontier. But it was by no means always the noble savage that was depicted; a double image was created—the savage as ignoble as well as noble. During this period, the first half of the 19th century, when the Indian was such a popular figure in American literature, it is particularly significantly that most of the authors who dealt with Indian themes derived their information from written sources rather than from direct observation. Cooper depended on Heckewelder's writings, and Longfellow on Schoolcraft's "Algic Researches" (1839). It has been said that "Cooper poured the prejudices of John Heckewelder into the Leatherstocking mold, and produced the Indian of nineteenth century convention." The authors who were busy writing about the Indians were far removed from the men who faced them on the new frontiers.

Two and a half centuries after Englishmen on the eastern frontier faced the Indian, American frontiersmen in the Mississippi Valley and the Far West found themselves in a parallel situation and regarded him in much the same hostile light—the Indian blocked the path of America's "manifest destiny." In 1867, the Topeka Weekly Leader spoke for the West when it characterized the Indians as "a set of miserable, dirty, lousy, blanketed, thieving, lying, sneaking, murdering, graceless, faithless, gut-eating skunks as the Lord ever permitted to infect the earth, and whose immediate and final extermination all men, except Indian agents and traders, should pray for." Cotton Mather's terser characterization of the "tawney serpents" seems almost mild and dignified beside this scathing blast.

Wrestling with his own day-to-day problems, with the Long Hairs not far off, the trans-Mississippi frontiersman was in no position to appreciate the extent to which the Indians already had affected American culture. And it would be interesting to know how many Americans on this frontier had read "Hiawatha." Certainly, few of them could have imagined that, when the West was won and the Indians were safely settled on reservations, native arts and crafts would be appreciated for their esthetic values and widely exhibited, musicians and poets would visit these remaining enclaves of Indian culture to study their music and songs at firsthand, and a museum devoted exclusively to the preservation and exhibition of Indian objects would be established in the largest city of the Nation. What would have surprised them more, perhaps, if they could have looked at a Boy Scout Handbook of the 20th century, is the statement that it "is a pity that most boys think of headdresses, war whoops, tomahawks, and scalps the instant Indians are mentioned. . . . There are so many thousands of beautiful and desirable things in their lives that it is safe to say that they can offer boys a mighty good code of sport and happiness." And among the other things that would strike the frontiersman forcibly would be the requirement that, in order to win a merit badge in Indian lore, the Boy Scout must learn the Omaha Tribal Prayer. Yes, the Omaha, one of those dastardly Siouan tribes—the gut-eating skunks!

But if the Midwestern frontiersman had been interested enough, he would have discovered that the word "skunk," which he could so glibly hurl at the Long Hairs as a derogatory epithet, was derived from an Indian language and had entered American speech in the 17th century. The borrowing of words as well as traits of Indian culture, like the use of corn, had been going on for a long time. Referred to by anthropologists as cultural diffusion, this kind of cultural borrowing is a process that has been occurring throughout the entire history of man. It has been one of the main stimuli of cultural change. When people of different cultures meet and social interaction takes place, this situation inevitably eventuates in some cultural borrowing on the part of either or both peoples.

In the past two decades, cultural anthropologists in this country have devoted increasing attention to detailed studies of the effects of Euro-American culture upon the Indians, that is, acculturation, rather than confining themselves, as was once the case, primarily to the collection of data that would make it possible to reconstruct an ethnographic picture of aboriginal life in its undisturbed form. On the other hand, although recognizing that in principle acculturation is seldom if ever a one-way process, anthropologists have paid scarcely any attention to the total effects upon American culture of our continuing contacts with Indians.

One of the things that anthropologists have discovered is that while Indians may "clothe" themselves, so to speak, with many of the accouterments of white man's culture, this is often no more than skindeep. Even when the Indian is brought into close contact with the white man for more than a generation, and despite missionary efforts and educational opportunities, there is a psychological lag to be taken into account which indcates a dimension of the acculturation process about which we know too little.

In contrast to this side of the acculturalization picture in the United States, it is interesting to recall, when white adults, and especially children, were captured in the 17th, 18th, and early 19th centuries by many different groups of Indians and lived among them in daily intimacy, the apparent ease with which these individuals adjusted themselves to Indian culture. Turner speaks of the "occasional instances of Puritans returning from captivity to visit the frontier towns, Catholic in religion, painted and garbed as Indians and speaking the Indian tongue, and the half-breed children of captive Puritan mothers." While there were many hundreds of white captives taken, we have detailed and reliable information on only a few cases, including individuals who were abducted as children. These "white Indians" often refused to return to the mode of life into which they had been born, even when given an opportunity. In the 18th century Crèvecoeur asked: "By what power does it come to pass, that children who have been adopted when young among these people, can never be prevailed on to readopt European manners?" Such individuals sometimes forgot their native speech, like Cynthia Ann Parker, captured by the Comanches in 1836 at the age of 9. When recaptured by the whites as a grown woman, all she could remember was her name. Other captives praised Indian character and morals and some of them adopted an Indian world view and religious beliefs. It was said of Mary Jemison, abducted in 1758 at the age of 15, that "she was as strong a pagan in her feelings as any Indian," that all her religious ideas conformed to those of the Senecas, and that "the doctrine taught in the Christian religion she is a stranger to." Of William Failey, abducted in 1837, his brother-in law and biographer wrote: "In fact, his long residence among the Indians has made him an Indian." Don Ryan in "The Warriors' Path" (1937) and Conrad Richter in "The Light in the Forest" (1953) have given this theme modern novelistic treatment. The latter book was soon republished in paperback form (1954), and Walt Disney has made a movie of it.

Benjamin Franklin must have been highly impressed by the attitude which the Six Nations assumed toward the values of their own culture as compared with that of the whites. An anecdote, in several forms, appears in his writings which presumably was derived from the considered response these Indians made when, during the Lancaster conference in 1744, it was suggested that if they so desired some of their boys might be sent to Williamsburg for a white education. The Iroquois countered with the proposition that "if the English Gentlemen would send a Dozen or two of their children to Onondago, the great

council would take care of their Education, bring them up in really what was the best Manner and make men of them."

These Indians not only felt secure in their own values; they felt free to appraise those of the white man. And the captives who became "white Indians" discovered that the actual manner of life of the natives was something other than the literary images of the noble savage or the fiendish red man. The Indian cultures contained values which the white child could assimilate, live by, and in adulthood refuse to relinquish. Old White Boy and all his sons became Seneca chiefs. Even aside from captives, there were white men on the frontier who became semiacculturated to Indian ways. Sam Houston, in his early days, lived with the Cherokees. It has not been sufficiently stressed that Leatherstocking, the most famous internationally of all characters in American fiction, falls into this category. Although a white man by "natur," he had Indian "gifts." He is said to have "acquired some knowledge of most of the Indian dialects." During his early life, he lived among the Delawares and long before they called him Deerslayer, he had successively borne three other Indian nicknames. On occasion, he identified himself with the Delawares and their aboriginal values. When contemplating torture by the Hurons, he says he will strive "not to disgrace the people among whom I got my training." And the Huron chiefs, uncertain about his return from the brief furlough granted him, entertained "the hope of disgracing the Delawares by casting into their teeth the delinquency of one held in their villages." While they would have preferred to torture his Indian comrade Chingachgook, they thought the "pale face scion of the hated stock was no bad substitute for their purposes." Quite aside from his characterization as the honest, resourceful, intrepid frontiersman and scout, the uniqueness of Leatherstocking as the first white man in fiction represented as acculturated in his youth to Indian languages, customs, and values, should not be overlooked.

From a contemporary vantage point, I believe that our relations with the Indians involve one distinct peculiarity which might have been difficult to predict at an earlier period of our history. Despite our achievement of political dominance, considerable race mixture, and the effects of acculturation on the native peoples, neither the Indian nor his culture has completely vanished from our midst. The question arises, have the Indian cultures of the postfrontier period completely ceased to influence us? The answer is no. One effect of the reservation system has been the conservation of those aspects of the native cultures that had survived all the vicissitudes of previous contacts with the white race. A new potential source of influence on our 20th-century culture was created. Before we can turn to the nature of this influence, however, it is necessary to obtain the wider historic perspective that a more systematic consideration of the older lines of influence will provide us.

In the first place, it could have been predicted that, as a result of the colonization of the New World, loan words would appear in various Indo-European languages that could be traced to aboriginal American languages. Besides the nouns borrowed to designate objects unknown in England, there are many expressions in American English that reflect Indian influence—*burying the hatchet, Indian summer, Indian giver, happy hunting ground*, and *war paint*, used by the American woman. *Buck* as a slang expression for *dollar* harks back to the Indian fur trade when prices had reference to beavers or buckskins. Place names of Indian origin are, of course, legion—the names of 26 States, 18 of our largest cities, thousands of small towns, most of the long rivers and large lakes, and a few of the highest mountains are of Indian derivation.

Having come to a country new to them, it was inevitable that the colonists, whose traditional culture had not prepared them to live as they had to live here, should be influenced by those aspects of Indian culture that had immediate practical advantages in daily life. In any case, the determinative importance of the fact that this was not in any sense a virgin land must not be forgotten. The countless generations of Indians had left their imprints upon the landscape. Without the plow, the soil had been cultivated, and the raising of native crops was as typical over wide areas as was hunting and fishing. It is still debatable how far the actual virgin terrain had been radically modified by burning, girdling, and tilling. There were narrow forest trails, trodden by moccasined feet, that were already old, and the whites made use of them in their own system of overland communication, developing some of them into highways eventually connecting great centers of American civilization. Then there were the earth-works of an older Indian population in the Old Northwest Territory which influenced the patterning of some early white settlements. The "pilgrims" who founded Marietta, Ohio, found it convenient to moor their flatboats "at the foot of a raised terrace the Mound Builders had once used as an avenue between their temple and the river." Circleville takes its name from the fact that in the laying out of the original town, concentric circles of aboriginal earthworks were closely followed by the outlying streets. An octagonal courthouse, surrounded by a circular green, became the hub of the town. And it is said that "in the Wabash River bottoms, in the early spring, many farmhouses stand high and dry on a wooded burial mound while all the fields are under water."

Among the early settlers, communication by water was everywhere the most important. While they were familiar with certain types of watercraft in their own culture, they and their descendants have been influenced by at least two types used by the Indians, the Chesapeake Bay log canoe and the bark canoe of the north.

From a European point of view, the Indians wearing moccasins, leggings, and breechclouts were considered to be relatively naked compared to themselves. However, considered in a very broad culture-historical perspective, their own style and that of the aborigines shared a generic trait in common: throughout the boreal regions of the Northern Hemisphere, clothing of the fitted or tailored type prevails, standing in marked contrast to the untailored style once found in the ancient Mediterranean region, Africa, and Central and South America. In all these latter regions, for example, nothing like the fitted footgear represented by the boot, shoe, or moccasin is found. While the practice never spread beyond the frontier itself, nevertheless there were white men who adopted the wearing of not only Indian moccasins, but leggings and a breechclout as well. The moccasins, of course, is the most noted item of Indian clothing that was used by white men very early. It was a fitted type of footgear, and if the colonists had been Romans, this item of clothing might not have been borrowed so quickly, or its use continued. Turner has noted that the General Court of Massachusetts once ordered 500 pairs each of snowshoes and moccasins for use in the frontier counties. Much later, footgear of this type was used by lumbermen. In the backwoods of Manitoba in the 1930's, a clergyman of my acquaintance always wore a pair of his best beaded moccasins in the pulpit on Sundays. It would be interesting to know more about the commercialization of the moccasin type of shoe which we see increasingly on the feet of Americans today.

It was, however, the discovery of the plants cultivated by the New World aborigines that from the very first produced the most profound impact on both European and American culture, revolutionizing the food economy and diet of Old World peoples and at the same time laying one of the foundations on which was to rise the distinctive structure of American agriculture. Of the several plants—maize, beans, pumpkins, squash, and others—maize in particular was important from the start, taking precedence over the grain which the settlers had brought from Europe. It became a primary factor in the acculturation of the Englishmen to an American way of life. We need think only of corn on the cob, cornbread, Indian pudding, hominy, mush, grits, succotash, and corn sirup; of breakfast cereals, cornstarch, and popcorn; or of corncob pipes and bourbon, to understand the extent of this Indian contribution to our civilization today.

Tobacco is an equally significant "gift" of the American Indians, symbolized by the once-familiar figure of the "wooden Indian" inextricably linked with the tobacco shop in the 19th century. The history and use of it in our culture present a number of features in cultural borrowing at large. Readaptation to the values of the borrowing people is well illustrated. The consumption of tobacco was completely divorced from the ceremonial context in which it appeared among the Indians and became purely secular.

Peruvian bark, now known as quinine, proved highly sensational since it was a specific for malaria. It reached Spain before the middle of the 17th century and was soon introduced into the English colonies. In Virginia, Governor Berkeley said in 1671 that whereas formerly one person in five had died of fever in his first year, now almost no one succumbed. When one considers that in this same century Governor Winthrop's famous

remedy for ulcers consisted of "one ounce of crabbe's eyes and four ounces of strong wine vinegar," the general state of colonial medicine can be well appreciated, and the reason why Peruvian bark, an Indian herbal, achieved such high fame can be easily understood. Indian medicine was likewise given a boost when, in 1738, Dr. John Tennent was awarded 100 pounds by the Virginia House of Burgesses for curing pleurisy with Seneca rattlesnake root. As William Fenton well says, when Western medicine met Indian herbalism, the former "was still carrying a heavy burden of medieval practices so that the first few physicians in the colonies were but several centuries advanced from the Indian shaman who selected his herbs thinking of the effect that their appearance might contribute to the disease, and guaranteed their efficiency with incantations and feats of magic. Moreover, the average settler had brought from the Old World a knowledge of herbs that in kind was not unlike that of the Indian, but as newcomers they were unfamiliar with New World plants, and although the level of their own popular medicine did not set them above adopting Indian remedies, the Indian herbalist whose knowledge was power was not always a ready teacher." In "The Pioneers," Cooper pictures for us how "Doctor" Elnathan Todd managed to steal one of John Mohegan's remedies.

Popular confidence in Indian medicine remained strong during the early 19th century, when the population was flowing over the Appalachians. The "yarb and root" doctor, red or white, played a prominent role in many communities. In 1813 in Cincinnati there was published "The Indian Doctor's Dispensatory." Other books followed, including Selman's "The Indian Guide to Health" (1836) and Foster's "The North American Indian Doctor, or Nature's Method of Curing and Preventing Disease According to the Indians" (1838). In a lecture given at the New York Academy of Medicine in 1936, Dr. Harlow Brooks (emeritus professor of clinical medicine, New York University) said:

The universal testimony of those qualified to judge has been that even within the memory of my generation we have incorporated into our pharmacopoeia and practice a good many practices and drugs of our Indian predecessors. . . . The leading doctor in my boyhood memory, in the district in which my parents settled, was an old Sioux medicine man, whose services were considered by the territorial government so valuable that when his tribe was removed to a reservation he was asked to remain with his white patients, among whom were my own parents. I am sure that much of the medicine I received as an infant and child was derived directly from the lore of this fine, learned, and much respected old man. In those days it was on the service of these men that our pioneers relied for medical help; otherwise, little or none at all was available to the early settler.

What is particularly interesting is not merely the incorporation in our pharmacopoeia of some aboriginal drugs, but the positive attitude toward Indian medicine and charms that has persisted into the 20th century. For instance, old Seneca families still sell wild flowers and sassafras on certain street corners in Buffalo, and the Pamunkey Indians of Virginia until a decade ago went to Washington every spring to sell sassafras and other herbs. In "Triple Western" (fall, 1954) there is a short item on "Medicine Man's Wisdom."

The potencies attributed to Indian herbal remedies have had still other manifestations in our culture, an important one being the medicine show. While not all these shows made use of the Indian, most of them did. It has been said that "as a symbol" the native "was as important to the med-show platform as the wooden Indian was to the tobacco shop." It exploited the image that had already been created of him as a "healer." When Chief Chauncey Kills-in-the-Bush Yellow Robe died, eulogies appeared in the theatrical press. Rolling Thunder, the owner of the Kiowa Indian Medicine and Vaudeville Company, commented on these as follows:

It is fine to see this intelligent recognition of the life work of an Indian. Too many people have always thought of the American Indian as next to a beast. There are some who are now learning the truth: that the Indian's drugstore was always the field and the forest, where the herbs he uses in his medicines are gathered as God placed them for him to use, and God gave the Indian the knowledge to gather and compound them. That is why the Indian as a healer has been a success.

The authors of "Show Biz" say that "when the Kickapoo Indian Medicine Company went on the block in 1911, after 30 years roaming the American plains and hamlets, it still brought $250,000. At one time, there were 150 medicine shows on the road, all of them featuring one or more Kickapoo Indians." It may be pointed out in passing that at the same time that the image of the Indian as a healer was being exploited in the medicine show, the old image of him as a bloodthirsty enemy was being dramatized by the Wild West show that William F. Cody took on the road in 1883 and which in various invarnations and imitations continued until 1931, when the 101 Ranch closed down.

The red man also became involved in another characteristic area of American cultural development in the years before the Civil War —religion. In Spiritualism, the United Society of Believers (Shakers), and the Church of Latter-day Saints (Mormons), the American Indians had special significance for the founders or adherents. According to Shaker tradition, "it was a native of the forest who first recognized the saintliness of Mother Ann. One poor Indian saw a bright light around her, and prophesied that the Great Spirit had sent her to do much good. In another story it is related that when Ann was returning from her eastern mission, she was met at the Albany ferry by a number of Indians, who joyfully cried: 'The good woman is come! The good woman is come!' " What other religious sect in the world has turned to an aboriginal people for validation of the saintliness of the founder? Besides this, some of the Shaker "gift songs" received in trance came from Indian spirits. Once the spirits of a whole tribe of Indians, who had died before Columbus discovered America and had been wandering homeless ever since, turned up at a Shaker meetinghouse, where they were made welcome. As described by an eyewitness, more than a dozen of the Shakers present became possessed by these Indian guests. A pow-wow ensued. There were yells, whoops, and strange antics. The Indian spirits asked for succotash, which they ate, and after some instruction were sent off under guidance "to the Shakers' heavenly world."

Although "speaking in tongues" had a long history in Europe as well as in America, one of the striking facts in the early developmental phases of American Spiritualism is the frequency of references to mediums speaking

Indian languages and to those who had an Indian "control" or "guide." The names of more than a dozen mediums, men and women and their Indian controls, appear in the "Encyclopaedia of Psychic Science." Such historic figures as Red Jacket, Black Hawk, and Tecumseh are on the list, as well as spirits with such names as White Feather, Bright Eyes, and Moonstone. What is particularly significant is that these Indian spirits were thought to be beneficent in their influence, especially because of their healing powers, although they often manifested themselves at seances in a somewhat rambunctious manner. As time went on and spirit photography was introduced, some of these spirits appeared in native costume in the photographs.

It would seem that no other American religious sect, with the possible exception of the Shakers, felt such a genuine affinity with the aborigines. While there was no question of borrowing Indian beliefs as such, nevertheless the Spiritualists saw analogies to their own views and practices. One of these was the "shaking tent" rite of the Algonkians of the eastern woodlands (which has been described elsewhere). Into a framework of poles covered with birchbark or canvas a conjurer goes; the tent sways and voices are heard which, however, are usually believed to be nonhuman. An early historian of American Spiritualism, writing in 1870, after referring to some of these rites, says:

Such are some of the phases in which communication exhibits itself amongst a people whom we call "savage" and whom, in comparison to our more advanced civilization, we may justly call so; and yet, does our knowledge of the occult and invisible forces in nature furnish us with any clue to the mystery of these astounding manifestations or the power by which the unlettered "savage" can avail himself of a knowledge which all our control over the elements fails to compete with? In a word, the red Indian can do what we can neither explain nor imitate.

This interest of the Spiritualists in the Indian and his ways has continued down to the present. At Lily Dale, N.Y., the summer mecca of Spiritualists, which commemorated its 50th anniversary in 1929, it has been customary to celebrate Indian Day with parades and dances given by natives from nearby reservations.

To turn now to the Church of Jesus Christ of Latter-day Saints, the attitude of the adherents of this indigenous American sect toward the Indians is in sharp contrast with that of the Spiritualists. According to "The Book of Mormon," the red men are essentially the degenerate posterity of a rebellious segment of a small group of Jews who, migrating to the New World before the beginning of the Christian era, brought with them an advanced culture. Consequently, it it said that "The Book of Mormon" supplements the Bible, since it is a history of God's dealings with remnants of Israel and the Saviour's ministrations among them in the Western Hemisphere. For in America, the great Nephrite prophecy has been fulfilled—the second coming of Christ. After the Resurrection He appeared to a multitude of nearly 3,000 people in Mexico, before a greater assembly the next day, and after this "he did show himself unto them oft." The occurrence of the legendary figure of a so-called "white god" with certain associated attributes among the Incas, Mayas, Aztecs, and Toltecs, the Mormons interpret as supporting eidence for the historic appearance of Christ in America.

In the Mormon view of the aborigines of the United States were the descendants of the Lamanites, the "bad" people of the Mormon epic. Unlike the Spiritualists, the Mormons had nothing they could look to them for; still, a strange affinity connected them with the Indians. In Mormon hymnals there are songs about the red man. In the days before the rise of archeology of anthropology in the contemporary sense, "The Book of Mormon" was representative of the speculations that had been going on in Europe for several centuries about the peopling of the New World. These earlier theories had to be reconciled first of all with the account given in the Bible of man's creation and dispersal. What is peculiar in the Mormon case, however, is the fact that a particular theory of the peopling of the New World was incorporated as a dogma of a religious sect. This could hardly have occurred anywhere but in early 19th-century America. The early Mormons easily reconciled their theory with the Bible, but since the sect has survived into a period of American culture when an enormous increase in our knowledge of New World prehistory from archeological investigations has taken place, a further reconciliation of the inspired history found in "The Book of Mormon" with this new knowledge is now being sought.

Outside the Mormon church, the consensus is that in its nondoctrinal aspects "The Book of Mormon" is derived from a romance written but not published by Solomon Spaulding, a clergyman who left the church and was in business in Ohio by 1812. There he dug into some mounds and became interested in the origin of the extinct people who had erected them. The theory that they were of Jewish origin was not original with him, since it was mantained by many prominent men in this country. If Spaulding's manuscript had been printed in its original form as fiction, he would have anticipated those writers in America who were soon to exploit the Indian in the historical novel. Even when "The Book of Mormon" was published in 1830, it fell precisely in the period when the Indian was assuming great prominence in American literature. Three of Cooper's "Leatherstocking Tales" had met with acclaim by this date, and at least 39 novels published between 1824 and 1834 included Indian episodes.

There was a parallel development in the drama. Barker's "Indian princess' (Pocahontas), staged in 1808, had a long line of successors. There were at least 30 so-called Indians plays staged between 1820 and 1840 and 20 or more between the latter date and the Civil War. Some of these were dramatizations of the novels of Cooper, Bird, and Simms. The peak in the popularity of these Indian dramas also falls within the period (1830-70) that has been called "the golden days of the American actor." Perhaps the most outstanding example is "Metamora, or The Last of the Wampanoags," which was in the repertoire of Edwin Forrest for almost 40 years. It was played in Philadelphia every year—except two —for a quarter of a century. Forrest had specifically advertised in 1828 for a play in which "the hero, or principal character, shall be an aboriginal of this country." William Cullen Bryant was the chairman of the committee which selected "Metamora" from the 14 plays submitted. It proved to be one of the most popular plays of the 19th-century American theater. "Metamora" was played even after Forrest's death, and a radio version was broadcast in 1939. During its theatrical lifetime, more Americans are said to have seen "Metamora" than "Abie's Irish Rose" or "Tobacco Road" in the 20th century.

In Poetry, the Indian had appeared as a subject ever since the time of Freneau, but there was nothing that could compare with the initial impact and continuing popularity of "Hiawatha." It became *the* poem of the American Indian. Before publication in 1855, there was an advance sale of 4,000 copies; in 5 months the sale had risen to 50,000 copies. It has been said that what was unique about Longfellow's poem was the fact that " 'Hiawatha' was the first poem of its kind in America based on Indian legend rather than on Indian history." While true enough, it is clarifying to note that until 1839, when Schoolcraft published his "Algic Researches," there were no reliable collections of Indian myths or tales on which a poet could draw. It was, therefore, a historical accident that Longfellow came to exploit Ojibwa material; he had no other choice. Paradoxically, Schoolcraft himself published a poem dealing with the Creek Indian wars 12 years before "Hiawatha" appeared. He did not know the Creeks at first hand, while he knew the Ojibwas intimately, his wife being of that tribe. Evidently it never occurred to him to use his Ojibwa myths as the basis of a narrative poem. Thus Schoolcraft epitomizes the force of the traditional literary approach to the use of Indian themes.

Longfellow bore the same sort of relation to Schoolcraft as Cooper did to Heckewelder. Generally speaking, there was no inclination on the part of eastern novelists, dramatists, or poets who selected Indian themes to become acquainted with living Indians of the contemporary frontiers as a background for their productions. Indeed, a volume of short stories, "Tales of the Northwest," about Indians in the Upper Mississippi region, written by one who knew them intimately, was ignored after its publication in 1839. William Joseph Snelling, the author, had insisted that "a man must live, emphatically, live with Indians; share with them their lodges, their food, and their blankets, for years, before he can comprehend their ideas, or enter their feelings." American writers were not yet ready for this early call to realism. But for American readers, a novel entitled "Altowan; or Incidents of Life and Adventure in the Rocky Mountains," by

Sir William Drummond Stewart, an eccentric Scot, who during the 1830's had spent 6 years in the West, was published in New York in 1846. Although the novel was undistinguished in writing and had some romantic trappings, in this case the author *had* seen a great deal of Indian life.What makes the book unique is that one of the leading characters, as pointed out by De Voto, is an Indian transvestite—a berdache—and this individual is depicted in highly realistic terms. The author pictures his behavior and dress in detail, and no doubt is left about what he was. "I know of no English or American novel of that time or for many years later that is half so frank about homosexuality," writes De Voto.

In painting and popular music there was a parallel romantic tradition. Gleanings from historical documents or tradition were tinctured by an extremely free use of imagination. It is obvious, for instance, that the artist who provided the frontispiece for Mrs. Morton's "Ouabi, or The Virtue of Nature" (1790) knew as little about Indians at first hand as did the author of this poem in the noble savage tradition. And Benjamin West's painting of one of Penn's treaties with the Indians, dating from about 1771, offers a direct parallel to the literary artist who drew on historical documents for his source material.

Part of Mrs. Morton's poem was set to music by Hans Gram the year after its publication. This composition, the first orchestral score published in the United States, was entitled "The Death Song of an Indian Chief," although there is no evidence that the composer knew anything about aboriginal music. In 1799, a musical arrangement of "Alk'-amoonok, the Death Song of the Cherokee Indians," reputedly based on a genuine Indian melody, was published and soon became very popular. It had been sung in "Tammany" (1794), the first American opera. An eccentric musician, Anton Philip Heinrich, who died in 1861, was the composer of the "Pocahontas Waltz" for piano and is said to have been the first to use Indian themes in larger orchestral works. The heroine of the big song hit of 1844, "The Blue Juniata," was an Indian girl, "Bright Alforata."

Actually, it is at this vernacular level that the backwash of the frontier is most clearly discernible in American music of the 19th century. This was due to the role of the Indian played in the subject matter of folk songs. In one group of songs, the Indian appears "merely as an incidental personality" and the attitudes toward him are vague. In a second group, however, negative attitudes are sharply defined since many songs in this class are long narrative ballads which depict actual frontier conflicts. Folksongs about historic events, "including songs about dramatic episodes in the relationships of Indians and White, have been sung regularly since the earliest days of colonization and have faithfully reflected changing relationships between the two culture groups at least down to the present century when modern techniques for the commercialization of popular songs may have beclouded the issue." A third category of songs reflects a positive attitude toward the Indian varying "from vague references to good Indians or Indians with heroic qualities, to songs and ballads exclusively about romanticized Indians, who are admired for their stamina and other heroic qualities." An anonymous, undated example of America's folk painting, depicting the rescue of John Smith, belongs to this earlier period. The same motif was subsequently as popular in prints as it was in fiction, drama, poetry, and music.

However, in the midst of all this romanticizing of the Indian, a trend toward greater realism developed, particularly in painting. Here and there in colonial times there had been some realistic paintings of the Indians; for example, the masterly portraits of Lenape chiefs painted in 1735 by Gustavus Hesselius (1682-1755). But about 1821, many of the western chiefs who came to Washington on business with the Government sat for their portraits. A collection of these became the nucleus of the famous "Indian Gallery." The magnificent reproduction of 120 of these portraits in a folio edition of 3 volumes (McKenny and Hall, "History of the Indian Tribes of North America, 1836-44") gave the eastern public an opportunity to see what contemporary Indians looked like. On the other hand, artists themselves began to go west (Seymour, Rindisbacher, Lewis, Catlin, Miller, Eastman, Stanley, Kane, Bodmer, Kurz), so that greatly enriched images of the natives, the kind of life they led, and the grandeur of the country they inhabited soon became more widely known to those living far removed from the contemporary frontier. It was the author of "Altowan" who induced Alfred Jacob Miller— now one of the most famous of these artists, whose true accomplishments have only become known to the public in recent years— to accompany him west in 1837. Catlin is particularly important, however, not only because he was a pioneer, but because he was a showman. He toured eastern cities in the late 1830's exhibiting his "Indian Gallery," which has been called the first Wild West show. It included Indian "curios," featuring pipes, and in exhibition halls he erected a real Crow tepee. Catlin appeared in person and, taking selected pictures as a point of departure, lectured to his audiences about Indian life. He would dress lay figures in Indian clothing and frequently had some Indians on hand to pantomime native activities. Although Catlin was not an anthropologist, his Indian Gallery did mediate to Americans a more realistic type of knowledge about the Plains tribes than had been available. After touring American cities, he took his show to England and the Continent. In 1954, an exhibition of Catlin's work, sponsored by the United States Information Agency, was again on tour in Europe, while in this country Bodmer's watercolors were being exhibited.

Even though Catlin "had been there," he had detractors, like Audubon, who challenged the accuracy of his paintings. The same thing had happened to Cooper and Longfellow. The romantic tradition in America was strong, and the application of a purely realistic standard of judgment was, in effect, an attack upon the tradition. Cooper may have idealized the Indian in some respects and erred in many details, but he idealized the pioneer and backwoodsman too. The Indian was enveloped in the romantic tradition and what is interesting is how long he has remained a part of it.

When the dime novel sprang into popularity in the 1860's, the Indians of the Cooper tradition became an integral part of this literature. In one way or another, Indians play a role in at least 45 percent of the 321 stories in the original dime-novel series. "Maleska, the Indian Wife of the White Hunter" (1860), the first one published by Beadle and Adams, actually was a reprinting of a story that had been serialized in 1839. "The death of the dime novel, if it ever really occurred, was accompanied by the birth of the nickelodeon, the motion picture, and the radio, which simply transferred the old stories of cowboys, desperadoes, and Indians to more dynamic forms." In fact, as soon as the silent cinema began to flicker, the Indian of the old romantic tradition was in. There was a screen version of "Hiawatha" as early as 1909, the "Deerslayer" was shown in 1911, the "Last of the Mohicans" in 1920. And, until very recently, what Stanley Vestal called the "Hollywooden Indian" has persisted in that typically American movie genre—the western.

On the other hand, there was an increasing awareness that authentic knowledge of the aboriginal cultures was relevant and desirable in the arts. Perhaps this attitude developed along with the emergence of a more realistic tradition in American writing. However this may be, I think that the publication of Edna Dean Proctor's "Song of the Ancient People" in 1893 represents a transitional case. While it is in the high romantic tradition, there is an appended commentary to this poem by F. H. Cushing (1857-1900), a pioneer anthropologist who went to the Southwest in 1879 and lived among the Zuñi for 5 years. He says he can bear witness to the poet's "strict fidelity of statement, and attempt to show, as one of the Ancient People themselves would be glad to show, how well she has divined their spirit." The volume was illustrated with realistic aquatints made by Julian Scott in the Hopi country. No other Indian poem had ever been offered to the public with such an aura of authenticity about it—it was bound in buckskin with a design taken from Southwestern pottery on the cover.

The inauguration of genuine Indian themes in American concert music is ordinarily attributed to Edward MacDowell, whose "Indian Suite" was first performed in 1896. But where did he find such themes? He was not a frontier boy. He entered the Paris Conservatory at the age of 14 and did not take up residence here until he was 27. The fact is that MacDowell exemplifies a repetition of the same kind of relationship to the source of his thematic material as was noted in the case of Cooper and Longfellow. He got them from Theodore Baker, the first trained musician to go into the field and study Indian music at first hand. Baker, a German, visited the Seneca Reservation and the Carlisle Indian School in the summer of 1880, offering the results of his analysis to Leipzig University as a doctoral dissertation. But he was not a composer, nor was Alice C. Fletcher, whose monograph on Omaha songs (1893) initiated the study of Indian music in American anthropology. However, two of the songs she collected, "Shupida" and the "Omaha Tribal Prayer," undoubtedly have been among the most widely circulated examples of authentic Indian music in American culture. Together with three other Indian songs, they appear in "Indian Lore," a pamphlet in the Merit Badge Series of the Boy Scouts of America. In the past 6 years, approximately 47,000 copies of this booklet have been printed. Scouts who aspire to the merit badge in Indian lore must be able to "sing three Indian songs including the Omaha Tribal Prayer and tell something of their meaning." Since 1911, there have been more than 18,700 American boys who have won this distinction.

Following the lead of MacDowell, other posers began to make increasing use of Indian themes, though only a few made direct contact with the reservation Indians. Among them were Burton, Cadman, Farwell, Jacobi, Lieurance, Arthur Nevin, Skilton, and Troyer, who found native music interesting to them, because as Skilton has said, "many devices of the ultra modern composers of the present day have long been employed by Indians—unusual intervals, arbitrary scales, changing tune, conflicting rhythm, polychoral effects, hypnotic monotony." Indian songs were harmonized and arranged for performance by white musicians; Indian themes were handled freely in the composition of original works, much in the same way that Longfellow handled Ojibwa myths.

In the field of operatic composition, despite the popularity of other compositions of Herbert and Cadman, neither the former's "Natoma" (1911) nor the latter's "Shanewis" (1918) became established in operatic repertoire. Some compositions based on Indian themes have received high acclaim in the repertoire of orchestral music, others as popular songs. Skilton's "Indian Dances," along with MacDowell's "Indian Suite," were among the 27 compositions of 12 American composers which had the greatest number of performances in the United States during the 7 years following World War I. Jacobi's "String Quartet on Indian Themes" was selected to represent American music at the International Festival of Contemporary Music at Zurich in 1926. Elliott Carter's "Pocahontas," presented in New York in 1939 (and later developed into a suite for orchestra) received the Juilliard Publication Award the following year. Cadman, who went to the Omaha Reservation in 1909 with Francis LaFlesche, an Indian anthropologist, wrote one of his most famous songs that year, "From the Land of the Sky Blue Water." It vied with "The Rosary" in popularity. He likewise wrote two operas on Indian themes. "By the Waters of Minnetonka" (1921), composed by Thurlow Lieurance, who had visited the western reservations as early as 1905, has had a phenomenal success. At midcentury it appears in the Victor Album "Twelve Beloved American Songs" along with "The Rosary" and "A Perfect Day." Nor should commercialized popular songs of a lower order—some Indian in name only—be forgotten. Among those composed early in this century were "Navajo" (1903), "Tammany" (1905), "Red Wing" (1907), and "Hiawatha's Melody of Love" (1920), to say nothing of "The Indian Love Call" (1924), and "Ramona," a hit of 1927.

In the early years of this century, some American poets, like the musicians, sought out the Indians, and those of the Southwest became a focal point of interest. These were the same people that Edna Procter had written about. They had been the subject, too, of a novel, "The Delight Makers" (1890), by A. F. Bandelier, said by Alfred L. Kroeber to be "a more comprehensive and coherent view of native Pueblo life than any scientific volume on the southwest."

A few American painters (Sharp, Phillips, Blumenschein) had also discovered the Southwest before the opening of the 20th century. Blumenschein's graphic commentary on the acculturation process, which shows two Indians mounted on merry-go-round horses, had appeared in Harper's Weekly in 1899.

Among the poets who became interested, Mary Austin soon took the lead. She became the key figure in the use of Indian material for literary purposes, and her extremely positive attitude toward the cultures of the Indians influenced many others to seek inspiration in their art. She characterized her "Amerindian Songs" as being "Reexpressed from the Originals." Some of these first appeared in "Poetry" (1917), along with comparable interpretations by Frank S. Gordon, Alice Corbin Henderson, and Constance Lindsay Skinner. Mary Austin wrote plays and stories, too. She seems to have moved from a romantic primitivism to a more and more realistic handling of Indian themes, as exemplified by her play "The Arrow Maker," produced on Broadway in 1911, and her "One-Smoke Stories" (1934), one of her last books. Nor should the fact be overlooked that four anthologies containing translations of American Indian songs and poetry have appeared in this century (George W. Cronyn, "The Path of the Rainbow," 1918 and 1934; Nellie Barnes, "American Indian Love Lyrics and Other Verse," 1925; Margot Astrov, "The Winged Serpent," 1946; and A. Grove Day, "The Sky Clears," 1951).

In the 20th century, the Indian has also reappeared in American plays, particularly in the work of the regional dramatists. While the setting is frequently the historic past, the problems the native faces in the acculturation process are sometimes dramatized. Both "Strongheart" (1905) and "Cherokee Night" (1936) are examples of this theme. In prose fiction, we also find that anthropologists, inspired by Bandelier and the stories collected in Elsie Clews Parsons' "American Indian Life" (1922), entered the field. "Laughing Boy," a Literary Guild book of 1929, by Oliver La Farge, and "Hawk Over Whirlpools" by Ruth Underhill (1940) are outstanding illustrations. In "America in Fiction," the authors call attention to the fact that "now that he is on reservations, not a military foe, and generally not an economic competitor, the Indian is a subject of great interest, so much so that more fiction has been written about him in recent years than about any other ethnic group except the Negro. In many works of fiction, he has been given central prominence, his cultural complex has been detailed, and much attention has been paid to his problems of adjusting himself to the dominating civilization that surrounds him." Their bibliography lists 37 novels or collections of stories published between 1902 and 1947. "Where once we had melodrama about the Indian with his bloody tomahawk," they say, "now we have clear-cut realism." Whatever the art form may be, what is striking is the more intimate acquaintance with contemporary Indians that

informs the work of the painter, musician, poet, dramatist, or novelist who has drawn upon aboriginal cultural forms or used the problems of the Indian for his thematic material.

Finally, it seems to me that among these more recent influences, the impact of the Indian on modern anthropology should not be omitted. The social sciences as they have developed in the United States during the past half-century have attained an unusual prominence in American culture. Among these, anthropology in its modern form was just getting under way about the time the frontier closed. It was in the 1890's that Franz Boas began to teach at Columbia University and to train students in fieldwork. Boas was a specialist in studies of the American Indian and a majority of his early students followed in his footsteps. Indeed, practically all the chief authorities on North American Indian ethnology, archeology, and linguistics have been American. A historical accident? Of course. But that is the point. It is only recently among the younger generation that more attention is being devoted to peoples in the South Seas, Africa, and Asia. But it was the study of the Indians, and the problems that emerged from the investigation of the Indian as a subject, that gave American anthropology a distinctive coloring as compared with British, French, and German anthropology. Recently an American psychologist has remarked that "if the word 'anthropology' were presented to a sample of psychologists in a word-association test I would venture 'culture' would probably be the most popular response, with 'Indians' a runner-up." The presumption, no doubt, is that these hypothetical responses would be those of American psychologists.

The more detailed and reliable accounts of native Indian cultures that have emerged from the fieldwork of American anthropologists have made possible a more objective appraisal of the values inherent in the aboriginal modes of life. To those who look at the record, the Indian no longer appears as either a noble or ignoble savage. He has moved into a clearer focus as a human being. Like our own, his traditional cultural background and historical situation have determined the nature of his experience and made him what he is.

Viewing the panorama of our colonial and national history as a whole, I have referred to many diverse aspects of our culture—speech, economic life, food habits, clothing, transportation, medicine, religion, the arts, and even a social science—which have been influenced by our relations with the Indians at different times and in differing ways. Some of these influences have been mediated directly, others indirectly. Contacts with the Indian on the frontier have by no means been the source of all of them.

In summing up, we may ask: how deeply have such influences penetrated our culture? To what extent are our relations with the Indians one key to our differentiation as Americans, not only culturally but psychologically? Constance Rourke once wrote, "The Backswoodsman conquered the Indian, but the Indian also conquered him. He ravaged the land and was ravaged in turn." Phillips D. Carleton, concluding his comments on the captivity literature, writes: "It emphasizes the fact that it was the line of fluid frontiers receding into the West that changed the colonists into a new people; they conquered the Indian but he was the hammer that beat out a new race on the anvil of the continent." Carl Jung, who has probably analyzed more persons of various nationalities than anyone else, thought he could discern an Indian component in the character structure of his American patients, and D. H. Lawrence asked whether a dead Indian is nought. "Not that the Red Indian will ever possess the broadlands of America," he said and then added, "But his ghost will."

In America we faced the Indian on receding frontiers for a long period; but outside the frontier there was the shadow of the Indian. This shadow is still upon us. We still mouth words and idioms that reflect intimate contacts with the aborigines of our land. We still make use of plants originally cultivated by them. We wear derivative forms of the footgear they wore. We have collected objects made by them in our homes and in our museums. Our artists have found inspiration in their artistic modes of expression. We constantly see the Indian sweep past our eyes on the movie screen. He persists in our historical novels and westerns. In 1954, "The Leatherstocking Saga" reappeared, compressed into one handsome volume. We Americans have seen the Indian come and go on the commonest national coins we have fingered. The first Bible to be printed in colonial America was in the Indian language, John Eliot's translation of the Old and New Testament into an Algonkian tongue. Over the generations thousands of American men have belonged to the more-than-a-century-old Improved Order of Red Men. American anthropologists have labored most industriously to provide more and more authentic information about aboriginal modes of life and the influence of American culture on the Indian. The Indian has never been rejected from the American consciousness. Perhaps his shadow upon us is even disappearing—he has become a part of us: in the "Dictionary of American Biography" will be found side by side with other famous Americans, Pontiac and Tecumseh, Blackhawk and Osceola. In 1931 a brief popular biography of Osceola—only a few pages in length—was printed at Palm Beach; it was entitled "Osceola the Seminole. Florida's Most Distinguished Historical Character!" And it is said that more statues have been erected of Sacajawea than of any other American woman.

Now that the frontier has passed, our children discover the Indian in the comic books, as well as in the library. They are familiar with Cooper's tales in "Classics Illustrated." Indeed, there appears to have been a marked increase in number, variety, and quality of children's books about Indians published in the last two or more decades. There are biographies of Indians famous in our history as well as historical romances. The stories of famous white captives have been retold; there are excellent books on Indian crafts and simplied but accurate accounts of tribal life, besides well-written stories which center around Indian children as major characters. Nevertheless, the average American is by no means aware of all the ramifications of Indian influence upon our culture. Perhaps the Red Indian ghost D. H. Lawrence saw here and what Jung discerned in the character of his patients provide clues to an aspect of the American ethos that invites deeper scrutiny in the future.

*selection 54*

# Where Are We Going If Anywhere? A Look at Post-Civilization

*Kenneth E. Boulding*

We are living in what I call the second great change in the state of man. The first great change is the change from pre-civilized to civilized societies. The first 500,000 years or so of man's existence on earth were relatively uneventful. Compared with his present condition he puttered along in an astonishingly stationary state. To judge by his artifacts, at least, generation succeeded generation with the sons exactly like their fathers, and the daughters exactly like their mothers. There may have been changes in language and culture which are not reflected in the artifacts, but if there were these changes are lost to us. The evidence of the artifacts, however, is conclusive. Whatever changes there were, they were almost unbelievably slow. About 10,000 years ago, we begin to perceive an acceleration in the rate of change. This becomes very noticeable 5,000 years ago with the development of the first civilization. The details of this first great change are probably beyond our recovery. However, we do know that it depended on two phenomena: the first was the development of agriculture, and the second was the development of exploitation. These two great inventions seem to have developed about the same time, perhaps independently —although we do not know this—in the Nile valley, in the lower valley of the Euphrates, and in the valley of the Indus. Agriculture, that is the domestication of crops and livestock and the planting of crops in fields, gave man a secure surplus of food from the food producer. In a hunting and fishing economy it seems to take the food producer all his time

*From* Human Organization, *Vol. 21, No. 2, 1962, pp. 162–167.* © *1962, The Society for Applied Anthropology. By permission of the author, and the publisher and copyright holder.*

to produce enough food for himself and his family. The moment we have agriculture with its superior productivity of this form of employment of human resources means that the food producer can produce more food than he and his family can eat. But this in itself is not enough to produce civilization. In some societies in these happy conditions, the food producer has simply relaxed and indulged himself with leisure. As soon, however, as we get politics, that is exploitation, we begin to get cities and civilization. Civilization, it is clear from the origin of the word, is what happens in cities, and the city is dependent in its early stages at any rate on there being a food surplus from the food producer and on there being some organization which can take it away from him. With this food surplus, the political organization feeds kings, priests, armies, architects, and builders and the city comes into being. Political science in its earliest form is the knowledge of how to take the food surplus away from the food producer without giving him very much in return.

Now I argue that we are in the middle, perhaps not even in the middle, of the second great change in the state of man, which is as drastic and as dramatic, and certainly as large if not larger, as the change from pre-civilized to civilized society. This I call the change from civilization to post-civilization. It is a strange irony that just at the moment when civilization has almost completed the conquest of pre-civilized societies, post-civilization has been treading heavily upon its heels. The student of civilization may soon find himself in the unfortunate position of the anthropologist who studies pre-civilized societies. Both are like the student of ice on a hot day—the subject matter melts away almost before he can study it.

These great changes can be thought of as a change of gear in the evolutionary process, resulting in progressive accelerations of the rate of evolutionary change. Even before the appearance of man on the earth, we can detect earlier evolutionary gear-shiftings. The formation of life obviously represented one such transition, the movement from the water to the land represented another, the development of the vertebrates another, and so on. Man himself represents a very large acceleration of the evolutionary process. Whether he evolved from pre-existing forms or whether he

landed from a space ship and was not able to get back to where he came from, is immaterial. Once he had arrived on earth, the process of evolution could go on within the confines of the human nervous system at a greatly accelerated rate. The human mind is an enormous mutation-selection process. Instead of the mutation-selection process being confined, as it were, to the flesh, it can take place within the image and hence, very rapid changes are possible. Man seems to have been pretty slow to exploit this potentiality, but one suspects that even with primitive man, the rate of change in the biosphere was much larger than it had been before, because of the appearance of what de Chardin calls the nöosphere, or sphere of knowledge.

Civilization represents a further acceleration of the rate of change, mainly because one of the main products of civilization is history. With the food surplus from agriculture it becomes possible to feed specialized scribes. With the development of writing, man did not have to depend on the uncertain memories of the aged for its records, and a great process of accumulation of social knowledge began. The past can now communicate, at least in one direction, with the present, and this enormously increases the range and possibility of enlargements of the contents of the human mind.

Out of civilization, however, comes science, which is a superior way of organizing the evolution of knowledge. We trace the first beginnings of science, of course, almost as far back as the beginning of civilization itself. Beginning about 1650, however, we begin to see the organization of science into a community of knowledge, and this leads again to an enormous acceleration of the rate of change. The world of 1650 is more remote to us than the world of ancient Egypt or Samaria would have been to the man of 1650. Already in the United States and Western Europe, in a smaller degree in Russia and in some other parts of the world, we see the beginnings of post-civilized society—a state of man as different from civilization as civilization is from savagery. What we really mean, therefore, by the anemic term "economic development" is the second great transition in the state of man. It is the movement from civilized to post-civilized society. It is nothing short of a major revolution in the human condition, and it does not represent a mere continuance and development of the old patterns of civilization.

As a dramatic illustration of the magnitude of the change, we can contemplate Indonesia. This is a country which has about the same extent, population, and per capita income as the Roman Empire at its height. For all I know it is producing a literature and an art at least comparable to that of the Augustan age. It is, therefore, a very good example of a country of high civilization. Because of this fact, it is one of the poorest countries in the world. It is very unhappy about its present state and visualizes itself as a poor country and it is desperately anxious to break out of its present condition. Jakarta is a city about the size of ancient Rome, although perhaps a little less splendid. All this points up the fact that the Roman Empire was a desperately poor and underdeveloped society, with a civilization that existed always on a shoe-string. The Roman cities seemed to have been always within about three weeks of starvation, and even at its height it is doubtful whether the Roman empire ever had less than 75-80 percent of its population in agriculture.

Civilization, that is, a state of society in which techniques are so poor that it takes about 80 percent of the population to feed the 100 percent. But we do have about 20 percent of the people who can be spared from food producing to build Parthenons, and cathedrals, to write literature and poetry, and to fight wars. By contrast, in the United States today we are rapidly getting to the point where we can produce all our food with only 10 percent of the population and still have large agricultural surpluses. But for the blessings of agricultural policy, we might soon be able to produce all our food with 5 percent of the population. It may even be that agriculture is on its way out altogether and within another generation or so we can produce our food in a totally different way. Perhaps both fields and cows are merely relics of civilization, the vestiges of a vanishing age. This means, however, that even in our society, which is at a very early stage of post-civilization, we can now spare about 90 percent of the people to produce bath-tubs, automobiles, and H-bombs, and all the other luxuries and conveniences of life. Western Europe and Japan are coming along behind the United States very fast. The Russians, likewise, are advancing towards post-civilization, although by a very different road. At the moment their ideology is a handicap to them in some places—especially in agriculture, where they still have 45 percent of the people. Even this, however, is a lot better than ancient Rome. And, if the Russians ever discovered that super-peasants are a good deal more efficient than collective farms, they may cut away some of the ideology that hangs around their neck and move even more rapidly toward post-civilized society.

I am not at all sure what post-civilization will look like and, indeed, I suspect there will be several varieties of it. But it will certainly be radically different from the civilized society which it is displacing. It will certainly be a worldwide society. Until very recently each civilized society was a little island in a sea of barbarism which constantly threatened to overwhelm it. Civilization is haunted by the spectre of decline and fall, although it is noteworthy that in spite of the rise and fall of particular civilizations, civilization itself expanded steadily in geographical coverage from its very beginnings. We must face the fact, however, that post-civilized society will be worldwide, if only because of its ease of communication and transportation. I flew last year from Idlewild to Brussels, and on glimpsing the new Brussels Airport out of the corner of my eye, I thought for a moment we had come back and landed at Idlewild again. I had for a moment a horrifying vision of a world in which we went faster and faster to places which were more and more like the places we left behind, until in the end of the process we flew at infinite speed to a place that was identical with what we left behind, and we might as well have stayed home. For the first time in history there is now a world style, at least in airports, which is a symbol of the coming post-civilization. We see this in art, in architecture, in music, in literature, and in all fields of life. What in Europe looks like Americanization, in America looks like Japanification. It is simply the creeping onset of post-civilized style.

The great problem of our age, however, is the disintegration of the institutions of civilization under the impact of advancing post-civilization. The characteristic institutions of civilization are, as we have seen, first agriculture, then the city, then war, in the sense of clash of organized armed forces, and finally, inequality, the sharp contrast between the rich and the poor, between the city and the country, between the urbane and the rustic. In classical civilization both birth and death rates average about forty per thousand, the expectation of life at birth is about twenty-five years. The state is based very fundamentally on violence and exploitation, and the culture tends to be spiritually monolithic, with a single church, or spiritual power perpetuating its doctrines because of its monopoly of the educational processes of transmission of the culture.

In post-civilization all these institutions suffer radical change. Agriculture, as we have seen, diminishes until it is a small proportion of the society, the city, likewise, in the classical sense, disintegrates. Los Angeles is perhaps the first example of the post-civilization, post-urban agglomeration—under no stretch of the imagination could it be called a city. War, likewise, is an institution in process of disintegration. National defense as a social system has quite fundamentally broken down on a world scale. The ICBM and the nuclear warhead has made the nation-state as militarily obsolete as the city-state, for in no country now can the armed forces preserve an area of internal peace by pushing violence to the outskirts. Poverty and inequality, likewise, are tending to disappear, at least on their classical scale. Post-civilized society is an affluent society and it produces large quantities of goods, even though it may fall rather short on services. It is a society furthermore in which the technology almost prohibits great inequalities in consumption. In civilized societies the king or the emperor could live in a Versailles and the peasant in a hovel. In post-civilized society, the proletariat disappears, everybody becomes at least middle-class, and when the product mix of the economy consists of automobiles, mass-produced clothing, domestic appliances, and the pre-fabricated homes, it is almost impossible for the rich to consume on a scale which is more, let us say, than ten times that of the poor. There is no sense in having more than ten automobiles!

Another profound change in the passage from civilization to post-civilization is the change in the expectation of life. In civilized society, as we have seen, birth and death rates tend to be about forty per thousand and the expectation of life at birth is twenty-five years. In post-civilized society the expectation of life at birth rises at least to seventy and perhaps beyond. At the moment we do not have the knowledge or techniques for prolonging the expectation of life much beyond seventy. We do not know, however, what lies in the future. It may be that we are on the edge of a biological revolution, just as dramatic and far-reaching as the discovery of atomic energy and that we may crack the problem of aging and prolong human life much beyond its present span. Whether or not, however, we go forward to Methuselah, the mere increase of the average age of death to seventy is a startling and far-reaching change. It means, for instance, that in an equilibrium population, the birth and death rate cannot be more than about fourteen-per-thousand. This unquestionably implies some form of conscious control of births and of the number of children per family. It means also a radical change in the age distribution of the population, with a much larger proportion of the population in later years.

There are, unquestionably, going to be many varieties of post-civilization and some are going to be more unpleasant than others. It is perfectly possible to paint an anti-utopia in which a post-civilized society appears as universally vulgar, or even universally dull. On the whole, however, I welcome post-civilization and I have really very little affection for civilization. In most pre-civilized societies the fact that the life of man is for the most part nasty, brutish, and short, does not prevent the poets and philosophers from sentimentalizing about the noble savage. Similarly we may expect the same kind of sentimentalizing about the noble Romans and civilized survivals like Winston Churchill. On the whole, though, I will not shed any tears over the grave of civilization any more than I will over pre-civilized society. Post-civilization is a realization of man's potential. On the whole its credit balance is large. It at least gives us a chance of a modest utopia, in which slavery, poverty, exploitation, gross inequality, war, and disease —these prime costs of civilization—will fall to the vanishing point. Neither the disappearance of the classical city nor the disappearance of the peasant fill me with much sorrow. Even in post-civilized society, of course, we can have cities of a kind, if we want to. We may even find culture cities in which vehicular traffic is prohibited and in which the rich indulge in the costly luxury of walking. In the meantime the masses will live scattered about the surface of the earth, commuting occasionally to quasi-automatic factories and offices, or will snuggle down with three dimensional T.V. at the end of the day.

Modest as these visions of utopia may be, there is no guarantee that we will reach them. The second great transition may be under way, but there is no guarantee that it will be accomplished. What we have at the moment is a chance to make this transition—a chance which is probably unique in the history of this planet. If we fail, the chance will probably not be repeated in this part of the universe. Whatever experiments may be going on elsewhere, the present moment indeed is unique in the whole four billion years of the history of the planet. In my more pessimistic moments, I think the chance is a slim one, and it may be that man will be written off as an unsuccessful experiment. We must, therefore, look at the traps which lie along the path of the transition, which might prevent us from making it altogether.

The most urgent trap is, of course, the trap of war. War, as I have suggested is an institution peculiarly characteristic of civilization. Pre-civilized societies have sporadic feuding and raiding, but they do not generally have permanently organized armed forces, and they do not generally develop conquest and empire; or if they do, they soon pass into a civilized form. An armed force is essentially a mobile city designed to throw things at another mobile or stationary city with presumably evil intent. As far as I know, not more than two or three civilizations have existed without war. The Mayans and the people of Mohenjodaro, seem to have lived for fairly long periods without war, but this was an accident of their monopolistic situation and they unquestionably occupied themselves with other kinds of foolishness. If pre-civilized society, however, cannot afford war, post-civilized society can afford far too much of it, and hence will be forced to get rid of the institution because it is simply inappropriate to the technological age. The breakdown in the world social system of national defense really dates from about 1949, when the United States lost its monopoly of nuclear weapons. A system of national defense is only feasible if each nation is stronger than its enemies at home, so that it can preserve a relatively large area of peace within its critical boundaries. Such a system is only possible, however, if the range of the deadly missile is short and if the armed forces of each nation lose power rapidly as they move away from home. The technological developments of the twentieth century have destroyed these foundations of national defense, and have replaced it with another social system altogether which is "deterrence." . . .

Even if we avoid the war trap, we may still fall into the population trap. Population control is an unsolved problem even for the developed areas of the world, which have moved the furthest toward post-civilization. We have not developed any social institutions which can adequately deal with the establishment of an equilibrium of population. An equilibrium of population in a stable post-civilized society may represent a fairly radical interference with ancient human institutions and freedoms. In a stable post-civilized society, as I have suggested, the birth and death rates must be of the order of fourteen per thousand, and the average number of children per family cannot much exceed two. There are many social institutions which might accomplish this end. So far, however, the only really sure-fire method of controlling population is starvation and misery. Insofar as this is true, the Malthusian spectre still broods over us.

In many parts of the world—indeed, for most of the human race for the moment—the impact on certain post-civilized techniques of civilized society has produced a crisis of growth, which may easily be fatal. In the tropics especially with DDT and a few simple public health measures it is easy to reduce the death rate to nine or ten per thousand, at the same time that the birth rate stays up at forty per thousand. This means an annual increase of population of three percent per annum, almost all of it concentrated in the lower age groups. We see this phenomenon dramatically in places like the West Indies, Ceylon, and Formosa; but thanks to the activity of the world health organization, it is taking place rapidly all over the tropical world. It is not the ultimate Malthusian equilibrium which is the problem here, but the strain which is put on the society by the very rapid growth of population, a rate of growth without precedent in history. Perhaps the most important key to the transition to post-civilization is heavy investment in human resources—that is in education. The conquest of disease and infant mortality, however, before the corresponding adjustment to the birth rate, produces enormous cohorts or children in societies which do not have the resources to educate them—especially as those in the middle-age groups, who after all must do all the work of a society, come from the much smaller cohorts of the pre-DDT era. There is an uncomfortable analogy here to 2-4-D, the hormone which kills plants by making them grow too rapidly. At the moment the human race is heading for monumental disasters in many parts of the world. The population disaster is perhaps retrievable in the sense that it may be confined to certain parts of the world and may simply delay the spread of post-civilization in these areas, without seriously threatening the transition in the already developed areas.

Even in the developed countries, however, population control presents a very serious problem. The United States, for instance, at the moment is increasing in population even more rapidly than India. The time when we thought that the mere increase in income would automatically solve the population problem has gone by. In the United States, and certain other societies, in the early stages of post-civilization, the child has become an object of conspicuous domestic consumption. The consumption patterns of the American spending unit seem to follow a certain *gestalt* in which household capital accumulates in a certain order such as the first car, the first child, the washer and dryer, the second child, the deep freeze, the third child, the second car, the fourth child, and so on. The richer we get, the more children we can afford to have at least on current income and the more children we do have. We now seem to be able to afford an average of something like four children per family, and as in a post-civilized society, these four children all survive, the population doubles every generation. A hundred years of this and even the United States is going to find itself uncomfortably crowded. It can be argued, indeed, that from the point of view of the amenities of life we are already well beyond the optimum population. One sees this clearly in California, which was a much more agreeable place thirty years ago than it

is today. When the United States gets to have a billion people, which we could easily have in less than a hundred years, its standards of life may be substantially reduced.

My only positive contribution to this problem is the suggestion that everyone should come into the world with a license to have just one child. A market can then be organized in these licenses and people who wish to be childless can sell their licenses to the philoprogenitive for a price determined by supply and demand. Nobody, I may add, has taken the suggestion very seriously up till now.

The third trap on the road to post-civilization is the technological trap. Our present technology is fundamentally suicidal. It is based on the extraction of concentrated deposits of fossil fuels and ores, which in the nature of things are exhaustible. Even at present rates of consumption they will be exhausted in a time span which is not very long, even measured against human history and which is infinitesimally small on the geological time scale. If the rest of the world advances to American standards of consumption, these resources will disappear almost overnight. Economic development, it appears is the process of bringing closer the evil day when everything will be gone—all the oil, all the coal, all the ores—and we will have to go back to primitive agriculture and scratching in the woods.

There are indications, however, that suicidal technology is not absolutely necessary and that a permanent high-level technology is possible. Beginning in the early part of the twentieth century it is possible to detect an anti-entropic movement in technology. This begins perhaps with the Haber process for the fixation of nitrogen from the air. A development of similar significance is the Dow process for the extraction of magnesium from the sea. Both these processes are anti-entropic. They take the diffuse and concentrate it, instead of taking the concentrated and diffusing it, as do most processes of mining and economic production. Sir William Crookes in the last years of the nineteenth century predicted that we would all be starving by the middle of the twentieth century because of the exhaustion of Chilean nitrates. This prediction was fortunately falsified by the Haber process. These anti-entropic processes foreshadow a technology in which we shall draw all the materials we need from the virtually inexhaustible reservoirs of the sea and the air and draw our energy from controlled fusion—either artifically produced on the earth or from the sun.

It may even be that the major consequence of space research will be the development of a more self-subsistent high technology on earth. From a strictly economic point of view I suspect space is not even for the birds. It seems to be remarkably empty of economic goods. The technology necessary to send man into space, however, may be much the same technology that will enable him to manage his own larger space ship, the good planet earth, with a true high-level husbandry. One can perhaps even visualize the almost completely self-sufficient household of the future living in a kind of grounded space-ship in which the water circulates endlessly through the kidneys and the algae, the protein and carbohydrates likewise. The power comes from solar batteries on the roof and the food from the algae tanks and man, thereby, greatly reduces the scale of the circulation in the midst of which he has to live. In this happy day everyone will live under his own vine and his own fig tree and presumably none shall make them afraid. This may be a long way off, or it may be closer than we think. It is clear, however, that a fundamental technological transition is still to be accomplished. . . .

Beyond these three traps one sees a distant fourth trap—the trap of inanition. Man is a profoundly problem-solving animal. He reacts best to situations of challenge and difficulty.

If he succeeds in solving the problems which now so thoroughly possess him, will he not in the very moment of his success die of sheer boredom? Our answers to this question must depend on our view of man's capabilities; but even here there is evidence, I think, in his religious life that he might survive even heaven. This is a problem, however, that I am prepared to let future generations take care of when they come to it. The business of our generation is more immediate. . . .

What we have to do now, however, is to develop almost a new form of learning. We have to learn from rapidly changing systems. Ordinarily we learn from stable systems. It is because the world repeats itself that we catch on to the law of repetition. Learning from changing systems is perhaps another step in the acceleration of evolution that we have to take. I have been haunted by a remark which Norman Meier, the psychologist, made in a seminar a few months ago, when he said that a cat who jumps on a hot stove never jumps on a cold one. I believe the remark may originally be attributed to Mark Twain. This seems precisely to describe the state we may be in today. We have jumped on a lot of hot stoves and now perhaps the cold stove is the only place on which to jump. In the rapidly changing system it is desperately easy to learn things which are no longer true. Perhaps the greatest task of applied social science, therefore, at the moment is to study the conditions under which we learn from rapidly changing systems. If we can answer this question, then there may still be hope for the human race.

*part 9*

# *Economic Anthropology*

# *Primitive Money*

## *George Dalton*

*From* American Anthropologist, *Vol. 67, No. 1, 1965, pp. 44–62. By permission of the author and the publisher.*

*In a subject where there is no agreed procedure for knocking out errors, doctrines have a long life.*
                                        *Joan Robinson*

Primitive money is a complicated subject for several reasons. There is not in common use a set of analytical categories designed to reveal distinguishing characteristics of markedly different systems: economies without markets and machines still tend to be viewed through the theoretical spectacles designed for Western economy. Second, francs, sterling, and dollars are only the most recent of a long series of foreign monies introduced into primitive economies. Earlier, Arabs, Portuguese, Dutch, English, and others introduced cowrie, manillas, beads, etc., with varying permeation and varying disruption of indigenous monetary systems. Only rarely do anthropologists succeed in disentangling the foreign from the indigenous in a way which reveals the nature of the old money and the consequences of the new.

Moreover, if one asks what is "primitive" about a particular money, one may come away with two answers: the money-*stuff*—woodpecker scalps, sea shells, goats, dog teeth—is primitive (i.e., different from our own); and the *uses* to which the money-stuff is sometimes put—mortuary payments, bloodwealth, bridewealth—are primitive (i.e., different from our own).

Primitive money performs some of the functions of our own money, but rarely all; the conditions under which supplies are forthcoming are usually different; primitive money is used in some ways ours is not; our money is impersonal and commercial, while primitive money frequently has pedigree and personality, sacred uses, or moral and emotional connotations. Our governmental authorities control the quantity of money, but rarely is this so in primitive economies.

Failure to understand the reasons for such differences leads to disputes about bride-wealth versus brideprice, to arguments about whether cows, pig tusks, and potlatch coppers are "really" money, to the assumption that modern coinage merely "replaces" indigenous forms of money, and to disagreement of authorities over minimal definitions of money. In these disputes the characteristics of American or European money are too often used as a model.

Some of the most respected comparisons between primitive and Western money fail to go deeply enough into comparative economic and social structure. Even Malinowski and Firth do not explain that it is nationally-integrated market organization which accounts for those Western monetary traits they use as a model of "real" money: "The tokens of wealth [*vaygua:* ceremonial axe blades, necklaces of red shell discs, and arm bracelets of shells] have often been called 'money.' It is at first sight evident that 'money' in our sense cannot exist among the Trobrianders. . . . Any article which can be classed as 'money' or 'currency' must fulfill certain essential conditions; it must function as a medium of exchange and as a common measure of value, it must be the instrument of condensing wealth, the means by which value can be accumulated. Money also, as a rule, serves as the standard of deferred payments. . . . we cannot think of *vaygua* in terms of 'money'."

Firth registers his agreement: "But according to precise terminology, such objects [strings of shell discs] can hardly be correctly described as currency or money. In any economic system, however primitive, an article can only be regarded as true money when it acts as a definite and common medium of exchange, as a convenient stepping stone in obtaining one type of goods for another. Moreover in so doing it serves as a measure of values. . . . Again it is a standard of value. . . ."

Malinowski and Firth use the bundle of attributes money has in Western market economy to comprise a model of *true* money. They then judge whether or not money-like stuff in primitive economies is really money by how closely the uses of the primitive stuff resemble our own—a strange procedure for anthropologists who would never use the bundle of attributes of the Western family, religion, or political organization in such a way. Quoting from Lienhardt—". . . most anthropologists have ceased to take their bearings in the study of religion from any religion practiced in their own society." And Gluckman and Cunnison write, concerning political organizations: "One important discovery made in . . . [*African Political Systems*] was that the institutions through which a society organized politically need not necessarily look like the kinds of political institutions with which we have long been familiar in the Western world, and in the great nations of Asia."

Dollars have that set of uses called medium of exchange, means of payment, standard of value, etc., precisely because our economy is commercially organized. Where economies are organized differently, non-commercial uses of monetary objects become important, and "money" takes on different characteristics. The question is not—as it is conventionally put—are shells, woodpecker scalps, cattle, goats, dog teeth, or *kula* valuables "really" "money?" It is, rather, how are the similarities and the differences between such items and dollars related to similarities and differences in socio-economic structure?

We shall show below the connections between Western money and economy, then go on to make some points about primitive money and economy, and finally will examine the case of Rossel Island money in detail.

## Capitalism: Market Integration Determines All Money Uses

In the economies for which the English monetary vocabulary was created, there is one dominant transactional mode, market exchange, to which *all* money uses relate. By contrast, in many primitive economies before Western incursion, market exchange transactions are either absent (as with Nuer) or peripheral (as in the Trobriands), but non-commercial uses of money do exist. Seeing non-commercial uses of money through the blinders of commercial money causes difficulty in understanding primitive monies. We must first be made aware of the blinders.

U. S. dollars may be called general purpose money. They are a single monetary instrument to perform all the money uses.

Moreover, the same dollars enter modes of transaction to be called redistribution and reciprocity, as enter into market exchange. These features of U. S. money are consequences of economy-wide market integration and require explanation in an anthropological context.

That U. S. economy is integrated by market exchange is explained by the wide range of natural resources, labor, goods, and services transacted by purchase and sale at market-determined prices, and by the extent to which people in our national economy depend for livelihood on wage, profit, interest, and rental income got from market sale. Natural resources and capital goods (land, labor, machines and buildings of all varieties), consumption goods (food, automobiles), personal and impersonal services (dentistry, electricity), are all purchasable "on the market." Goods and services which are ceremonial and religious, or which serve as prestige indicators, are purchasable in the same way and with the same money as subsistence goods. In market-integrated economy very different items and services are directly comparable, because all are available at prices stated in the same money. The subject of price determination of products and resources under varying conditions of supply and demand (price and distribution theory) is an important field of economics because market exchange is our dominant transactional mode.

## Commercial uses of money in a market-integrated national economy

Except for economic historians, most economists and all economic theory were (until recently) concerned exclusively with European and American types of economy. Economists do not find it necessary to distinguish among the transactional modes of market exchange, reciprocity, and redistribution, because market exchange is so overwhelmingly important. For the same reason economists do not find it necessary to describe at length the different uses of money in our own economy: with only a few exceptions they all express market exchange transactions.

To make this point clear I will attach to each of the money uses an adjective describing the transactional mode, thereby pointing up how they all serve commercial transactions: medium of (commercial) exchange; means of (commercial) payment; unit of (commercial) account; standard for deferred (commercial) payment.

The medium of (commercial) exchange function of money in our economy is its dominant function, and all other commercial uses of money are dependently linked—derived from—the use of dollars as media of (commercial) exchange. For example, dollars are also used as a means of (commercial) payment of debt *arising from* market transactions. It is purchase and sale of resources, goods, and services which *create* the money functions of means of (commercial) payment and standard for deferred (commercial) payment. All the commercial uses of money are consequences of market integration, simply reflecting the highly organized credit and accounting arrangements that facilitate market purchases. This is why economists in writing about our economy need not attach the qualifier "commercial" to the money uses. Indeed, we in our market-integrated national economy sometimes regard the terms "money" and "medium of exchange" as interchangeable. But for primitive communities where market transactions are absent or infrequent, it would be distorting to identify money with medium of (commercial) exchange, as Einzig warns us: "Since, however, money has also other functions and since in many instances [of money used in primitive economies] those functions are more important than that of the medium of exchange, it seems to be unjustified to use the term as a mere synonym for 'medium of exchange'."

## Non-commercial uses of money

Dollars are also used as a means of non-commercial payment: traffic fines paid to local government and taxes to all levels of government. A structural characteristic of Western economy is that redistributive transactions—obligatory payments to political authority which uses the receipts to provide community services—are made with the same money used as medium of (commercial) exchange in private transactions. The consequences are important and far-reaching.

In all societies having specialized political authority, there must be some institutionalized arrangement for the governing authorities to

acquire goods and services for their own maintenance and to provide social services (defense, justice) to the community. In this sense,
we may regard the redistributive function
(acquiring and disbursing such goods and
services) as an "economic" component of
political organization. Exactly how the arrangements vary for political authority to acquire
and disburse goods and services is one way
of differentiating between the organization of
Soviet, American, and (say) Bantu economies.

In U. S. economy the government makes
use of the market in the process of redistribution: medium of (commercial) exchange money
earned as private income is used by households and firms as means of (redistributive)
payment of politically incurred obligation
(taxes). The government then buys on the
market the services and products it requires
—civil servants, guns, roads—to provide community services.

In our system, the same can be said for
another mode of transaction, reciprocity, or
gift-giving between kin and friends. The same
money serves the different transactional modes:
in purchasing a gift, the money paid is used
as medium of (commercial) exchange; giving
the gift is part of a reciprocal transaction (a
material or service transfer induced by social
obligation between the gift partners). If cash
is given as a gift, it is means of (reciprocal)
payment of the social obligation discharged
by the gift-giving.

Here is yet another reason why economists
in dealing with our own economy need not
distinguish among transactional modes: redistribution and reciprocity make use of
market exchange and make use of the same
money used in market exchange. In Western
economy, therefore, tax and gift transactions
appear as simple variations from the private
market norm—special types of expenditure
or outlay—which present no theoretical difficulties.

American reliance upon market sale for livelihood and upon the price mechanism for
allocating resources to production lines does
the following: it makes the medium of (commercial) exchange use of money its dominant
attribute, it makes other money uses serve
market transactions, and it confers that peculiar *bundle* of traits on our general purpose
money which mark off dollars from non-
monetary objects. It is our market integration

which makes it necessary to institutionalize
all uses of money in the same money instrument. As with Malinowski and Firth, we
thereby come to think of "money-ness" as this
*set* of uses conferred on the single monetary
object. And because ours is a market economy,
we come to think of medium of (commercial)
exchange as the single most important attribute of "money-ness."

## Limited-purpose monies

In primitive economies—i.e., small-scale
economies not integrated by market exchange
—different uses of money may be institutionalized separately in different monetary objects to carry out reciprocal and redistributive
transactions. These money objects used in
non-commercial ways are usually distinct
from any that enter market place transactions.
And the items which perform non-commercial
money uses need not be full-time money, so
to speak; they have uses and characteristics
apart from their ability to serve as a special
kind of money.

In U. S. economy, objects such as jewelry,
stocks, and bonds are not thought of as
money because (like cattle among the Bantu)
these come into existence for reasons other
than their "money-ness." Each is capable of
one or two money uses, but not the full range
which distinguishes dollars, and particularly
not the medium of (commercial) exchange use
of dollars. It is worth examining these because,
we shall argue, primitive monies used in reciprocal and redistributive transactions are the
counterparts of these limited or special purpose monies, and not of dollars as media of
(commercial) exchange; they resemble dollars
only in non-commercial uses (paying taxes
and fines, and gift-giving).

Dollars serve as a store of (commercial
and non-commercial) value because dollars
can be held idle for future use. But this is
true also for jewelry, stocks and bonds, and
other marketable assets. However, in U. S.
economy jewelry is not a medium of (commercial) exchange because one cannot spend
it directly, and it is not a means of (commercial or non-commercial) payment because
it is not acceptable in payment of debt or
taxes.

As a measuring device (rather than as tangible objects) dollars are used as unit of
account and standard for deferred payment

of debts. Now consider the accounting and payment procedures used by a baby-sitting cooperative in which a number of households club together to draw on each other for hours of baby-sitting time. Family A uses four hours of sitting time supplied by family B. Family A thereby incurs a debt of four hours it owes the co-op; family B acquires a credit of four hours that it may draw upon in future from some member of the co-op. Here, baby-sitting labor time is a unit of (reciprocal) account and a standard for deferred (reciprocal) payments—a limited purpose money in the sense that it performs two of the subsidiary uses of dollars. Other examples (trading stamps, blood banks) could be given. The point is that even where dollars perform all the money uses for all modes of transaction, there are situations in which a limited range of money uses are performed by objects not thought of as money. These limited purpose monies become important in small-scale communities without market integration and, therefore, without a general purpose money.

### Control over the quantity of money; absence of status requisites

In national market economies, governments deliberately control the quantity of general purpose money because dollars (francs, sterling) carry out market sales which the populace depends on for livelihood. Roughly speaking, if the authorities allow too much money to come into use as medium of (market) purchase, the result is inflation. If the authorities allow too little money to come into use, the result is deflation and unemployment (a contraction in the rate of market purchasing below the full employment capacity rate of production). The need to deliberately vary the quantity of money is a direct result of economy-wide market integration.

It has often been noted that in primitive societies there is seldom any conscious control by political authority over money objects. Such is not merely a difference between primitive *monetary* systems and our own, but one that reflects differences between their *economic* systems and ours. In economies not integrated by market exchange, non-commercial monetary transactions are only occasional events (e.g., bloodwealth, bridewealth), and non-commercial money is not usually connected with production and daily livelihood.

That the non-commercial money-stuff may be fixed in quantity for all time (Yap stones), or increase in quantity only through natural growth (cows, pig tusks) does not affect production and daily livelihood (as would be the case with us if dollars were fixed in quantity).

What is also true of our market economy based on contract rather than status, is that having the money price is a sufficient condition for buying most goods. Not only is Western money anonymous, so to speak, but money users are also anonymous: the market sells to whoever has the purchase price and only rarely imposes status prerequisites on the use of money as medium of (commercial) exchange. In contrast, there usually are status prerequisites in non-commercial uses of primitive money. For example, in the use of cattle as means of (reciprocal) payment of bride-wealth, status requisites such as lineage, age, rank of the persons, must be compiled with. The money users are not anonymous, and a special kind of limited purpose money is necessary to the transaction.

### Primitive Money and Socio-economic Organization

Einzig points out that: "The overwhelming importance of unilateral non-commercial payments in primitive life as compared with payments arising from [commercial] trade is altogether overlooked by practically all definitions [of primitive money]. It is assumed that money must be essentially commercial in character and that any object which serves the purposes of non-commercial payments may safely be disregarded even if its use is of first-rate importance in the economic, political, and social life of primitive communities."

When anthropologists employ Western monetary terms to describe uses of money-stuff in non-commercial transactions, a crucial misunderstanding may result: when cattle or seashells perform some money uses in ways unrelated to market purchase and sale, they are not media of (commercial) exchange, or means of (commercial) payment.

The uncritical use of our general purpose money as the model of true money obscures the point that special purpose monies used for non-commercial transactions express salient features of underlying socio-economic structure. When we consider money in communities not integrated by market exchange—the Nuer, the Trobriands, the Tiv—it becomes essential to distinguish among the several transactional modes and among the several money uses: *primitive money-stuff does not have that bundle of related uses which in our economy is conferred on dollars by market integration and by the use of dollars in both commercial and non-commercial transactions.* The differences between cattle-money or shell-money and dollars are traceable to the differences in the transactional modes which call forth money uses. When Malinowski says that *kula* valuables are different from Western currency, he is really pointing out that reciprocal gift-giving is different from market purchase and sale. Indeed, anthropologists use Western monetary terms ambiguously whenever they fail to distinguish between the market and the non-commercial modes of transaction. Reining, for example, states: "There seems to have been little exchange among households although iron tools and spears made from locally smelted ore had a limited application as a medium of exchange, being used primarily for marriage payments."

If Western monetary terms are to be used by anthropologists in the meanings they convey for our own economy, the unqualified phrase "medium of exchange" must mean medium of market (or commercial) exchange. Since brides are not acquired through impersonal market transactions by random buyers and sellers, the iron tools are not used as media of (market) exchange, but as media of (reciprocal) exchange: as part of a non-commercial transaction in which a man acquires a bundle of rights in a woman and her children in return for iron tools and other indemnification payments to her kin.

It seems useful to regard the bridewealth items as special purpose "money" because the iron tools and spears—or in other societies, cows or goats—are the *required* items, and because they carry out money uses which do have counterparts in our own society. Whether one calls them special purpose monies or highly ranked treasure items necessary to the transaction for which one may not substitute other items only matters when the subject of money uses in primitive compared to Western economies is raised. Then we can show that cows and armbands of shells do perform some of the uses of dollars but in noncommercial situations. The goal is always to state the role of bridewealth or kula items, or other limited purpose money, from the viewpoint of the analyst concerned with comparative economy, but without distorting the folk-meaning of the items and the transactions they enter.

## Money uses in primitive and peasant economies

Because money and money uses in market-dominated economies differ sharply from money in other economies it is useful to classify economies in accordance with the importance of market exchange transactions.

TYPE I: MARKETLESS   In marketless communities, land and labor are not transacted by purchase and sale but are allocated as expressions of kinship right or tribal affiliation. There are no formal market-place sites where indigenously produced items are bought and sold. These are "subsistence" economies in the sense that livelihood does not depend on production for sale. The transactional modes to allocate resources and labor as well as produced items and services are reciprocity

### Underdeveloped Communities

| primitive (or subsistence) economies | | peasant economies |
|---|---|---|
| type I | type II | type III |
| marketless | peripheral markets only | market-dominated |
| Sonjo | Trobriand Islanders | Malay Fishermen |
| Nuer | Tiv | Jamaica |
| Lele | Rossel Islanders | Haiti |
| Arnhemlanders | | Kipsigis |
| Bemba | | Cantel ⎫ Guatemala |
| Kwakiutl (1840) | | Panajachel ⎰ |
| | | Kwakiutl (1890) |

and redistribution. In marketless economics, then, transactions of labor, resources, material goods, and services are of non-commercial sorts—obligatory gifts to kin and friends, obligatory payments to chiefs and priests, bridewealth, bloodwealth, fees for entering secret societies, corvée labor, mortuary payments, etc.—which immediately marks off as different from our own any money-stuff used. Items such as cattle, goats, spears, Yap stones, and pig tusks, take on roles as special purpose money in non-commercial transactions: they become means of (reciprocal or redistributive) payment, as is the case with bloodwealth and mortuary payments; or media of (reciprocal) exchange, as is the case with bridewealth.

TYPE II: PERIPHERAL MARKETS ONLY Everything said above about marketless economies holds true for those with only peripheral markets, with one exception: market-place sites exist in which a narrow range of produce is bought and sold, either with some money-stuff used as medium of (commercial) exchange, or via barter in the economist's sense (moneyless market exchange). We call these market exchanges "peripheral" because land and labor are not bought and sold and because most people do not get the bulk of their income from market sales. In such small-scale subsistence economies market-place prices do not function—as they do in our national economy—as an integrative mechanism to allocate resources to production lines: labor and land use do not respond to changes in the prices of products transacted in peripheral market places. Malinowski's *gimwali* are peripheral market transactions of an occasional sort without the formal trappings found in African market places.

TYPE III: MARKET-DOMINATED (PEASANT) ECONOMIES Small-scale market-dominated communities share with our own nationally integrated market economy the following features: (i) a large proportion of land and labor as well as goods and services are transacted by market purchase and sale; (ii) most people depend upon market sale of labor or products for livelihood; (iii) market prices integrate production. Labor and land move into and out of different production lines in response to profit (and other income) alternatives, as in-

dicated by market prices. In such economies, the medium of (commercial) exchange function of money is the most important; the other commercial uses of money facilitate market transactions, and the same money is used for non-commercial transactions.

Peasant economies, differ from primitive (subsistence) economies in that peasant producers depend upon production for sale. However, both peasant and primitive communities differ from large-scale, developed, nationally integrated Western economies on two counts: modern machine technology is largely absent, and traditional social organization and cultural practices are largely retained.

## Rossel Island Money

Rossel Island money is famous in anthropological literature because it has for so long been a puzzler. Although it was reported at an early date, and by an economist who was in the field for only two months, re-analysis in the light of points made earlier in this paper allows a different interpretation of Rossel Island money and economy.

### Armstrong's theoretical presentation

Armstrong asserts that Rossel Island money is a rough equivalent of our own: that it is a medium of exchange used to purchase a wide range of goods and services, and that it is a standard of value for stating prices. He uses Western monetary and economic terms throughout to describe the Rossel system—medium of exchange, standard of value, buy, sell, price.

| Armstrong's numbering system for classes of ndap shell money (1928:62) | number of individual ndap shells in each class |
|---|---|
| 22 | 7 |
| 21 | 10 |
| 20 | 10 |
| 19 | 10 |
| 18 | 20 |
| 17 | 7 |
| 16 | 7 |
| 15 | 10 |
| 14 | 30 |
| 13 | 30–40 |

Total in classes 13–22 ≅ 146

The Rossel Islanders use two types of shell money, *ndap* and *nko*. Ndap money consists of individual shells (Armstrong calls them coins), each of which belongs to one of 22 named classes or denominations, which Armstrong ranks from 1-22, a higher numbered class indicating a higher valued shell.

Armstrong could not determine the number of ndap shells in each class below 13, but he guesses there are fewer than 1,000 in all, which would mean 800 or so in classes 1-12.

Armstrong's theoretical concern is with the value relationships among the ranked shells. He tells us that (as in Western economy) all goods and services on Rossel bear a money price stated as a piece (coin) of a specific class (1-22) of ndap, so that a big house costs a No. 20 ndap shell, and a pig a No. 18. But the shells are not quite like dollar bills numbered 1-22 with a No. 20 (say), bearing twice the value of a No. 10, or an item priced at No. 20 purchasable with two shells of No. 10 variety. In Armstrong's view it is merely an aberration due to custom, and, perhaps, to unsystematic thinking that the Rossel Islanders insist that something priced at No. 20 must be paid for with a No. 20 shell, rather than with lower denomination pieces adding up to 20. He sees this as an inefficiency in their system as compared to ours—in which all bills and coins are directly convertible into each other. He therefore shows that the Rossel system requires elaborate borrowing to allow a person who does not happen to own a piece of No. 20 money to acquire an item "priced" at 20, and argues that it is the borrowing system that reveals the value relationships among the ranked coins. This is a cumbersome equivalent of our own system—a model T, so to speak—which does the same job as our own media of exchange, but with more work and fuss because one cannot substitute two $10 bills for something priced at $20. Armstrong writes: ". . . the necessity for continual loans is largely the result of the peculiar nature of the system. The same 'amount' of money, where the values are simply related and 'change' can always be given, could perform the same amount of real service (i.e., effect the same number of purchases) with perhaps a tenth or less of the amount of lending necessitated by the Rossel system."

If one borrows a No. 12 for a short time, he will have to repay a No. 13; but for a longer time he will have to repay a No. 14, 15, etc. Therefore, he says, the value relationships among the denominations 1-22 conform roughly to compound interest, which shows the relationship of an initial sum lent to its repayment equivalent, depending upon the rate of interest and the time the initial sum is outstanding. Theoretically, a No. 1 shell is related to any other number, 2-22, by the length of time a No. 1 loan is outstanding before repayment must be made in any higher number.

Armstrong's analytical interpretation may be summarized: ndap shell money functions like dollars in that it is a medium of exchange, standard of value, standard for deferred payments, etc. Debts are calculated and goods and services priced in shells of stated denomination. The peculiar (different from our own) feature of the system is that the shell denominations are not freely convertible into one another, which makes necessary frequent borrowing at interest to acquire the exact denomination shell needed for a given purchase.

### Contradictory evidence

There are two faults in Armstrong's analysis from which stem the subsidiary difficulties in his interpretation of the Rossel monetary system.

1. He assumes all ndap shells function as media of (commercial) exchange. He does not distinguish among modes of transaction (reciprocity, redistribution, market exchange), but regards all transactions as commercial purchases; brides cost a No. 18 shell, just as baskets cost a No. 4 shell. He writes: ". . . any commodity or service may be more or less directly priced in terms of them [*ndap* shells]." Armstrong never doubts that Rossel Island money is essentially like our own media of (commercial) exchange. One could sum up his ethnocentric theorizing in a syllogism: ndap shells are "money"; money is a commercial instrument; therefore Rossel Island is a market economy.

2. This market preconception leads him to do what the Rossel Islanders do *not* do: to number the ndap classes 1-22. By so doing he can assume that convertibility via borrowing and repayment is practiced throughout the

*entire* range, so that one could start by lending a No. 1 shell, and by continual loans at interest, wind up eventually with a No. 22 shell. For example, "Any [*ndap* shell] value can thus be regarded as any lower value plus compound interest for the number of time units equal to the number of values by which the two are separated, so that No. 22, for example, is No. 1 plus compound interest for 21 units of time."

By ranking them 1-22 Armstrong implies that the differences between ndap shell classes are cardinal differences: that a No. 22 is 22 times more *valuable* than a No. 1, in the sense that a $20 bill is 20 times more valuable than a $1 bill. There are no such cardinal differences among ndap shells. To number them 1-22 is to give a false impression of similarity between ndap shell classes and Western money denominations and a false impression about the commensurability or the "purchasing power" relationship between lower and higher numbered ndap shells.

The characteristics of monetary transactions on Rossel that lead us to doubt Armstrong's interpretation may be set out with the following provisos kept in mind: Rossel Island economy is not integrated by market exchange; ndap shells (except for the lowest few classes) are not media of (commercial) exchange; and convertibility throughout the entire range could not be practiced.

There are (on the basis of Armstrong's own data) at least three groups of ndap shells, the shells in each group being necessary for a different range of transactions, and convertibility via borrowing and repayment being possible *within* the lowest two groups, but not *within* the highest group, and not between groups.

The shells Armstrong classes 1-8 or 9 are the only ones capable of increase in quantity. The individual shells in each of these classes do not bear separate names, and some of them, at least, enter low echelon transactions, casual market exchange between individuals. In one of the rare descriptions of how shells below class No. 18 are actually used, Armstrong tells us that one may buy a basket, a lime stick, or a lime pot with a No. 4 shell. However, the question, "what goods and services will *each* shell class 1, 2, 3, . . . 22 'buy,' or what transactions does each enter?" is not answered except for ndap shells Nos. 4, 18,

20, and 21. What is clear, however, is that shell classes 18-22 are used for a very special range of important transactions which mark them off sharply from lower echelon shells, and that shells below No. 18 are not convertible into shells 18-22 by borrowing and repayment. One cannot start with a No. 1 or 17, and by lending, work it up to a No. 18-22.

Armstrong writes: "Nos. 18-22 seem to be in a somewhat different position from the lower values and one would imagine that they are not related to each other and the lower values in the precise manner set out in generalized form above [i.e., according to the compound interest formula linking the entire series, 1-22]." Convertibility via borrowing and repaying a higher class shell most certainly breaks down between Nos. 17 and 18. I suspect but cannot so readily document from the data that it does so, between Nos. 10 and 11 as well. If such is the case, convertibility is possible among Nos. 1-10, and among Nos. 11-17, but not between the two sets, and not among Nos. 18-22. It is very clear that the entire series is not linked because the uses to which shells 18-22 are put are of an entirely different order from the uses of lower shells. "As a matter of fact, a peculiarity enters as soon as we reach No. 18, which is not, as a rule [when borrowed] repaid by a coin of higher value."

Nos. 18-22 (of which there are fewer than 60 shells in all), are obviously treasure items like especially venerated kula bracelets and potlatch coppers, items with individual names and histories, which must be used to validate important social events and transactions in the same sense that bridewealth items validate a marriage. The folk-view toward these shells helps to explain their role as limited purpose money in reciprocal and redistributive transactions. "Nos. 18-22 are peculiar in one other respect. They have a certain sacred character. No. 18, as it passes from person to person, is handled with great apparent reverence, and a crouching attitude is maintained. Nos. 19 to 22 are proportionately more sacred, are almost always kept enclosed, and are not supposed to see the light of day, and particularly the sun . . . I am inclined to think that there may be a real gap [in sacredness and prestige] . . . between Nos. 17 and 18 . . . [No. 22 shells] are said to be inherited in the male line and to be owned by the most powerful chiefs on the island."

To have regarded Nos. 18-22 as especially valuable media of (commercial) exchange—high denomination bills—with which to buy especially high-priced merchandise, is the most telling error Armstrong makes. Nos. 18-22 cannot be acquired by any amount of lower class shells, and there is no way of gauging how many times more valuable a No. 18 is compared to a No. 6 because they enter entirely different transactions.

Without exception, Nos. 18-22 enter non-commercial transactions exclusively: they are used as means of (reciprocal or redistributive) payment or exchange in transactions induced by social obligation. Payments of a No. 18 are a necessary part of ordinary bridewealth, as well as necessary payment for shared wives, and for sponsoring a pig or dog feast, or a feast initiating the use of a special kind of canoe. No. 20 is a necessary indemnity payment to the relatives of a man ritually murdered and eaten, a transaction which is part of mortuary rites for the death of a chief. Moreover, there is a connection between shells 18-22 and lineage affiliation which Armstrong notes but makes nothing of. ". . . Nos. 18 to 22 are regarded as property peculiar to chiefs, though continually lent by the latter to their subjects."

The implication throughout is that there exists (as with us) an impersonal money market in which anyone may borrow from anyone else at the going interest rate. This is doubtful. Unfortunately, Armstrong is silent on the question, "who may borrow from whom, and with what penalties for failure to repay?"

As with special purpose money for non-commercial transactions elsewhere, there are status requisites involved in the acquisition and use of the high echelon shells on Rossel. Just as marriage is not a market purchase of a wife by anyone who acquires a No. 18 ndap, but rather a reciprocal transaction between two lineage groups (the ndap payment being one of the several necessary conditions within the social situation), so too with pig feasts on Rossel. Only persons of correct status may sponsor the feast and pay the ndap shell. In this case Armstrong notes that social requisites determine who may use upper ndap shells, but he does not see this as a

symptomatic difference between Rossel and Western money, i.e., between non-commercial means of (redistributive) payment, and our Western media of impersonal (commercial) exchange. What Armstrong says of pig feasts is equally true of marriage, and all the other *social events* which require payment of high echelon ndap shells:

There are . . . complex social factors determining who shall have a pig to sell, [sic] and who shall be in a position to buy, [sic] and the buying and selling is not a simple economic occurrence, but a much more significant and complex social occurrence. We must suppose a complexity of social facts, which I am not in a position to define, that determine most of the general relations of a particular pig feast. . . . A particular individual provides a particular *ndap*. . . . A certain readjustment of social relations thus results from the holding of the feast . . . though we abandon the view that the monetary operations at a feast of this nature are to be regarded merely as a collective buying from a collective seller, it still remains that this is a useful way of describing these operations.

It is about as useful to describe a pig feast on Rossel as buying a pig with a No. 18 ndap as it is to describe marriage in America as buying a wife with a wedding ring. To describe the pig feast as a market purchase one must ignore the social requirements of the transaction and the folk-view of the event, both of which differentiate this redistributive transaction from market exchange. Armstrong is forced to use market terms, purchase and sale, to describe pig feasts and bridewealth, because he regards ndap shells as media of (commercial) exchange in a market system.

One bizarre feature of the Rossel system, that a transaction requires a single shell of a specifically named class, and neither a shell from a higher class nor several from lower classes would do, may be examined in the light of what has been said above. "A man may have to borrow, even though he has money of a higher value in his possession than he requires at the moment. He may have Nos. 11 and 13, but not No. 12 which he requires at the moment. He cannot get change as a rule, for No. 13 is not a simple product of any lower value."

The higher values have nothing to do with commercial purchase and sale. One could not use five petty shells, like No. 4 (which buys a pot), to perform a transaction such as bloodwealth (which requires that special treasure Armstrong numbers 20), for much the same reasons that in the Trobriands, one cannot "buy" a renowned kula valuable with the pots bought from hawkers in a gimwali.

One final point. In comparing primitive money with our own, it is important that the writer describe the frequency of different kinds of monetary transactions. Only so can one gauge what role, if any, the money item(s) play in the production system. Armstrong concerns himself with social and ritual events— marriage, death, redistributive feasts, fines —and says almost nothing about production, subsistence goods, natural resource and labor transactions, and all the other ordinary concerns of money and pricing in our own economy. That he nevertheless asserts that Rossel money is much like our own, should make one wary. Einzig is properly suspicious: "It is a pity that there is not enough evidence to show to what extent, if at all, *ndap* and *nko* are used as a medium of exchange in everyday transactions, apart from the purchase [sic] of pigs."

If all the ndap shell transactions which Armstrong describes were abolished, subsistence livelihood of Rossel Islanders would remain unimpaired. It is a pity he did not hit upon that distinction which is useful to analyze economies not integrated by market exchange. DuBois writes concerning this: ". . . I should like to make a distinction between subsistence and prestige economy. By subsistence economy is meant the exploitation of the . . . natural resources available to any industrious individual. By prestige economy on the other hand, is meant a series of social prerogatives and status values. They include a large range of phenomena from wives to formulae for supernatural compulsion."

The upper values of ndap shells (and probably the middle values as well—Armstrong is silent here) enter prestige spheres in noncommercial uses. From the Westerner's viewpoint these transactions are outside the production system and subsistence livelihood. Despite Armstrong's assertion to the contrary, there is no evidence that one could opt out of the social and ritual games (through which upper ndap shells are paid and received) by converting upper shells into land, labor, or

products, except perhaps as occasional events in emergency situations.

### Rossel Island money: a case of red herrings

"The study of economics in simple communities should properly speaking be a job for economists. But so far few economists have tackled it, and most of the investigation has perforce been done by anthropologists."

All social scientists are either Sherlock or Mycroft Holmes. Anthropologists are Sherlock: they go to the scene, observe minutely, gather their threads of evidence from what they observe, and—like Sherlock—sometimes reach Paddington before reaching conclusions. Economic theorists are Mycroft: they do not go to the scene to observe minutely. They have no equivalent to field work because economists are not concerned with social organization or human behavior, but rather with the behavior of prices, income determinants, capital-output ratios, and other impersonal matters relating to the performance of nationally-integrated, industrialized, market economies (for which fieldwork is unnecessary). Institutional matters, personal roles, and the social implications of economic organization have long since been consigned to the limbo of sociology. Neither the problems of interest nor the methods of analysis are the same in economics and economic anthropology.

Armstrong is an economist who played at anthropology. His mistake was to bring Mycroft's tools to Sherlock's subject (and without realizing he was doing so). The result— to mix my metaphors—was to create a sort of Piltdown Economic Man, Melanesians with monetary denominations which fit the formula for compound interest. Armstrong's pioneer work is not a hoax, but a red herring; and the lesson to be learned is not analytical—what primitive money is all about—but methodological: how not to do anthropology.

### Conclusions

The distinctions spelled out in this paper may be used to answer questions of interest to economic anthropology, comparative economy, and economic development.

1. Anthropologists do not hesitate to contrive special terms for special actions and institutions when to use terms from their own so-

ciety would be misleading. They do not talk about *the* family, but about nuclear, extended, and matrilineal families. The same should be done with economic matters.

Those aspects of primitive economy which are unrelated to market exchange can only be understood by employing socio-economic terms: ceremonial-prestige and subsistence goods; reciprocity and redistribution; spheres and conversions; limited purpose money. Such terms contain a social dimension and so allow us to relate economic matters to social organization, and to express the folk-view toward the items, services, persons, and situations involved. The economist dealing with monetary transactions in Western economy need not concern himself with personal roles and social situations because of the peculiarly impersonal nature of market exchange. The anthropologist dealing with marketless transactions cannot ignore personal roles and social situations and still make sense of what transpires.

Kula armbands, potlatch coppers, cows, pig tusks, Yap stones, etc., are variously described as money of renown, treasure items, wealth, valuables, and heirlooms. Malinowski says kula valuables are regarded like crown jewels or sports trophies in Western societies. Writers on East Africa say that cows are regarded like revered pets. Such treasures can take on special roles as non-commercial money: their acquisition and disposition are carefully structured and regarded as extremely important events; they change hands in specified ways, in transactions which have strong moral implications. Often they are used to create social relationships (marriage; entrance into secret societies), prevent a break in social relationships (bloodwealth, mortuary payments), or to keep or elevate one's special position (potlatch). Their "money-ness" consists in their being required means of (reciprocal or redistributive) payment.

2. Subsidiary characteristics of Western money-stuff, such as portability and divisibility, are actually requirements for media of (commercial) exchange. In peasant and national economies integrated by market exchange, purchases of goods and services are a daily occurrence, and so money must be portable; market purchases are carried out at widely varying price, so the medium of (commercial) exchange must be finely divisible.

Yap stones, cows, kula armbands, and Ros-

sel Island shells are not divisible, and some are not conveniently portable. But neither are they media of (commercial) exchange; they are not used for daily purchases of varying amount. Their use as non-commercial money makes their lack of divisibility and portability unimportant. Here we see one way primitive money-*stuff* is related to primitive money *usage*. As means of (reciprocal or redistributive) payment used infrequently to discharge social obligations, it does not matter that the money-stuff lacks those characteristics required of a medium of (commercial) exchange.

3. Economics textbooks err in citing primitive monies *indiscriminately* as equivalents of Western media of (commercial) exchange, for the same reason that Armstrong errs in treating Rossel Island monies as a single type and as a crude equivalent of our own. By giving the impression that *all* primitive monies perform the same primary function as dollars, they quite wrongly imply that all primitive economies may be regarded as crude market systems.

Economists are correct in saying that some unusual money-stuffs have functioned as media of (commercial) exchange. They have in mind situations such Colonial America where "primitive money-stuffs" (commodity money such as tobacco and cotton) functioned just as dollars do today, or Prisoner of War camps where cigarettes (primitive money-stuff) became used as media of (market) exchange.

But to conclude that because some primitive money-*stuffs* do perform the primary function of dollars, *all* primitive monies may be regarded as crude media of (commercial) exchange, is an important error. As we have seen in the case of Rossel Island, this market preconception impedes our understanding of marketless economies and those with peripheral markets only. It implies that market exchange is the only transactional mode ever to exist, and so—as economists do in our own economy—one may ignore the social situations in which monetary transactions occur and the folk-view toward the persons, events, and items involved. It is precisely this sort of ethnocentrism that regards all "exchanges" as commercial transactions, and equates all money payments with market purchases, with the result that brides and murder are said to have a price, just as pots and yams in the market place have a price.

4. A situation of special interest is one

where cowrie (in times past), or sterling or francs (in recent times), acquired initially in external market exchange, became used internally for commercial and non-commercial transactions. Such cases of monetary incursion deserve examination for reasons which are of interest to students of community economic development as well as economic anthropology.

Cowrie inflation, wampum inflation, and bridewealth inflation are related cases. Cowrie and wampum became used as media of (commercial) exchange through external trade with Europeans in situations where the quantity of money-stuff was uncontrolled and increased rapidly in supply. Similarly, where bridewealth comes to be paid in sterling or francs, the sum increases when earnings of Western money through market sale of labor or produce increase faster than the number of marriageable females. What might be called "potlatch copper inflation" is a similar case: when the Kwakiutl became increasingly enmeshed in Canadian market economy, they used their market earnings to increase the stakes in the potlatch. The limited number of coppers (like the limited number of brides, elsewhere) fetched a larger bundle of market-purchased goods. All such cases may be described as "upward conversions": newly expanded market earnings are used to acquire treasure items and brides which indigenously were not transacted through market exchange.

Western money does much more than merely displace primitive monies where the latter were not media of (commercial) exchange indigenously. It allows non-commercial payments and obligations of traditional sorts (such as bridewealth) to be discharged with general purpose money earned in market transactions—instead of with traditional items of special-purpose money. In economies which formerly were marketless or had peripheral markets only, a structural link—Western cash—now exists between spheres of exchange which formerly were separate. Western money therefore has inevitable repercussions on traditional social organization and cultural practices. In brief, market earnings can now be used for reciprocal and redistributive payments (just as in Western economy goods purchased on the market enter gift-giving, and money earnings are used to pay taxes and tithes).

5. One source of ambiguity in the literature is the quest for a single, all-purpose definition of money that would include our own kind (and presumably Soviet money), as well as the welter of types in use in primitive and peasant economies widely differing in organization. Einzig writes: "It must be the ultimate goal of the study of primitive money to try to find the common denominator—in so far as it exists—in terms of which both the well-established rules of modern money and the apparently conflicting conclusions on primitive money can be explained."

To concentrate attention on what all monies have in common is to discard those clues—how monies differ—which are surface expressions of different social and economic organization. Money is not an isolated case. Much the same can be said for external trade and market places, which (like money) also are made use of in economies differing markedly in organization (say, the U. S., the Soviet, and the Tiv economies). Money traits differ where socio-economic organization differs. To concentrate attention on money traits independently of underlying organization leads writers to use the traits of Western money as a model of the real thing (while ignoring the structure of Western economy which accounts for the money traits). Then any primitive money which does not have all the traits of the Western model money is simply ruled out by definition—it is not money. This does not get us very far towards understanding primitive and peasant economies.

Two distinctions which allow us to contrast primitive and Western money are the distinctions between commercial and non-commercial uses of money, and between marketless economies, those with peripheral markets only, and market-integrated economies. In sum, money has no definable essence apart from the uses money objects serve, and these depend upon the transactional modes that characterize each economy: as tangible item as well as abstract measure, "money is what money does."

# The Organization of Economic Life

## Manning Nash

*From Sol Tax (ed.),*
Horizons in
Anthropology. *Aldine*
*Publishing Company,*
*1964, pp. 171–180.*
*Copyright © 1964, Aldine*
*Publishing Company.*
*By permission of the*
*author, and the publisher*
*and copyright holder.*

The Economic Life of man shows a great variety over time and space. In the New Hebrides islands, the main economic concern is the accumulation of pigs. Men raise pigs, exchange pigs, lend out pigs at interest, and finally in a large ceremonial feast destroy the pig holdings of a life time. Among the Bushmen of the Kalahari desert there is no private property in productive goods, and whatever the hunting band manages to kill is shared out among the members of the group. In the Melanesian islands every gardener brings some of the yams from his plot to the chief's house. There the pile of yams grows and grows, and eventually rots, to the greater glory of the tribe. The Indians of Guatemala and Mexico live in communities each with its own economic specialty. One group produces pottery, another blankets, another lumber and wood, and the next exports its surplus maize. These communities are tied together in a complex system of markets and exchange.

How are these economic activities to be interpreted and explained? What body of ideas can make sense of the gift-giving of the Plain Indians, the personalized markets of Haiti, the elaborate ceremonial of exchange in the Solomon islands? Less than half a century ago the differences among economic systems were explained by the hypothesis of social evolution. Different economic systems were assigned to levels or stages of the evolution of human society and culture. It was assumed that there had been an evolution from simple hunting bands, with communal property rules, to villages with settled agriculture and clan or family property, and that was followed by a stage of political units with advanced technology and private or state property. This view of economic evolution has not fared well in the face of modern field research. Two chief things have made this mode of explanation lose its force. First, the rising tide of field investigation of economic systems revealed a whole host of economic arrangements which this crude classification by stages could not contain. And second, the idea of stages of evolution shed very little light on the actual processes of economic change. A new model of the variables to explain economic systems and their changes over time is now being fashioned. This model rests on about four decades of accumulated information, and on methods and theories developed in the act of gathering and interpreting that data.

Method in studying economic systems is basically the same as in the rest of social and cultural anthropology. Method is a device to study social regularities, and to give meaning to those regularities. In the study of non-monetary, or partially monetized economies, getting the basic facts is often a test of the observer's ingenuity. Many new ways of getting measurable or nearly measured data have been invented, and recent research is marked by an emphasis on quantities or relative magnitudes of economic activities.

The distinguishing features of peasant and primitive economic systems fall along four axes. The first is *technological complexity and the division of labor.* These are relatively simple societies, technologically. A simple technology means that the number of different tasks involved in any productive act are few. Usually it is the skill of a single or a few producers which carries production from beginning to end. Many primitive and peasant technologies are ingenious, marvelously fitted to a particular environment, requiring high levels of skill and performance, but still very simple. The Bemba of Rhodesia [see Selection 24, p. 167] wrest a living from poor soil with uncertain water supply by an intricate method of cultivation. With good rains and luck they harvest their crop of finger millet. The system is one of balance in a precarious ecological niche, but the task structure is simple, and the tools involved require only human energy to operate. The specialized operations involved are not the kind which make an interrelated web of occupations. Men do most of the agricultural work among the Bemba, and one man is virtually as good as another in his agricultural skills.

The division of labor follows the natural axes of sex and age. An occupational list in a peasant or primitive society is not a long one. Persons tend to learn their productive skills in the ordinary business of growing up, and within age and sex categories there is high interchangeability among productive workers. Work and tasks are apportioned to the appropriate persons, without much regard to differences in skill or productivity. The technology also sets the limits of the size of combined working parties. Except at peak periods—planting or harvesting in agricultural communities, an organized hunt at the height of the animal running season—large working parties are not found. Effort and work are closely tied to a pattern fitted to the annual and ceremonial cycle, not to the continuous demands of a highly organized economy with a wide social division of labor.

The second feature of peasant and primitive economy is the *structure and membership of productive units.* The unit of production, the social organization carrying out the making of goods, is dependent on, and derived from, other forms of social life. Peasant and primitive societies do not have organizations whose only tasks are those of production, and there are no durable social units based solely on productive activities. The bonds of kinship which structure families, clans, and kindreds are often the bonds which organize economic activities. Territorial bonds may serve to create local producing organizations. And the political structure, especially in societies with hereditary nobilities, is often used as a mechanism for forming productive units. This dependence of economic units on prior kinds of social relations has a typical series of consequences. Productive units tend to be multipurposed. Their economic activities are only one aspect of the things they do. The economic aspect of a family, a local group, or a compound composed of patrons and clients, is just one area where the maintenance needs of the group are being met. Therefore, in these societies there tend to be many productive units, similarly structured, all doing the same sort of work. These productive units are limited in sorts of personnel they are able to recruit, the capital they are able to command, and the ways in which they may distribute their product. There does not exist a labor market, nor a capital market, nor a system of distribution to factors of production. A striking example of productive units based on relations derived from the organization of social groups only partially oriented to economic activity is the Indian pottery-making community in southeastern Mexico. This community is composed of 278 households. Each household is engaged in the production of pottery for sale, with virtually the same technology. Every household looks like every other in its productive organization. Or again, from Mexico, among the people of Tepoztlan many make their living by the sale of services at a wage. Yet people must be sought out for employment, and hiring a fellow member of the community is a delicate social job. The transaction cannot appear as a strictly economic one.

The third distinguishing feature of peasant and primitive economies is *the systems and media of exchange*. In an economy with a simple technology, productive units which are multi-purposed and derived from other forms of social organization, and with a division of labor based chiefly on sex and age, a close calculation of the costs of doing one thing or another is often impossible, or merely irrelevant. The advantages of a change in the use of time, resources, and personnel are arrived at through the logic of social structure, through a calculus of relative values, not in terms of the increase of a single magnitude such as productivity. This inability to estimate closely the costs and benefits of economic activity is aggravated by the absence of money as *the* medium of exchange. Most of the world now has some familiarity with the use of money. In fact, some societies developed full, all purpose money prior to contact with the industrial and commercial West. And many societies have standards of exchange like the Polynesian shell currencies, or the tusked pigs of Melanesia, the salt currency of the horn of Africa, or the cocoa beans of the Aztecs. But this is quasi-money, or special purpose money; it is merely the standard with the widest sphere of exchange. Special purpose money is confined to a particular circuit of exchange, and the circuits of exchange in the economy are only partially tied together. Among the Siane of New Guinea there are different kinds of exchange of goods, and each kind of goods is limited to its particular circuit. Some goods can be exchanged only for subsistence items, others only for luxury items, and others only

for items which confer status and prestige. The Tiv of Nigeria have similar multicentered exchange system with media appropriate to each sphere of exchange. Food is exchanged for food, and can be exchanged for brass rods; brass rods exchange for the highest valued goods, women and slaves. And a reverse or downward movement of exchange items was severely resisted and considered illogical and unfortunate among the Tiv.

The media of exchange and the circuits of exchange are set into various kinds of systems of exchange. The most common systems of exchange are markets, redistributive system, reciprocal exchange, and mobilization exchange. The market system is widespread among peasants, and in Meso-America tends to be free, open, and self-regulating. In Haiti the market is competitive, free, and open, but special bonds of personal attachment grow up between some buyers and some sellers which cut down some of the risk and uncertainty involved in small peasant trading. Rotating market centers, with a central market and several subsidiary markets, are a fairly common feature in Burma among the Shans, in several parts of Africa, north and south of the Sahara, and in many places in the Near and Far East. These market systems usually operate without the presence of firms, and lack investment in expensive facilities of exchange, including the spread of information. The single complex of markets, firms, capital investments, entrepreneurs, deliberate technical investment, and property rules to facilitate accumulation and exchange is apparently a historical precipitate peculiar to the West. In the ethnographic record it does not appear as a necessary bundle or sequence of events.

Reciprocity of exchanges is exemplified by the practices of gift-giving or kula exchange of the Solomon Islands and tends to lack much bargaining between, to rest on fixed sets of trading partners, and to occur between equivalent units of the social structure. Thus clans exchange with clans; barrios or wards with wards; households with households; tribes with tribes; or communities with communities. The reciprocal exchange is for near equivalences in goods and services. The rates of exchange tend to be fixed. Redistributive trade takes place in societies with some systems of social stratification, but not organized for market exchange. An African paramount chief may collect tribute in the form of goods and redistribute it down the social hierarchy through his clients and kinsmen. Or administered trade at fixed prices, with a political center exchanging with its peripheries is another common example. Redistributive exchange keeps a political and status system operating without great gaps in wealth between the different classes of status groups. A system of mobilization for exchange collects goods and services into the hands of an elite for the broad political aims of the society. The irrigation empires of the early civilizations apparently had these sorts of exchange systems, and some of the new nations of Asia and Africa have systems like this in conjunction with some aspects of market, redistribution, and reciprocal exchange.

The fourth dimension of variation in economic systems is in *the control of wealth and capital*. Generally, investment takes the form of using resources and services to buttress or expand existing sets of social relations. The chief capital goods in peasant and primitive societies are land and men. Tools, machines, terraces, livestock, and other improvements in productive resources are controlled in a manner derived from the conventions of control and allocation of land and human beings. Land tenure is an expression of the social structure of a peasant and primitive society, and the allocation of land results from the operation of the system of kinship, inheritance, and marriage, rather than through contracts or transactions between economic units. Even in those societies where corporate kin groups like clans do not exist as landholding bodies, special devices like the establishment of titles, or kindred-based landholding corporations may be invented as on Truk. Manpower, like land, is also organized to flow in terms of given social forms, not to abstract best uses.

For peasants and primitives to maintain their societies, capital, or property rules, or economic chance may not be permitted to work in ways disruptive of the values and norms of the society. A fairly common device for insuring that accumulated resources are used for social ends is the leveling mechanism. The leveling mechanism is a means of forcing the expenditure of accumulated resources or capital in ways that are not necessarily economic or productive. Leveling

mechanisms may take the form of forced loans to relatives or coresidents; a large feast following economic success; a rivalry of expenditure like the potlatch of the Northwest Coast Indians in which large amounts of valuable goods were destroyed; or the ritual levies consequent on office holding in civil and religious hierarchies as in Meso-America; or the give-aways of horses and goods of the Plains Indian. At any rate most peasant and primitive societies have a way of scrambling wealth to inhibit reinvestment in technical advance, and this prevents crystallization of class lines on an economic base.

This schematic presentation of the major features of peasant and primitive economies serves to place them in a comparative series of economic organizations and to extend the range of social contexts for economic analysis. But charting the range and diversity of economic systems is only a part of the task of anthropology. How economic systems relate to the total social system is a question of major theoretical importance. Economic action is only a part of the system of social action. It is tied to the whole social system in three ways: First by normative integration, second by functional interdependence, and third by causal interaction. The ends sought in the economic sphere must be consonant, or complementary, with goals in other spheres. Economic activity derives its meaning from the general values of the society, and people engage in economic activity for rewards often extrinsic to the economy itself. From this point of view, there are no economic motives, but only motives appropriate to the economic sphere. In peasant and primitive societies the norms and values used to define a resource, a commodity, control over goods and services, the distributive process, and standards of economic behavior, are the norms governing most social interaction. The economy is not so different from the rest of society so that one set of values holds there, and other values hold in other contexts. The economic system does not exhibit an ethic counterposed to the regnant value system.

The functional interdependence of economy and society stems from the fact that the same persons are actors in the economic, the kinship, the political, and the religious spheres. The role of father must fit in some way with the role of farmer, and these must fit with the role of believer in the ancestor cult, and these must fit with authority position in the lineage, to take an example from the Tallensi. The interdependence of parts of a society means that there are limits to the sorts of economies and societies that may coexist in one time and space continuum. These limits only now are being charted. But it is plain that a system of reciprocal exchange rests on social units that are nearly equivalent in status, power, and size. The marriage and descent system of the Nayar (where husbands were warriors who lived away from wives and where descent was matrilineal) is an instance of the functional compatibility of an occupational and status system with a marriage and descent system.

The causal interaction of economy and society turns on the pivot of the provision of facilities. For given forms of social structure a given variety and volume of goods and services are required, and if there are shifts in facilities available, there will be shifts in the rest of society. Conversely, shifts in the social structure will change the volume and variety of goods and services a society produces. The empirical way of finding these causal interactions is to study peasant and primitive societies undergoing change. The facts of change are the only sure guides to generalizing on the sequences, forms, and processes of economic and social interaction. Much of the change in the economic life of peasants and primitives comes from the expansion and spread of the Western forms of economic activity.

The expansion of the economic frontier can be seen in places like Orissa, the hilly tribal region of India. Here economic opportunity in the wake of the spread of the money economy has allowed some castes to move quickly up the status ladder and forced some traditional high status castes downward. The economic frontier in the form of money and new opportunities tends to change the role of corporate kin groups and place more emphasis on smaller familial units, to introduce a re-evaluation of the goods of a society, and to put pressures on traditional authority systems.

The chief way that peasants and primitives get involved in the world economy is through entering a wage-labor force, or by producing something that can sell in international trade. The effects of entering a wage-labor force often start conflicts between generations, raise problems about the control of income, and sometimes depopulate the society so that its social structure collapses. A rural proletariat may replace a tribal society. Income from entrepreneurial activity by peasants poses larger problems for the social system. It may result in greater wealth differences, in modifications of the use of capital, in loosening the integration of the society, and in changing the authority patterns. The boom involved in peasant agriculture often involves a change in religious and ethical concepts, and an increase in the importance of economic activity relative to other forms of social activity.

The introduction of factories to peasant primitive societies provides, in theory, the widest possibilities for transformation. The change induced by a factory may be akin to that from the increased use of money from wage labor, or the expansion of the economic frontier, but it tends to tie the community more closely to a national and international economic network, to provide a new context for political change, to give a base for new voluntary groupings, and to exert great pressures on extended familial networks, and above all to demand a sort of flexibility and mobility of persons and institutions usually not found in traditional societies.

What the studies of economic change have taught is that modifications in economic activity set up a series of pressures and tensions in the society and culture and that there are limited possibilities for their resolution. There is no generally agreed upon sequence of change, and hardly more consensus on final forms, but the evidence seems to indicate that economic systems are among the most dynamic parts of a society, and that economic activity, in the sense of the provision of facilities for the organization of the rest of society, is one of the most pervasive and determinative aspects of social life. It sets the limits within which social structures and cultural patterns may fall.

The field of economic anthropology has mainly, thus far, worked on the description and interpretation of small-scale societies, but by principle and method it is not limited to them. It is moving into problems of economic and social change, and illuminating the relations of economy and society, and the causal interaction of economic variables and other parts of society and culture. Its greatest challenge and potential is the fashioning of a theory encompassing both economic and noneconomic variables in a single explanatory system. It may then provide a framework for a truly comparative study of the form, function, and dynamics of economic systems.

*selection 57*

# The Impact of Money on an African Subsistence Economy

## Paul Bohannan

*From* The Journal of Economic History, *Vol. 19, No. 4, 1959, pp. 491–503. Copyright 1959, The Economic History Association. By permission of the author, and the publisher and copyright holder.*

It has often been claimed that money was to be found in much of the African continent before the impact of the European world and the extension of trade made coinage general. When we examine these claims, however, they tend to evaporate or to emerge as tricks of definition. It is an astounding fact that economists have, for decades, been assigning three or four qualities to money when they discuss it with reference to our own society or to those of the medieval and modern world, yet the moment they have gone to ancient history or to the societies and economies studied by anthropologists they have sought the "real" nature of money by allowing only one of these defining characteristics to dominate their definitions.

All economists learned as students that money serves at least three purposes. It is a means of exchange, it is a mode of payment, it is a standard of value. Depending on the vintage and persuasion of the author of the book one consults, one may find another money use—storage of wealth. In newer books, money is defined as merely the means of unitizing purchasing power, yet behind that definition still lie the standard, the payment, and the exchange uses of money.

It is interesting that on the fairly rare occasions that economists discuss primitive money at all—or at least when they discuss it with any empirical referrent—they have discarded one or more of the money uses in framing their definitions. Paul Einzig, to take one example for many, first makes a plea for "elastic definitions," and goes on to point out that different economists have utilized different criteria in their definitions; he then falls into the trap he has been exposing: he excoriates Menger for utilizing only the "medium of exchange" criterion and then himself omits it, utilizing only the standard and payment criteria, thus taking sides in an argument in which there was no real issue.

The answer to these difficulties should be apparent. If we take no more than the three major money uses—payment, standard and means of exchange—we will find that in many primitive societies as well as in some of the ancient empires, one object may serve one money use while quite another object serves another money use. In order to deal with this situation, and to avoid the trap of choosing one of these uses to define "real" money, Karl Polanyi and his associates have labeled as "general purpose money" any item which serves all three of these primary money uses, while an item which serves only one or two is "special purpose money." With this distinction in mind, we can see that special-purpose money was very common in pre-contact Africa, but that general purpose money was rare.

This paper is a brief analysis of the impact of general purpose money and increase in trade in an African economy which had known only local trade and had used only special purpose money.

The Tiv are a people, still largely pagan, who live in the Benue Valley in central Nigeria, among whom I had the good fortune to live and work for well over two years. They are prosperous subsistence farmers and have a highly developed indigenous market in which they exchanged their produce and handicrafts, and through which they carried on local trade. The most distinctive feature about the economy of the Tiv—and it is a feature they share with many, perhaps most, of the pre-monetary peoples—is what can be called a multi-centric economy. Briefly, a multi-centric economy is an economy in which a society's exchangeable goods fall into two or more mutually exclusive spheres, each marked by different institutionalization and different moral values. In some multi-centric economies these spheres remain distinct, though in most there are more or less institutionalized means of converting wealth from one into wealth in another.

Indigenously there were three spheres in the multi-centric economy of the Tiv. The first of these spheres is that associated with subsistence, which the Tiv call *yiagh*. The commodities in it include all locally produced foodstuffs: the staple yams and cereals, plus all the condiments, vegetable side-dishes and seasonings, as well as small livestock—chickens, goats and sheep. It also includes household utensils (mortars, grindstones, calabashes, baskets and pots), some tools (particularly those used in agriculture), and raw materials for producing any items in the category.

Within this sphere, goods are distributed either by gift giving or through marketing. Traditionally, there was no money of any sort in this sphere—all goods changed hands by barter. There was a highly developed market organization at which people exchanged their produce for their requirements, and in which today traders buy produce in cheap markets and transport it to sell in dearer markets. The morality of this sphere of the economy is the morality of the free and uncontrolled market.

The second sphere of the Tiv economy is one which is in no way associated with markets. The category of goods within this sphere is slaves, cattle, ritual "offices" purchased from the Jukun, that type of large white cloth known as *tugudu*, medicines and magic, and metal rods. One is still entitled to use the present tense in this case, for ideally the category still exists in spite of the fact that metal rods are today very rare, that slavery has been abolished, that European "offices" have replaced Jukun offices and cannot be bought, and that much European medicine has been accepted. Tiv still quote prices of slaves in cows and brass rods, and of cattle in brass rods and *tugudu* cloth. The price of magical rites, as it has been described in the literature, was in terms of *tugudu* cloth or brass rods (though payment might be made in other items); payment for Jukun titles was in cows and slaves, *tugudu* cloths and metal rods.

None of these goods ever entered the market as it was institutionalized in Tivland, even though it might be possible for an economist to find the principle of supply and demand at work in the exchanges which characterized it. The actual shifts of goods took place at ceremonies, at more or less ritualized wealth displays, and on occasions when "doctors" performed rites and prescribed medicines. Tiv refer to the items and the activities within this sphere by the word *shagba*, which can be roughly translated as prestige.

Within the prestige sphere there was one item which took on all of the money uses and hence can be called a general-purpose currency, though it must be remembered that it was of only a *very limited range*. Brass rods were used as means of exchange *within the sphere*; they also served as a standard of value within it (though not the only one), and as a means of payment. However, this sphere of the economy was tightly sealed off from the subsistence goods and its market. After European contact, brass rods occasionally entered the market, but they did so only as means of payment, not as medium of exchange or as standard of valuation. Because of the complex institutionalization and morality, no one ever sold a slave for food; no one, save in the depths of extremity, ever paid brass rods for domestic goods.

The supreme and unique sphere of exchangeable values for the Tiv contains a single item: rights in human beings other than slaves, particularly rights in women. Even twenty-five years after official abolition of exchange marriage, it is the category of exchange in which Tiv are emotionally most entangled. All exchanges within this category are exchanges of rights in human beings, usually dependent women and children. Its values are expressed in terms of kinship and marriage.

Tiv marriage is an extremely complex subject. Again, economists might find supply and demand principles at work, but Tiv adamantly separate marriage and market. Before the coming of the Europeans all "real" marriages were exchange marriages. In its simplest form, an exchange marriage involves two men exchanging sisters. Actually, this simple form seldom or never occurred. In order for every man to have a ward (*ingol*) to exchange for a

wife, small localized agnatic lineages formed ward-sharing groups ("those who eat one Ingol"—*mbaye ingol i mom*). There was an initial "exchange"—or at least, distribution—of wards among the men of this group, so that each man became the guardian (*tien*) of one or more wards. The guardian, then, saw to the marriage of his ward, exchanging her with outsiders for another woman (her "partner" or *ikyar*) who becomes the bride of the guardian or one of his close agnatic kinsmen, or—in some situations—becomes a ward in the ward-sharing group and is exchanged for yet another woman who becomes a wife.

Tiv are, however, extremely practical and sensible people, and they know that successful marriages cannot be made if women are not consulted and if they are not happy. Elopements occurred, and sometimes a woman in exchange was not forthcoming. Therefore, a debt existed from the ward-sharing group of the husband to that of the guardian.

These debts sometimes lagged two or even three generations behind actual exchanges. The simplest way of paying them off was for the eldest daughter of the marriage to return to the ward-sharing group of her mother, as ward, thus cancelling the debt.

Because of its many impracticalities, the system had to be buttressed in several ways in order to work: one way was a provision for "earnest" during the time of the lag, another was to recognize other types of marriage as binding to limited extents. These two elements are somewhat confused with one another, because of the fact that right up until the abolition of exchange marriage in 1927, the inclination was always to treat all non-exchange marriages as if they were "lags" in the completion of exchange marriages.

When lags in exchange occurred, they were usually filled with "earnests" of brass rods or, occasionally, it would seem, of cattle. The brass rods or cattle in such situations were *never* exchange equivalents (*she*) for the woman. The only "price" of one woman is another woman.

Although Tiv decline to grant it antiquity, another type of marriage occurred at the time Europeans first met them—it was called "accumulating a woman/wife" (*kem kwase*). It is difficult to tell today just exactly what it consisted in, because the terminology of this union has been adapted to describe the bridewealth marriage that was declared by an administrative fiat of 1927 to be the only legal form.

*Kem* marriage consisted in acquisition of sexual, domestic and economic rights in a woman—but not the rights to filiate her children to the social group of the husband. Put in another way, in exchange marriage, both rights *in genetricem* (rights to filiate a woman's children) and rights *in uxorem* (sexual, domestic and economic rights in a woman) automatically were acquired by husbands and their lineages. In *kem* marriage, only rights *in uxorem* were acquired. In order to affiliate the *kem* wife's children, additional payments had to be made to the woman's guardians. These payments were for the children, not for the rights *in genetricem* in their mother, which could be acquired only by exchange of equivalent rights in another woman. *Kem* payments were paid in brass rods. However, rights in women had no equivalent or "price" in brass rods or in any other item—save, of course, identical rights in another woman. *Kem* marriage was similar to but showed important differences from bridewealth marriage as it is known in South and East Africa. There rights in women and rights in cattle form a single economic sphere, and could be exchanged directly for one another. Among Tiv, however, conveyance of rights in women necessarily involved direct exchange of another woman. The Tiv custom that approached bridewealth was not an exchange of equivalents, but payment in a medium that was specifically not equivalent.

Thus, within the sphere of exchange marriage there was no item that fulfilled any of the uses of money; when second-best types of marriage were made, payment was in an item which was specifically not used as a standard of value.

That Tiv do conceptualize exchange articles as belonging to different categories, and that they rank the categories on a moral basis, and that most but not all exchanges are limited to one sphere, gives rise to the fact that two different kinds of exchanges may be recognized: exchange of items contained within a single category, and exchanges of items belonging to different categories. For Tiv, these two different types of exchange are marked by separate and distinct moral attitudes.

To maintain this distinction between the two types of exchanges which Tiv mark by differ-

ent behavior and different values, I shall use separate words. I shall call those exchanges of items within a single category "conveyances" and those exchanges of items from one category to another "conversions." Roughly, conveyances are morally neutral; conversions have a strong moral quality in their rationalization.

Exchanges within a category—particularly that of subsistence, the only one intact today—excite no moral judgments. Exchanges between categories, however, do excite a moral reaction: the man who exchanges lower category goods for higher category goods does not brag about his market luck but about his "strong heart" and his success in life. The man who exchanges high category goods for lower rationalizes his action in terms of high-valued motivation (most often the needs of his kinsmen).

The two institutions most intimately connected with conveyance are markets and marriage. Conveyance in the prestige sphere seems (to the latter-day investigator, at least) to have been less highly institutionalized. It centered on slave dealing, on curing and on the acquisition of status.

Conversion is a much more complex matter. Conversion depends on the fact that some items of every sphere could, on certain occasions, be used in exchanges in which the return was *not* considered equivalent (*ishe*). Obviously, given the moral ranking of the spheres, such a situation leaves one party to the exchange in a good position, and the other in a bad one. Tiv says that it is "good" to trade food for brass rods, but that it is "bad" to trade brass rods for food, that it is good to trade your cows or brass rods for a wife, but very bad to trade your marriage ward for cows or brass rods.

Seen from the individual's point of view, it is profitable and possible to invest one's wealth if one converts it into a morally superior category: to convert subsistence wealth into prestige wealth and both into women is the aim of the economic endeavor or individual Tiv. To put it into economists' terms: conversion is the ultimate type of maximization.

We have already examined the marriage system by which a man could convert his brass rods to a wife: he could get a *kem* wife and *kem* her children as they were born. Her daughters, then, could be used as wards in his exchange marriages. It is the desire of every Tiv to "acquire a woman" (*ngoho kwase*) either as wife or ward in some way other than sharing in the ward-sharing group. A wife whom one acquires in any other way is not the concern of one's marriage-ward sharing group because the woman or other property exchanged for her did not belong to the marriage-ward group. The daughters of such a wife are not divided among the members of a man's marriage-ward group, but only among his sons. Such a wife is not only indicative of a man's ability and success financially and personally, but rights in her are the only form of property which is not ethically subject to the demands of his kinsmen.

Conversion from the prestige sphere to the kinship sphere was, thus, fairly common; it consisted in all the forms of marriage save exchange marriage, usually in terms of brass rods.

Conversion from the subsistence sphere to the prestige sphere was also usually in terms of metal rods. They, on occasion, entered the market place as payment. If the owner of the brass rods required an unusually large amount of staples to give a feast, making too heavy a drain on his wives' food supplies, he might buy it with brass rods.

However, brass rods could not possibly have been a general currency. They were not divisible. One could not receive "change" from a brass rod. Moreover, a single rod was worth much more than the usual market purchases for any given day of most Tiv subsistence traders. Although it might be possible to buy chickens with brass rods, one would have to have bought a very large quantity of yams to equal one rod, and to buy an item like pepper with rods would be laughable.

Brass rods, thus, overlapped from the prestige to the subsistence sphere on some occasions, but only on special occasions and for large purchases.

Not only is conversion possible, but it is encouraged—it is, in fact, the behavior which proves a man's worth. Tiv are scornful of a man who is merely rich in subsistence goods (or, today, in money). If, having adequate subsistence, he does not seek prestige in accordance with the old counters, or if he does not strive for more wives, and hence more children, the fault must be personal inadequacy. They also note that they all try to keep a man

from making conversions; jealous kinsmen of a rich man will bewitch him and his people by fetishes, in order to make him expend his wealth on sacrifices to repair the fetishes, thus maintaining economic equality. However, once a conversion has been made, demands of kinsmen are not effective—at least, they take a new form.

Therefore, the man who successfully converts his wealth into higher categories is successful—he has a "strong heart." He is both feared and respected.

In this entire process, metal rods hold a pivotal position, and it is not surprising that early administrators considered them money. Originally imported from Europe, they were used as "currency" in some part of southern Nigeria in the slave trade. They are dowels about a quarter of an inch in diameter and some three feet long; they can be made into jewelry, and were used as a source of metal for castings.

Whatever their use elsewhere, brass rods in Tivland had some but not all of the attributes of money. Within the prestige sphere, they were used as a standard of equivalence, and they were a medium of exchange; they were also a mode for storage of wealth, and were used as payment. In short, brass rods were a general purpose currency *within the prestige sphere.* However, outside of the prestige sphere—markets and marriage were the most active institutions of exchange outside it—brass rods fulfilled only one of these functions of money: payment. We have examined in detail the reasons why equivalency could not exist between brass rods and rights in women, between brass rods and food.

We have, thus, in Tivland, a multi-centric economy of three spheres, and we have a sort of money which was a general purpose money within the limited range of the prestige sphere, and a special purpose money in the special transactions in which the other spheres overlapped it.

The next question is: what happened to this multi-centric economy and to the morality accompanying it when it felt the impact of the expanding European economy in the 19th and early 20th centuries, and when an all-purpose money of very much greater range was introduced?

The Western impact is not, of course, limited to economic institutions. Administrative organizations, missions and others have been as effective instruments of change as any other.

One of the most startling innovations of the British administration was a general peace. Before the arrival of the British, one did not venture far beyond the area of one's kinsmen or special friends. To do so was to court death or enslavement.

With government police systems and safety, road building was also begun. Moving about the country has been made both safe and comparatively easy. Peace and the new road network led to both increased trade and a greater number of markets.

Not only has the internal marketing system been perturbed by the introduction of alien institutions, but the economic institutions of the Tiv have in fact been put into touch with world economy. Northern Nigeria, like much of the rest of the colonial world, was originally taken over by trading companies with governing powers. The close linkage of government and trade was evident when taxation was introduced into Tivland. Tax was originally paid in produce, which was transported and sold through the Hausa traders, who were government contractors. A few years later, coinage was introduced; taxes were demanded in that medium. It became necessary for Tiv to go into trade or to make their own contract with foreign traders in order to get cash. The trading companies, which had had "canteens" on the Benue for some decades, were quick to co-operate with the government in introducing a "cash crop" which could be bought by the traders in return for cash to pay taxes, and incidentally to buy imported goods. The crop which proved best adapted for this purpose in Tivland was beniseed (*sesamum indicum*), a crop Tiv already grew in small quantities. Acreage need only be increased and facilities for sale established.

There is still another way in which Tiv economy is linked, through the trading companies, to the economy of the outside world. Not only do the companies buy their cash crops, they also "stake" African traders with imported goods. There is, on the part both of the companies and the government, a desire to build up "native entrepreneurial classes." Imported cloth, enamelware and ironmongery are generally sold through a network of dependent African traders. Thus, African traders are linked to the companies, and hence into international trade.

Probably no single factor has been so important, however, as the introduction of all-purpose money. Neither introduction of cash crops and taxes nor extended trading has affected the basic congruence between Tiv ideas and their institutionalization to the same extent as has money. With the introduction of money the indigenous ideas of maximization —that is, conversion of all forms of wealth into women and children—no longer leads to the result it once did.

General purpose money provides a common denominator among all the spheres, thus making the commodities within each expressible in terms of a single standard and hence immediately exchangeable. This new money is misunderstood by Tiv. They use it as a standard of value in the subsistence category, even when—as is often the case—the exchange is direct barter. They use it as a means of payment of bridewealth under the new system, but still refuse to admit that a woman has a "price" or can be valued in the same terms as food. At the same time, it has become something formerly lacking in all save the prestige sphere of Tiv economy—a means of exchange. Tiv have tried to categorize money with the other new imported goods and place them all in a fourth economic sphere, to be ranked morally below subsistence. They have, of course, not been successful in so doing.

What in fact happened was that general purpose money was introduced to Tivland, where formerly only special purpose money had been known.

It is in the nature of a general purpose money that it standardizes the exchangeability value of every item to a common scale. It is precisely this function which brass rods, a "limited-purpose money" in the old system, did not perform. As we have seen, brass rods were used as a standard in some situations of conveyance in the intermediate or "prestige" category. They were also used as a means of payment (but specifically not as a standard) in some instances of conversion.

In this situation, the early Administrative officers interpreted brass rods as "money," by which they meant a general-purpose money. It became a fairly easy process, in their view, to establish by fiat an exchange rate between brass rods and a new coinage, "withdraw" the rods, and hence "replace" one currency with another. The actual effect, as we have seen, was to introduce a general purpose currency in place of a limited purpose money. Today all conversions and most conveyances are made in terms of coinage. Yet Tiv constantly express their distrust of money. This fact, and another—that a single means of exchange has entered all the economic spheres—has broken down the major distinctions among the spheres. Money has created in Tivland a unicentric economy. Not only is the money a general-purpose money, but it applies to the full range of exchangeable goods.

Thus, when semi-professional traders, using money, began trading in the foodstuffs marketed by women and formerly solely the province of women, the range of the market was very greatly increased and hence the price in Tiv markets is determined by supply and demand far distant from the local producer and consumer. Tiv react to this situation by saying that foreign traders "spoil" their markets. The overlap of marketing and men's long-distance trade in staples also results in truckload after truckload of foodstuffs exported from major Tiv markets every day they meet. Tiv say that food is less plentiful today than it was in the past, though more land is being farmed. Tiv elders deplore this situation and know what is happening, but they do not know just where to fix the blame. In attempts to do something about it, they sometimes announce that no women are to sell any food at all. But when their wives disobey them, men do not really feel that they were wrong to have done so. Tiv sometimes discriminate against non-Tiv traders in attempts to stop export of food. In their condemnation of the situation which is depriving them of their food faster than they are able to increase production, Tiv elders always curse money itself. It is money which, as the instrument for selling one's life subsistence, is responsible for the worsened situation—money and the Europeans who brought it.

Of even greater concern to Tiv is the influence money has had on marriage institutions. Today every woman's guardian, in accepting money as bridewealth, feels that he is converting down. Although attempts are made to spend money which is received in bridewealth to acquire brides for one's self and one's sons, it is in the nature of money, Tiv insist,

that it is most difficult to accomplish. The good man still spends his bridewealth receipts for brides—but good men are not so numerous as would be desirable. Tiv deplore the fact that they are required to "sell" (*te*) their daughters and "buy" (*yam*) wives. There is no dignity in it since the possibility of making a bridewealth marriage into an exchange marriage has been removed.

With money, thus, the institutionalization of Tiv economy has become unicentric, even though Tiv still see it with multicentric values. The single sphere takes many of its characteristics from the market, so that the new situation can be considered a spread of the market. But throughout these changes in institutionalization, the basic Tiv value of maximization—converting one's wealth into the highest category, women and children—has remained. And in this discrepancy between values and institutions, Tiv have come upon what is to them a paradox, for all that Westerners understand it and are familiar with it. Today it is easy to sell subsistence goods for money to buy prestige articles and women, thereby aggrandizing oneself at a rapid rate. The food so sold is exported, decreasing the amount of subsistence goods available for consumption. On the other hand, the number of women is limited. The result is that bridewealth gets higher: rights in women have entered the market, and since the supply is fixed, the price of women has become inflated.

The frame of reference given me by the organizer of this symposium asked for comments on the effects of increased monetization on trade, on the distribution of wealth and indebtedness. To sum up the situation in these terms, trade has vastly increased with the introduction of general purpose money but also with the other factors brought by a colonial form of government. At the same time, the market has expanded its range of applicability in the society. The Tiv are, indigenously, a people who valued egalitarian distribution of wealth to the extent that they believed they bewitched one another to whittle down the wealth of one man to the size of that of another. With money, the degree and extent of differentiation by wealth has greatly increased and will probably continue to increase. Finally, money has brought a new form of indebtedness—one which we know, only too well. In the indigenous system, debt took either the form of owing marriage wards and was hence congruent with the kinship system, or else took the form of decreased prestige. There was no debt in the sphere of subsistence because there was no credit there save among kinsmen and neighbors whose activities were aspects of family status, not acts of money-lenders. The introduction of general purpose money and the concomitant spread of the market has divorced debt from kinship and status and has created the notion of debt in the subsistence sphere divorced from the activities of kinsmen and neighbors.

In short, because of the spread of the market and the introduction of general-purpose money, Tiv economy has become a part of the world economy. It has brought about profound changes in the institutionalization of Tiv society. Money is one of the shatteringly simplifying ideas of all time, and like any other new and compelling idea, it creates its own revolution. The monetary revolution, at least in this part of Africa, is the turn away from the multicentric economy. Its course may be painful, but there is very little doubt about its outcome.

*selection 58*

# Maximization Theories and the Study of Economic Anthropology

## Robbins Burling

*. . . Economics is the study of the allocation of scarce means to multiple objectives, or more broadly "the science which studies human behavior as a relationship between ends and scarce means which have alternative uses" (Robbins).*

Many anthropologists who have concerned themselves with economic problems have recently used similar definitions, including Firth in his latest discussion of anthropological economics, and Herskovits. But these authors, after indicating choice, allocation, and "economizing" to be the core of economic behavior, slip back to a consideration of "economizing" among material objects and ends, or only among the objects which *we* include in our market system. It is this mistake that Robbins

From American Anthropologist, *Vol. 64, No. 4, 1962, pp. 802–820.* By permission of the author, and the publisher.

avoids and it is for this reason that I have found his essay so valuable and so much more satisfying logically than the formulations of most anthropologists who have dealt with these problems.

Robbins points out that there is no economic problem if unlimited means are available for achieving some goal, and furthermore we do not have to economize if something has no alternative use whatsoever. "When time and the means for achieving ends are limited, *and* capable of alternative application, *and* the ends are capable of being distinguished in order of importance, then behavior necessarily assumes the form of choice" (Italics in the original). One must choose between scarce means and apply them to the variously valued ends. The unity of economic science, says Robbins, lies in the forms assumed by human behavior in disposing of scarce means. Neither ends nor means can necessarily be measured in monetary terms, and neither need consist of material objects, and so economics defined in this way has no necessary connection with the use of money or material objects. Since we are disposing of scarce means in virtually everything we do, economics in this view focuses on a particular *aspect* of behavior and not on certain kinds of behavior. The woman organizing her housework, the man allocating his time between his family and his club, the child deciding whether to play baseball or fly a kite, the political leader distributing patronage, and the feast giver who "gives" away food in order to accumulate prestige, are making "economic" decisions whether or not money has anything to do with their choice, and whether or not they are dealing with "material" objects. If Robbins, like other economists, goes on to study those types of behavior in which the economic aspect (choice and allocation) can to a certain extent be measured in money, it is not because of the principles of economics, but because of expedient and supplementary assumptions about what kinds of behavior are more and less important or more easily analyzed. Clearly, in turning to a primitive society, this alternative of restricting ourselves to priced phenomena does not exist. The implications of seizing upon the "economizing" aspect of behavior, as central to the study of economics, are a good deal more far reaching than has some-

times been realized, and my major criticism of both Herskovits and Firth, for instance, is that neither follows out the implications of his own definitions. If all behavior involving allocation is economic, then the relationship of a mother to her baby is just as much an economic one, or rather has just as much of an economic aspect, as the relationship of an employer to his hired laborer. A farmer hoeing his yams is being no more economic than when he is chatting with his cronies in the men's house. The economic aspect of behavior —choice, allocation of scarce means, including time and energy and not just money—is present in all this behavior. From this point of view it is quite hopeless to speak of an institution or group as being economic in nature. All groups have an economic aspect.

It is possible to look upon a society as a collection of choice-making individuals, whose every action involves conscious or unconscious selections among alternative means to alternative ends. The ends are the goals of the individual colored by the values of his society toward which he tries to make his way. They may include prestige, love, leisure, or even money. The means are the technical skills and knowledge at his disposal, including skill at oratory or endurance at the hunt as well as technical knowledge as such. There are no specifically economic techniques or economic goals. It is only the relationship *between* ends and means, the way in which a man manipulates his technical resources to achieve his goals, that is economic.

Now, strictly speaking, given a set of technical skills and knowledge and given a set of scalable ends or values, there is only one best way to use one to reach the other. The economist is not usually interested in either ends or means themselves but rather in the way in which means are manipulated to reach ends, and he is above all interested in working out the most efficient possible way of achieving certain ends, given the means. It is at this point that economists are likely to express their lack of interest in the economics of primitive people, because the most economic procedure for a primitive is presumably no different than it is for anyone, granted of course that both ends and means may be different in another society than in our own. To most economists it hardly matters how the members of any particular society make their choices. If they are inefficient and do not direct their means to rational accomplishment of their ends, why then, so much the worse for the people.

In practice, of course, economists have not worried about the general problem of how all of the varied ends of an individual can be met. They have limited their problem by asking how a particular man, say an entrepreneur, can best accomplish the end of a large money profit—how can money be maximized. This has an air of unreality when applied to a primitive society. People work and try to achieve their goals. They want more food, or more wives, or more prestige, and they clearly work to achieve these aims, but the ends they have in mind are never so simple as those dealt with by economists who speak of high money profit. Of course, the entrepreneur's aims are not really so simple either, but the grossness of the oversimplification becomes inescapable when looking at a primitive society.

Polanyi and his associates recognize that "economics" has often been used in this sense, to refer to situations of choice in areas of limited means. They argue that price setting markets are found only in a limited segment of human history. They seem to conclude that for this reason it is difficult to study choice-making in other societies, but their interests are simply not centered on choice-making. Nevertheless, it may be worthwhile to examine choice-making even in societies where money and price-setting markets are absent. One can hardly argue that "economization," the careful calculation of choices with an eye to one's prospects, is missing simply because the particular institutional framework which helps us to make *some* economizing decisions (the market) is missing. Primitives are presumably neither more or less rational than any of us, although they may use different institutions through which to express their rationality. Of course, the system of market regulated prices cannot be studied in the absence of market regulated prices, but it may still be useful to study rationalizing calculation. Furthermore, certain characteristics of price-regulating markets may be readily seen even in societies very different from our own and in very different institutional settings. Where doweries are substantial or bride-price is required, the amount to be paid may be a matter of careful bargaining. The total bride-price may depend upon the desirability of the girl, either personally or as derived from her family's social status. Instances of curtailment or increase in the amounts of cattle available for bride-price (through disease or otherwise) show that the price also depends upon the supply of cattle. It seems entirely reasonable to suggest that certain characteristics of our marketing system that go under the name of "the law of supply and demand" are applicable in a much broader context than our own markets. This possibility would be obscured if we have to limit the range of meaning of economics to a consideration of material goods, as suggested by Polanyi. If we can get back to the initial assumptions of economists about scarcity of means and unlimited wants we may find that they are still useful assumptions even in the absence of markets and prices.

Here, then, is a final area of behavior to which the term "economic" might apply, the area of choice and allocation of scarce resources to alternative goals. It would study an aspect of behavior, not a type of behavior, and it would be an aspect of behavior that has no more connection with the material aspects of life than with others, and no necessary connection with the objects which are priced in our society. One of the troubles with our understanding of the economics of primitive people has surely been that we have confused the various possible definitions of economics and have persuaded ourselves that allocation of resources was somehow more characteristic of behavior that deals with material goods than with other behavior, or that the use of money coincided with the use of material goods or that only by using money could we rationally economize. It is clear, however, that economizing calculation, material goods, and items exchanged through price-setting markets, each refer to something distinctly different.

Once we focus upon choice and allocation, it becomes apparent that there have been a number of strands of thought in the social sciences that have looked upon human behavior from this essentially economic view. For the rest of this paper I will investigate just one of the implications of regarding human behavior as if governed by an attempt to allocate scarce resources in a rational way. I find it convenient to call this the principle of "maximization," but it is closely related to the idea of "rationalizing calculation."

## Maximization Theories

The notion that human behavior is somehow oriented toward a maximization of some desired end has appeared in a great range of social science theory. Maximization is, of course, a fundamental concept in economics, for a central axiom of that discipline is that human wants are unlimited, but that we constantly strive to maximize our satisfactions. More specifically, all of microeconomics, the study of how an entrepreneur or a firm should behave, assumes that he or it is trying to maximize money profit. Such questions as what will happen to profit if price is increased, or how a decrease in production will effect the ratio of income to costs, are at the heart of a great deal of economic theorizing, and they assume that the end in view is to make as much money as possible. Of course we know, and to give them their due I believe that economists know also, that not even entrepreneurs always strive to maximize money profit, but that sometimes they may prefer something else—leisure, conceivably even good human relations—rather than more money. This is not to deny that these entrepreneurs are trying to maximize something, but only states that they sometimes have to choose between money and some other desired end. The assumption that it is money that is being maximized is only a convenient simplification in line with the general attention of economists to those instances of choice and behavior in which money is involved. . . .

People do not always try to maximize money, or basic biological satisfactions, or power, though all of these certainly do enter into our decisions, and, in a general way, the more we have, the happier we expect to be.

The most explicit theory of maximization which I know of is that of George Zipf, who wrote an incredible book called *Human Behavior and the Principle of Least Effort*. Kluckhohn reviewed this book as being ". . . fertile and suggestive, mad, irrelevant," and indeed it was all of these things. Zipf believed that all of our behavior is oriented toward the minimization of effort. Now, taken literally, and the delight of Zipf's book is that he stated his principles with no leeway for ambiguity, this is nonsense. Athletic events and taking a walk to work up an appetite are hardly understandable within this framework. This among other flights of fancy has led most people who have stumbled upon his book to reject his principles, even while recognizing the fertile mind which produced them and the remarkable collection of data which he believed would support them. However, even some of his principles may deserve an examination. Like the economist, the Freudian psychologist, or like Leach or Lasswell when they look at political behavior, Zipf assumes that people are trying to orient their behavior, that is, make their choices in such a way that they will obtain the greatest possible amount of something. Zipf recognizes, and in fact he spells out in detail, how a man in trying to minimize effort may be led a long way around to reach his ultimate goal. It may pay in the long run (in terms of less effort) to stop work and make a new tool because, even though it takes effort to make the tool, the total effort expended may eventually be less when the tool is used. He discusses how various factors may make it more or less desirable to have many specialized tools or a few more generalized ones. He demonstrates with an enormous collection of data that the words we use most frequently are the shortest ones and says that in the long run this means a lesser expenditure of effort in speaking. He also points out that there is a point beyond which the planning to minimize effort is itself more costly of effort than the amount saved, and it is therefore extramarginal. One does best, in terms of saving energy, not to plan beyond that point. Now all this is rather neat, and it is reminiscent of the discussions of economists on how to maximize money income, except, of course, that it is so absurd to set up the minimization of effort as the overriding goal which guides all of our behavior. Perhaps it is no more extreme than the idea that maximization of income, or sex, or power is the main dynamo of human behavior, but the people who have suggested these other motivations have hedged more cautiously than Zipf did. Money income is a convenient simplification to the economist, "pleasure" is a broad enough concept to include all of our motivations, and Leach suggests power only for the particular purposes of a particular analysis. Zipf's mistake was to give himself no loophole, but to maintain that effort minimization was the one and primary motive of all human behavior. His lack of ambiguity, however, even though it may have led him to be rapidly rejected as a somewhat mad genius, allowed a more explicit formulation of the implications of a maximization theory than any of the others, except perhaps for technical economics.

All of these theories are disconcerting for much the same reason: all are too simple. Clearly the things we want are more complicated than expressed by any of these simple motivations. Certainly we are sometimes happy to avoid effort, and we often seek money or power, but these are not always sought after by all people. More significantly, we often have to choose *between* these things. We must decide whether leisure (minimum effort) is more or less important to us at the moment than an increase in money income, or whether power is to be sought after instead of either of these, and it is here that Zipf presents an intriguing argument. He points out that it is quite impossible to maximize two things at once. One might, for instance, offer a prize to the submarine commander who sinks the greatest number of ships in a given interval of time. Alternatively, one might offer the prize to whoever sinks a given number of ships in the shortest possible time: "Yet when we offer a prize to the submarine commander who sinks the *greatest number* of ships in the *shortest possible time*, we have a double superlative—a *maximum* number and a *minimum* time—which renders the problem completely meaningless and indeterminate, as becomes apparent upon reflection." Similarly, one cannot simultaneously try to maximize both sexual satisfaction and the acquisition of money, because there may come a time when there is a choice between the two, and to increase one will at the same time decrease the other. This is precisely the same argument that Robbins used in denying that economics could in principle be restricted to material ends, since one often has to decide between material and nonmaterial objectives. To scale one's ends and distinguish them in the order of importance implies some general standard against which the more specific goals can be measured. This presumably is what economists mean when

they speak of achieving satisfactions as the ultimate goal.

Now to say that an individual strives to maximize his satisfactions is to state little more than a truism. Unless satisfactions are expressed in some more concrete form, such as money, they are ill defined and of course may shift from time to time for the same person and also be different for various individuals. All that is really said is that our behavior is goal-oriented and that the various immediate goals are themselves measurable with respect to one another and can be scaled. It certainly does not help us to predict human behavior, since the only way we know what is desired is to watch which choices people make. So, we are faced with a dilemma. If we state that people act so as to maximize something broad enough ("satisfactions") to subsume all our more specific goals, we say very little. If we state that we act so as to maximize one particular goal—power, money income, or whatever we choose, then usually we are incorrect. But the idea of maximization cannot be abandoned since any discussion of purposive or goal-oriented behavior, or any analysis of choice, does imply a maximization theory and we may as well make explicit a common notion in the social sciences, and for that matter in all of our everyday thinking. It does bring us closer to one of the basic postulates of economics.

Economists have assumed that our wants are infinite. This does not mean that any *particular* want is unlimited, and specifically the desire for material goods may conceivably not be unlimited. Western industrialism has increased material goods so greatly that one can at least imagine that the desire for these may eventually be satiated. Some goals, however, have inherent limitations. Power and prestige cannot be multiplied for everybody since the implication of more power or prestige for some people in a society is that others must have less. For every winner in the race for prestige, just as in a running race or football game, there is also a loser. As has long been pointed out, moreover, much of modern purchasing is not based so much on the desire for material objects, anyway, as for the prestige that it is hoped these objects—cars, swimming pools, or filled book cases—will bring. The principle that our wants are unlimited is a statement that is hardly susceptible of proof, but it may be a useful axiom which can be assumed to lie at the base of human behavior and which can bring sense to a good deal of man's actions. Similarly, it seems reasonable to accept the principle that the means of achieving our desires are limited so that we can only manipulate our means so as to satisfy as many of our wants as possible. Interpreted in this way and stripped of their connotation of money profit, these basic postulates of economics may be worth incorporating into a more general theory than that of market analysis.

From this point of view, we are "economizing" in everything we do. We are always trying to maximize our satisfactions somehow, and so we are led back to the notion that economics deals not with a type but rather with an aspect of behavior. This economic view of society becomes one way, or if one prefers, one model for looking at society. It is a model which sees the individuals of a society busily engaged in maximizing their own satisfactions —desire for power, prestige, sex, food, independence, or whatever else they may be, in the context of the opportunities around them, including those offered by their own culture. Since one makes choices partly with an eye to the expected choices of others, it is not unreasonable to view this pursuit of satisfactions as a great and continuing game of strategy. It makes no sense at all for anthropologists to try to limit economics to mean the pursuit of one particular goal.

If we now focus upon the individual who is caught in the web of his society, and who is trying to maximize his satisfactions, we are led to the investigation of his actual behavior in situations of choice. This is the crucial economic question. In the first place, one must allocate his own resources. A woman must allocate her attention between her husband and her children, and for that matter save a bit for her mother. Attention, like money or time, must be economized. Patronage must be allocated among followers. Admiration or prestige must be granted to some people, denied to others. Each person has at his disposal a certain amount of love, of admiration, and of power, as well as of labor or money or energy, and these must all be distributed. It is reasonable to suppose that they are dis-

tributed with the intention of maximizing one's own satisfactions. They are granted with the idea of return in some form. One gives prestige in return for bride-wealth, or labor in return for wages, or care of children in return for affection or social approval, and it is totally irrelevant whether money or material goods happen to be part of the equation in these various types of exchange, though in a sense we are acting so as to make a profit in all of this exchange behavior. We feel that the prestige gained is worth more than the food we give away, or that the power gained is worth the distribution of patronage, though of course the person with whom we are trading must feel differently, or we could never come to terms. This leads to a conception of social organization as a whole as a system of exchange, a broader concept than that of the particular and limited systems of exchange mentioned earlier.

George Homans not long ago suggested that an exchange model would be a useful one in uniting various lines of social science research:

. . . [small-group research] would be furthered by our adopting the view that interaction between persons is an exchange of goods, material and non-material. This is one of the oldest theories of social behavior, and one that we still use every day to interpret our own behavior, as when we say 'I found so-and-so rewarding'; or 'I got a great deal out of him'; or even 'Talking with him took a great deal out of me.' But, perhaps just because it is so obvious, this has been much neglected by social scientists.

Homans goes on to consider several experiments in sociology and even in animal psychology and uses terms such as "cost," "value," and "profit" to describe them and even constructs the formula: Profit = Reward − Cost. He uses these terms in very much the same way that they are defined in the elementary economics textbook referred to earlier, but Homans realizes that in his experiments as in much of life, these cannot possibly be measured in money. Exchange, like maximization, is certainly close to the heart of economics, and in fact an exchange model of society is remarkably similar to conventional economic analysis, even though it takes into account far more than our primitive notion of economics. It should be possible to speak of the supply of prestige, the demand for power, and the cost of authority. I see no reason why one should not even speak of the marginal utility of loving care. Each man can be regarded as an entrepreneur, manipulating those around him, trading his products of labor, attention, respect, etc., for the most he can get in return.

The trouble with this is, of course, that there seems to be little prospect for quantification. The contrasting beauty, perhaps a spurious beauty, of traditional economics is that one can assign figures to the commodities and services that are exchanged, because they have prices, and one can then manipulate the figures. But unless the anthropologist uses concepts of economics, cost, value, demand, supply, etc. in a much broader context than is the custom of the economist, over a range of meaning far wider than that which is priced, he had better stop talking about economics.

The view of society as a system of exchange, and the view that men act so as to attempt to maximize satisfactions, are fundamentally economic ones and are close to the way in which economists look upon their subject matter. However, unlike anthropologists, economists have not ordinarily been interested in finding out *whether* people economize intelligently, but only in figuring out *how* they can economize more intelligently. This difference in objectives creates an almost unbridgeable gap between economics and anthropology, because an anthropologist is always most interested in the actual behavior of men in concrete situations. I think, however, that a clear conception of this broader "economic" or

"exchange" view of society might, if followed out consistently, be of interest even to the economist. The problems that have to be wrestled with in describing a society in this manner make themselves known most insistently where money value is not used as a means of measurement. Once this problem is clearly faced, it is obvious that the same problem exists in our own society. There are many things which we do not price, and our behavior can never be understood if we focus only on those limited types of behavior which are priced. We must constantly choose between monetary and nonmonetary goals. Even if an economist is interested only in advising people how they ought to behave if they want to maximize their satisfactions (and not just their money income), he will have to take nonmonetary goals into account. From this point of view I think that anthropology could play its time-honored role of broadening the viewpoint of others and making even our own society more understandable, because of the attention it has directed towards differing cultures. Of course, we will have to get economists to listen to us first, but we cannot possibly expect economists to listen to us until we get some clear idea of what economic science is trying to achieve, and of what "economic" means. As long as we stumble along with the extraordinarily ethnocentric notion that somehow economics is primarily connected with food production, or with material culture or land tenure, or certain restricted types of labor, then we are missing any opportunity for fruitful communication with our economist colleagues.

# The Natural Experiment, Ecology and Culture

*Morris Freilich*

*From* Southwestern Journal of Anthropology, *Vol. 19, No. 1, 1963, pp. 21–37.* © *1963, Department of Anthropology, University of New Mexico. By permission of the author, the publisher, and the copyright holder.*

## Introduction

Alfred North Whitehead has described modern science as an interest in relating stubborn facts to general principles; a "union of passionate interest in the detailed facts with equal devotion to abstract generalisation." Modern anthropology has a passion, indeed, for the detailed facts, but couples this with a nebulous attachment to abstract generalization. It has therefore a wealth of facts but a paucity of principles.

A problem that must concern us as scientists is: How can our ethnographic facts be used more efficiently to increase our stock of general principles? Or, differently put, how can anthropology be made more scientific in terms of modern scientific goals?

Modern science, it is generally acknowledged, dates from the introduction of the experimental method. In the sister social sciences of sociology and anthropology, and particularly in anthropology, minimal use has been made of this method. Explanations usually given for the minimal use of the experiment include: the complexity of the data, the related problems of vested interests and maintaining objectivity, the problem of sampling, the problem of control and the problems—both moral and methodological—of manipulating humans. Experimentation as a regular part of anthropological methodology would lead, I submit, to a sharpening of concepts, a sophistication of measuring devices and finally to an increase in empirically based principles. It is therefore most urgent that this method be carefully re-examined for its possible incorporation into the study of culture.

The essence of the experiment lies in the close observation of phenomena where the critical variables are controlled. Two points here are worth noting. First, variables considered "critical" are needed for an experiment. Second, control over such critical variables is a relative matter; we can speak only of experiments with superior or inferior controls. As Festinger has remarked about recent laboratory studies in the social sciences: "we must include under the term 'laboratory experiment' a wide range of studies with varying degrees of control and precision."

In *Research Methods in the Behavioral Sciences* three major types of experiments are discussed: the laboratory experiment, the field experiment and the natural experiment. Let us examine these forms further and see to what extent all, or some of them, can be usefully incorporated into general anthropological methodology. The laboratory experiment is "one in which the investigator creates a situation with the exact conditions he wants to have and in which he controls some, and manipulates other, variables." The field experiment is "a theoretically oriented research project in which the experimenter manipulates an independent variable in some real social setting in order to test some hypothesis." And the natural experiment is "a change of major importance engineered by policy makers and practitioners and not by social scientists. It is experimental from the point of view of the scientist . . . (since) it can afford opportunities for measuring the effect of the change on the assumption that the change is so clear and drastic in nature that there is no question of identifying it as the independent variable."

It is undeniable that human animals living in society and behaving according to the dictates of historically derived cultures represent extremely complex phenomena for study in a laboratory. However, some scholars have shown that complex phenomena can be reduced to a minimal number of critical variables and these can be studied in laboratory situations. For example, Guy Swanson has provided evidence that the behavior of crowds of all sizes can be expressed in the behavior of three people acting under controlled conditions. Rose and Felton have shown the possibility of creating culture in laboratory conditions. By the careful selection of critical elements in society and culture, Rose and Felton were able to construct models of sociocultural systems which enabled them to study,

under laboratory experimental conditions, such concepts as: closed and open societies, invention of culture and diffusion of culture.

Anthropologists of diverse theoretical orientations appear to share a common commitment to the natural history approach; it is doubtful therefore that the laboratory experiment would be used by many of them, even as an additional methodological tool. However, in the field and natural experiments man is studied in his natural environment; and such studies would therefore be more congruent with existing practices of, and ideas about, anthropological field work.

The field experiment has been used to good advantage by many highly reputable anthropologists. Researchers such as Allan Holmberg and associates have combined planned change endeavors and experimental work and have both assisted communities to become independent and provided important theoretical statements. Although the work of many applied anthropologists has been sophisticated both in design and general methodology, applied anthropology is treated by many social scientists as an illegitimate sibling of "theoretical" anthropology. A common charge that has been made against applied anthropology is that it is unscientific. Apparently, for many non-applied anthropologists, field experiments and similar work done by the applied anthropologist represent too radical a change from the natural history approach to be acceptable. For many, particularly those whose training or identification is "Boasian," it is "the exhaustive collection of data" which is the typical province of anthropology and not the manipulation of such data.

The most conservative of anthropologists, however, can find little argument with the natural experiment, for such studies differ minimally from traditional anthropological field work. The importance of the natural experiment for anthropology warrants some further discussion of the tactics and methodology here involved.

### The Natural Experiment

Following the discussions in Festinger and Katz's important book, I have described the natural experiment as one where the researcher selects a situation for study where *change of a clear and dramatic nature* has occurred. In essence the argument of the natural experimenter is that this type of change can be treated as an independent variable in an experimental setting, and its effects can be observed and recorded. Or, differently put, the socio-cultural system in which a clear and dramatic change has occurred is, for a given time, a natural laboratory, where given variables are in a state of control so that the effects of an independent variable (the change) can be studied. Thus, the argument would here continue that it hardly matters how control is achieved; what is important is that it is there and can be used for experimental purposes. The role of the researcher using the natural experiment is then to opportunistically capitalize on situations which exist. Following French, the opportunism of the researcher lies in searching for situations where change of a clear and dramatic nature has occurred and using such situations as "natural" laboratories.

It should be noted that change of a clear and dramatic nature can be represented by a whole series of phenomena: cultural, social, ecological, demographic, and so forth. Further, such changes become most useful for experimental purposes when they are related to a theoretical framework. For example, the work of Steward and associates in Puerto Rico (which I would call a natural experiment) is important theoretically not only because this was an experimentally oriented study with a number of controls built into it, but also because the study was directly related to a theoretical framework—cultural ecology. Similarly, Goldschmidt's recently completed study in East Africa is important for theoretical anthropology both for its experimental design and its relationship to a theoretical framework. Studies such as these add to our library of detailed facts and increase our ability to make abstract generalizations.

To summarize, the anthropologist can do various kinds of natural experiments using a change in culture, ecology, demography, etc., as his independent variable. The factors that all natural experiments would have in common irrespective of the particular problem under investigation would be (1) a natural history orientation, (2) a socio-cultural system where an independent variable is in a state of natural isolation, (3) the possibility of studying the effects of the independent variable on the dependent variables, since other factors which may influence the dependent variables are in a state of natural control, and (4) a problem under investigation which is related to a theoretical framework.

In order to stay within the naturalistic and non-manipulating tradition of anthropological field work, the anthropologist engaged in natural experiments would give up some of the control available to his colleagues who do field and laboratory experiments. However, in doing natural experiments anthropologists would not be simply giving up some control in order to maintain the tradition of their discipline. Indeed, as Katz has shown, natural experiments have certain inherent advantages over both field and laboratory experiments. Their major advantage is "that the manipulation of variables is much more powerful. The real world can and does produce role reversals, drastic changes in groups norms, institutional revolutions, and group conflicts in a fashion impossible in the laboratory." In addition, natural and field experiments have certain advantages over laboratory experiments. First, these studies can continue over longer periods of time. Thus, if a process (p) is isolated in system (s) at time (t) the validity of this finding can be checked by studying system (s) at time (t + 1); other things being equal (p) should be still part of the system. Second, direct observation of phenomena is possible and there is less need to make inferences from limited data. Third, these studies permit the experimenter to use multiple measures for the study of given phenomena. In the laboratory it is frequently necessary to use a single measuring instrument, and correlations obtained from a single instrument may be influenced by various side effects.

The natural experiment, although differing minimally from traditional anthropological field studies, thus parallels in structure the laboratory experiments done in the physical and biological sciences. Although some control is lost by going outside of man-made laboratories, compensations are to be had in (1) the powerful manipulation of variables that is possible, (2) the checks available on the validity of the findings and (3) the possibility of observing man in his natural habitat so that real problems, rather than manufactured ones, can be solved. As suggested above, anthropologists, although rarely referring to their work as "experiments," have done what is here being called "natural experiments." Apart from the natural experiments done by Steward and associates and Goldschmidt and associates there is Linton's famous study of the effects on Tanala social organization of a change in food production. These and other similar studies have shown that it is possible to arrive at empirically based generalizations by conducting natural experiments. However, the natural experiment has, as yet, not become a formal aspect of anthropological methodology; and the minimal use of an experimental approach remains a basic defect in the study of man. As Stouffer has put it: "One of the greatest weaknesses of social science has been the infrequency of its use of deliberately designed controlled experiments, which are the only sure method of determining whether a change in one variable actually will be followed by a change in another."

The study which follows attempts to illustrate further the scientific possibilities inherent in the use of the natural experiment. The paper as a whole is an attempt to stimulate greater interest in experimental work, so that anthropology can share in the benefits which accrue to experimentally oriented sciences.

### Theory, Hypothesis, Procedures and Methods

In conducting a natural experiment anthropologists, like their colleagues in the physical and biological sciences, can begin with a theoretical framework, and derive a hypothesis therefrom for testing. In the natural experiment the next step is to *find a situation* where the critical variables of the hypothesis are in a state of "natural" control and where it is possible to study the effects of the independent variable.

The theoretical framework used in the study which follows is *cultural ecology*, as described by Julian Steward. Steward defines cultural ecology as the *interaction between technology and the culturally defined manner of exploiting the environment*. According to cultural ecological theory, such interaction is a "creative process," an important determinant of culture change. As Steward puts it, "over the millenia cultures in different environments have changed tremendously, and *these changes are*

*basically traceable to new adaptations required by changing technology and productive arrangements.*" (italics inserted).

Working within this framework, I derive the following hypothesis: *If two groups which differ considerably in cultural traditions make the same cultural ecological adaptation, then there should be a core of culture shared by both groups which is related to the common mode of adaptation.* The hypothesis was tested in the village of Anamat, in Eastern Trinidad, where East Indians and Negroes live together in neighborly enmity and do peasant farming in terms of a common "folk science" technology.

To test this cultural ecological hypothesis it was necessary to collect certain kinds of data, to analyze such data into comparable categories and to accept or reject the hypothesis on the basis of the data collected. The data collection procedures followed the usual anthropological field techniques. The writer and his wife spent approximately eleven months in the village of Anamat and became accepted members of the Anamatian community. Observation of and participation in community activities was for the first month of field work the major method used. In the months that followed, although the observation and participation method was continued, it was used as a subsidiary method to the following: informal and formal questionnaires, life histories, group seminars with East Indians and Negroes on their cultural practices, special informants and analysis of records kept by the Anamatian peasants relating to their land holdings. In addition local field assistants were hired to obtain certain kinds of confidential data which I had difficulty in obtaining. It was also possible for me to get the part-time assistance of a clerk in the office of Registrar General of Trinidad. The latter was able to provide historical data on land holdings for Anamat and land in the immediate vicinity of this village.

Two major types of data were collected from both the East Indians and the Negroes—ecological and cultural. The ecological data were collected to verify that the adaptations of East Indian and Negro peasants were indeed similar. The cultural data were collected in order to observe to what extent similarities in ecological adaptations had led to similar cultural practices in areas of social life not directly connected with subsistence activities.

*Table 1  Land Holdings of Negro and East Indian Peasants in Anamat, Trinidad*

|  | 10 acres or less | 11–19 acres | 20–30 acres | over 30 acres | total no. of holdings |
|---|---|---|---|---|---|
| Negroes | 6 | 11 | 8 | 6 | 31 |
| East Indians | 7 | 8 | 13 | 3 | 31 |
| Totals | 13 | 19 | 21 | 9 | 62 |

To verify that the cultural ecological adaptations of both groups were the same, I obtained data on the size of the land holdings, the relative fertility of the land of each group (East Indians and Negroes), the nature of the land holdings (freehold title, rent, lease, etc.), the cash and subsistence crops grown, the personnel who worked the land, the time spent working the land, the technology used, the crop yields and the incomes obtained. The data collected led to the conclusion that the East Indians and the Negroes had the same general environmental conditions and made specific ecological adaptations which were similar enough to be considered "the same" for the purposes of this natural experiment.

General environmental conditions were the same because East Indians and Negroes worked land all of which was situated in the same small village of Anamat. They both therefore shared common climatic conditions, such as rainfall, temperature, humidity, hours of daylight; they had common transportation facilities to and from their land holding and to and from market areas.

Specific ecological adaptations were considered the same for the following reasons: First, both groups worked similar sized land holdings (see Table 1). The average East Indian peasant worked a holding of 20.6 acres; the average Negro peasant worked a holding of 21.9 acres.

Second, the land of East Indians and Negroes was dispersed throughout Anamat. No part of the village could be considered "East Indian" or "Negro." Since the land of both groups was scattered throughout the community, it is possible to assume that the fertility of the soil was essentially the same for both groups.

Third, nearly all of the land worked by both groups was owned by freehold title by those who worked it. The East Indians owned 96.7 percent of the land they worked; the Negroes owned 92.9 percent of the land they worked. Both groups rented the balance of the land they worked.

Fourth, the major cash crop for both groups was cocoa and for both an additional cash crop was coffee. For a small minority of peasants, both East Indian and Negro, extra income was obtained from the sale of bananas and dasheen (*Araceae*).

Fifth, crops grown for home consumption were mainly such root crops as the following: yams (*Dioscoreaceae*), sweet potatoes (*Convolvulaceae*), cassava (*Euphorbiaceae*), tannia (*Marantaceae*) and dasheen (*Araceae*).

Sixth, although both groups had strong attachments to consanguineal families (see below), they both mainly lived in nuclear family households, and the land was mainly worked by the members of such a household. The head of the house (usually a male for both groups) did most of the work on the land. He was assisted by his wife and children, particularly during the crop time when the cocoa and coffee had to be picked.

Seventh, the time spent working the land was extremely similar for both groups. For both, the working week was generally Monday through Friday with a half day of work on Saturday. Both groups of peasants found it difficult to tell me exactly how much time they spent working on the land each day. Both stated that it all depended on what had to be done at a certain time of the year. When I urged them to provide me with an estimate of how long they believed they worked on an average day, I received data which averaged 7.5 hours a day for the East Indians and 7.6 hours a day for the Negroes. For most of the peasants, both East Indian and Negro, the working day started around 7:30 to 8:00 in the morning and ended about 4:00 to 4:30 in the afternoon. All the peasants told me that when they had a lot of work that had to be finished at a given time they worked until it got dark, and at such times work on Sundays was not uncommon. Such long working weeks occurred mainly during the heavy cocoa crop seasons—November through December, parts of January and April. The Negroes spent more time away from the land than the East Indians during such féte seasons as Christmas and Carnival. This time, however, was approximately balanced by East Indians participating in family *pujas* (prayer meetings) and other Hindu religious observances.

Eighth, both groups used a technology which in terms of recognized practices of working cocoa estates could be considered as unscientific. They both practiced what could be called a folk-science of agriculture. This was mostly based on information which was passed down orally from their peasant farming parents and which was shared by the whole community. In addition "MacDonald's Farmer's Almanac" was used by some of the farmers as an extra guide. This almanac was considered by a number of East Indian and Negro peasants as an important source of farming information. The nature of the information contained in this almanac can be deduced from its cover, which states in bold type: "Tells When to Plant and Harvest by the Moon . . . (makes) Predictions about Crops, The Weather, Sickness and Lucky Days."

Finally, the crop yields and the income for both groups were extremely similar. Although it might be possible to deduce that peasants working similar sized holdings in similar unscientific ways would have similar crop yields and income, I attempted to obtain information in this area directly. On the basis of a limited number of records I was allowed to examine, together with the answers I received on questionnaires about crop yields and income, I was able to come to the following conclusions. The average yield per cocoa tree per year was 0.76 lbs. for East Indians and 0.70 lbs. for Negroes—this, when it is possible with scientific methods to average 2.73 lbs.! Further, the average income per acre was $86.18 for the East Indians and $81.35 for the Negroes.

Statements made by the Anamatian peasants on the farming abilities of East Indians and Negroes further supported the conclusion that the two groups had similar average incomes. To the question: "Who are better farmers, Negroes or East Indians?" the general answer first received was related to the cultural affiliation of the person being questioned—Negroes stated "Negroes" and East Indians stated "Indians." After a short discussion, however, when the questioned person was asked to name "good" and "poor" farmers in Anamat, it was usually concluded by the informant that both groups had a fairly equal share of good and poor farmers. Put differently, it was agreed by most of my informants that East Indians and Negroes farmed about equally well.

To summarize, both groups were considered as making the same cultural ecological adaption since both:

1. shared the same climatic conditions,
2. worked land of similar acreage,
3. worked with similar biotic and edaphic (soils, relief and drainage) features,
4. spent similar amounts of time working the land,
5. used the same folk-science technology,
6. used the same kind and number of personnel (head of the house) to do most of the farming,
7. worked to produce the same cash crops: cocoa and coffee,
8. worked to produce the same crops for home consumption (root crops),
9. shared the same market and transportation facilities,
10. obtained similar incomes from their subsistence activities.

### Cultural Data

In collecting cultural data from East Indians and Negroes in Anamat, special care was taken to spend approximately equal time with both groups so as not to bias the data. This balance was maintained by careful planning and record-keeping of interactions with Anamatians. Initially each group tried to monopolize my time, each respectively trying to demonstrate that only they had a culture which could interest an anthropologist. Within a short time, however, it became generally known and accepted that I was a strange kind of individual who liked East Indians and Negroes equally well.

Cultural data was obtained from both groups on economic practices, marriage, the family, extended kinship ties, authority patterns, leisure activities, expressive symbols, religious practices, involvement in community affairs—both social and political—and on the various roles in their respective systems. The cultural data collected showed that although East Indians and Negroes made a similar ecological adaptation and earned similar incomes, their cultural practices, in areas of social life not directly connected to subsistence activities, were extremely different.

Money was spent differently by East Indians and Negroes. Although the average Negro household contained only one child and the average East Indian household had 3-4 children, both groups spent similar amounts for food and clothing. Thus, per family member, the East Indians spent far less on food and clothing than the Negroes. The East Indians, however, spent more money on housing than the Negroes. Fourteen of the East Indian peasants (45%) lived in brick houses as against eight of the Negro peasants (26%) who lived in brick houses. The balance of the peasants of both groups lived in galvanized-roofed houses (14 East Indians and 20 Negroes) and karat huts (3 East Indians and 3 Negroes).

The East Indians also spent more money on education than the Negroes. At the time of this study two sons of East Indian peasants were studying in universities in England and one other East Indian youth was planning to go to England. None of the Negro peasants had sons studying in a university, nor did any of the Negro youths plan on going to a university.

The Negroes spent more money than the East Indians on pleasure or what they called "féte." A féte, for the Negro, was a situation which contained at least two of the following: people, talk, rum, music, dance and sexual play. If all or most of these phenomena were present in a given party, the Negro would consider himself to be in a "big féte" or "real féte." The East Indians spent more money than the Negroes on religious matters. These usually took the form of the *puja*, the family prayer meeting, which was held in the house or the yard of the person "making a *puja*."

In short, Indians spent more money on capital items which would affect their future (housing, education, religion), while Negroes spent more money on noncapital items which were fairly quickly consumed and which re-

lated to a present rather than future time orientation. Going along with a different use of money by East Indians and Negroes was a different use of time. The *pujas* of the East Indians brought them into frequent contacts with members of their extended families; the féting of the Negroes was usually done with friends rather than family and frequently took the Negro male away from his nuclear family. Thus East Indians spent more time with the members of their family than did the Negroes. To the extent that the use of time may represent an operational measure of values, it could be said that "the family" was far more valued by East Indians than by Negroes. Such a conclusion would be congruent with the following facts: (1) East Indians bringing religious services into the home, the place which houses the family; and (2) East Indians building more expensive and permanent housing than the Negroes.

The East Indians lived in a joint family setting: a life-long household economy of three generations, with patrilineal inheritance, patriarchal authority and patrilocal residence rules. Although the joint family household frequently split into nuclear households, the latter were usually placed within close proximity of each other and close contacts were had between the members of a joint family. While a given Indian might be living in his own house and be relatively independent economically, the directives of a father or an elder brother were still orders and not suggestions.

The Negroes lived in nuclear households but had strong affectionate ties to a matrifocal family: a three generation consanguineal unit with a minimal membership of a mother, her brother, her son and daughter and her daughter's children. Authority patterns were here equalitarian. Directives were given by elder members of the family in the form of "advice" rather than orders.

The marriages of the East Indians were arranged by their elders; and the father of a young Indian girl would attempt to get a youth for his daughter who was of "good family" (i.e. of a caste which was, at least, of equal status with his own) and who lived in a village other than his own. The marriage was supposed to last for life. The Negroes selected their own mates and understood that a given marriage was only supposed to last

*Table 2   Points of Reference for Two Cultural Models*

| | |
|---|---|
| Time | What is the basic time orientation of the group; is it the present, the past or the future? |
| Space | In what area is most living done, and under what circumstances is there an extension of this area? |
| People | What is the basic kinship unit of the group, and what is the nature of associational activities? |
| Authority Structure | What is the nature of order-giving and order-receiving in the group? |
| Exchange System | What kinds of exchanges occur with respect to a) goods and services, b) women, c) symbols? |
| Sanctions | What sanctions effectively control behavior in the group? |
| Goals | What kinds of behavior receive most prestige per unit of time, energy, and expense incurred? |

for as long as man and wife "cooperated"; when one or both parties thought that the proper "cooperation" no longer existed, it was time for them to separate. As the Anamatian Negro put it, a marriage was a "now-for-now" affair.

In terms of associational patterns the East Indians maintained a sharp separation of the sexes in all social activities. Be it at a family *puja* with fifty or more people congregating in and around one house or during a friendly visit of a man and his wife, the Indian women would rarely interact with any of the males present. The Indian women understood and accepted the fact that their place was with the other women who were present. The Indian men would similar consider it improper to have social intercourse with the women on these occasions. Social intercourse across sex lines was greatly limited in Indian culture and occurred mostly between a man and his wife when they were alone.

For the Negro a get-together without members of the opposite sex being present would represent a very dull party. The associational activities of the Negro peasants in Anamat thus usually included interactions between members of both sexes. At such times some of the men would have opportunities to talk to some of the women present, in private. Part of the content of these conversations frequently included the male "beggin' for a brush" (proposing that the woman and he meet later for sexual play). If a given woman agreed, it was understood by both parties that the man was to be the recipient of a favor

which must be later repaid in terms of some goods or services. Thus sex was for the Negroes of Anamat a medium of exchange along with money (British West Indian dollar). The use of sex as a medium of exchange fitted in well with the cultural system of the Negroes: it facilitated the serial polygyny which was practiced; it led to a more equalitarian distribution of goods and services and was congruent with the fête complex which was a major goal of this system.

In summary, the East Indian and Negro peasants in Anamat were part of two extremely different cultural systems, the former having a way of life which in many important areas was similar to the cultural practices of the Hindu peasants in India, the latter maintaining cultural practices developed in the slavery plantation system of the New World. It is outside the scope of this paper to describe more completely the cultural practices of East Indian and Negro peasants in Anamat; most of such information has been presented by the writer elsewhere. It is possible, however, to summarize the data I collected in Anamat in terms of two systems, presented as mechanical models. The models were constructed by using the following points of reference as structural categories: *time, space, people, authority, exchanges, sanctions* and *goals*. In terms of these categories, questions were asked and answered on the basis of the ethnographic data collected in Anamat. For example, in reference to the category *time* the question asked was: "What is the basic time orientation of the group: is it past, present or future?'' Similar questions were posed for each of the categories of the models (see Table 2). The mechanical models used here were, in actuality, the sum of all the content (i.e., answers to questions posed) of all the structural categories.

In terms of these categories East Indians in Anamat can be described as: (1) being future oriented in time, (2) using village space for most of their interactions, but extending such space to include the villages of the members of their extended family, (3) being members of a joint family, (4) possessing a hierarchical authority system, (5) exchanging goods and services by using money as a medium of exchange, (6) exchanging women (indirectly) with joint families of other villages, (7) exchanging information by the use of the English language, (8) having supernatural, polytheistic sanctions and (9) having ''family improvement'' as a major goal.

The Negroes, in terms of the same categories, can be described as: (1) being present oriented in time, (2) using the village space for most of their interactions, but extending this space, mainly, by traveling to fétes in other communities where they interacted with friends, (3) being members of a matrifocal-consanguineal family, (4) possessing a loose, equalitarian authority system, (5) exchanging goods and services by using money and the sexual services of women as media of exchange, (6) exchanging women (indirectly) with other matrifocal families on a temporary basis, (7) exchanging information by the use of the English language, (8) having social sanctions and fatalism as major forms of sanctions and (9) considering ''being in a big féte'' as a major goal.

A comparison of the cultural systems of East Indians and Negroes in Anamat will show that they are extremely different (see Table 3). The content elements which are similar—use of the village for most interactions, use of money as a medium of exchange and use of English as a means of exchanging information—cannot be related to the shared mode of cultural ecological adaptation. The use of the village for the majority of the interactions of the Anamatians is very similar to village life in most cultures; it cannot therefore be related to the common adaptations of the East Indian and Negro peasants. The use of money as a medium of exchange and the use of the English language are also unrelated causally to cocoa and coffee peasant farming. The money (British West Indian dollar) and language used in Anamat is the

*Table 3   Models of East Indian and Negro Cultural Systems*

| points of reference | cultural systems | |
|---|---|---|
| | East Indian | Negro |
| Time | The future | The "now" |
| Space | Village; extended by permanent villages of kin | Village; extended by temporary féte centers |
| People | | |
| Kinship Unit | Joint family | Consanguineal-matrifocal |
| Associational Patterns | With family | With friends freely chosen |
| Authority | Patripotestal, rigid, hierarchical | Loose, equalitarian |
| Exchange | | |
| Goods and Services | Money medium of exchange | Money and sexual services media of exchange |
| Women | Indirect, permanent, between joint families | Indirect, temporary between matrifocal families |
| Symbols | English | English |
| Sanctions | Supernatural, polytheistic | Social (natural) plus fatalism |
| Goals | Family improvement | Féte |

same as that used all over Trinidad and is directly related to the fact that till recently this was a British colony.

Since the independent variable—a common form of cultural ecological adaptation—did not lead to a common core of culture shared by East Indians and Negroes, and since the cultural elements similar in the two groups cannot be related to the independent variable, the hypothesis proposed had to be rejected.

## Summary and Conclusions

A type of cultural ecological adaptation was considered in this study as an independent variable of change, and two cultural traditions treated as dependent variables. A situation was selected with natural controls to test the hypothesis that a shared mode of cultural ecological adaptation would lead East Indians and Negroes to show cultural similarities related to the shared mode of adaptation. The data collected necessitated the rejection of the hypothesis. It must be concluded then that the type of cultural ecological adaptation here considered is not a causal factor of change.

Julian Steward acknowledges that cultural ecological adaptations may at times not be deterministic, that they may at times allow considerable latitude or potential variation in socio-cultural types. "Where latitude is possible," writes Steward, *"historic factors* may determine the nature of the society" (italics inserted). That such historic factors are of minor importance for Steward may be deduced from his generalizations about cultural ecology as a determinant of change, and from the minimal treatment, in Steward's works, given to situations where environment allows latitude.

I would submit that what Steward calls "historical factors" are of far greater import and deserve far more attention than he would allow. Such historic factors are in part the cultural traditions of groups. The importance of culture as a persisting element in human life is both implicit in general anthropological usage and attested by various empirical studies.

Steward's model of change stipulates that (1) the cultural ecological adaptation is *the* independent variable and (2) at times the influence of this independent variable approaches zero (the environment *allows* latitude). A slight modification of the model would explain better the results obtained in Anamat. The fact that East Indians and Negroes do not share similar cultural forms may be more a factor of the *cultures* considered than the form of the ecological adaptation. That is, perhaps we are dealing with two cultural traditions which are highly resistant to change, two cultures that would tend towards non-change in any kind of environment.

For a more predictive model of change, cultural tradition must be given a less passive role to play. In a previous work which more completely described this study, I proposed a model of change utilizing four polar concepts, two cultural and two ecological. The concepts suggested were: *generalized* and *specialized cultures*, and *permissive* and *deterministic ecologies*. It was suggested that the cultural concepts be used in a fashion analogous to their usage in evolutionary biology. A *specialized culture* would be one whose cultural forms are functionally related to one and only one type of ecology. A *generalized culture* would be one whose cultural forms show no specific functional relationships to any type of ecology.

A *specialized culture* which changes its environment would tend to react in terms of either culture change or cultural extinction. A *generalized culture* which changes its environment may well survive with minimal cultural changes. In terms of these concepts the hypothesis here discussed may have been rejected because of (1) a permissive ecology, (2) generalized cultural systems, or (3) a combination of both. For clear-cut generalizations using these concepts, many additional studies relating culture and cultural ecology are required.

That limited conclusions are available from this experiment should not greatly concern us; rarely does an experiment in any science produce much more. Further, as Freedman, Hawley and associates have stated, the findings of a single experiment are much less likely to be conclusive in the social sciences than in physics and chemistry, and therefore "more man hours of work will probably be required in the development of theory in the former fields." What should be noted is that this kind of experimentation uses the process that is today considered "science." As James Conant writes: "Science emerges from the other progressive activities of man to the extent that new concepts arise from experiments and observations, and the new concepts in turn lead to further experiments and observations."

One final point: it was stated above that the data collected necessitated the rejection of the hypothesis tested. More accurately it should have been said that *within the limits of the experimental design, data collection and data analyzing techniques and the conceptual scheme used for this study, the hypothesis had to be rejected.* To make these limits minimally limiting we must attempt to improve the general methodology of our studies. A side effect of doing natural experiments, of no small importance to the science of man, is that of being forced by this technique to improve our models, to operationalize our concepts and to develop more accurate measuring devices.

*part 10*

# *Applied Anthropology*

# The Uses of Anthropology

## Sol Tax

*From Sol Tax (ed.),*
Horizons in
Anthropology. *Aldine
Publishing Company,
1964, pp. 248–257.
Copyright © 1964,
Aldine Publishing
Company. By permission
of the author, and the
publisher and
copyright holder.*

In this series of essays, nineteen of our younger anthropologists have described some of the directions of their thought and their research. In so doing they have given us some view of man and his works, past and present. They have also given us a view of the sciences of mankind which together we call anthropology. It will be recalled that in 1859 the leading anthropologist of France, Paul Broca called for just such a "general anthropology" to unite the several disciplines studying man. This has become now a reality, perhaps more in America than in any other land. Each of the nineteen anthropologists has described particular phenomena of biology and of culture; of archeology, linguistics, or ethnography; of politics, society, economics, religion, or the arts. All of us are specialists, but despite the diversity of our interests, we are nevertheless closely united in the science of man.

General anthropology today not only unites scholars of all of the disciplines which converge to study mankind; it also is the most world-wide of sciences, uniting scholars of mankind wherever they are. For over a century, anthropologists more than any other group of scientists have vigorously maintained personal communication, through congresses and correspondence and travel. . . . It is not surprising that we are the first to find a way to overcome the formidable political and financial barriers that isolate the pieces of a world otherwise so shrunken in size. Through the journal *Current Anthropology* we have developed a "communications coöperative" through which almost all of the anthropologists of the world ("wherever the post office reaches") are in constant contact, aware of who the others are and what they are doing.

The science of man thus marches on with new vigor. More and more scholars are trained;

the methods of study improve every year; the exchange of ideas and knowledge increases rapidly; and the results of our labors accumulate at an ever increasing rate. These results—some of the newest of which have been recounted in these essays—and the interesting discoveries just beyond the horizon, are sufficient justification for anthropology. The discovery of man and culture is one of the noblest endeavors of the human spirit. But we also live in a world beset with problems; thus it is a fair question whether anthropology also has something to offer to help to solve them.

Like other scientists, we anthropologists believe that our greatest service to mankind is in pursuit of knowledge. This is why society trains us. If we stop being scientists and scholars, what are we? So for the most part we pursue scientific problems, not practical or political or social problems. . . .

The question remains, then, as to how anthropology finds its uses.

One answer to this question might be suggested by the phrase "applied anthropology." Engineering and medicine are professions which can be said to apply the knowledge gained by the physical and the biological sciences. After this pattern, some have awaited the development of a profession that would apply the findings of anthropology. Indeed, since 1941 we have had in the United States a Society for Applied Anthropology which has attempted to build such a profession. Although this society has encouraged the use of anthropological knowledge by government and private organizations, a profession of applied anthropologists has not come into being, either in the United States or elsewhere. Anthropological knowledge is used by administrators and managers with the wit to use it. If they wish professional assistance, they must turn to anthropologists. Anthropologists indeed become involved in management and administration, just as in social work, education, and public health. These anthropologists are sometimes distinguished from those who work for museums, research institutions, and universities; but in contrast to analogous medical sciences, they do not form a class of practitioners. Instead, all anthropologists conceive of themselves both as pursuing academic research and as putting their knowledge to social use. If an outsider

seeks anthropological counsel, he must search out a genuine anthropologist; the anthropologist who gives him counsel will not dissociate himself from either the name of his discipline or his academic pursuits.

Anthropologists study man. Each anthropologist pursues a particular special study—this is what we mean by research—but all are actively interested in the whole study. We are highly specialized as social anthropologists, or human paleontologists, or linguists, for example, but we are equally general anthropologists. As we learn and we teach our specialties, we also learn from other specialists and we teach in a context which we share with them.

Here then we come to the second answer to the question. It is as teachers of the lessons of the whole of anthropology that we put our science to use; and we teach not only in the classroom, important as that is to most of us, but wherever we work and live. Anthropology has become for us a way of life, a set of values to pass on to whomever we touch: our parents and our children; our colleagues at work or play; our fellow citizens wherever they are. . . . The first attraction of anthropology is the very breadth of our subject matter—the study of mankind as a whole—which brings and holds us together, and gives us the special character which we then pass on. Man as an animal, as a population, as a species; man's behavior and his culture, and the behavior of his culture; the origin, characteristics, and distribution of the varieties of man, his language, social forms, ideas; man's genetics, prehistory and history, and the laws of history, which explain all of these in all time over the whole earth; comparative anatomy, personality, religion and ethics, law, sociology, and science; national characteristics, acculturation, socialization— all of these and whatever else may become relevant are parts of the grand problem which anthropologists have chosen to study.

The original anthropologists were anatomists, philologists, geographers, and antiquarians who met together in Paris, in London, in Moscow, or in New York to listen each to the others. It was their interest in the all-inclusive problem that drew them together and that made all-inclusiveness a virtue to be felt and extolled. The anatomists might come to read papers on craniometry to philologists and to students of customs, and to listen in turn to papers on chipped-stone industries, on grammar or on folklore. Those first anthropologists surely contributed not only breadth, but a great tolerance for variety in subject matter and in techniques of study. They established these as values for which anthropology ever since has tended to select.

It is not surprising that anthropology should characteristically form a society of scholars open to new techniques, tools, ideas, and men. The tools brought in range from the "law of uniformity" from geology to a Freudian model, or a Carbon-fourteen dating from chemistry. We have freely adopted, reinterpreted, and made our own whatever has appeared useful to our varied problems. People of other fields are drawn in because they are wanted and needed. But if men are not so drawn in, their ideas still are. Sometimes whole new fields of study are added, like culture and personality, but of course all that are added are new answers to the heterogeneous problems already there. Anthropology always has been as broad in conception as it is possible to be; in wandering correspondingly widely for its data and tools, it absorbs into the tradition of the discipline those new men with special ideas who accept the breadth of anthropology.

The breadth, eclecticism, and openness of boundaries of our subject matter are associated not only with an unusual tolerance for a variety of subjects and tools, but also for surprising ambiguity. It is not possible to be (as we say) "wholistic," to take into account all at once all aspects of a problem if we also require a clear structure. Given a choice between fully understanding one piece of a whole, but not in context, or only half understanding a larger whole, we generally prefer the second. This choice is related to our predilection for dealing with the real world. Unlike economists and others who deal with abstractions comfortably, we reflect our origins in natural history by feeling more comfortable the closer we are to nature, and to substantive rather than to theoretical or methodological problems.

The original interest of anthropologists in "other people" is also related to our concern with the reality of man through all time and space. Knowing mankind is to know all varieties of mankind; knowing people means seeing them as people. This is one source of our "liberal" view of other peoples and cultures. When it is recalled that the original Ethnological Society of Paris was formed by members of the Aborigines Protection Association, it is not surprising that anthropologists have generally taken the side of the oppressed. But it is not only tradition, and the circumstance of our founding, that lends us our character. Our tradition takes us out to study different peoples and cultures; though we see them in the broadest context, it is living people whom we come to know. It is because we live with them and come to know them that we learn from them. We keep our liberal tradition because we are the pupils of other peoples. Even if the "other peoples" are only archeological remains (or even not "peoples" at all, but baboons or gorillas!) our point of reference is still other living peoples and cultures, whose accomplishments give us humility and perspective and make us, too, "other" people.

It is precisely our tradition of general anthropology that makes it possible not only to use specialized knowledge, but also to recognize the relevance of new specialties. The question is not whether any piece of specialized knowledge is directly useful, but how the insights of general anthropology can be put to the service of society. Hence that second answer to the question posed: we serve by passing on to others the point of view and the understandings that we have ourselves gained. We have learned and we teach that the peoples of our species are equally human, thus equally able to achieve what is great and what is base. We have learned and we teach that the different peoples have from the very beginning of time developed particular ways and particular values; it is part of being commonly human to differ not simply as individuals, but systematically as communities of individuals. We teach our concept of culture and our tolerance of cultures. We have learned and we teach that a people values its identity, and resists changes which threaten it; that nobody but a people itself can judge what is important in its values, and what is threatening. Thus we teach the wisdom of discovering rather than assuming what other people want and fear, an undertaking the more difficult and the more important as the cultural difference is greater. These lessons we can teach in the classroom, on the lecture platform, in books, and hope that they will become part of a liberal education to be internalized by the many.

What else? When we are asked, we can go farther specifically to influence programs which deal with other peoples. Now it becomes important to distinguish among the kinds of people in a nation or in a community. We have learned that at an operating level we deal not with a culture at all but with many cultures; not even with the many cultures but rather with groups of people who are influenced not only by their cultures but by their position and by their interests as they perceive them. The programs in which we become involved concern what are now called "new nations." A new nation characteristically has an elite culturally perhaps less separated than we are from its tribes and its villagers, but with interests often opposed to theirs. Anthropologists generally see the problem from the village point of view, the administrators of programs, from that of the governing elite with whom they deal. The problem is now not one simply of teaching what we have learned; to be helpful means to become political, and at this point most scientists properly leave the task to others.

Suppose, however, that we stay with the problem: even now—at a time when there are differences of interest and perspectives to which education is not an effective answer —how can knowledge derived from the study of man be deliberately put to the service of man?

"The service of man" is a large phrase. If it could be limited to, say, the service of one's own country, the problem would be more manageable. The country—any nation—is governed by people—in specific Departments, Bureaus, Committees, and as administrators; the scientist simply places his knowledge at the service of one of these, and his problems are resolved. He becomes a technician, an instrument. Indeed the capitals of nations are crowded with social scientists who do just this. This is not to say that they are weak, immoral, dishonorable. Often they will have personal points of view to press: recently I met a young economist working with the Alliance for Progress, in Washington, who described how the younger men in the agency were fighting to change a philosophy inherited from an older agency. They obviously were passionately working from the inside and probably effecting policy more than if they operated on the outside as independent critics. . . . The anthropologist who puts his knowledge to the service of his country need not therefore lose his integrity or his freedom of action, although he may well lose his patience. The difference between serving one's conscience and one's boss; one's boss and one's country; one's country and mankind—the difference in each case is neither clear nor absolute. It is easy to rationalize one's own behavior—whatever it may be—or to blame the next anthropologist.

It is characteristic of the anthropologist that if he does continue his work of education into what is close to the political realm, he acts as an independent agent, taking upon himself the ultimate responsibility for satisfying his conscience in terms of the obligations he feels toward his colleagues and toward his fellow men. It may be because anthropologists cannot comfortably have clients or work for others that a class of applied anthropologists does not develop. The scientist has, as Broca said, but one master, the truth as he learns it, and to teach it requires also the freedom of the academic profession.

Let us accept the independence of the anthropologist. Supposing him to be a research scientist serving only the one master and responsible only to his conscience and to his colleagues, let us give him this problem: What are the circumstances in which a community of people achieves its own goals, or is on the contrary frustrated? Assuming that there is basic agreement on what is wanted, communities of people still fall short of their goals. This happens whether the community one has in mind is a modern city unable to keep itself clean and orderly; or a nation unable to control the growth of a strangling bureaucracy; or even the faculty of a University unable to protect its academic freedom. The problem is one for the tools as well of political science, economics, and sociology; but it is the sort of general problem which anthropologists characteristically tackle, borrowing what tools we need. We would think of beginning the anthropological research in a small community of a culture different from our own, since this is our special method of objectifying the problem; but we would hope to end up with some general understanding of the processes involved. Should we succeed in learning how any community of people can better achieve its own goals, we would have put anthropology to important use.

The method of research that is suited to this problem, however, appears to violate the canon that the anthropologist should not become involved in public affairs. In the three or four cases where the problem has been successfully pursued, the anthropologists found that they had to interfere quite deliberately in social processes. To study such a problem requires helping the people of the community to discover their goals; but since there are competing goals and wants and forces in the society, this cannot be a simple educational process. (If it were so simple, there would be no problem to begin with.) So the anthropologist takes a special position in the community and becomes an actor as well as an observer. He helps people to try various ways of discovering their goals and the ways of achieving them which suit their own cultural norms and their own self-perceived interests. One well-known example of this sort of research is Allen Holmberg's work at Vicos in Peru, where the researchers from Cornell University had to lease a plantation and become the *patrón* of the serf-like Indian community in order to bring the community into a position where it could act freely for itself. The community responded remarkably; and Holmberg's experiment proved an important point not only for anthropology but also for the people of Vicos and Peru, for all others in similar circumstances, and for the policymaking powers in the world. Similarly the University of Chicago's experiment in helping a small community of North American Indians to resolve its problems has led to understandings not only about American Indian problems in general, but about those of other population enclaves like the Maori of New Zealand or tribal peoples in India or Africa. The general lesson that they will adjust to the modern world when their identity and their own cultural values are not threatened is important because such threats may not really be necessary. The understandings gained by this method of research by the anthropologists of Cornell and Chicago could probably not have come in any other way. The results are proving themselves in an understanding of the problems of new nations, of North American cities, even of the organization of universities. Indeed, the unique community of anthropologists of the world that I mentioned as being now in existence was helped into being directly by what was learned from American Indians. The same understanding may some day help the peoples of the world to achieve the common goal of peace.

This new method of research . . . is often called "action anthropology." It does not fit the distinction frequently made between pure and applied research. It requires the intellectual and the political independence that one associates with a pure researcher; it depends upon university and foundation connections and support rather than those of a client or government. But it also requires that the anthropologist leave his ivory tower and that without losing his objectivity he enter into some world of affairs which becomes for the time being his laboratory. But since we are ethical men, and our laboratory is a community of people who are not to be sacrificed for our purposes or for science or even for some larger humanity, the anthropologist who undertakes such research is selected from those who are willing and able to take on unusual burdens and risks. Like a physician with his patients, he accepts the problems of a whole community as his own problems. Since he can never be wholly successful, he must be prepared for disappointments and frustrations, without even the satisfaction of blaming others besides himself. It is no wonder that this method of research has not become common, or indeed fully accepted as legitimate. The stakes are high and the game dangerous; but action anthropology is nevertheless quite in the tradition and spirit of general anthropology, and promises to provide the best demonstration of its meaning and its use.

# *Anthropological Engineering: Its Use to Administrators*

## *Eliot D. Chapple*

If these are the concerns of the practical man —first, the maintenance of equilibrium in a system, whether it is made up of one institution such as a factory or an aggregate of institutions as in the political system, and, second, the restoration of it after a crisis— then the anthropologist is specially equipped to assist him. The anthropologist has at his command a science of human relations, crude though it may be at present, and he has developed principles and techniques which are specially fitted for just such problems. On questions of a technological nature, he is not trained to give judgment; he is not primarily concerned with the comparative efficiency of two methods of farming, nor with the value of a new system of cost accounting. What he can do is to predict what will happen to the relations of people when such methods are introduced. It is the administrator's business to make the decision, weighing the evidence furnished by the anthropologist and the technical expert.

By using anthropological methods, the administrator can attain a control in the field of human relations comparable to that which he already has in the field of costs and production. He can understand and estimate the effects of change, and see what steps have to be taken to modify his organization or to restore it to a state of balance. He can do this both through acquiring a knowledge of anthropological principles, and by using anthropologists to make analyses of existing situations. In short, the administrator has available what may properly be called anthropological engineering. It is based upon scientific principles and it therefore produces workable results.

*From Anthropological Engineering: Its Use to Administrators.* Applied Anthropology, *Vol. 2, No. 2, 1943, pp. 28–32. By permission of the author and the publisher.*

But anthropological engineering in the proper sense, involving the use of quantitative methods of analysis, has only been developed during the last three or four years. The use of anthropological methods and principles by the administrator goes back over a decade. There have been three areas of development: in industry, in political administration in this country and in England, and in the work of private charitable and philanthropic agencies.

## The History of the Use of Anthropology in Modern Problems

One of the most notable applications of anthropological methods is the research program carried out by the Western Electric Company, Hawthorne Works, Chicago, particularly in its later phases. Here in the bank wiring observation room the first study ever made of a group in industry working under actual operating conditions was based directly upon anthropological procedures. As a result of this study a system of personnel counselling was instituted by which an interviewer (counsellor) was placed in each department. This individual's job is to keep a continuous check on the human relations situation in the department and to build up with the workers a relationship in which they come freely to him to make complaints, to tell their troubles, or to make suggestions. Since the direction of activity in a hierarchical institution like a factory proceeds from supervisor to supervisee, the counsellor acts as a stabilizing force, whose job is to maintain or restore the equilibrium of the workers by providing an outlet for activity in the other direction. When administrative changes are planned, or when difficulties are encountered in the organization, the research staff, though its counsellors, has available a continuous record of the situation in the affected department. By this means, the management is able to make adjustments in its policies in the light of the underlying system of relations in the factory.

In a number of other industries anthropologists have been utilized from time to time, although ordinarily under the label of personnel or industrial relations experts on account of the current prejudice against the name anthropology. . . . The present author and Professor C. M. Arensberg of the Massachusetts Institute of Technology have developed and applied quantitative methods to the study of human relations in industry which are too technical to discuss here. Some aspects of these methods will be mentioned a little later in connection with the Penncraft project.

In the field of political administration, the first use of anthropological methods was in England in the field of colonial administration. Here the anthropologist, who was merely concerned with recording the behaviors of primitive people, was able to be of service to the administrator in preventing crude misunderstandings and hasty political activity. As early as the end of the last century, anthropological surveys of colonial peoples were instituted, but only since 1929, under the urging of Professor Malinowski, did any realization of the part anthropology might play as an aid to the administrator become common. Most of the work has been done in connection with the International Institute of African Languages and Cultures, and their publications provide a convenient summary of much of this work. In 1935, an interesting collaboration between an anthropologist and an administrator was undertaken in Tanganyika. It was, however, largely of the factual type earlier mentioned. Most of the English work is of this character, and is only suggestive in that it shows the direction in which anthropology is going.

In the United States, anthropology has been in use by the Office of Indian Affairs for some time, but the most significant use has been in the Department of Agriculture. Anthropology in the Indian Service is, of course, comparable to the use made of it in colonial administration in England. Anthropologists have traditionally been concerned with primitives, and their knowledge of the Indian naturally made them useful under an administration interested in producing a satisfactory adjustment for the Indian rather than in merely turning them into white men by executive fiat. Anthropological procedures have been of considerable utility in the field of Indian Education, where it has been realized by the administrators that the educational program was definitely failing to produce results. The Indians were unable to make a satisfactory adjustment off the reservation, though their training in the Indian schools was primarily directed to that end. Several studies by Dr. G. McGregor and Mr. A. Sterner illustrate the type of problem faced by the Indian Service and the kind of recommendations made in this field.

In the work of the Department of Agriculture, under the leadership of M. L. Wilson, we find for the first time the use of anthropological methods and principles as an aid to administrators not primarily concerned with the so-called primitives. Their efforts have taken at least two directions: first in the use of anthropological methods and procedures in rehabilitation and resettlement under the direction of Dr. John H. Provinse of the Bureau of Agricultural Economics, Department of Agriculture, and second, in the program, still in the process of formulation, of using anthropology as an aid in understanding the way of life of the American farmer. It is now clearly understood that "the farmer" does not represent a single system, duplicating itself all over the country, but rather that there are many different systems based upon the type of agriculture and differences in the regional situation. These cultural differences in techniques and activities are recognized by the Department officials as the agents which bring about different systems of relations and different adjustments between individuals.

The last field in which anthropology is in use is in the work of private charitable and philanthropic institutions. I wish particularly to discuss the research connected with the Penncraft Resettlement project of the American Friends Service Committee, with which I am associated because it presents several points of interest for the administrator. It illustrates in a simple way the use of anthropological engineering methods which I have mentioned, and is a good indicator of the direction in which anthropology is moving.

At this project, in the depressed coal mining areas of Wstern Pennsylvania, fifty families have been settled on a two hundred acre lot. The intention of the Friends is to develop initiative and cooperation among the homesteaders, and ultimately to produce a self-supporting and cooperating community. It is hoped that the experience learned from this project will be applicable to resettlement projects generally throughout the country.

Mr. F. L. W. Richardson, Jr., and I had to estimate objectively the degree to which the community of fifty families were developing initiative and cooperation, qualities desired by the Friends. The following steps were taken: (1) Simple measurements at successive periods were made on the system of relations developed by the homesteaders and the management. These measurements included the amount, frequency and order of the interactions in each relation, measures I haven't the time to discuss further. (2) From these periodic samples estimates of the amount of change in each relation and in the system as a whole were made, and the reason for the change determined; *i.e.*, which of the four areas, environment, technology, personnel, or outside institutions was responsible. (3) From the analysis of these periodic samples, we then set up a tentative blueprint of the kind of equilibrium which could be developed from the existing situation, which would fulfill the objectives of the Friends, defined in our terms. (4) The blueprint then becomes the basis for recommendations by the investigators, of changes in administrative policies; it also provides the measuring stick by which the success of these policies can be estimated. (5) The recommendations have to be framed in terms of specific cultural techniques which can be introduced to produce increased cooperation or initiative; they include analyses of proposed policies to see how they contribute to the development of the kind of community desired, and suggestions as to the ways in which the techniques of getting a living, such as farming or manufacturing, can be adapted to the requirements of the individuals in the community.

The Penncraft project thus illustrates the importance of anthropological methods in another way. Much of the analysis has to be based upon determinations of the effect on the community of the techniques and activities of getting a living, the geographical locations of houses, and the environmental limitations on agricultural production. Since administrative policy is to a large degree based upon the analysis of these situations, the task of the anthropologist is to show the precise way in which these cultural activities affect and control human relations. For example, in answering the question of what is the best way of getting a cash income, the choice of any given occupation must also be evaluated from the point of view of its effect upon the equilibrium of the group.

## How the Anthropologist Can Prescribe Remedial Changes in Policy

The anthropologist's third premise, his recognition of the part played by the techniques and activities in the relations of individuals, is of great value to the administrator. Due to the anthropologist's interest in culture, he is able to suggest how changes necessary to stabilize the relationships in a group can be brought about by introducing specific techniques to which the individuals have been or can become conditioned. Thus if it is desired to bring certain individuals together more frequently, he can suggest how this may be done; he can also show how the changes required by new techniques will upset the existing equilibrium and what ought to be done about it. Such changes in technical activities have to be predicated upon the analysis of the relations of individuals, and I have elsewhere suggested how these methods can be used as a basic tool in mental therapy. The extension of these methods to administrative work is much simpler. Since the organization ordinarily requires the performance of a number of associated techniques, administrators do not have to improvise them in an artificial environment as the therapist is compelled to do.

## Conclusion

It has recently been the fashion among editors and scholars to deplore the changes brought about in human relations by science and technology and to swear that salvation can only be attained if we turn back to the humanities, and have less rather than more science. It seems to me that the reverse is true, and that it is the ignoring of the place of science in the field of human relations which has caused our difficulties.

Throughout this paper, my remarks could be taken as an answer to this proposition. In discussing what anthropology is and what it can do, we have seen that changes in technology produce their results by disturbing the equilibrium of individuals and groups. If we are to keep technology from running away with us, this can only be done by using an-

thropological methods, that is, by utilizing the science of human relations. But if this is to come about, administrators and others working in this field will have to use anthropology not merely in accomplishing a desired objective; they must also learn to formulate their objectives in terms of known principles of anthropology.

Ordinarily, anthropologists are called in only after the administrator has decided on his policy. Very often this policy is not devised to utilize the existing system of relations, but to do something about a problem which is never clearly defined. A good example of this is to be found in the field of resettlement. It is customary to try to rehabilitate an area by setting up new communities, and selecting its members without regard for their existing systems of relations. Under almost any conditions, only a small proportion of the people can be so resettled; except in rare instances outside the government where work exchange methods can be used, it is very costly. The development of a technology by which a cash income can be obtained is very difficult owing to the economic influence of the depressed area, in which it is located. Moreover, such a method breaks down the existing institutions of the people, it breaks up and separates leaders and their followers, and instead of utilizing what there is, a new system has to be built up over a long period of time before any equilibrium is reached. It may be that this is sometimes necessary, but anthropological considerations certainly suggest that it would be considerably cheaper per person rehabilitated, and much more effective, to adjust relations within existing settlements. In this way, the already operating institutions could be made the basis for change, and it would then be possible to take up the problem of improving the economic institutions of the area as a system rather than nibble away at one small part of it. By defining the problem and the policy in the light of anthropological principles, a more effective result will be obtained than if the anthropologist is merely employed as a trouble-shooter, a specialist who can make useful suggestions after the administrator has got himself into difficulties.

Moreover, the use of anthropological method and principles enables the administrator to estimate the state of equilibrium in the system of human relations in the institution for which he is responsible, and make such adjustments as are necessary to make it more stable. By instituting methods of control through periodic sampling of the human relations and thus determining the precise nature of the adjustments at any given time, he is able to anticipate and avert disturbances. Through such methods, he will be able to perfect his organization and bring about a more satisfactory adjustment for all the individuals who compose it.

But this can be done only if the organization is not merely brought into a state of equilibrium in its internal relations, but if also it is part of a larger system, itself in equilibrium. Here again anthropological principles have to be taken into consideration. A stable equilibrium for an individual or a group is one in which adjustments to change occur within the limits of tolerance of the system. If an individual, or an institution, or a society is to withstand the effect of external forces, the compensatory changes brought about by the impression of a force on the system, must not throw it into a prolonged state of disequilibrium. A democratic society, in anthropological terms, is one in which the system of relations provides habitual channels for such compensatory movements, and thus for the maintenance or restoration of the individual's equilibrium. The administrator issues orders to and controls the activities of the administered, but the latter, through their representative or directly at hearings, conferences, and so on, are able in turn to act upon the administrator. Where this kind of balance does not obtain, serious maladjustments of personality occur and compensatory movements take a violent form. If our society is to move more completely toward a democratic system, the engineers of human relations will have to devise methods by which all our institutions are made more efficient, more adjustable to change, and more permeable to suggestions from all its members. In so doing, they will be able to bring about a society where increased technical efficiency is coincidental with increased human adjustment.

*selection 62*

# Anthropology as an Applied Science

*H. G. Barnett*

I

. . . A concern over the future of applied anthropology led, in 1951, to an experiment in the use of anthropology in the administration of the Micronesians who are under the jurisdiction of the United States. At that time seven anthropologists held civil service positions with the governing agency, the Trust Territory of the Pacific Islands, one anthropologist being associated with each of the six regional divisions of the area and one with the Headquarters

*From* Human Organization, *Vol. 17, No. 1, 1958, pp. 9–11. Copyright 1958, The Society for Applied Anthropology. By permission of the author, and the publisher and copyright holder.*

Staff of the Commissioner for the Territory. All had been employed on a so-called job description. As it happened, this was a very permissive professional charter laying out broad areas of activity with respect to research, advice, and program evaluation. It was positively phrased and was so inclusive in its implications that no generally understood boundary existed between the duties of the anthropologists and other personnel concerned with the same problems. A more objectionable feature of the situation, as it was viewed in the latter part of 1951, was the engagement of the anthropologist in the policy-making process at both the Headquarters and the District levels. This often produced differences of opinion, based upon what was considered to be good or bad for the Micronesians, with the views of the anthropologist —avowedly a specialist on human behavior— at stake.

In order to eliminate this source of confusion, as well as to lay out an area for scientific contribution, it was decided to restrict the anthropologist's participation in decision making to the submission of data for which he could show evidence, and to relieve him of any duty requiring the implementation of a decision. He was thus to be treated as a technical specialist and not as an administrative officer. He was to accept directives and refer policy-making to his executive associates, confining his efforts to social, economic, and other analyses which would enable those officers to arrive at their decision or take into account the consequences of their past actions for future determinations.

This generalized statement of the anthropologist's role in the Trust Territory administration was ultimately particularized and a rationale given for its premises and safeguards in a memorandum issued by the Commissioner in 1952. The key assertions in this document were as follows:

1. Since anthropologists are concerned with collecting information about, and maintaining an intimate knowledge of, the indigenous cultures of the area, they should be in a position to contribute to effective administration in three principal ways:

a. Advising on the implementation of departmental i.e., educational, economic, judicial, etc. projects and on the solution of problems arising from such implementation. . . .
b. Evaluating the success of particular departmental programs in the light of their objectives. . . .
c. Independently formulating and implementing researches of theoretical interest to the anthropological profession and/or of practical importance to the administration. . . .

2. The anthropologist has the obligation to collect, in a reliable and systematic way, information that is useful to the administrator. This obligation cannot be met adequately if he assumes or is called upon to assume, the role of an agent of control or enforcement. Apart from the question of job training, there is the important fact that the anthropologist must maintain, insofar as possible in the eyes of the people, a neutral position with respect to administrative policy and action. Anything which tends to identify him as a government official invested with the power to impress his ideas detracts by so much from his usefulness as a source of unbiased information, because it jeopardizes confidential relationships with his informants and frequently involves him in factional struggles. . . .

3. In line with the observations contained in the last section, it is desirable that the anthropologist be accorded the freedom and the facilities to interview informants under the most favorable conditions. It is to be expected that at times information will be given him in confidence. Allowance should be made for this in local housing and office arrangements wherever possible. . . .

4. . . . It is evident that the anthropologist's familiarity with, and his acceptance by, the people [Micronesians] of his district give him knowledge that is otherwise unobtainable by outsiders. . . . From both an ethical and a practical standpoint, he is obligated to preserve confidences. . . .

II

While the announced purpose of this work plan was to promote more effective cooperation between administrators and anthropologists, its significance was more far-reaching than that. Behind it lay the conviction that anthropology is or can be an applied science.

Under it lay the premise that science can demonstrate means but not ends. Supporting it was the understanding that the anthropologist must confine himself to statements of fact and probability, leaving to the administrator the responsibility for making policy decisions based on those facts and probabilities.

It is appreciated that these determinants of the role of anthropology in Trust Territory administration are not widely accepted as guides to action by anthropologists or other social scientists. They derive by analogy from the characteristics of the applied physical sciences. Since on that count their validity may be debatable, and since they raise questions of truth or necessity, it may be well to elaborate on them.

As to the possibility of a scientific application of anthropological knowledge, it must be admitted at once that the findings and the constructs of academic anthropology are rather sterile for this purpose. For one thing, as Gouldner has emphasized, theoretical science of any kind can rarely be translated directly into practice. At the least it must be adapted; and in many instances it must be modified to accommodate empirically derived concepts. Beyond that, applied science must develop its own insights and methods. This is especially true of applied social science, for its primary concern is with change, whereas theoretical sociology and anthropology deal with structures which are inherently static even though one is supposed to flow into or become another. Serious attention to the results of empirical studies of cultural change cannot fail to reveal that much has been learned or can be learned about dynamic regularities in human behavior. It is not too much to say that we are often in a position to predict and control such changes, granted the ordinary limitations imposed upon any applied science; namely, the demands for rigor in analysis, attention to specificity, stipulation of conditions, and conclusions stated as probabilities.

## III

There is yet another reason for the valid objection that traditional anthropology offers little insight into practical problems, and it is intimately related to the first. In spite of its acknowledgments of, and gestures toward, psychology and psychiatry it does not incorporate their insights into its contributions to the study of man. It satisfies itself with abstract forms and hypostatized forces rather than with human beings and their motivations. Presumably an unapplied anthropology can operate with this separation of man from his works; but the student of change, observing human beings reacting to the stresses of novelty, cannot long remain insensitive to its artificiality and its unproductivity. It is difficult to escape the conclusion that human behavior is a socio-psychological phenomenon to the understanding of which psychology and psychiatry have quite as much to offer as does anthropology. A conjunction of these disciplines, and others, to form a social instead of a departmental science, holds considerable promise for the future. That the effort can be significant and useful is evident from the formulations attempted by such workers as Leighton and Mead.

The anthropologist seeking to apply his knowledge must further beware of the illusion that science means certainty. Modern science does not state its propositions as absolutes. All generalizations and the predictions based upon them are conditional and probability statements. It is true that the most assured social scientist is an amateur in forecasting and control as compared with the laboratory physicist or the engineer. He has much more in common with the meteorologist, who must take daily and hourly readings and even then refuse to forecast the weather for point X at time Y except within wide limits and when subject to stipulated conditions.

The course of human affairs runs no more smoothly than does the weather, but social scientists know more about its turbulencies and their causes than most people are willing to grant. There seems to be no reason for assuming that a human being is more difficult to understand or control than is an atom. In all science, including that of things social, it is the prediction of causes, not effects, that is risky. Under natural conditions —that is, conditions which are not externally manipulated—the conjunction of events that is necessary and sufficient to produce another event has itself such a complex of antecedents that it is rarely possible to do more than to say that it is likely to occur. For this reason, in anthropology as in physics, a regularity, hence a prediction, is properly phrased in the conditional tense: if A happens, then B is likely to follow.

Anthropological forecasting in the Trust Territory was not pretentious and it was not spectacular. It was undertaken with hesitation and with full realization of its fallibility, but in the conviction that any rational guide to procedure is better than one based on preconception, ignorance, or dedication. It was replete with qualifications: a particular sequence *could* occur or *might* occur; it is more likely or less likely, possible, or expectable. The reasoning which produced such projections rested on analogy with what is known to have occurred elsewhere or at another time among the same people under comparable conditions. Sometimes the result was nothing more than an objectively organized compilation of common sense; but even this can be valuable in an emotionally charged atmosphere.

Scientific activity, like any other, is governed by a set of values. In himself, the scientist prizes open-mindedness, caution, and detachment. In his work he strives for rigor, evidence, thoroughness, and proof. Whether he is right is less important than whether his methodology is appropriate to its purposes; that is, whether it answers the questions asked in ways which can be verified by others. Adherence to this set of values is the result of a choice—opposed, for example, to reliance upon answers by doctrine or intuition—and it is a preference which cannot be supported by employment of scientific methods. It is true that values can be studied scientifically; so can science itself. In any case, though, the method operates under the dictates of its supraordinate value system representing ends which may be accepted or rejected—by appeal to other values—but cannot be shown to be true or false.

## IV

Just as science cannot turn upon itself and validate its goals, neither can it justify other goals or procedures except by granting the values which dictate them. It can grade, rate, and evaluate alternatives and preferences, granting the ends they seek as givens; but it cannot evaluate those ends except by reference to other ends accepted as givens. In short, science can deal with means and not ends, but neither ends nor means are absolutes. What is an end in one value framework, may become a means or an instrument in another. There are scientific means to save human lives, but no scientific justification for them—unless we can demonstrate that they are means to some other granted end, such as happiness, which may in its turn be demonstrated to be a means to social solidarity or some other unquestioned value, and so on indefinitely. The suitability of means to relative ends can therefore be demonstrated. So can the wisdom of a choice between alternative means; but again, only under the command of a scientifically extrinsic criterion operating as a value. There are costly as well as inexpensive means to save life, healthful as well as unhealthful avenues to happiness.

The crux of the matter is that science can ascertain properties; it cannot discover or adjudicate their virtues. It can rate them in terms of stated criteria, not in terms of their desirability. Its findings cannot be translated into good and evil. That requires the imposition of a scale of moral values about the validity of which there can be debate but no proof. In Kant's terms, science deals with hypothetical not categorical imperatives.

The allocation of policy making to the Trust Territory administrator arose from the desire not only, or even primarily, to establish effective collaboration with the anthropologist, but even more to ensure a division of function based on competence and acknowledged responsibility. The administrator, by the terms of his employment, was expected to make decisions concerning Micronesian welfare and to assume responsibility for their consequences. Since there could be no scientific determination of the ends to be sought in this decision-making process, it followed that the anthropologist, acting as a scientist, was not professionally qualified, nor was he charged with the responsibility, to definite the purposes of government. It may be argued that the administrator was not qualified either, but this is a matter of opinion and cannot be demonstrated except, again on certain value assumptions. In any case, the argument does not qualify the anthropologist, for it does not follow that those who know a people best know what is best for them.

This division of function did not preclude expressions of opinion or value judgments by the Trust Territory anthropologist. Indeed, he was often urged to state his opinions, and probably offered them more often than he was asked. It did place on him the obligation to make clear when he was expressing a personal taste, a preference, or a prejudice with acknowledgment of the values from which it stemmed. Contrary to the contention sometimes voiced by social scientists, this obligation did not require a schizophrenic personality any more than do the demands on a man to act both as a father and a physicist, or a biologist and a Democrat. It does ask that men claim no more distinction for their preferences than they are entitled to as social philosophers. And it is a safeguard against the prevalent view that anthropologists are just another brand of intellectual with an axe to grind.

## V

This brings us to the heart of the matter as far as the utilization of anthropology is concerned. Quite apart from the question of whether we should aspire to the ideal of an objective treatment of our data, there is the fact that the anthropologist is not widely regarded as an authority on human affairs and his reputation in this respect does not show evidence of increasing. Even more important, however, can be the damaging effects of a reaction against a discipline of knowledge which offers opinions under the panoply of science. Today, when opportunities for non-academic employment are multiplying, this prospect might well be a matter for serious reflection.

This leads to a more serious question which will not have escaped the reader; namely, do we want a rigorous science of human behavior? And if so, are we prepared to deal with its consequences? We share this dilemma with the physicists, but are more deeply involved; for we propose to understand and, by so much, to provide a basis for the human direction of human affairs. The decision weighs heavily because science, any science, and its applications are neutral instruments; and they can operate for the good or ill of mankind, depending on the value system of the man who puts them into play.

*selection 63*

# *Interventionism and Applied Science in Anthropology*

## *Lisa R. Peattie*

### I

. . . "Applied anthropology" and "action anthropology" as the terms are now used seem to be new. If intervention and taking-up causes are as old as organized anthropology, the notion of scientific intervention seems on the whole to be a more modern phenomenon in the profession. The members of the Ethnological Society in working for the abolitionist

*From* Human Organization, *Vol. 17, No. 1, 1958, pp. 4–8. Copyright 1958, The Society for Applied Anthropology. By permission of the author, and the publisher and copyright holder.*

cause, seem to have been expressing an interest which they naturally felt *as anthropologists* in the native peoples, but they do not seem to have felt that their work for the cause was in itself an application of general scientific principle to solve particular practical problems either. "Applied anthropology" in this sense is thought of as the general moral and practical enlightenment which anthropology can provide men in considering the problems of their day. . . .

Applied anthropology as it appears today may be looked upon as having two roots. One is the element of concern and of special knowledge arising out of the peculiar position of the anthropologist. He is a member of the western peoples who have been rapidly making themselves rulers of the world, and whose way of life is still sweeping over the other peoples. He nevertheless knows the native peoples in the path of that civilization as informants and friends, and, to a degree unique among westerners, he sees the natives as having moral systems, esthetic sensibilities, and ways of life complete and proper in their own terms. His own society will accept this special concern because his special knowledge is useful to that society, trying to cope with the job of dealing with all sorts of people of different ways of life. The anthropologist is thus the man in the middle, and he tends to take on himself the job of speaking for the native to the west, and at the same time interpreting and filtering the forces of the west down to the native. This root—represented in those early ethnological societies—is the older of the two.

On the other hand, applied anthropology may be seen as part of a general movement of social science away from the humanistic studies, and toward the model of the physical and biological sciences. So anthropology strives for a higher degree of predictive precision, and sees as a goal the possibility of scientific management of social situations. It becomes possible to think of anthropology as doing more than giving men a certain enlightened perspective on themselves and their problems in the way that Brinton and Boas thought. Now we imagine the applied anthropologist as curing the ills of society through science, as the doctor of medicine uses science to cure the ills of the body.

If modern applied anthropology and action anthropology are looked upon as springing from these two roots, one sees that there is at times a tendency of one or another root to appear the dominant one, and even at times for there to be marked lines of cleavage, of incompatibility, between these two aspects of anthropology in action. The first root arises out of the special interest of the anthropologist in native and minority peoples. The second affirms the possibility and urges the value of disinterested consideration of social phenomena—as a biologist might view protozoa on his microscope slide. Action anthropology is in part an attempt to treat interest disinterestedly. Applied anthropology tries to move back and forth between value-interest and disinterested consideration of relevant fact. Anthropology in action is suspended between these two poles and swings between them.

## II

There are many different kinds of applied or action anthropologists, and as situations vary, even more kinds of applied or action anthropology.

In the first place, the action and scientific components of the hyphenated creature are variously divided. At one extreme, there is the kind of applied anthropology represented by a considerable part of research in Africa, in which the anthropologist is supported by government funds in order to do what is essentially pure research relevant to administration. The anthropologist's job is here to describe the cultural reality with which the administrator must deal; he tells the administrator what the golden stool means to the Ashanti, or describes the native legal system of the Tswana. In other instances, the anthropologist has a closer relationship to the taking of action and the exercise of power; he may be commissioned to find the facts with regard to some particular problem with which administrators are to take action— ritual murders in Basutoland, or the functioning of medical services in Latin America. Still more closely allied to action are those anthropologists who become regular, specialized members of the administrative group, with a mandate like that of the Staff Anthropologist in the Trust Territory to "recommend practical measures to achieve given program objectives." From this role it is not far to the single individual who combines under one hat the roles of scientific observer and actor, whether anthropologist turned administrator, administrator with anthropological training, or "action anthropologist" with a diffuse personalized power ("influence") not derived from a role in a formal managerial system.

Applied anthropologists have also variously conceived the balance between science and action in their work. Applied anthropology has been thought of as scientific experiment, with the interests of the subjects enhanced as well as protected: as social service using the conceptual apparatus of anthropology; and (as in the Fox program) a blend in which "helping" and learning-from are equal goals, inextricably blended. But even the most "scientistic" of the applied anthropologists seem to worry a good deal about the ethics of their operations.

There have been a number of instances in which anthropologists have worked among people of their own general culture, in ways which are more or less "applied" science. The field of "anthropology in industry," the community studies made for the Bureau of Agricultural Economics, and some more recent studies in the mental health field are examples. But it is still true that the largest part of the situations in which applied anthropology comes into being are those in which western government impinges upon peoples of other culture, whether in European colonies in Africa, technical assistance programs in the underdeveloped countries, or on Indian reservations in the United States. The typical applied anthropologist works in a cross-cultural situation, and tends to find his patent to practice in the traditional concern of his profession with non-western and especially the primitive peoples.

The typical applied anthropologist works with such peoples in a situation of great disparity of power, and, most typically, he is supported by and responsible to management (or is, as in Vicos, himself management). Although I know of anthropologists who have informally put themselves at the service of the "underdog," I do not know of any clear case of the underdogs hiring themselves an anthropologist.

The typical situation of the applied anthropologist is thus to find himself working for or at least with those who have power over other people with different values from themselves, and with regard to whose values the anthropologist is somewhat more sensitive

than the other members of the administering group. It is not remarkable, then, that applied anthropology is sensitive on the subject of values and is attentive to the ethical problems surrounding the ends towards which power may legitimately be exercised and the degree to which the anthropologist may legitimately associate himself with the exercise of power. This concern in turn adds force to the anthropologist's worries lest the applied branch of his profession fail to measure up as science. The attempt to remain value-neutral in the interests of science may appear a dodging of the responsibilities inherent in his relation to power; the attempt to use his skill and his relation to power to "do good" may appear unscientific special pleading; the attempt to avoid power while using his special skills to clarify and to mediate between conflicting values may seem to involve him in philosophical and practical difficulties of hopeless complexity.

## III

The roles which applied anthropologists have taken have been shaped in part by the necessities of particular situations, and in part by the feelings of the anthropologists concerned towards these problems. So, too, criticism of these various roles must recognize that there are various sets of postulates, usable and used by anthropologists, relevant to such judgment.

The first axis along which the species and varieties of applied and action anthropologists range themselves may be identified by the question: What sort of science should anthropology be?

There is, at one extreme, a group of anthropologists who hope for, from their profession, a kind of prediction and control and of precise, compendent generalization similar to that in the natural sciences. There are, at the other end of the scale, those for whom their profession's center of gravity lies somewhere closer to the humanities, and who conceive of their science as offering mainly illuminating insights and useful organizing concepts for experience and action. Men in the former category are likely to conceive of applied anthropology, on the action side, as a process of applying scientific generalization to particular practical instance and, on the scientific side, as a process of experimental testing of generalizations. They strive for a precise stating of goals and predictions, and for a paring-down of a factorial complexity in such a way as to make their science-action program fit the picture of the laboratory experiment. Those in the second category tend to operate in the way which Sol Tax speaks of as "clinical"; they "work in a way that does not assume or require much firmness or precision in (their) predictive findings"; they are characterized by "empiricism," "trial and error correction," ad hoc "inventiveness," and sensitivity to a "multiplicity of cues." Workers in the first category try to so arrange their intervention that its nature, time, and place are clearly marked, and then withdraw—actually or conceptually—to watch the results, as the laboratory technician, having planted a bit of tissue in his mouse, waits to see its growth. Men in the second or "clinical" mode of working tend to remain in continuing involvement with the social situation which is their subject-matter, and which they are both altering and observing at the same time. They find in this way of working a greater stimulus to the illuminating observation and the useful new concept which is for them the chief fruit of scientific endeavor; an accompanying loss of precision which would distress the scientistic applied anthropologist does not so much distress them, partly because they hoped for less from that precision at the outset.

Anthropologists differ also in their conceptions as to the prevailing and proper relationships between science and values. Within anthropology, the extreme positivist viewpoint which would debar value from the field of proper *subjects* of study is not importantly represented; values, indeed, have for many social anthropologists occupied the center of their field of subject-matter. Anthropologists have differed, and continue to differ, however, as to the *bearing of values on science* and of *science on values*.

With regard to the first of these issues, the way in which values should properly affect scientific anthropology, three general sorts of position may be distinguished. There is first the "conservative" view that anthropology is and must be an intellectual discipline in its own right, needing no justification in practical utility, and indeed in danger of digressing from its own proper aims or of ceasing to be

science at all if it is too responsive to the demands of men of affairs for help in solving practical problems. Thus Evans-Pritchard writes:

It may be held that it is laudable for an anthropologist to investigate practical problems. Possibly it is, but if he does so he must realize that he is no longer acting within the anthropological field but in the non-scientific field of administration. Of one thing I feel quite certain: that no one can devote himself wholeheartedly to both interests; and I doubt whether anyone can investigate fundamental and practical problems at the same time.

Men holding this view are unlikely to hold any great enthusiasm for applied anthropology; in any case, they do not comfortably become applied anthropologists.

A second view is frequently held today by those who are glad to own themselves applied anthropologists. In this view, it is proper and indeed laudable for the anthropologist to let values and practical concerns set his problem and define his subject matter, but he must then, in the interest of proper scientific objectivity, keep his values strictly out of his work. Men conceiving of their work in this way may or may not hold it proper for the anthropologist also to express his own value-based preferences for what should happen. But in any event, it is considered that the more the anthropologist can keep his observations and descriptions separate from his valuings, the better the quality of his scientific production will be.

There is a third view—that in Nadel's words "value judgments are inseparable from an investigation" and may indeed contribute to it. So Redfield finds that without the personal value-laden reactions which the ethnologist brings to the cultural reality he is observing he would not observe so well nor be able to describe that reality so precisely; "valuing is part of the ethnologist's work." This view of the science of anthropology is by no means the same as an insistence that anthropology should be of practical utility, that its problems should be set in terms of values. For both men cited, this value-infused observation is a way of carrying out scientific enterprises of no direct practical utility. But from this position, the value-involvement of the applied or action anthropologist in his scientific problem may appear less a disadvantage than it does to the would-be "pure scientist." It may even seem an advantage to be maximized and used, rather than a kind of "friction" to be reduced.

We come then to the question: What is the relevance of science for values? What can knowledge of the Is tell us of the Ought? A good many anthropologists—including applied anthropologists have taken Max Weber's position with regard to this question; their answer is that knowledge of fact can never tell us anything as to what should be; science can never contribute to making a choice between *values*. In this view, the applied anthropologist can in his professional role only point out the factual consequences of alternative modes of action, or recommend the best technical means for bringing about an end previously value-determined. If he presumes to urge one course of action as against another, he has moved outside the realm of science.

Within anthropology there have been, however, many who have considered it possible to draw value-deductions from science. There is, first, a point of view connected with functionalism, and related to the notion of biological adaptability, in which that is good which can be shown to contribute to the survival of men—and by extension, of cultures. There has been also the attempt to identify "universal" values and to find a sanction for these in the demonstration of their universality. At the opposite pole, there is that anthropologically based value theory which finds the sanction for value-systems to lie not in universality but in particularity; the doctrine of cultural relativism. Although in the first instance asserting the relativity of values and thus negative in reference, this has clearly been expanded into positive injunctions to protect other cultures from destruction and to conform to one's own culture. There have also been in anthropology those who have found the good, not in comparing cultures laterally, but in tracing the evolution of cultural life vertically along the axis represented by time: evolutionists, old and new. So even Boas in 1908 seems to have seen a more than descriptive significance in the observation that mankind was evolving away from narrow nationalisms. So Kroeber sees trends in human history which make it possible to speak of "higher" cultures.

But these various tendencies to derive at least some Ought from the descriptions of the Is which anthropologists make have, by and large, not been so much an occasion for intervention, or for taking action, as a third position, standing somewhere outside the question as to whether or not science can tell us anything of values. This is the position which finds the anthropologist obligated to speak or to act just because of his special knowledge. Anthropologists need not, in feeling such obligation, believe that they can prove their values by their science; they know that they do hold some values, and when these are endangered in a field which touches their subject-matter and in which they feel involvement—Nazi racism, government policy towards the American Indian, racial segregation in education—they feel somehow a *duty* to act. Nor do they feel in most cases that, in thus stepping outside the realm of descriptions of what is, they cease to be anthropologists; it is because they are anthropologists, with certain special knowledge and special interests, that they feel obliged to act as they do.

This is intervention in the tradition of the early ethnological societies—or it is disciplined and combined with a scientific discovery goal into action anthropology, or cast still more into the traditional mold of science as an "experiment" in cultural change.

## IV

In such action, it must be noted, anthropologists do in fact draw value deductions from their science—even when they claim the impossibility of doing so on a logical basis. Is not the emphasis placed on cultural self-determination an example of an implicit extension of methodology into ethical imperative? In studying the various ways of life other than his own the anthropologist learned to suspect judgment, to regard, for that time, those practices and beliefs as having their own internal logic and their own validity. The study of culture demanded cultural relativism. So also the stress, in many statements on applied anthropology, on restoration of equilibrium and the prevention of friction and violence in social relations, while representing a value general in the society from which the anthropologists are drawn, seems to be given special force by the functionalist approach in anthropological theory, and the general tendency of many descriptions to center around the concepts of equilibrium and integration.

It may even be argued that the recent tendency of anthropologists to put greater stress on values surrounding the well-being and self-fulfillment of individuals, as contrasted with the stability and integration of cultural wholes, is in itself partially a result of the experience of anthropologists with applied anthropology and the underdeveloped peoples. Anthropologists have been drawn into the great current of change connected with the attempts of such peoples to get the things which the West has, and they have become identified with it, and come to see the needs of the peoples who are their subject matter in a new way because of it.

Applied anthropology thus contains within itself two distinct strains of value-emphasis: one concerned with "the relativity of values," the "right of cultural self-determination," the values of "integration"; the other speaking of universal individual needs, satisfied better by some cultures than others. "Every cultural shoe pinches somewhere." Typically, a single anthropologist uses both these sets of values, implicitly carrying in his own mind a working separation of areas into one category or the other. Technology is usually seen as an area in which one has a right to work for change, as also medical care; they are thought of as means, farther from a central core of value, and as closely related to the universal biological needs of man. So new plows yes, new religion no. Sorcery is seen as violating some universal right to mental health, a particular kinship structure as representing the right of cultural self-determination. Such a gradient may be argued as one representing greater to less disturbance to the person, or it may appear simply as a given.

## V

In summary, then, the following seem to be some of the main problems for discussion—in most cases, continuing, not-capable-of-resolution discussion—with regard to applied or action anthropology.

Applied anthropology will always continue to raise the great unsolvable questions of ethics. What is the good life for man? To what extent is it proper for present generations to undergo discomfort in the interest of the (presumed) advantage of future generations? To what extent has one man or group of men a right to exert power over others, even in their own interest? To what extent may men ever be said to have free choice, and in what circumstances?

These fundamental philosophical questions raise also others which are, in theory at least, capable of some empirical investigation. It would seem worthwhile, for example, to investigate the forms of power and influence in applied anthropology. To what extent, for instance, may the members of the Fox field project be said to be exerting power over the Fox through their questioning, clarifying, and occasionally persuading functions? How may the rationality of human choices be increased? And how may mechanisms be developed for expressing these choices?

It seems clear that applied or action anthropology is bound to be qualitatively different, as science, from traditional anthropology. At least it is evident that it is adding to anthropology a greater interest in process, in small group dynamics, in what has been called "mood," in the relations between social groups, and in phenomena, such as leadership and factionalism. In the literature of the Fox project we find described, for instance, a field of interpersonal relations in which relations of power and items of "mood" are quite as important as those societal bonds and cultural uniformities more traditionally at the center of the anthropologist's field of investigation.

The methodology of such investigations is still in need of refinement. Most especially we need in applied anthropology attention to the methodology of validation. Much of the literature of applied anthropology is a fairly impressionistic description of "what happened when." We need better. Anthropology will have to develop ways of better recording of process and better measurement of change—in attitudes and in interpersonal relationships. Most especially I am struck by the lack, so far as I know, of any really thorough and convincing account of how a group of applied anthropologists are seen by their "clients"—and this although one of the advantages of applied anthropology should be that it takes the effects of the investigator into account in description. To put a group of "pure" scientists to studying the interaction of the applied scientists with their clients may be a humiliating solution, but it is at least a logically possible one.

*selection 64*

# The Research and Development Approach to the Study of Change

### Allan R. Holmberg

I

. . . In 1952, quite by design, although unexpectedly and suddenly, I found myself in the delicate position of having assumed the role of *patrón* (in the name of Cornell University) of a Peruvian *hacienda*, called Vicos, for a period of five years, for the purpose of conducting a research and development program on the modernization process.

As you can readily imagine, such action on my part clearly shook (or perhaps I should say shocked) the Board of Trustees—to say nothing of the some 2,000 residents of the *hacienda* and no few of my anthropological colleagues—to the extent, I might add, that had events subsequently taken other turns than they eventually did, I would probably not be writing this and would be much more in disgrace as an anthropologist and human being than I presently am. Moreover, had I known then what I now know, I am not so sure that I would be willing to repeat the experience, even though it has been one of the most rewarding ones of my whole professional career. My doubts lie not so much with the fruitfulness or legitimacy of the research and

*From* Human Organization, *Vol. 17, No. 1, 1958, pp. 12–16. Copyright 1958, The Society for Applied Anthropology. By permission of the author, and the publisher and copyright holder.*

development, as contrasted with the strictly research, approach to the study of the social process but more with the wear and tear that it might cause to the inadequately financed or inadequately staffed anthropologist or other behavioral scientist who is brash enough to attempt to apply it, especially in a foreign area. On this point I shall have more to say later. For the moment, suffice it to say that having recently retired—again quite by design —from playing the dual role of God and anthropologist (the status of Vicos has recently changed from a dependent to an independent community) and having again assumed the role of a plain anthropologist, I find the change in status a highly comforting one. Nevertheless, on the basis of the past five years of experience at Vicos, I remain convinced that the interventionist or action approach to the dynamics of culture, applied with proper restraint, may in the long run provide considerable payoff in terms both of more rational policy and better science. My concern here, therefore, will be with some of the reasons why I believe this to be the case. What, then, are some of the implications— the advantages and disadvantages, the gains and losses—of the application of the research *and* development approach to the study of change, both from a value and scientific point of view?

## II

On the question of values—in the ethical sense—I really have little to say, more than to state my stand. No one—professional or layman—can scientifically justify intervention into the lives of other people, whether they be of his own kind or of a different breed. However, by its very nature, the social process is an influencing process among individuals and social groups, one upon which the very existence of society depends. It is no less a necessary condition for the study of social life. Even the most "pure" anthropologist imaginable, conducting his research with "complete" detachment and objectivity, cannot avoid influencing his subjects of study or in turn of being influenced by them. In some instances, I believe, this has led to very salutary effects, both on anthropologists and their informants. Certainly the science of anthropology has been greatly enriched by

those informants who were influenced by anthropologists to become anthropologists, even though it may be more questionable, perhaps, that native cultures have been correspondingly enriched by those anthropologists who were influenced by their informants to go native. While this may seem beside the point, I simply want to emphasize the fact that influence and consequently the values which motivate that influence are always part of the process of human interaction and while they can be studied by science, their validation must rest on other grounds.

This does not mean that any anthropologist —pure or applied—can manipulate his subjects without restraint. Some code of ethics must govern his behavior, as the Society for Applied Anthropology long ago recognized. In the case of Vicos, however, where power was held by us, this became an especially delicate issue because having assumed the role of *patrones* we expected and were expected to intervene in the lives of the people. It was at this point that the question of values entered and it was at this point that it was very necessary to take a value stand. What then was this stand?

I long ago made the decision for myself, which is shared by a great many people and communities of the world, that the best kind of a community in which to live is one that is, to quote Aldous Huxley, "just, peaceable, morally and intellectually progressive" and made up of "responsible men and women." To my way of thinking, and I am by no means unique in this view, the best way of approaching this Utopian state of affairs is to pursue as a goal the realization of basic human dignity to which every individual is entitled. And by basic human dignity I mean a very simple thing: a wide rather than a narrow sharing of what I regard as positive human values, some expression of which, as Professor Harold Lasswell has so clearly shown, is found in every society and towards a wider sharing of which, if I interpret Professor Robert Redfield correctly, the broader course of civilization itself has been moving for a considerable period of time.

For lack of better terms of my own to express the meaning I wish to convey, let me again refer to Lasswell who speaks of the following categories of value: power, wealth, enlightenment, respect, well being, skill, affection, and rectitude. The wide sharing of such values among members of the Vicos community was essentially the overall basic value position and policy goal to which we subscribed. In other words, everyone, if he so desired, should at least have the right and the opportunity, if not the responsibility, to participate in the decision-making process in the community, to enjoy a fair share of its wealth, to pursue a desire for knowledge, to be esteemed by his fellowmen, to develop talents to the best of his ability, to be relatively free from physical and mental disease, to enjoy the affection of others, and to command respect for his private life. While no such value stand, of course, can ever be validated by science we and a surprising number of Vicosinos, as I have said elsewhere, and, as revealed by a baseline study, believed them "to be good and desirable ends."

Movement towards such goals, of course, rests on a couple of fundamental assumptions (or better, expectations) in which I happen to have a very strong faith: 1) that human traits are such that progress can be made towards the realization of human dignity, and 2) that the natural order (physical nature) is such that with greater knowledge and skill, human beings can turn it progressively to the service of social goals.

In stating this overall value position, I have not meant to suggest that movement towards these goals can occur only through a single set of institutional practices. Like most anthropologists I subscribe to the doctrine of the relativity of culture and I firmly believe that people have the right of self-determination, as long as they respect that right in others. From the very beginning at Vicos we recognized this principle. In short, we used our power to share power to a point where we no longer hold power, which is just as matters should be.

Before leaving these value and policy matters let me simply cite a few of the developmental changes that have come about as a result of the application of the research *and* development approach to change at Vicos:

1. *Organization.*

*1952.* Vicos had an *hacienda*-type organization. Outside renters not only had free use of *hacienda peones* for labor and personal services, but also of their animals and tools. Power was concentrated in the hands of *patrón.*

*1957. Hacienda* system and free services have been abolished; new system of community organization now in march is based on shared interests and local control.

2. *Land ownership.*

*1952.* No title to land, although Vicosinos had tried on numerous occasions to purchase the land on which they had been living as *peones* for 400 years.

*1957.* Based on reports of development by the Cornell-Peru Project, the Institute of Indigenous Affairs asked the Peruvian Government to expropriate Vicos in favor of its indigenous population. This expropriation has now taken place.

3. *Local authority.*

*1952.* Under the *hacienda*-type organization there were no responsible secular authorities within the community.

*1957.* The Vicosinos have organized a board of their own delegates elected from each of 6 zones of the *hacienda.* They have the legal responsibility for the direction of community affairs.

4. *Income.*

*1952.* The indigenous community of Vicos had no source of income of its own.

*1957.* Former *hacienda* lands are now farmed for the public good, providing a steady income for the payment of lands and the development of public service.

5. *Education.*

*1952.* In the aspect of education Vicos had a very small school, with one teacher, 10–15 students.

*1957.* Vicos now possesses the most modern school in the whole region, recently made a *nucleo escolar,* with a capacity of 400 students. There are now 9 teachers and about 200 students, many of whom have had five years of continuity in school.

6. *Production.*

*1952.* Low economic production—each *hectare* of potato land produced a value of only $100.

*1957.* Each *hectare* of potato land is now producing a value of $400–$600.

7. *Health facilities.*

*1952.* There were no modern health facilities.

*1957.* A modern health center has been built by the Vicosinos and a neighboring community; a clinic is held twice a week and a public health program is underway.

Most of the cost of these developments have

been borne by members of the community themselves.

As a final development outcome I should perhaps mention that the Cornell-Peru Project has had considerable impact outside of the area of Vicos. When originally undertaken there was not a single project of its kind in Peru. At the present time, the Institute of Indigenous Affairs is directing five programs of a similar nature in other areas of the country. And attached to all are Peruvian anthropologists, many of them trained in part at Vicos.

But more important have been the effects on the outside produced by the Vicosinos themselves. Word of their freedom has got around. Let me cite but one example. Recently an *hacienda* community, in conditions similar to those obtaining at Vicos in 1952, sent a commission to Vicos for advice. Their *hacienda*, a public one as Vicos has been, was about to be rented at public auction for a period of ten years and they were desirous of freeing themselves from service to a *patrón*. One of the ways in which this can be done is for the residents of an *hacienda* to rent it directly from the government themselves. But in the case of this community sufficient funds were not immediately available.

The Vicosinos sent a return commission to *Huascarán*, a fictitious name for the community under discussion. On the recommendation of this commission the community of Vicos, which had funds in the bank, lent the community of Huascarán sufficient money to rent their *hacienda* directly from the government, thus freeing them from service to a *patrón*. More than that when the commission from Vicos first went to Huascarán they noticed that the Huascarinos planted their fields by somewhat antiquated methods and suggested more modern methods of agriculture which were originally introduced into Vicos by the Cornell-Peru Project. These are the kind of developmental effects that give the applied anthropologist an occasion for joy.

## III

Now what of the scientific implications of the research and development approach to the study of change? Here again I take a positive view, particularly in a situation like Vicos, where it was possible to work in a complete cultural context, where it was possible to specify social goals for almost all aspects of culture, and where it was possible for the anthropologist to maintain some control over the interventions and variables involved. In such an environment, hypotheses can be tested by comparing actual goal achievement with predicted goal achievement.

Actually in the natural sciences, research and development are inseparable. It is even common to join them in one formal project as is the case in many technologically advanced industries, in government, and in private institutions. But whether formally joined or not, scientific discovery is sooner or later inevitably put to the test of success or failure through the application of research results in engineering and technology. In other words, a great strength of, if not a necessary condition for, natural science is feedback through development.

Anthropology, like other behavioral sciences, profits little from such corrective feedback. In part this is because it is not systematically employed in social decision-making, as let us say, physics is employed in missile or building construction. But even if it is employed the results are either not fed back to the anthropologist or they are fed back too slowly to facilitate rapid scientific advance. Moreover, research and development work in behavioral science are seldom joined, even though they were to some extent in Vicos, for the systematic exploitation of their reciprocal benefits, as they are in the research and development laboratories of the natural sciences. To get the feedback necessary for rapid advance in a behavioral science like anthropology, policy is needed, even if policy does not need science.

The connection between research and development in anthropology and other behavioral sciences is probably even closer than it is in the natural sciences. In science, as everyone knows, every generalization is both an insight and a prediction, even though its explicit statement is usually cast in one form or another. Now when a generalization on behavior is communicated to people who are also its subjects, it may alter the knowledge and preferences of these people and also their behavior. Thus a scientific generalization on behavior, by altering behavior, appears to falsify or obsolesce itself. This is called "pliancy factor" by my philosophical colleague at Cornell, Max Black.

In general this complication has been viewed as a cross that the behavioral scientist must bear. Actually, a generalization about behavior is not falsified when predictions based upon it are made obsolete when the subject to whom it is made known prefers to modify himself rather than to conform to an earlier prediction. It is simply that the possibility of modification of behavior must be taken into account and turned to scientific advantage. In the continuous interplay between scientific generalization and goal-seeking behavior, the insight-feedback of a scientific generalization can be employed both for goal revision and as empirical data for research. This is one of the great advantages of the research and development approach. Perhaps an example will illustrate what I mean.

One of the developmental goals of the Vicos program was to bring decision-making bodies of the community up to a level of competence at which we, the *patrones*, could be dispensed with but without the community's falling victim to its most predatory members as has sometimes been the case. Thus, arrangements had to be made for group survival and stability and, through controlling the complexity of the problems dealt with and by other devices, the groups gradually brought to their highest level of competence. This required that hypotheses be formulated and acted upon—hypotheses concerning the requirements of viability and competence of groups. Once acted upon the hypotheses were tested by their results. Hence each successive developmental step was a step in the isolation of another variable for research.

Concretely, both development and research interests merge in following the consequences of such successive steps as the following, at least some of which were taken for one group of potential decision-makers at Vicos: 1) the group was asked for advice in the settlement of land disputes; 2) it was invested with prestige by calling public attention to its role; 3) the group was given the opportunity to settle land disputes; 4) the group was provided, through skilled observers, the feedback of an understandable analysis of its performance; 5) the *patrón* was withdrawn from the group meeting, reserving only the right to veto under certain conditions; 6) the jurisdiction of the group was enlarged with gradually decreasing veto.

While this detail is much abbreviated, it suggests how research on the developmental steps provides an opportunity for the dogged pursuit of whatever variables one wishes to isolate. Every insight into the variables can be put to a test; and, where predictions are disappointed, a reformulation of the hypothesis can be followed by a further test until predictions are no longer disappointed. By no means will all the unknowns of human behavior become unveiled, but development requires correct insights, hypotheses, and analytic models. It compels their never-ending revision until they pass the test of application.

The essence of the connection between research and development in this illustration is that each developmental intervention—say, introducing legal principles by which land disputes might be resolved—is both a necessary step towards reaching community goals and in the research sense a method of varying the group situation to isolate another variable in group dynamics—in this instance isolating the effect of introducing formal principles against which individual cases are to be judged. It is precisely because of feedback to the researcher from the development application that research needs development just as much as development needs research.

Whatever the particular example, the story is much the same. The researcher is compelled to follow through, to keep on trying for the refinement of an hypothesis or model that will stand the test of application. If, for example, he wants to know what is necessary to break down prejudice between Indians and Mestizos, his research is not terminated when he has tested one popular hypothesis and found it invalid, because his developmental objectives require that he try a whole series of interventions until prejudice begins to decline.

In the case of Vicos, attempts were made in collaboration with several colleagues to lay out about 130 specific possible lines of research and development, each matched to a specific developmental goal such as the diversification of agriculture, the development of community leadership, the reduction of social distance between Indians and Mestizos, the increase of educational opportunities for both children and adults, etc. Wherever possible an attempt was made to make fairly precise statements about the goals in question. To lay out the various possibilities in order subsequently to develop a strategy of research and development, each line of possible intervention was represented in a semi-diagrammatic way by a column on a very large bulletin or map board taking up the walls of a room. The diagram below represents how 3″ x 5″ cards were used to lay out visually the research and development sequences, subject to constant revision as research and development continues:

| |
|---|
| An ideological goal or end point |

| |
|---|
| A corresponding institutional goal or end point |

| |
|---|
| Program plans for probes, pretests, interventions, and appraisals |

| |
|---|
| Present ideological situation with respect to above goals summarized |

| |
|---|
| Present institutional situation with respect to above goals summarized |

| |
|---|
| Record of past interventions |

| |
|---|
| Base line ideological situation |

| |
|---|
| Base line institutional situation |

At the top of the column is posted for some end-point date the particular goal in question to be reached. At the bottom of the column are posted the counterpart institutional and ideological situations found at the base line period before interventions. Above them are summarized any interventions so far made, and above them the present institutional and ideological situation with respect to this one line of development. The remainder of the column is given over to a proposed schedule of probes, pretests, interventions, and appraisals.

By utilizing such a method, interventions are not likely to be hit or miss and their developmental and research gains can be fully appreciated. Scheduling them requires the careful appraisal of the facts describing the existing situation and trends, probes of readiness of the community to take the proposed step, pretests of interventions on a small scale, then the intervention itself and subsequent appraisal, which in turn becomes the first step in a still further intervention. Hence in diagrammatic terms, the upper part of the column, including the goals themselves, is constantly undergoing revision on the basis of the growing lower part of the column representing past experience.

To illustrate the distinctiveness of research, where the whole life of the community is available for study, as it was to a considerable extent in Vicos, it may be helpful to visualize a great many columns such as have just been described, set side by side. The interrelationships among these columns can hardly go unnoticed, and it becomes both possible and necessary to consider these interrelationships in devising a research and development strategy.

One more thing should be said about this contextual mapping in a research and development approach to change. It makes possible, for *development*, an economy of intervention. For example, one way in which to reduce social inequality between Mestizos and Indians is to schedule public functions in Vicos attractive enough to draw neighboring Mestizos in and then conduct these functions in such a way as to break down the traditional acceptance of segregation. One can conceive of an experiment along this line that might test the hypothesis that prejudice between Indians and Mestizos will be reduced by contact under conditions of social equality.

Now with reference to quite a different goal of reducing communal binges, movies are an effective competitor with alcohol because the Vicosinos prefer to be sober when watching a movie. Movies are also an obvious method for adult education, including literacy. Finally, the importation and showing of films may become the nucleus of a small-scale experiment in Indian entrepreneurship. Hence a variety of lines of desirable research and development converge on a movie program for Vicos. Actually such an experiment is now underway at Vicos and a skillful plan for introducing movies into the community may turn out to be a strategically sound intervention because many birds may be killed with one small stone.

I have now said enough to indicate what

I believe some of the value and scientific implications of the research and development approach to the study of change to be. Most of what I have said is positive and I have not suggested that this approach be applied to the exclusion of others. My greatest doubts about it, on the basis of my experience at Vicos, stem from the unlikelihood of mobilizing sufficient funds and personnel to do a research and development job well. It is a man's job that a boy cannot be sent to do. I hope that the powers supporting research will soon take cognizance of this fact.

*selection 65*

# A Cross-Cultural Outline of Education

## Jules Henry

### INTRODUCTION

. . . A few anthropological monographs contain sections on education, though others make reference to the subject merely in passing. Recently, a review of problems in education appeared as a collaborative work of anthropologists and educators.

In surveying these publications, it seemed that it might be useful if a general outline of the educational process could be provided for the anthropological field worker. With such an outline, the scientist would not need to rely solely on his creative imagination and on works that are often incomplete and focused on particularistic interests, for he would have available also a methodological tool that might help increase the scope of his observations.

As industrial cultures become more and more the target of anthropological interest, anthropologists will sooner or later have to study their educational systems too, so that an outline of education for anthropologists should take account not only of pre-literate culture but of industrial society also.

Much material that one might wish to see included in an outline of education is con-

*From* Current Anthropology, *Vol. 1, No. 4, 1960, pp. 267–304. Copyright 1960, Wenner-Gren Foundation for Anthropological Research. By permission of the author, the publisher, and the copyright holder.*

cerned largely with personality, with physiological pathways to enculturation, and with the conditioning of the very young child while feeding, eliminating, or, in general, in close physical contact with his family. The present outline, however, deals primarily, though not exclusively, with children about six years of age and older, and concentrates on the formal, conscious aspects of education. Furthermore, since the outline and text are concerned solely with education as a social process, no attention is given to knowledge the child acquires while alone.

Education can be looked at from the standpoint of the adult educator and from that of the child who is learning. The adult generally wants to do something to the child, and sees education as a process through which the child should become what the adult wants him to be. From the position of the child, however, education is also finding a way to certainty: the child wants to know what he should do about everything, and how he should do it, and he looks to the adult—to the educational process—to help him. This outline and text take account only of the first view.

### Origins of the outline

While the outline derives in part from the work of others and in part from my own field experience in non-industrial cultures, much of it has grown out of research on cultural factors in learning that was begun seven years ago at Washington University. Several hundred protocols of direct observation of American classrooms have been collected by me and my students, and it was the analysis of these observations that made necessary the bulky (but by no means complete!) outline. The research continues.

The records collected during this research are factual, relatively unscreened process notes of what the observer saw. The major selective factor was the observer's concentration on teacher-pupil interaction.

### Some theoretical problems

Humans must learn much more than other animals, and the evolution of *Homo sapiens* has been characterized by a great expansion of his dependence on learning and of his capacity to learn. This has been accompanied by an increase in the number of teaching devices. For these reasons the outline contains a partial inventory of the materials humans must learn and of teaching methods.

Although in the past thirty years or so the dependence of lower animals on learning has become apparent, due particularly to the work of the comparative psychologists, learning in *Homo sapiens* differs from that in other animals in some striking ways. Among these are the following. (1) In man, learning is dominated by symbolic processes. (2) In man, the motivational organizors of learning are more variable—that is to say, much less subject to innate determinants than in sub-human species. (3) There are apparently, in man, no innate limits on learning: the outer limits of the capacity of human beings to learn have not yet been discovered. (4) A striking feature of man is the extent to which his learning is polyphasic, that is, affected by a strong innate tendency to learn more than one thing at a time. While it is true, as Pavlov has shown, that animals also learn more than one thing at a time, polyphasic learning is much more extensive in man.

The combination in *Homo sapiens* of genetic variability, absence of obvious, biologically determined limits on learning, and great capacity for polyphasic learning, has brought it about that the social processes of learning have become extremely complex, and therefore require long-sustained and meticulous observation and recording by the researcher. The net, but by no means final, result of an effort to catalogue the actual—as distinguished from laboratory—learning *events* in human children is a long and complicated outline like the one offered here. When, to this, we add the dimension of cultural variability, the catalogue becomes even more impressive. It then becomes clear that the education of humans cannot be understood through conceptually reducing the entire process to a simple reward-reinforcement system.

The paradoxical aspect of human education is that in spite of the overshadowing tendency of human learning to variability and expansion, educational procedures have regularly taken as a model the innate release mechanism postulated by ethology. That is to say, it would appear that human societies have tried repeatedly to accomplish in their members a completely predictable response system. The model, though not the reality, of the educated human, is the mass tendency of an American audience to rise to its feet whenever it hears the national anthem: the response is predictable and almost automatic. Teachers in American elementary schools rely heavily on the culturally determined and learned tendency of children to raise their hands whenever the teacher wants the answer to a question; Pilagá mothers depend on the learned tendency of their children to recoil from the village boundaries or to duck into their houses whenever an adult shouts the term "sorcerer." The processes whereby these tendencies to respond predictably to single or complex symbols are internalized in the child form the matrix of education everywhere. The outline, particularly the sections on teaching methods (II) and on conduct control (IX), attempts to take account of these processes.

Thus, as one peruses the outline, one cannot but be struck by the fact that what it represents, in part, is a measure of the extent to which human learning has departed from that of lower animals. Stated another way, if one wished to obtain an answer to the question, "How does human learning differ from animals?" a first step might be to examine this outline, for here, quite apart from the general theoretical points raised, the mere catalogue of the dimensions of human education serves to place human learning on an entirely different plane from that of even the higher primates. . . .

I. On what does the educational process focus?
1. Enivronment (other than human)
   1. Flora
   2. Fauna
   3. Climate
   4. Geographical features
   5. Anthropomorphized flora
   6. Anthropomorphized fauna
   7. Anthropomorphized or zoomorphized machines
   8. Anthropomorphized or zoomorphized natural phenomena other than flora or fauna (winds, rivers, mountains, etc.)
   9. Space
   10. Time
   11. Motion
   12. Space-time-motion

13. The world view of the culture
    1. Isolate-static
    2. Communicate-changing
       1. Engulfing
    3. Hostile or pacific
       1. Hostile
       2. Pacific
       3. Selectively hostile or pacific
    4. Geographical position of places studied
       1. Near: own town, state or province, village, tribe
       2. Near-distant: other states or provinces, nation in general; other villages or tribes
       3. Distant: other lands
    5. Temporal position
       1. Immediate
       2. Contemporary
       3. Near past
       4. Distant past
       5. Mythological past
14. Clothing
15. Food
16. Transportation and communication
2a. Values
   1. Good and bad: moral rules
   2. Work, success, failure
   3. Being on time
   4. Culture
   5. Proper dress
   6. Strength, activity, power
   7. Beating the game
   8. Politeness, tact
   9. Cooperation, helpfulness, togetherness
   10. Patriotism
   11. Cleanliness, orderliness
   12. Thrift, saving, don't waste
   13. Parents are good
   14. Prettiness, beauty
   15. Love
   16. Mother, motherhood
   17. Happiness
   18. Competitiveness
   19. Equality
   20. Novelty, excitement
   21. Pride
   22. Knowledge as value
   23. The "beautiful person"
   24. Private property
   25. Democracy
   26. Family

27. Responsibility
28. Generosity, doing more than required, noncommercialism
29. The state
30. Deference
31. Enlightened self-interest
32. Independence, toughness
33. Physical intactness
34. Sense of emergency
35. Constancy
36. Solicitude for others, kindness
37. Composure under stress
38. Courage
39. Knowledge as means to an end
40. Compromise
41. Fun, relaxation
42. Friends, friendship, faithfulness
43. Fairness
44. Flattery, empty praise
45. Honor (integrity), personal autonomy
46. Self-restraint
47. Trying hard, don't give up
48. Fame, ambition
49. Honesty
50. Prestige
51. Niceness, likeableness
52. Respect for authority
53. Excitement
54. Gentleness, non-violence
55. Speed, alertness
56. Sacredness, etc., of parents
57. Flexibility
58. Modesty
59. Tolerance
60. Freedom
61. Peace
62. Progress
63. Wealth
64. U.S.A.
65. Loyalty
66. Money, greed, etc., are corrupting
67. Smartness, cleverness, thinking
68. Profit
69. Size
2*b*. Value conflict
3. Institutions
    1. Social structure
    2. Religion
    3. Economic system
4. Technology, machines
5. Reading, writing, and arithmetic
6. Social manipulation
    1. Recognition-seeking behavior
        2. Manipulation of others
        3. Manipulation of self
    7. Responsibility
    8. How to complete
    9. How to take care of others
    10. Use of the mind
        1. How to think
        2. Disjunction
            1. When to disjoin
            2. How to disjoin
            3. From what to disjoin
        3. Concentration
            1. Interest stimulation defining purpose; motivation
            2. Force
            3. Shutting out external stimuli
            4. Visualization
            5. Focused retention
        4. Preparation of the mind
        5. "Mental discipline"
    11. Body parts or functions
        1. The voice
        2. The sphincters
        3. Care of the body (like getting enough rest)
        4. Posture
        5. How to relax
        6. The mouth
    12. Art
    13. History
    14. Some other facts about which information is communicated
        1. About systems of rewards and punishments
        2. About what the culture promises its members
        3. About permitted and forbidden activities
        4. About how to get pleasure and avoid pain
        5. About whom to love and whom to hate
        6. How to handle frustration
        7. The difference between the real and the manifest (this refers to situations in which an effort is deliberately made to enable the child to see "behind" the obvious)
        8. About death
        9. About sex relations
        10. About race, class, or ethnic differences
15*a*. Instruction in identifiable adult tasks
15*b*. Teaching about adult tasks

16. Scientific abstractions
17. Science (general)
18. Routine procedures
19. Childish handiwork
20. Cultural stereotypes
21. Warfare and associated activities
22. Safety
23. Songs, music
24. Mythology
25. The object system
26. Games
27. Cultural fictions

II. How is the information communicated (teaching methods)?
1. By imitation
2. By setting an example
3. By instruction in schools, ceremonials, other formal institutions
4. By use of punishments
5. By use of rewards
6. Problem-solving
7. Guided recall
8. Giving the child tasks to perform beyond his immediate capacity
   1. Jamming the machine
9. Mechanical devices
10. By kinesthetic association
11. By experiment
    1. By teacher
    2. By pupil
12. By doing
13. By symbolic association
14. By dramatization
15. By games or other play
16a. By threats
16b. By trials
17. By irrelevant association
18. By relevant association
19. Through art
    1. Graphic
    2. Music, general
    3. Songs
    4. Literature (stories, myths, tales, etc.)
20. By stating the opposite of the truth ("Water's a solid, isn't it?"); writing antonyms
21. By holding up adult ideals
22. Acting in undifferentiated unison
23. Physical force
24. By positive or negative assertion
25. Repetition
26. By specifically relating information to the child's own body, bodily function, or experience
27a. Through ego-inflation
27b. Through ego-deflation
28. Through use of humor
29. By telling
30. By watching
31. By listening
32. Question and answer
    1. Teacher question, pupil answer
    2. Pupil question, teacher answer
33. Holding up class, ethnic, national, or religious ideals
34. By doing something on his own
35a. By repeating the child's error to him
35b. By repeating the child's correct answer
36. By accusing
37. By following a model
    1. Human
    2. Non-human
38. By comparison
39. By filling in a missing part
40. By associative naming (e.g., a book mentions gingham as a material, and teacher asks students if they can name other materials)
41. By identifying an object (like going to the board and underlining "a noun" in a sentence)
42a. By group discussion
42b. By class discussion
43. Physical manipulation
    1. Bodily manipulation
    2. Bodily mutilation and other physical stresses
44. Rote memory
45. By working together with a student (as when teacher and student work together to make a battery, or as when teacher and student go over reference books together)
46. Through special exhibits
47. By having children read substantive materials (e.g., reading the chemistry lesson in the reader)
48. By putting the child on his mettle ("Now let's see how well you can read.")
49. Through group projects
50. By giving procedural instructions
51. By demanding proof
52. Through reports by students
53. By pairing (e.g., one child gives a word and calls on another child to give a sen-

tence with the word; one child gives the state and another gives the capital)
54. By asking for volunteers
55. Through isolating the subject

III. Who educates?
1. Males or females?
2. Relatives or others?
3. On which age group does the burden of education fall?
    1. Peers
        1. Boy
        2. Girl
    2. Older children
        1. Male
        2. Female
    3. Adolescents
        1. Male
        2. Female
    4. Adults
        1. Male or female
        2. Younger or older
        3. Married or unmarried
    5. Others
4. Is education by "successful" people?
5. What rewards accrue to the educator?
    1. Enhanced status
    2. Material rewards
    3. Emotional satisfactions
6. Are there education specialists?
7. Does the educator wear distinctive dress or other insignia?
8. Is the educator of the same or of a different social group from that of the person being educated? (national, racial, class, etc.)

IV. How does the person being educated participate? (What is his attitude?)
1. Accepting
2. Rejecting, resistive
3. Bored, indifferent
4. Defiant
5. Inattentive
6. Social closeness of teacher and child
7. Social distance of teacher and child
8. Fnds the process painful?
9. Finds the process gratifying?
10a. Competitively
10b. Cooperatively
11a. With inappropriate laughter
11b. Ridiculing peers
12. Laughter at humor of peers or teacher

13. Overt docility
14. Eagerly
    1. Facial expression
    2. Hand-raising
    3. Talking out
    4. Heightened bodily tonus
15. Through making independent decisions and suggestions
16. Asks for clarification, direction, etc.
17. Through spontaneous contributions or other demonstrations not precisely within the context of the lesson
18. Through spontaneous contributions within the context of the lesson
19. Attentively
20. Spontaneously humorous
21. Spontaneously expressive
22. Approaches teacher physically
23. Mobile—free
24. Immobile—constricted
25. Through performing special assigned tasks
26a. Hostile to peers
26b. Protective of peers
27. Diversion to peers
28. Anxiously
29. Disjoined hand-raising
30. By whispering to teacher
31. Laughs at peers
32. Corrects teacher
33a. Disruptively
33b. Critically
34. By carping criticism
35. By praising work of peers
36. Dishonesty, cheating, lying, etc.
37. Attempts to maintain order
38. Guilty
39. With sense of inadequacy
40. With sense of adequacy
41. By copying from peers
42. Attempts to control the class
43. No response
44. Uses teacher's last name
45. Uses teacher's first name
46. Calls out to teacher
47. Uses kinship term
48. By public performance

V. How does the educator participate? (What is his attitude?)
1. Eagerly
    1. Facial expression
    2. Bodily movement

3. Tone of voice
4. Heightened bodily tonus
2. Bored, uninterested, etc.
3. Embarrassed
4*a*. Dominative
4*b*. Integrative
5. Insecure
6. Politely
7. Enjoys correct response
8. Resents incorrect response
9. Can't tell
10. Seeks physical contact with person being educated
11. Acceptance of blame
12. Putting decisions up to the children
13. Discouraging
14. Encouraging
15. Hostile, ridiculing, sarcastic, belittling
16. Relatively mobile
17. Relatively immobile
18. Personalizing
    1. Use of request sentence with name
    2. Use of name only
    3. Use of hand-name technique
    4. Use of equalizing, leveling term like "comrade"
19. Depersonalizing
    1. Use of class seating plan for recitation in succession
    2. Use of "next" or some such impersonal device
    3. Use of "you" instead of name
    4. Pointing, nodding, looking
20. Irritable
21. Accepts approach
22. Repels approach
23. Accepting of child's spontaneous expressions
24. Rejecting of child's spontaneous expressions
25. Humorous
26. Handles anxiety, hostility, discomfort, etc.
27. Acts and/or talks as if child's self-image is fragile
28. Acts and/or talks as if child's self-image is irrelevant
29. Defends child against peers
30. Responds to non-verbal cue other than handraising
31. Excessively polite
32. Keeps word
33. Fails to keep word

34. Praises and rewards realistically
35. Praises and rewards indiscriminately
36. Critical (does not point out good things in student's work)
37. Does not reward correct answer or good performance
38. Does not punish incorrect answer or poor performance
39. Acknowledges own error
40. Uses affectional terms like "honey" or "dear"
41. Awakens anticipation ("Now we are going to get some nice new books.")
42. The inclusive plural

VI. Are some things taught to some and not to others?
    1. Do different age groups learn different things?
    2. Do the sexes learn different things?
    3. Are different groups taught different things?

VII. Discontinuities in the educational process
    1. Discontinuities between age-periods
        1. In regard to techniques
        2. In regard to values
    2. How do all of these apply between the sexes?
        1. Are discontinuities different for boys and girls?
        2. The secrecy of initiation rites

VIII. What limits the quantity and quality of information a child receives from a teacher?
    1. Methods of teaching
    2. Available time
    3. Quality of equipment
    4. Distance from the object
    5. Ignorance or error of teacher
    6. Stereotyping of the object
    7. Failure of teacher to correct pupil's mistakes
    8. Failure of teacher to indicate whether the pupil's answers are right or wrong
    9. Failure of teacher to respond to a question
    10. General vagueness or fumbling of the teacher

IX. What forms of conduct control (discipline) are used?

1. Relaxed
2. Tight
3. Sense of propriety
4. Affectivity
5. Reprimand
    1. Direct
    2. Gentle
    3. Mixed ("We like for you to have an opinion but it is childish for you to shout out your numbers like that.")
    4. Impersonal ("Some of you are holding us up.")
6. Ridicule
7. Exhortation ("How can I teach you if you keep making so much noise?")
8. Command
9. Command question or request
10. "We" technique
11. Instilling guilt
12. Cessation of activity
13. Group sanction
14. Threat
15. Putting the child on his mettle
16. Non-verbal signal
17. Reward
18. Promise of reward
19. Special strategems
20. Awakening fear
21. Using a higher power
    1. Human
    2. Non-human
22. Exclusion
23. Punishment
24. Encourages peer group control

X. What is the relation between the intent and the results of education?
    1. Relatively high correlation between intention and results
    2. Relatively low correlation between intention and results

XI. What self-conceptions seem reinforced?
    1. Ego-forming factors
        1. Syntonic: praise, support, status inflation
            1. Grandiose self-conception
        2. Dystonic: blame, shame, guilt, fright, exclusion, depersonalization

XII. How long does the process of formal education last? . . .

## Summary and Conclusions:
## Some Ancient and Abiding Characteristics of Human Education

1. Use of reward stimuli to learning: primarily praise, appreciation, and status elevation.

2. Use of pain stimuli to learning: ridicule, accusation, physical pain, physical confinement (restriction of movement).

3. Use of role-occupant as role-instructor (teaching of archery by archers, of agriculture by farmers, of warfare by warriors, of mathematics by practitioners of mathematics, of carpentry by carpenters, etc.) This has undergone radical change since the emergence of modern mass education.

4. In high civilizations: low status of teachers, unless they teach sacred matters.

5. In high civilizations: a correlation between (*a*) love of knowledge for its own sake, with (*b*) status of teachers, and with (*c*) the interest of students in learning.

6. Confinement of creativity to gifted individuals (creativity never a mass phenomenon).

7. Absence of the assumption of a natural impulse to learn. (This does not mean that children are not everywhere naturally investigative, but there is no evidence that children will not lose interest in learning when it requires work.)

8. Congruence of status change with education, coupled with definite marks of adult recognition of status change.

9. Unity of the social sphere, including education, in non-literate cultures outside the stream of industrialization.

The main point deriving from this cross-cultural study of education is that *Homo sapiens* learned long ago that there is no such thing as "natural maturation" in a social sense, and that the central problem for human beings is the adaptation of each new generation to culture. This includes learning the techniques for survival each particular culture has found reliable.

It would appear that, on the whole, adult *Homo sapiens* has rarely taken it for granted that children could or would just naturally learn by spontaneous imitation. At the same time, the children of *Homo sapiens* have not assumed that they would just naturally grow into adulthood. Rather, children have always been aware that they have to validate their status as adults by learning adult techniques from older teachers. It follows that *Homo sapiens* has been born on a kind of status machine—a status escalator or a status treadmill, depending on the culture—from which there has rarely been any socially acceptable escape. . . . Furthermore, he has always had to rely on those superior to him in knowledge and social status to enable him to raise his own status. On the other hand, it is not clear that adults have always assumed that children would naturally wish to be adult. Over and over again, the data shows that children have had to be urged up the status ladder by rewards, punishments, and other even more complex devices. From the point of view of the adults this is absolutely necessary, for otherwise the children would remain dependent and disgracefully deviant in other ways. From the standpoint of the child, he must climb the status ladder or suffer the consequences of dependence and deviance. It is likely, meanwhile, that this compulsion and the inner conflict involved leave a lasting impression on the child, so that as a mature adult these memories can provide a fertile soil for social change, for if conditions arise that seem to provide an opportunity to eliminate the sources of the pains of childhood growth, adults may be happy to take advantage of the situation and push for change, often, perhaps, not knowing the real sources of their readiness.

Also deriving from this study is an insight into the enormous effort that *Homo sapiens* has put into narrowing the perceptual sphere of the individual. To this end he has employed ridicule, praise, torture, admonition, etc., etc., with all the ingenuity his great brain has been able to devise. Thus, though *Homo sapiens* has been also *Homo inquisitor*—man the curious, the inquirer—he has always worried that his careful arrangement of cultural patterns would be destroyed if he *learned without limit.*

Finally, protecting himself from *inundation by stimuli,* *Homo sapiens* has erected the categories of his languages and his culture patterns. Of course, in the long run these intellectual walls crumble because of the inherently variable mental constitution of *Homo sapiens,* because many devices he uses for narrowing the perceptual sphere are unrewarding and self-defeating, because of the polyphasic nature of human learning, and because of the indeterminate factors that are always present in human learning. Thus, the dialectic of man's effort to understand the universe has always decreed that he should be alternately pulled forward by what has made him *Homo inquisitor* and held back by the fear that if he knew too much he would destroy himself, i.e., his culture. So it is that though language has been an instrument with which man might cleave open the universe and peer within, it has also been an iron matrix that bound his brain to ancient modes of thought. And thus it is that though man has poured what he knows into his culture patterns, they have also frozen round him and held him fast.

# Some Relations of School and Family in American Culture

## Robert F. Spencer

*From Symposium:*
*A School is to Learn. . . .*
Proceedings of the
Minnesota Academy of
Science, *Vol. 29, 1961.*
*pp. 128–239. Copyright*
*by the Minnesota*
*Academy of Science.*
*By permission of the*
*author, the publisher,*
*and the copyright holder.*

Virtually any statement made about the contemporary American system of education can be subjected to infinite documentation. What the school should accomplish, what it has accomplished, what its curricula ought to be, how far it should or has become a kind of surrogate for the family, church or other institution, emerge as vital questions for the professional educators, questions, clearly, for which there is no single answer. Judgments become normative, ameliorative, critical, and certainly, nearly always fraught with overtones of emotionalism. This leaves the non-specialist who attempts to gain an over-view of the nature and image of the educator and his field in the dilemma of adequately finding his way. Still, the school is a social institution. As such, it can be subjected to analysis in quite the same behavioral terms as any other human group activity. Rather, therefore, than to move into the areas of the ideal—what a school and the system associated with it ought to be—it may be possible to consider the educational institutions in terms of their structure and function, thereby analyzing the interrelations between school system and other institutional facets of contemporary society.

This paper is written from the point of view of the behavioral sciences, specifically, from the vantage point of the anthropologist whose concern lies in the comparison of the various aspects of human behavior at all times and places. For indeed, if a society seeks to learn about itself, it gains perspective only through an observation of alternative solutions to human problems which have been reached by human groups possessing different historical backgrounds and whose view of man, his nature and destiny, is couched in fundamental assumptions and premises different from those of *Homo americanus*.

Further, the anthropologist is accustomed to see a society and its associated culture in holistic terms, arguing that all aspects of behavior in a historically conditioned and determined context are intimately interrelated, that they interact with each other and are so systematically fashioned as to support one another. In other words, any facet of behavior in a society has a function, the end of which is to maintain and perpetuate the whole. From comparative studies of other peoples, whether civilized or so-called primitives, the anthropologist affirms the essential dynamically functional nature of any institution in society. This can never exist in a vacuum but becomes an integral element in a complex system. By this reasoning, it is rank error to divorce the educational institution of this or any other human society from the total social matrix.

But to speak of a total American society and culture poses an almost insurmountable problem for some investigators. Ours is, it is true, a vastly proliferated system what with its many interest groups, its varied ethnic backgrounds, its abundant organizations, or its geographical and ecological diversity. Yet a failure to admit the organic integrity of American culture and society is to ignore the forest. Indeed, there is enough of a uniformity in contemporary American society to suggest that size does not necessarily make for complexity and that the concept of complexity is stressed far too much. In this paper, I submit that there is an American culture, that the school system is a vital part of the total society, and that, in interacting with other social institutions, e.g., the family, the school functions to affirm and preserve not only ideological and ideational norms, but more pointedly, aspects of behavior which promote the maintenance of the totality of American society as we know it.

The anthropologist is aware at once that the analytic points he makes are not necessarily reflective of popular consensus or wish. A question which nearly always confronts him at once relates to the applications of what he and his fellow behavioral scientists have

to say. This is, in fact, a recognizable pattern in American culture, one which demands constantly applications of any line of scientific inquiry. A point which must be left open here is that respecting science itself. Even if science is a vital part of contemporary culture, something which seems to offer a panacea to modern man, scientific values are not necessarily social values. Indeed, one may ask if science, taken as an entity essentially supercultural, can ever be normative. Theoretically, of course, it should not be. A description of the physiological function of the pancreas is not the same as a course of treatment prescribed for diabetes. In this paper, I seek to do no more than call attention, on the basis of what is empirically known about American society and culture, to some of the existing interrelationships between school system, family, and society. I should wish respectfully to leave to the investigator whose interest is application the solutions to the specific problems which arise out of culture pattern and human behavior.

It is possible to make a series of statements, a summary of propositions which reflect an empirically derived scientific commitment to the problem at hand. These are, in effect, to "call the shots" as one sees them; they are not to define solutions. They are:

1. There is a total system definable as American culture and society.

2. This system, tightly bound in some areas, extremely loosely in others, depends on essentially ephemeral human relationships.

3. The ephemeral quality of the human relationship is an outgrowth of the primary cultural definition of the worth of the individual.

4. On the significant formative level, i.e., that of socialization, making the individual one with his culture and society, family and school function together to produce a desired result.

It may thus be affirmed that the family and the system of contemporary American education meet in the area of a dynamic social cross-fertilization. If the ensuing processes are examined functionally, a picture reflecting the vitality of institutional relations can be proffered.

## American Culture and Society

To say that contemporary America constitutes not one, but a series of diffuse subcultures is to do violence to the anthropological concept of culture. To identify, as some sociologists do, a depressed urban area where crime is rampant as a criminal sub-culture fails to take into account the fact that even deviant behavior is structured and patterned according to the norms of the so-called majority. Sub-culture as concept is not only unfortunate but is dangerous in presenting a distortion of existing uniformity. One need not move into the psychoanalytic formulations of national character as has been done for America by Margaret Mead or Geoffrey Gorer to recognize that there is an essential structural sameness to American life. Into this, individuals and groups, whether in the form of the Sons of Erin, the Sons of Hermann, or the Japanese-American Citizens' League, are inextricably drawn. An ethnic minority is a separate cultural segment only if it refuses to be assimilated into the prevailing modes of the majority, such as may be the case of the traditional Chinatown. Here, however, one is not dealing with a Chinese sub-culture but rather with a segment of Chinese culture encysted within the larger body. When the minority of whatever kind comes to act within the majority group and framework it has forfeited its distinctness. Thus in the fieldwork experience of the writer, it is noted that the Buddhist temple of Japan, when transplanted to America, possesses the organization of the Christian churches. It has a minister, an order of service, a Sunday School, a board of deacons or elders, a hymnology, and so on. There is every indication that the aspirations of American life, indeed, the problem of survival itself, are met by conformity. If one considers merely that the individual is confronted with a value system, a legal system, a uniform pattern of aims, aspirations, and goals, there is an organic integrity and wholeness to American culture.

The concept of culture as employed by anthropologists has been subject to some rather unfortunate misunderstandings on the part of other social scientists, whether objective or applied. For culture is not necessarily behavior, however much the terms society and culture are confused. In the concept of culture one may understand the definitions which lie behind action and behavior. In other words, men act because they hold certain truths to be self-evident. It is the ostensibly self-evident truth with which one is concerned in the cul-

ture concept; it is the definition of the situation, the evaluation of the relations between man and man, between man and the supernatural, between man and the universe. The line between culture and values is admittedly difficult to draw. But culture and values are not the same things; given the definition of the situation, men proceed to build systems of values on the basis of truths which they consider to be fundamental and intrinsic. Values, as a result, can only be viewed as relative, never as absolutes. But it is in culture that there lies a basis of prediction, not of the course of specific events, but rather or what the individual will do in a given circumstance. If I remark to my small boy—"but boys don't cry," I have not only indicated that such behavior falls short of the expected, i.e., the predictable, but I have also gone far to enculturate. I have not only informed the child of the behavior expected of him but I have succeeded in some measure in internalizing in the child the beginnings of self-image in the male role in this culture.

It is often said that society precedes culture. Men, in other words, must live together before they can establish the ground rules necessary to further living together. It is here that the comparative knowledge brought out by the anthropological approach is of assistance. One may consider, for example, the case of the Apache Indians for whom the anthropologist Morris Opler notes: "Childhood is not an end in itself, but a period of preparation for adulthood." This statement is significant only when American and Apache norms are compared. Clearly, in American culture of today, childhood is viewed, however implicitly, as an end in itself. One has merely to consider the vast array of items designed to preoccupy children—the school itself, the toy industry, television programs, Santa Claus, the Easter Rabbit, and Disneyland with its complex associations. It is evident also that the transition from childhood to adulthood, given this cultural definition among ourselves, can be traumatic and result in the storm and stress of adolescence. As Margaret Mead has shown, the Samoans, with a different cultural definition of childhood, never experience the griefs of transition.

Or one might go further down the line and consider other cultural premises as they affect man in modern society in the United States. American action, for example, clearly rests on the premise that the world and the nature of man are inherently good and improvable. This means, of course, that contemporary society accepts the view that man can triumph over nature and that man can and does rise to new heights of progress. This premise rests, one may be sure, in the history of Western civilization and in the Judeo-Christian ideology of the triumph of good over evil. But whatever the origins of the concept, behavior among ourselves is couched in terms of these fundamental assumptions, so much so, in fact, that individuals are not only not capable of verbalizing them, but tend to start in alarm when the question of their validity is raised. American culture welcomes change, technological change especially, forgetting that this may have marked repercussions for the total social structure, the way in which the individual relates to his fellows, and to the place occupied by him. On the sociological level, this is the time-honored example of the cultural lag: the disparity between material achievement and the solution to the problem of living socially with it.

It is scarcely necessary to call attention to the corollaries of the fundamental assumptions of American culture. With the sociologist, for example, one can point to the changing composition of rural populations, to the fact that they no longer exist as such but are, by virtue of increased communications and mobility, drawn into the urban orbit. Or one may show how urbanism in the traditional sense is gone, being replaced by the burdens of an industrialized society with its decentralization of industry and its growing pattern of suburban living. Again, one can point to the whole problem of mobility as an important factor in the fragmentation of human relationships, as for example, in the increasing nucleation of the family, the breakdown of deeper, more permanent, and supportive relationships, with both kinsmen and friends.

Here is obviously not the place to consider at length the area of individuation and the essential isolation of the person as features characteristic of American society. One may consider Weber's view, as well as that of Tawney, of the individualized capitalistic Protestant ethic, go with Max Lerner into his analysis of the distinctive attributes of American culture, or hold with Riesman and Whyte in respect to mass society and its nature. Regardless of prophecies of doom, one can be objective. There does seem to be a loss, as a result of individualized separateness, of some of the features which characterized the frontier or which anthropologists find diagnostic of peasant or folk societies. Such a loss is seemingly a concomitant of our cultural surroundings and is perhaps a reflection of industrialization and its effects on social living. The Soviet Union, for all its vaunted collectivism, obviously faces the same kind of problem. Nor does totalitarian control do other than shift men's loyalties away from the organic society to the artificially conceived state. While American society has not done this, and happily never will, it still pays a price for increasing industrialization, a price measured in the gradual departure from the deep roots of tradition. If there is regarded as desirable in human activity a sense of support, a deeply founded series of expressions relating to dependence between man and man rather than independence (points which are of course debatable), American society has tended to lose in depth in favor of momentary fulfillment. Such statements, it is true, could not be made were it not for the data collected from other cultures which make comparison possible. Nor is this to say that American society and culture are found wanting. It is merely to note that there are alternative solutions to the problems of human living. If American society can be viewed with greater objectivity, some of the issues which confront the social worker and the educator might more readily be resolved.

## The American Family

It is axiomatic that no society can operate effectively without the family. This is the primary institution, the instrument of procreation, the agent of socialization. One need examine only a fraction of the extensive literature on the family, that produced by the professional sociologist, to gain the impression that in American life today the family and its associated kinship system have taken on a special coloring. The sense of personal independence and autonomy relates closely to family aspirations with the result that the extended kinship unit of the past is in eclipse. Perhaps, as family size increases, and we are told that this is a trend, the individualism which is fostered by the present system will to some degree fade. But in these present decades the notion that the young married couple should forage for itself, set up its independent household, raise its children independently of the grandparental generation or the extended family, find its social outlets in a peer group of like age, retain the most casual relations with the extended kindred of both, and so on through a host of isolating features like these remains uppermost. It is significant that the cultural premises of American life create a situation in which the unmarried person creates a problem; his status both socially and psychologically remains in doubt. This may, in fact, be an important factor in reducing the age of marriage in American society. It is curious that a society which stresses so heavily a moral tone should find it easier to accommodate the divorced person than the bachelor. But it is also significant that the primary function of the family, that of socializing the young, is not materially altered. Conceptually, at least, in legalistic terms, in terms of societal expectations, the family assumes a responsibility at this level. What has changed is the depth and extent of the view of the family as a socializing agent. At what point, it may be asked, does family responsibility for a child come to be shared with the total society itself?

The above suggests then that there are some quite specific functions of the family in American society. This is a tightly structured society in its quite limited prescription of the ways in which a child may be handled and the extent of freedom accorded the parent. One has only to consider the overview of American culture and society which comes from the pen of Dr. Benjamin Spock and his imitators or from the accurate predictive analysis of Gesell and Ilg. Conversely, however, the parent has certain alternative ways of acceptable action open to him. Both parents may be employed and the very young child farmed out to the sitter or the nursery school. There is marked mobility in American culture with the result that the nucleated family may move at random to any part of the geographical limits of the society. These are elements which suggest a looseness of organization and which point to an important aspect of modern American life—the family must operate

within quite precisely defined vertical limits, even if these are not wholly deeply rooted, but it is free to expand horizontally. On the level of child rearing, and bearing generally help from an extended kinship group, this means that the society must utilize institutions other than the family to enhance the socialization process. It is here that there is a functional and structural reason for the school and the educational institutions generally. A school is not to learn. It is in large measure to substitute for the socializing and social institutions which in the European ethnic backgrounds out of which most Americans come were of another kind.

One should anticipate some disagreement with these remarks on the part both of the social worker and the educator. In answer, attention may be called to a discussion based on social system, on the issue of how the American family exists as an entity different from the family of the Japanese, the Arabs, or various of the modern Europeans. Because of the nature of the social system of which the American family forms a part, it can be asserted that there is actually little latitude in behavior or choice for individuals. This is not to say that freedom of choice is wholly precluded. But such freedom is meaningful only with defined limits. The polygynous family, for example, cannot exist. Or one may learn from the sociologist that there may be differences in expectations on the parts of persons coming from different backgrounds. And there is a profuse and consistent body of information on matters of this kind. Not only is the nature of the American child rearing process known in some detail, but the expectations and goals of varying elements in the society are also understood. Thus the differences as between social classes, that defined on the basis of economic status as well as educational attainment, are further reflected in attitudes toward child rearing, toward goals in education, and in respect to the achievement and expectation of success. These are important and meaningful on certain levels. In the end, however, they become minutiae when viewed against individualized, competitive, and isolating elements characteristic of the total social fabric.

How does the family in American society act as a socializing agent? Students of personality as related to socio-cultural systems have repeatedly demonstrated how the socializing elements resident in social systems reach the individual, are channeled, integrated, intensified, internalized, so as to produce a personality oriented in a specific direction. Ego strength, development of the super-ego, the severity or laxness of pressure in one or another direction have their bearing on the development of the adult personality and its relations to the values systems which become characteristic of any cultural milieu. Thus as one anthropologist has pointed out, there are those cultures which stress sanctions of shame as against those which concern themselves more deeply with an internalized sense of guilt. Or similarly, the whole problem of integrated anxiety or of any other aspect of covert development is involved here. Since it is generally regarded as axiomatic that the child is father to the man, socialization, enculturation, the fixing of values and personality patterns occur at the earliest age levels.

Clearly, in American society, the moral role attributed to the family in inculcating the value systems of American life suggests that the family is by no means becoming blurred in its functional outlines. That it has changed in composition is unquestionable. The days are clearly gone when the socializing agency might lie in alternate generations, such as between grandparent and grandchild. The parent himself in the nucleated family system of today is obliged to assume a good many socializing roles, more indeed than would have been the case among pioneer and rural families of tradition, and certainly more than is true of other Western areas, such as in Europe. The child learns at home, from his peer groups, through mass media, and through the recognized moral institution of the church, the latter especially becoming a surrogate for the family and implementing and complementing the school system. Not only does the family in American society fix the primary personality patterns, those which reflect the unconscious orientations leading to the formation of a modal personality type, but regardless of social class and background, the child learns certain kinds of information. His orientations toward the world, his views about acceptable and unacceptable behavior, his basic moral code, i.e., the total "good" and "bad" pattern, folkways and folklore are imparted through the socializing agencies relating to the very young, to the infant and

child whose world the culture itself must define. But more than this, learning involves initially language, it relates to the formation of the major motor responses, and it does not omit such aspects as food preferences, manner of sleeping, postures, gestures, and a host of related psycho-biological features. Thus when the child finally comes to school, he has already been patterned, his likes and dislikes are defined, his moral sense is on the way to realization, and it is to all these that the educational institutions give additional enforcement. The child, in short, approaches the school system as a functioning member of society.

What has been said here of the enculturative process is of course true of all societies. Differences lie not only in the varying kinds of information imparted and the kind of personality system developed, but also in the depth or intensity of the processes of internalization and learning. It has been so often remarked of contemporary society and culture that its variations preclude any generalizations. From what has been noted above this criticism is scarcely applicable. When social class, for example, is viewed as an independent variable influencing the enculturative process among ourselves, as a good many studies have attempted to show, there is a corresponding lack of attention to differences or variations in the consequent personality type. The demands of the culture, in spite of conceptual pluralism, create an American personality mode, one operative within the framework of individualized competitiveness but at the same time one which must accommodate itself to the demands of mass society. This paradox creates a modern problem. It is a problem which becomes vital in regard to the interrelations of school and society or family in American life and it reflects the great difficulty of defining the functions of school and family and their respective allocation. If the age of school attendance is reduced, and clearly this seems to be happening, then some of the traditional functions of the family are being arrogated by impersonal social institutions.

### The Educational Institutions—Manifest and Latent Functions

Traditionally, "a school is to learn . . ." This means, of course, that in the history of Western culture, especially as it has unfolded since the Protestant Reformation, the emphasis on individual responsibility and achievement has grown over the centuries, reaching a kind of apogee in the scientism of the nineteenth century. Since then, learning for learning's sake has tended to be refocused. A Ph.D., that degree reflective of German pedantry and ostensibly pointless investigation, tends now to require that the holder occupy a position of service in society, at least, that his researches find some ultimate or, more likely, some immediate application. These views stand in sharp contrast to the old-fashioned view that the person be learned and cultured and that this is the primary of education.

In terms of the concepts which underlie education in modern society the mere idea that only academic skills are to be acquired is clouded by the multi-pronged aims of the school. Philosophies of education do, it is true, differ from community to community, but the pendulum seems to swing gradually away from an orthodox Deweyism. Despite marked variation in approach, at least as they are seen and defended by vocal protagonists, the problems of the educator, as indeed of the social worker, appear to arise in the contrast between training for individual attainment and achievement for the ends of society. "Helping people to help themselves," the cliche of the social worker, a view implicit in professional education, poses paradox in pitting social desiderata against individual realization. The resolution at present seems to lie at varying points on a complex continuum. But the issue, as seen by the social analyst, is not which method is better but rather how the educational institutions function to stabilize the total social fabric.

The school, in addition to the problem of imparting knowledge and skills, is confronted with wholly new issues. One can readily sympathize with the educator whose task is to fashion a frame of reference in which to resolve them. What the school does, therefore, is not a cause of the disharmonies in the social body; it is apparent that education must come to grips with a change in the total configuration and patterning of American social behavior and values. On the manifest level, with the increasing nucleation of the family over the past five decades, the school has the task of molding sound character and enhancing the formation of a wholesome personality. Inevitably, it is faced with the problem of creating a sound social adjustment for those entrusted to its care, a fact which is probably borne out in the "conformist" tendencies of the modern teen-ager. Similarly, in effecting preparation for life, the school becomes the guardian of the culture, being left with the necessity for instilling the sense of democratic citizenship and of spiritual and moral values. Add to this the concerns with vocational skills and their inculcation, the problem of helping the individual "discover himself," and the task is endless. It is small wonder that points of view differ and that the spirit of individualism should conflict with the ends of the social aggregate.

But of course these are areas in which the educator as professional has been vitally concerned. He is aware of the problems but finds difficulty in drawing the lines of definition. Whether he does so in terms of the so-called "child-centered school" or whether he moves into a more conservative area, he is still operating in terms of the overt, in the area of the socio-cultural commonality of understanding which assigns manifest functions to the school system. In other words, while there may be disagreement in detail and implementation, the concept that the "school is to learn" continues to underlie any concept of education.

From a strictly objective viewpoint, however, one which attempts to utilize the methods of science without associated value judgments, any institution has latent functions. There are aspects of institutional organization of which those involved, whether in a participant or directive capacity, are not necessarily wholly aware. To take a cross example, while all of us, as citizens, welcome the changing social status of the Negro in America and applaud the legal edicts which have made this so, we may also, as scientists, recognize that racial tensions, particularly in the Deep South, reflect a stability of social institutions, that the scapegoat psychology directed toward the Negro may have a function in channeling the aggressive and hostile drives of some individuals and groups. To modify these by legislation is not wholly to resolve the problem. In other words, racial tensions as they have existed among ourselves, however much we as individuals may dislike them, have to be seen objectively as serving some kind of purpose and function. Hearts may, it is true, bleed for the Negro; this does not alleviate the hatred, the hostility, or indeed the anxiety arising because of the appearance of certain kinds of disreputable conservatism.

Thus, if the school has taken over all the manifest functions noted above, what is left? What does the educational institution do covertly in maintaining the social whole and how does it interfunction with other segments of the society? Because institutions interact, it may be affirmed that the changing functions of the family cause the school to assume a greater share of the burden of socialization than was formerly the case. Are the schools creating a longer and longer day for the child because the parent wishes to be free of the obligations of parenthood? Or conversely, is there talk of reducing vacation time because the school believes that its sphere of influence is being intruded upon? This is not a "chicken and egg" proposition but rather one which is reflective of an interaction between school and family. The effects, in any case, are clear; the child is removed more and more from his family group. The number of people who formerly would be thrown into closest contact with children becomes increasingly reduced. This takes place not only through the general length of the school day but also through the group aims of the educational system and its ancillary elements.

If one considers that the child in America of today has a long school day, one realizes that his activities are highly diffuse and that he is put in the position of interacting with a host of people and groups. Monday through Friday, involved in the day itself, a period of hours, it may be noted, far longer than is the case in the school system of the various countries of Europe, the child becomes further involved in a mass of extra-curricular activities. In American life today, urbanized as it is, Saturday calls for still further activity ranging from the involvements of the various voluntary associations, participation in spectator or consumer activities and sports, the cinema, the television medium, while Sunday is frequently given to yet another aspect of education in church and Sunday School, and otherwise follows the pattern of Saturday. The total result, one which even the most dedicated of educators in the American system must recognize, is the shift toward greater impersonality. Time is simply lacking to pause, to assess personal achievement, or to formulate depth in human relationships. There is, as the folklorists have shown, a great change in levels of participation—the spontaneous games which some of us knew as children are on the way out, being replaced by play engineered by institutional authority —and the end is worth spelling out. It is loss of creativity and a lessening dependence on the rich traditions of the culture.

The constant push to be occupied, the "busyness" of which American culture makes so much, unquestionably has its effects on the formation of the value system of the child. The idealized adult tends less to be a family member and more to involve an impersonal associate of the society at large—a teacher, a minister, a scoutmaster. This means that images become inconsistent, undependable, and that the cultural traditions take on a diffuse quality. Where formerly an authoritarian grandparental figure might emerge, one predictable in terms of his strengths or weaknesses, but wholly predictable also in terms of enforcing cultural norms, the child of today can readily transfer his allegiance and find his ideal in a host of vaguely defined figures. The end result is that the skill of the child in interacting with other individuals is in itself changed. He is not necessarily less efficient nor yet less able but he lives in a society which accords worth to horizontal human relationships and tends to veer away from those reflecting emotional depth. By the same token, he is trained and socialized to accept essentially ephemeral human relationships. This is no more than affirmation of the fact that the cultural traditions are not deeply set. It is here that a real problem lies. It is expressed pointedly in a recent evaluation of the views of James B. Conant.

There is strong evidence that our ideal of classless middle-class society has been translated to mean that children must be molded into so-called democratic "look-alikes," if not "think-alikes." Our experience in two world wars has done much to encourage the idea of national society in uniform and in lock-step. There is a possibility that in a society influenced so greatly by the media of mass communication the individual, as an individual, can be lost. We may be in a new crisis in which it is necessary to defend the right of the individual as a scholar, as an artist, as a person, to discover himself and to express himself.

The educational institutions are confronted with the dilemma of substituting in some measure, indeed, extensively, for the family, of reaching the individual at a younger and and younger age. The school has been concerned with the "needs" of the individual in his development but finds difficulty in defining these needs as against those of the society itself. The end result is makeshift. Our culture is confronted with the dilemma of abhorring the collective and yet at the same time of realizing the Judeo-Christian ethic of the responsibility of man for man. Progressive education did not resolve the issue nor does a return to the rigid disciplining of pure subject matter curricula seem to hold much promise. What is indeed more practical is a recognition on the part of the educational system of its specific function in the whole society, an awareness that ours is a cultural tradition worth imparting and worth preserving both in its historic past and in its changing present.

*selection* 67

# *Healing Ways*

## *Lyle Saunders*

*From* Cultural Difference and Medical Care. *Russell Sage Foundation, 1954, pp. 141–173. Copyright 1954, Russell Sage Foundation. By permission of the author, and the publisher and copyright holder.*

With regard to illness and its treatment, as in other aspects of their culture, the Spanish-speaking people of the Southwest have many traits in common with the Anglos. Like most other people, they have minor ailments that they tend to disregard. Like all people, they occasionally have aches and pains, chills and fever, and other insistent symptoms that force them to seek relief. And, as in the case of most other people, what they do, how they do it, and when, are determined by the "knowledge" they have of the meaning and cause of their symptoms, and of what can or should be done about them. Such knowledge is a product of association with other people may be as restricted or expansive, as consistent or contradictory, as the range of their associations permits it to be. . . .

Illness and disease, it must be remembered, are social as well as biological phenomena. On the biological level they consist of adaptations of the organism to environmental influences; on the social level they include meanings, roles, relationships, attitudes, and techniques that enable members of a cultural group to identify various types of illness and disease, to behave appropriately, and to call upon a body of knowledge for coping with the condition as defined as an illness. *What is recognized as disease or illness is a matter of cultural prescription* [italics added], and a given biological condition may or may not be considered an "illness," depending on the particular cultural group in which it occurs. Infestation by intestinal worms is generally regarded as a type of disease by people in the United States. Among other people, for example the inhabitants of the island of Yap, worms are thought to be a necessary component of the digestive process. *Mal ojo, susto,* and *empacho* are examples of diseases that are common in Latin America but unknown in the United States— with the exception of the Spanish-speaking Southwest—although the symptoms which give rise to diagnoses of any or all of these are fairly common in this country. What should be done about a given condition defined culturally as "illness" and the proper relationships of a sick person to other people are also culturally prescribed. An individual thus has cultural guides that enable him to know when he or others may be regarded as sick, something about the cause and nature of the sickness, what may be done to alleviate or remedy the condition, and the behavior expected of him and of others in the situation. . . .

In adopting new ideas about illness and new materials and techniques for treating it, the Spanish-speaking people have not necessarily abandoned any of their old ideas or healing methods. Some individuals may have dropped certain practices used by their parents or grandparents in treating certain disease conditions, or may have failed to learn them, but in the Spanish-speaking population viewed as a whole most of the old ways persist in some form. Drugstores in the "Mexican" sections of Anglo cities in the Southwest do a thriving business in herbs and other folk remedies. *Parteras, curanderas, médicas, albolarias,* and even *brujas* still find a demand for their services in both rural and urban areas. Alternative types of medical service and methods of treatment are seldom mutually exclusive, so that the adoption of the new does not necessitate giving up the old. The new is merely added to the old body of knowledge or belief, and either or both are drawn upon, depending on the circumstances. The Spanish-speaking person who puts himself in the hands of an Anglo institution and practitioner for a surgi-

cal operation expects to receive the utmost benefit from Anglo knowledge and skill. If, subsequently, he wears a piece of *oshá* over the incision, this does not necessarily indicate any lack of faith in Anglo methods but rather his reliance on a wider range of "knowledge" than that possessed by the Anglos who are treating him. Penicillin and the other antibiotics admittedly reduce or prevent infection, but so, in his opinion, does *oshá*, and it does no harm to be doubly certain of results by using both.

**Folk Medicine**

Three of the four sources from which the Spanish-speaking people derive their ideas about sickness and its treatment provide them with types of knowledge, belief, and practice that may be classified as folk medicine. Folk medicine differs from "scientific" medicine in a number of ways. In any culture, it is generally the common possession of the group. In a folk culture, there is relatively little division of knowledge with respect to medicine, so that what one adult knows about illness and its treatment is usually known by all other adults. Although knowledge of the origins of folk medical practices and beliefs may have largely been lost, the practices and beliefs themselves are often so rooted in tradition that they seem a part of the natural order of things and are as much taken for granted as is the daily rising and setting of the sun. Folk medical lore is transmitted from person to person and generation to generation by informal methods and through what sociologists like to call unstructured situations. One learns it, much as he learns other elements of his culture, as an incidental part of his everyday associations. Folk medicine is usually well integrated with other elements of a folk culture and is reinforced by them. The expected attitude toward a given element of folk medicine is one of uncritical acceptance. Failure does not invalidate a practice or shake the belief on which it is based. A remedy is tried, and if it works no surprise is evinced, since that it what was expected. If it does not work, the failure is rationalized and something else tried. In most illnesses the patient ultimately either recovers or dies. If he gets well, the remedial technique is credited with effecting the cure. If he dies, the reason is not that the remedy was inappropriate, but that the patient was beyond help. Folk medicine, like scientific medicine, undoubtedly derives much of its prestige and authority from the fact that the majority of sick persons get well regardless of what is done.

If practitioners of scientific medicine think of folk medicine at all, they are likely to regard it as mere superstition or as a somewhat curious and outdated survival, having about the same relationship to medical science that astrology has to astronomy. But folk medicine, even in cultures with a well-developed tradition of scientific medicine, is a flourishing institution, and many folk practices have survived because they undoubtedly do get results. Although they are in general uncritically accepted by those using them, folk medical practices are subjected over a period of time to a rough empirical evaluation. Those that seem successful frequently come to be more and more used and thus firmly entrench themselves in the minds and behaviors of the group using them. Those that consistently fail to do what is expected of them tend to be used less and less frequently and, in time, may be dropped altogether. There thus operates a selective process that tends to weed out the ineffective practices and to strengthen those that prove to be effective.

Between scientific medicine and folk medicine there is a constant two-way interchange. Remedies that have been developed by scientific medicine become a part of the pharmacopoeia of folk medicine (for example, aspirin to relieve headaches or other minor aches and pains) and others with a long history of folk use are "discovered," analyzed, tested, and ultimately become a part of scientific medicine (for example, curare, quinine, cocaine). It is not the materials or procedures that determine whether a given technique represents folk or scientific medicine, but rather the way in which they are used and the body of knowledge or belief that lies behind the use. Scientific medicine is rooted in a precise knowledge of cause and effect relationships and a critical attitude toward both practices and results. Folk medicine is neither precise nor critical. It is rooted in belief, not knowledge, and it requires only occasional success to maintain its vigor.

The folk medicine of a given people, however, is usually not a random collection of beliefs and practices; rather, *it constitutes a fairly well-organized and fairly consistent theory of medicine* [italics added]. The body of "knowledge" on which it is based often includes ideas about the nature of man and his relationships with the natural, supernatural, and human environments. Folk medicine flourishes because it is a functional and integrated part of the whole culture, and because it enables members of cultural groups to meet their health needs, as they define them, in ways that are at least minimally acceptable.

The Spanish-speaking people of the Southwest, as has been indicated, draw their medical beliefs and practices from many sources. One of these, and one that particularly influences the medical beliefs and practices of the two groups we have called Mexicans and Mexican-Americans, is the folk medicine of Mexico. . . .

One widely dispersed body of knowledge and practice is that related to concepts of heat and cold as qualities both of disease conditions and of materials used in therapy. These concepts provide a means of determining what remedy may be used for a particular illness and what the consequences are likely to be if the wrong treatment is used. Illnesses are classified as hot and cold, without respect to the presence or absence of fever, and the correct therapy is to attain a balance by treating "hot" diseases with "cold" remedies and "cold" diseases with "hot" remedies. Foods, beverages, animals, and people possess the characteristics of "heat" or "cold" in varying degree, and it is thought wise always to maintain a proper regard for the principles of balance. "Hot" foods, for example, should never be combined, but rather should be taken in conjunction with something "cold," with care being used to see that extremes of heat and cold are not taken together. A person with a "cold" disease is endangered by being given "cold" remedies or foods, since these are likely to aggravate his condition. There is no general agreement on exactly what is "hot" or "cold"; therefore, the classification of a given material or condition may vary from place to place.

Another fairly common body of belief and practice in Mexico relates to the concept of the clean stomach and includes the idea that the maintenance of health requires a periodic purging of the stomach and intestinal tract. At least one disease, *empacho*, is thought to be directly due to failure to achieve a clean stomach, and the rather large number of purgatives used are evidence of the extent to which the concept is accepted.

Blood is considered important in the balance of health and disease and many folk remedies serve the function of purifying the blood or otherwise improving its quality. Loss of blood for any reason, even in the small amounts necessary for laboratory tests, is thought to have a weakening effect, particularly on males, whose sexual vigor is thereby believed to be impaired.

Illness is conceived primarily in terms of not feeling well. Conditions that are not accompanied by subjective feelings or discomfort are generally *not classified as illness* [italics added]; hence, there is no obligation to do anything about them. Health is looked upon as a matter of chance and it is felt that there is very little that a person can do to keep it. Minor discomforts usually are not sufficient motivations to seek treatment, and frequently persons are seriously ill before they begin to seek or accept help. There is a tendency to conceal illness, partly deriving from the idea that to be sick is a manifestation of weakness.

Air is considered potentially dangerous, particularly if cold or if it is blowing over one. Night air is more dangerous than day air, and persons already ill are thought to be particularly susceptible to the harm that air can bring. Consequently, sickrooms are not ventilated, and special care is taken to see that all windows and doors are closed at night.

Pregnancy requires adherence to many dietary restrictions and a reduction in the amount of water drunk, lest the head of the foetus grow too large for an easy delivery. Frequent bathing and regular exercise in the prenatal period are thought to facilitate the delivery process, which frequently takes place with the woman in a squatting or kneeling position. After the delivery the mother remains in bed for an extended period of time, and then she takes or is given a steam bath. During the first three days following delivery the diet is restricted to a small amount of "cold" foods. Thereafter, "hot" foods again may be eaten.

With respect to etiological factors, three types of causation are recognized: empirical, magical, and psychological. Empirical or "natural" diseases are those in which a known external factor operates directly on the organism to produce the illness. Any disorders resulting from exposure to bad air, invasion by microorganisms, contact with an infected person, eating improper foods, failure to keep a clean stomach, and similar hazards are considered "natural" diseases. A long list of illnesses, including pneumonia, rheumatism, diarrhea, colds, smallpox, worms, tuberculosis, and venereal disease, is placed in this category. Magical diseases are those in which the causative factors lie outside the realm of empirical knowledge and cannot be thus verified. Such a disease is *mal ojo*, or evil eye, which is produced in young children, often without intention, by persons who have a "strong glance." Some kinds of *susto*, a type of illness resulting from fright, are of magical etiology in that they are felt to be caused by the possession of an individual by an evil spirit. And there are, of course, many kinds of bewitchment in which a person with evil intent and magical power can cause illness symptoms in another. Psychological diseases are those in which a strong emotional experience causes the appearance of the disease symptoms. Examples are *susto* when it occurs in young children who have suffered a severe fright, or epilepsy, which is believed to result from strong emotional feelings.

For most illnesses there are appropriate remedies. The number and range of remedial measures are so great that only some of the major categories can be indicated here. Herbs are widely used in a variety of ways and for a large number of conditions. Tea made by boiling leaves or stems in water is a common remedy. Herbs are also taken with foods, are used in aromatic preparations whose fumes may be inhaled, are applied to external surfaces in the form of powder, and are worn in bags or cachets over parts of the body, much as the Anglos not so many years ago wore asafetida to ward off colds. Massage or some other form of manipulation of body parts is considered efficacious for some illnesses, and poultices and plasters of various kinds are used to produce both mechanical and magical effects. Salves and ointments are not uncommon; foods are both prescribed and withheld for remedial purposes; and various types of bathing are practiced. Prayer and the reciting of religious formulas are common forms of dealing with sickness, and where the illness is thought to be magical in nature, spells, charms, incantations, and other ritualistic practices may be utilized. In recent times, practices and materials have been borrowed from scientific medicine, and injections or "shots" have become a common form of treatment.

Mild disorders are treated by the afflicted person or by some member of his family. More serious cases, or those that do not yield to home treatment, may require calling in someone with more specialized knowledge. Who is called and when, depends on the type and seriousness of the disease, the degree of discomfort, the availability of specialized help, and the probable cost of obtaining assistance. If the disease is a "natural" one that is fairly serious or uncomfortable, a physician may be called in to assist rather early in its course, provided a doctor is available and the problem of payment is not insuperable. Physicians, it is felt, understand "natural" diseases and are able to do something about them. But if the disease is thought to be of magical or psychological origin, assistance is more likely to be sought from a *curandera*, a *bruja*, or some other type of folk specialist, since they are assumed to be more familiar with and, hence, better able to treat such diseases. A complaint of *susto* or *mal ojo* will be listened to understandingly by a folk specialist, and the patient will be assured that his ailment is being treated. But to make such a complaint to a practitioner of scientific medicine would be to expose oneself to the possibility of skeptical disbelief, condemnation, or even ridicule, a circumstance that most patents and their families prefer to avoid. . . .

Probably one of the most widely used, and certainly one of the most efficacious, remedies of the Spanish-American villages was *oshá*, a plant of the parsley family, to which reference has already been made, whose properties were probably learned from the Indians. The healing qualities of *oshá* are largely concentrated in the root, which may be used in many ways to treat a wide variety of illnesses. Chewed raw or ground into a powder and made into a tea, it prevents flatulency and soothes the stomach. Drunk in hot water with sugar and whiskey, it will break up a cold and help to cure such respiratory illnesses as influenza, pneumonia, and pulmonary tuberculosis. Taken internally it will also reduce fevers. Applied directly to a wound in powdered form, or worn over a wound, *oshá* promotes healing. An ointment for the relief and cure of cuts and sores can be made from mutton fat, candle wax, and turpentine into which is mixed some powdered *oshá* root, *manzanilla* (camomile), and *contrayerba* (caltrop). Mixed with olive oil, *oshá* can be used as a liniment in the treatment of rheumatic pains, and it is also useful, in the form of a paste, to draw out the poison from snakebites. In addition, this highly versatile plant is used as the basis of an enema, as a remedy for colic in children, and as a means of protection against snakes, which are believed to be repelled by its pungent odor. *Oshá* has recently entered into Anglo folk medicine as an ingredient in a cough remedy prepared and sold by a Denver druggist. It is also useful as a seasoning for soups and stews.

The familiar onion of Anglo home remedies is also put to many uses by the Spanish-Americans. Roasted and applied hot, *cebollas* are thought to be effective in treating chilblains. Teething babies are allowed to chew the leaves and stems to relieve the pain of swollen gums. A cough syrup made of the juice of fried or roasted onions sweetened with honey or sugar is thought to be an excellent treatment for colds, particularly in the case of babies. *Inmortal* (spider milkweed) likewise has many uses. Powdered and mixed with water, it can be drunk to reduce headache or chest pains or to bring down a fever. Made into a paste and used as a poultice, it will relieve pains of various kinds. It is also useful in childbirth. Rubbed on the abdomen or taken with cold water it will reduce labor pains, and drunk with hot water after delivery it helps to expel the placenta. Asthma, shortness of breath, and similar afflictions may be helped by drinking a tea made of *inmortal*.

Not even a representative sample of the many plants used in the folk medicine of Spanish-Americans can be given here. But some indication of the extent of the list and of the familiarity to Anglos of many items on it may be obtained from a brief mention of the popular Anglo names of a few of the plants used: cattails, garlic, cottonwood, basil, apricot, camphor, alfalfa, lavender, aster, licorice, sunflower, anise, sagebrush, cocklebur, pumpkin, thistle, elderberry, lupine, algae, oleander, milkweed, corn, mustard, golden-rod, tansy, and mint. And not only plants but animals, animal products, and nonorganic substances find their place in the list of reme-dies, as can be seen in a mention of rattle-snake oil, cowhide, lime, rennet, milk, red ants, bones, alum, earth, and rock of various kinds, each of which, along with many other substances, is used in the treatment of some type of illness. . . .

## Folk Medicine and Scientific Medicine

Anglo practice and village practice with re-gard to childbirth differ in several important respects. Anglo physicians, who are in a posi-tion to advise practicing midwives, recom-mend that the patient be delivered in bed to lessen the possibility of postpartum hemor-rhage. They advise that the mother should remove her clothing, that the *partera* should scrub her hands and arms with strong soap before approaching the mother, that the scis-sors used for severing the cord be washed in soapy water, that the mother be given a sponge bath soon after delivery. There has been a strong tendency, however, for many of the *parteras* to look upon Anglo medical ways as different from but not appreciably better than their traditional medicine and to continue to use their own more familiar meth-ods. Or, if the Anglo methods are adopted, their efficacy may be reduced by the failure of the *partera* to grasp the reasons behind their use. The scissors, after being washed with soap, may be dried with an unsterile cloth or placed on a table that has not been cleaned. Water that has been boiled may be poured when cool into an unsterile container. The acceptance of Anglo ways may represent merely the adoption of new elements into an old pattern in which the new procedures are not understood in terms of the Anglo reasons for their use, but instead are fitted into the already existing pattern of understanding with respect to causation and healing of illness and disease. Just as Anglo medical personnel tend to see many of the Spanish-American folk practices as either worthless or danger-ous, so Spanish-Americans are inclined to be skeptical about the efficacy, necessity, and safety of some of the Anglo healing practices, and may be at times reluctant to accept them. Surgical procedures, in particular, are fre-quently regarded as harmful, dangerous, and unnecessary, and many villagers can tell of someone who was done irreparable damage by an operation or who, being advised by an Anglo physician that an operation was abso-lutely necessary, was thereafter cured by some folk procedure.

The transition from Spanish-American folk-ways to the acceptance and use of Anglo sci-entific medicine is complicated by the fact that folk medical knowledge is widely dissemi-nated, so that anyone giving medical care is subject to the critical attention of relatives and friends of the patient, who are always ready to step in and insist on changes in treatment or to add to what is being done if they feel that proper care is not being given. Thus, the *partera* who has learned some new techniques from a physician or from the train-ing program of the State Department of Pub-lic Health may find herself constrained by the pressure of family opinion to forego her new knowledge and to continue with old ways. Knowing as well as she what herbs may be used to hasten delivery or check postpartum bleeding, the family have provided them, and they are likely to interpret the failure of the *partera* to use them as resulting from igno-rance or indifference to the welfare of the patient. They *know* these traditional remedies assure comfort and safety for the patient, and they are likely to feel that no treatment proc-ess can be good which withholds them.

Among many Spanish-American villagers, Anglo medicine is regarded as something to be used chiefly as a last resort when all other known procedures have failed. Consequently, for a long time, the Anglo record of success-ful treatment was less good than it need have been because too frequently Anglo practition-ers were not consulted until the case was practically hopeless. Most of the successes in treatment were thus credited to folk practices; many of the failures were charged to Anglo medicine. As a result, another barrier to the acceptance of Anglo medicine was raised through the development of the belief, which could be supported by reference to known cases, that Anglo medical institutions were places where people went to die.

The continued use of their own medical practices by Spanish-Americans sometimes leads the Anglo, who knows his ways are better, to characterize Spanish-Americans as ignorant or superstitious, to accuse them of being indifferent to the well-being of their families and friends, and to become impatient and annoyed at their failure to see the obvious benefits of Anglo procedures. What such Anglos fail to appreciate is that Spanish-Americans also *know* that their ways are superior and that their use, far from constituting neglect of or indifference to the needs of sick relatives and friends, actually constitutes the provision of first-rate medical care. The Anglo may argue that by the pragmatic test of results his *is* the best medicine and that the Spanish-American ought to have enough sense to see it. But the evidence of the superiority of Anglo medicine is not always available to the Spanish-American in a form that has meaning to him and, in any case, what is or is not "good sense" is relative to culture. In utilizing his own knowledge and that of his friends, relatives, and neighbors, and when that fails, in calling in a *médica* or *curandera* or even a *bruja*, the Spanish-American villager is acting in a way that is eminently sensible in the light of his convictions about the nature of disease and the proper ways to deal with it. To behave otherwise, to disregard what he knows and subject himself or a member of his family to a course of treatment that may bear no particular relationship to his understanding of disease, simply because some Anglos say that it is what he should do, would constitute a very strange kind of behavior indeed.

Sickness, particularly if it be serious, is likely to be viewed as a crisis, and in situations of crisis people in all cultures tend to resort to those patterns of thinking and acting that have been most deeply ingrained in them as a result of their cultural experiences. To meet a crisis with the resources of one's culture, whatever they may be, is to behave in a manner that is both sensible and sound; it is, in fact, to behave in the only way that most human beings can under such circumstances. The Spanish-American, in utilizing the medical ways of his culture is neither ignorant nor indifferent. If he knew no way of dealing with illness, he might be called ignorant. But he does know something to do, frequently many things. If he did nothing, he might be called indifferent. But he does something, and continues to do something while his resources remain undepleted or until he achieves results. The sequence in which he does things is determined by the differential value he places on the various procedures as they apply to the particular situation. If the seeking of Anglo medical care is, for a given illness, well down on the list, it is because this is the way he sees the particular procedure in relation to the others that are available to him. That an Anglo, in a similar situation, might have a different set of resources and a different order of importance for them, cannot be expected to have any considerable influence on his behavior. . . .

## Reasons for Anglo Medicine Not Being More Extensively Used

A number of explanations can be found for the failure of Spanish-speaking people in close contact with Anglo culture to adopt completely its medical ways. One such factor is certainly the extent to which Anglo medical services and facilities are available. Although the Spanish-speaking are rapidly becoming urbanized, many of them still live in rural areas where medical personnel and facilities are not readily available. Large numbers of Spanish-speaking people live in sparsely settled areas where one has to drive many miles to see a physician or enter a hospital. A map of health facilities in New Mexico, prepared in 1946 for the New Mexico Health Council, showed four counties to be completely without medical facilities and a large part of the state to lie outside a 30-mile radius from any type of health facility. In parts of Colorado, Arizona, and Texas, similar conditions exist. The present widespread distribution of automobiles and recent improvements in rural roads have done much to make Anglo medicine more readily available to rural Spanish-speaking people and have undoubtedly contributed to its somewhat greater use. But there still remain many areas where, either because of sparseness of population or a high concentration of Spanish-speaking people among the residents of the areas, it would be quite difficult to get to an Anglo doctor or hospital even if one were highly motivated to do so.

Another factor related to availability is that of cost. Anglo medical care is expensive and the Spanish-speaking, as a group, are poor. In many instances they cannot afford, or do not feel that they can afford, the services of a physician or a sojourn in a hospital. Anglo medicine involves bills for home or office calls, some likelihood of being given an expensive prescription, and the possibility of surgery, or hospitalization for some other reason, which may be very costly. A *médica* usually does not charge much and under certain circumstances can be paid with products instead of cash, a definite advantage to those living in rural areas. Her medicines are not likely to cost much, and there is little likelihood that she will recommend hospitalization or an operation. Diagnosis and treatment by oneself and one's family cost little or nothing, and for many minor illnesses can be quite satisfactory. These differences in costs certainly constitute an influence in the readiness or reluctance with which an individual or family makes the decision to seek any given type of medical care.

Lack of knowledge of Anglo medical ways is probably another factor in the extent to which Spanish-speaking people do or do not use Anglo practitioners and facilities. The simple matter of getting in touch with a doctor and putting oneself under his care can seem complicated to a person who is not at ease in either the English language or Anglo medical culture. How does one find a doctor? How can one be sure that the chosen doctor will be either competent or *simpatico*? How is a doctor approached? How can one know in advance how much the treatment will cost or what will be the expected manner of payment? What illnesses may properly be taken to a physician? These and other questions, the answers to which most of us take for granted, can be puzzling to persons not wholly familiar with Anglo culture, and can be effective barriers to the initiation of a doctor-patient relationship, particularly when the potential patient may not be highly motivated in the direction of wanting Anglo medicine.

Closely related to a lack of knowledge of Anglo medical ways as a deterrent to seeking Anglo medical care is the factor of fear. That which is strange or unknown is often feared, and there is much in Anglo medicine that is strange and fear inducing even to Anglo laymen. The instruments used, the pain that sometimes accompanies their use, and the unfamiliar surroundings of the office, clinic, or hospital in which they are used, all can arouse fear. So can the unfamiliar elements in the medical routine—the examination procedure, the invasion of one's physical and mental privacy, the uncertainty of the diagnostic procedure, the incomprehensible language that may be used. For a Spanish-speaking person, for example, a physical examination can be a very unpleasant experience, particularly if it involves the participation of persons of the opposite sex. The fear of being examined by a man is sometimes enough to keep Spanish-speaking women away from Anglo medical practitioners and to make traumatic for others the contact they have with Anglo medicine. Foster reports the failure of a considerable proportion of women coming to a prenatal clinic in Mexico City to return for a follow-up visit after their initial experience, which included an unexpected physical examination. It is not without significance for the medical relations of Spanish-speaking and Anglos in the Southwest that most of the healing personnel in the culture of the Spanish-speaking are women, whereas proportionately more of those in the Anglo culture are men. Spanish-speaking men, too, are likely to have some reluctance to subjecting themselves to examination by Anglo physicians and to being placed in potentially embarrassing situations with Anglo nurses.

Another possible factor that may operate is resistance to being separated from one's family and being isolated for an indefinite time in an Anglo institution, where all relationships are likely to be impersonal. Good medical care, from the Anglo point of view, requires hospitalization for many conditions. Good medical care, as defined in the culture of the Spanish-Americans, requires that the patient be treated for almost any condition at home by relatives and friends, who are constantly in attendance and who provide emotional support as well as the technical skills required in treatment. In time of sickness one expects his family to surround and support him, and to supervise closely and critically, if not actually carry on, the treatment process. Members of the family, in turn, feel obligated to remain close to the patient, to take charge of his treatment, and to reassure him as to his place in and importance to the family group. The Anglo practice of hospitalization, with the treatment being taken over by professional strangers and the family relegated to the meager role permitted by the visiting regulations, runs counter to the expectation patterns of the Spanish-speaking and, thus, may be a factor in the reluctance of some members of the group to seek or accept Anglo medical care.

There are some illnesses for which Anglo medical care is not sought because, as has already been noted, the type of sickness is not ordinarily known to Anglo practitioners. A patient suffering from *mal ojo, susto,* and similar conditions seeks relief, if at all, from someone who is familiar with these diseases and who, therefore, may be expected to know something about the proper method of treatment. This difference between the two cultures in the conceptualization of disease serves to restrict the range of conditions for which Anglo medical assistance might be sought to those recognized by both cultural groups and gives to the folk practitioner almost exclusive influence in dealing with those conditions that are recognized only by the Spanish-speaking group.

A final factor that may be mentioned as possibly contributing to the hesitancy of Spanish-speaking people to use Anglo medicine is that such attempts as are made often do not provide the satisfactions that the Spanish-speaking expect. With the *curandera* and *médica* the whole process of diagnosis and treatment moves along in an atmosphere of informal cooperation and collaboration between patient, family, and the healer. Alternative procedures are discussed and courses of treatment agreed upon, with the opinions of patient and family frequently being given much weight in the final decisions. The folk practitioner works less as an independent specialist than as a consultant and technician who implements the therapeutic plans of the patient or his family, all of whom remain very much in the picture throughout the treatment period. All know what is going on and why. All are free to offer suggestions and criticisms. The diagnosis and treatment of illness thus involve active participation by the patient and members of his family in a situation in which the relationships are mainly personal and informal. Diagnosis is usually easy and swift, and treatment follows immediately.

By contrast, Anglo medicine is likely to be somewhat impersonal and formal. It is expected that the patient will be turned over to the physician, who will then direct the diagnostic and treatment procedures, largely without the benefit of advice or suggestion from either the patient or his family. Information may be sought from both, but usually only for the purpose of getting at the present complaints or learning the patient's medical history. Diagnosis may be slow and may involve techniques that are not understood by the patient or his family. Treatment may be delayed pending the establishment of a definite diagnosis and, when instituted, may involve hospitalization of the patient. The patient and his family are expected to be relatively passive participants in a situation in which most of the new relationships established are impersonal, businesslike, and, frequently, very unsatisfactory. In treatment by either folk practitioner or physician the possible range of outcomes is about the same. The patient may get better, may remain as he is, may get worse, may die. There being no conclusive evidence of the relatively greater frequency of desirable results when using Anglo medicine than when relying on folk healers, the amount of satisfaction that patient and family get in the medical relationship becomes an important factor in determining which of the two types of medicine they will select.

The most important differences between Spanish-American folk medicine and Anglo scientific medicine that influence the choice of one or the other are these: Anglo scientific medicine involves largely impersonal relations, procedures unfamiliar to laymen, a passive role for family members, hospital care, considerable control of the situation by professional healers, and high costs; by contrast the folk medicine of Spanish-American villagers is largely a matter of personal relations, familiar procedures, active family participation, home care, a large degree of control of the situation by the patient or his family, and relatively low costs. Given these differences, it is easy to understand why a considerable motivation would be necessary for a Spanish-American to have any strong preference for Anglo medicine over that which is not only more familiar and possibly psychologically more rewarding —or at least less punishing—but also less expensive.

Despite the many factors that operate to hinder the seeking and acceptance of Anglo medical care by Spanish-speaking people of the Southwest, however, Anglo medicine is rapidly coming to play an increasingly larger part in the total complex of attitudes and activities of the Spanish-speaking people with respect to illness and health. In cities where Anglo medical facilities and personnel are accessible, the use made of them by the Spanish-speaking probably is not greatly different in either amount or kind from that of Anglos of comparable social class status. In some rural areas, activities of private practitioners, medical groups, health cooperatives, local and state health departments, and, particularly, public health nurses have brought a considerable amount of Anglo medicine within the reach of Spanish-speaking people and have done much to develop the attitudes necessary to the acceptance and use of Anglo medical ways. If we think of the Spanish-speaking population as distributed along a continuum ranging from complete reliance on their own folk medicine at one pole to the complete acceptance of Anglo scientific medicine at the other, the greatest numbers would be concentrated near the center, with the highest proportion probably being found on the Anglo half of the continuum. . . .

*selection   68*

# *Salvage Archaeology*

## *J. O. Brew*

. . . In 1945 a group of archaeologists realized, suddenly, the tremendous amount of destruction that was threatened in the River Basin projects of the United States Bureau of Reclamation and the Corps and Engineers. At that time 108 dams had been authorized in the Missouri Basin alone. Since almost all of the prehistoric and early historic occupation of the Missouri was on the banks of the main stream and its tributaries, a large part of our heritage there was scheduled to go under water. In North and South Dakota, the Oahe Lake alone is to be 308 miles long and lakes almost as large are now filling up immediately upstream and downstream from it. And the threat lies not only in the Missouri, but in river basins all over the country, from Oregon to New England and from Minnesota to Texas.

To meet this threat an independent group, the Committee for the Recovery of Archaeological Remains, was organized to represent the archaeologists of the nation. It was sponsored by the American Council of Learned

*From Introduction.*
*In Fred Wendorf,*
*A Guide for Salvage*
*Archaeology, Museum*
*of New Mexico Press,*
*1962, pp. 14–25.*
*Copyright 1962, The*
*Museum of New Mexico*
*Press. By permission of*
*the author, the publisher,*
*and the copyright holder.*

Societies, the Society for American Archaeology, and the American Anthropological Association. The task seemed overwhelming, and to archaeologists a frontal attack upon the forces of bureaucracy was almost appalling. But a few were found who, inexperienced as they were in the Washington maelstrom, nonetheless, recognized the dire necessity, and assumed the chore.

Enthusiastic assistance was obtained at the outset from the archaeologists in the Smithsonian Institution who prepared specific estimates of ways, means, and costs. On the administrative side, the officers of the National Park Service, under the authority of the Antiquities Act of 1906 and the Historic Sites Act of 1935, provided valuable guidance. After a number of conferences, a series of inter-agency agreements was drawn up between the scientific agencies, the National Park Service and the Smithsonian, on the one hand; and on the other, the two construction agencies involved, the Bureau of Reclamation and the Corps of Engineers. After more conferences, testimony before committees, and period of alternating hope and dismay, Congress made an appropriation which enabled the program to get started. . . .

From very small beginnings in 1946, surveys and excavations have been carried out in reservoir pool areas in all of the major and many of the minor river basins of the country. In a pamphlet issued by the Committee for the Recovery of Archaeological Remains, with the assistance of the American Council of Learned Societies, the following rough totals are given for the work accomplished by federal agencies under the program during the years 1946 through 1957. Archaeological, historical, and paleontological surveys had been made in 310 reservoirs in 42 states. More than 9,000 sites had been located and recorded, including prehistoric villages, burial grounds, trails, quarries, fur-trading posts, military forts, pioneer cabins and early frontier settlements. Excavations had been conducted in 69 reservoir areas in 31 states. Over 4,000,000 specimens had been found. . . .

For small cost we are gaining knowledge of our prehistoric and early historic past far beyond the dreams of a preceding generation of archaeologists, and historians. At first many deplored the demands of the program, fearing

that it would pull men away from researches they had planned in order to cope with emergencies. This has not proved to be the case. There is more excavation going on outside the river basins than ever before, while within the basins we are deciphering the main lines of cultural development and the movement of prehistoric populations. Archaeologists themselves, for the most part, still do not realize the extent of the record that is being compiled by the river basin studies. The pre-Columbian inhabitants of the New World did not possess the wheel and, with this limitation on land transport, it is estimated that eighty per cent of the inland population lived along the rivers. In the Missouri Basin the proportion was much higher and all of the known sites of five prehistoric cultures in Nebraska and the Dakotas are going under water behind the dams. In comparison with the rate of normal archaeological research the compulsion exerted by this emergency has advanced our knowledge by decades if not by centuries.

Salvage archaeology, however, is not restricted to the river valleys. Shortly after the establishment of the River Basin Program a new threat to our prehistoric past arose. The demand for oil and natural gas had reached the point where tank car transport could not keep up and engineers perfected methods of moving these commodities through pipelines. Huge trenching machines began cutting ditches through hundreds of miles of countryside. Particularly in the southwestern states, this again meant the destruction of sites. So pipeline salvage came into being and archaeologists are now standard personnel on major pipeline projects. They are employees of the companies in many cases, and the costs of the work, and of the preparation and publication of reports, are included in the project estimates. . . .

When all this is put together, along with the individual local salvage projects in connection with new airfields, factories, motel developments, land clearance for farming and the like, the significance of the development becomes clear. In 1945 we had considerable knowledge of our prehistory in only a very few areas; really, in only a very few places. Between these places were gaps, many of them of great size, about which we knew nothing. The salvage work in the river basins and along the roads and pipelines is filling in these gaps with surprising rapidity. . . .

This presentation is not intended to give the impression that the achievements of the various salvage programs in the United States during the past fifteen years have been perfect. There have been irreparable losses in the river basins and there will be more if the Congress does not increase the appropriations for the coming year. Constant vigilance by archaeologists and the public will be necessary to protect our sites from destruction in road and building construction.

The results of the various programs, however, in the increase to our knowledge of the prehistoric and historic past have been noteworthy and exciting. Systematic information is rapidly becoming available about areas and early cultures of which, previously, we knew little or nothing. And to the world of scholarship in general perhaps the most significant fact is that salvage archaeology has become far more than a mere emergency rescue operation for saving individual sites and buildings. Geologists, palaeontologists, botanists, and zoologists are joining with the archaeologists and historians. The ecological studies program in the most recent of our river basin projects, the Upper Colorado, is a good example of this.

Climatic changes and the effects of drought, erosion, flooding, and silting upon populations through time, all have become part of the research. The Missouri Basin Chronology Program of the Smithsonian Institution demonstrates the assistance being received from the physical sciences with their rapidly developing dating techniques, of which Carbon-14 analysis is the most striking. In all parts of the country many fields of knowledge are bringing their resources to bear to make these programs truly interdisciplinary, to discover and describe as much as possible about past human occupancy, and to insure that the historic record does not disappear forever as a victim of our progress. . . .

In summary, salvage archaeology can probably best be judged by a list of some of its extraordinary achievements during its short life as a recognized segment of our scientific operations.

It is turning the major river valleys of the world into vast archaeological laboratories.

It has built a museum in the middle of what was once the Zuider Zee.

It delayed the construction of new buildings in the centers of the bombed-out cities of Europe while archaeologists deciphered the remains of the earliest life in those cities.

It has joined together in a major scientific program, effectively and for the first time, such diverse agencies of government as our Department of Defense, National Park Service, Federal Power Commission, Smithsonian Institution, and the Bureau of Public Roads. . . .

And it has brought about, for the first time, a truly useful and effective cooperation involving archaeology, the earth sciences, and the discipline of history. The full force of this common approach has been seen in the United States during the last decade in the major river basins, notably the Missouri, the Columbia, and the Upper Colorado. The next decade will witness the same scientific productivity in the valley of the Nile, where already botanists, geologists, palaeontologists, and climatologists are teaming up with prehistorians, egyptologists, historians, and specialists in arid lands technology to study the vast living text-book, proving-ground, and laboratory which is Nubia, before it disappears forever beneath the waters of the new inland sea to be created by the high *Saad el Aali Dam* above the First Cataract at Aswan.

# Index